Explorations in CORE MATH

for Common Core GPS Analytic Geometry

HOUGHTON MIFFLIN HARCOURT

Cover photo credit: ©Daniel Dempster Photography/Alamy

Printed in the U.S.A.

7 8 9 10 0928 23 22 21 20 19 18 17 16 15 14

4500483813 C D E F G H I

Contents

Unit 2 Right Triangle Trigonometry 189

Correlation of *Explorations in Core Math* to the Common Core GPS for Analytic Geometry

Standards	Lessons
Number and Quantity: The Real Number System	
Extend the properties of exponents to rational exponents.	
MCC9-12.N.RN.1 Explain how the definition of the meaning of rational exponents follows from extending the properties of integer exponents to those values, allowing for a notation for radicals in terms of rational exponents. *For example, we define* $5^{\left(\frac{1}{3}\right)}$ *to be the cube root of* 5 *because we want* $\left[5^{\left(\frac{1}{3}\right)}\right]^3 = 5^{\left[\left(\frac{1}{3}\right)\times 3\right]}$ *to hold, so* $\left[5^{\left(\frac{1}{3}\right)}\right]^3$ *must equal* 5.	**This standard is addressed in the Student Edition.**
MCC9-12.N.RN.2 Rewrite expressions involving radicals and rational exponents using the properties of exponents.	**This standard is addressed in the Student Edition.**
Use properties of rational and irrational numbers.	
MCC9-12.N.RN.3 Explain why the sum or product of two rational numbers is rational; that the sum of a rational number and an irrational number is irrational; and that the product of a nonzero rational number and an irrational number is irrational.	**This standard is addressed in the Student Edition.**
Number and Quantity: The Complex Number System	
Perform arithmetic operations with complex numbers.	
MCC9-12.N.CN.1 Know there is a complex number i such that $i^2 = -1$, and every complex number has the form $a + bi$ with a and b real.	**Lessons 13-1, 13-2**
MCC9-12.N.CN.2 Use the relation $i^2 = -1$ and the commutative, associative, and distributive properties to add, subtract, and multiply complex numbers.	**Lesson 13-2**
MCC9-12.N.CN.3(+) Find the conjugate of a complex number; use conjugates to find moduli and quotients of complex numbers.	**Lesson 13-2**
Use complex numbers in polynomial identities and equations.	
MCC9-12.N.CN.7 Solve quadratic equations with real coefficients that have complex solutions.	**Lesson 16-3**
Algebra: Seeing Structure in Expressions	
Interpret the structure of expressions.	
MCC9-12.A.SSE.1 Interpret expressions that represent a quantity in terms of its context.*	**Lessons 8-1, 14-1, 14-2, 14-3, 15-2, 15-3, 16-1**
MCC9-12.A.SSE.1a a. Interpret parts of an expression, such as terms, factors, and coefficients.*	**Lessons 14-1, 14-2, 14-3, 15-2, 15-3, 16-1**

(+) Advanced   * = Also a Modeling Standard

Standards	Lessons
MCC9-12.A.SSE.1b b. Interpret complicated expressions by viewing one or more of their parts as a single entity. For example, interpret $P(1+r)^n$ as the product of P and a factor not depending on P.*	**Lessons 15-1, 15-2, 15-3, 16-1, 16-2, 16-3**
MCC9-12.A.SSE.2 Use the structure of an expression to identify ways to rewrite it. For example, see $x^4 - y^4$ as $(x^2)^2 - (y^2)^2$, thus recognizing it as a difference of squares that can be factored as $(x^2 - y^2)(x^2 + y^2)$.	**Lessons 8-1, 14-1, 14-2, 14-3, 15-1, 16-1, 16-3**
Write expressions in equivalent forms to solve problems.	
MCC9-12.A.SSE.3 Choose and produce an equivalent form of an expression to reveal and explain properties of the quantity represented by the expression.*	**Lessons 15-1, 15-2, 15-3, 16-1, 16-2, 16-3**
MCC9-12.A.SSE.3a a. Factor a quadratic expression to reveal the zeros of the function it defines.*	**Lessons 14-1, 14-2, 14-3, 16-1**
MCC9-12.A.SSE.3b b. Complete the square in a quadratic expression to reveal the maximum or minimum value of the function it defines.*	**Lessons 16-2**
Algebra: Arithmetic with Polynomials and Rational Expressions	
Perform arithmetic operations on polynomials.	
MCC9-12.A.APR.1 Understand that polynomials form a system analogous to the integers, namely, they are closed under the operations of addition, subtraction, and multiplication; add, subtract, and multiply polynomials.	**Lessons 14-1, 14-2, 14-3**
Algebra: Creating Equations*	
Create equations that describe numbers or relationships.	
MCC9-12.A.CED.1 Create equations and inequalities in one variable and use them to solve problems. Include equations arising from linear and quadratic functions, and simple rational and exponential functions.*	**Lessons 8-1, 8-3, 8-4, 9-1, 9-2, 10-1, 10-2, 10-3, 11-1, 11-2, 11-3, 12-2, 12-3, 12-4, 16-1, 16-2, 16-3**
MCC9-12.A.CED.2 Create equations in two or more variables to represent relationships between quantities; graph equations on coordinate axes with labels and scales.*	**Lessons 15-1, 15-2, 15-3, 16-1, 16-2, 16-3, 16-4, 17-2, 17-3**
MCC9-12.A.CED.4 Rearrange formulas to highlight a quantity of interest, using the same reasoning as in solving equations. *For example, rearrange Ohm's law $V = IR$ to highlight resistance R.**	**Lessons 11-1, 11-2, 11-3, 11-4, 16-3, 17-2, 17-3**

(+) Advanced   * = Also a Modeling Standard

Standards	Lessons
Algebra: Reasoning with Equations and Inequalities	
Solve equations and inequalities in one variable.	
MCC9-12.A.REI.4 Solve quadratic equations in one variable.	**Lessons 16-1, 16-2, 16-3, 16-4**
MCC9-12.A.REI.4a a. Use the method of completing the square to transform any quadratic equation in x into an equation of the form $(x - p)^2 = q$ that has the same solutions. Derive the quadratic formula from this form.	**Lessons 16-2, 16-3**
MCC9-12.A.REI.4b b. Solve quadratic equations by inspection (e.g., for $x^2 = 49$), taking square roots, completing the square, the quadratic formula and factoring, as appropriate to the initial form of the equation. Recognize when the quadratic formula gives complex solutions and write them as $a \pm bi$ for real numbers a and b.	**Lessons 16-1, 16-2, 16-3, 16-4**
Solve systems of equations.	
MCC9-12.A.REI.7 Solve a simple system consisting of a linear equation and a quadratic equation in two variables algebraically and graphically. *For example, find the points of intersection between the line* $y = -3x$ *and the circle* $x^2 + y^2 = 3$.	**Lesson 16-4, 17-2**
Functions: Interpreting Functions	
Interpret functions that arise in applications in terms of the context.	
MCC9-12.F.IF.4 For a function that models a relationship between two quantities, interpret key features of graphs and tables in terms of the quantities, and sketch graphs showing key features given a verbal description of the relationship. Key features include: intercepts; intervals where the function is increasing, decreasing, positive, or negative; relative maximums and minimums; symmetries; end behavior; and periodicity.*	**Lessons 15-1, 15-2, 15-3, 17-3**

(+) Advanced   * = Also a Modeling Standard

Standards	Lessons
MCC9-12.F.IF.5 Relate the domain of a function to its graph and, where applicable, to the quantitative relationship it describes. For example, if the function $h(n)$ gives the number of person-hours it takes to assemble n engines in a factory, then the positive integers would be an appropriate domain for the function.*	**Lessons 15-1, 15-2, 15-3, 17-3**
MCC9-12.F.IF.6 Calculate and interpret the average rate of change of a function (presented symbolically or as a table) over a specified interval. Estimate the rate of change from a graph.*	**Lesson 15-3**
Analyze functions using different representations.	
MCC9-12.F.IF.7a Graph functions expressed symbolically and show key features of the graph, by hand in simple cases and using technology for more complicated cases.* **a.** Graph linear and quadratic functions and show intercepts, maxima, and minima.*	**Lessons 15-1, 15-2, 15-3**
MCC9-12.F.IF.8a Write a function defined by an expression in different but equivalent forms to reveal and explain different properties of the function. **a.** Use the process of factoring and completing the square in a quadratic function to show zeros, extreme values, and symmetry of the graph, and interpret these in terms of a context.	**Lessons 14-1, 14-2, 14-3, 16-1, 16-2**
MCC9-12.F.IF.9 Compare properties of two functions each represented in a different way (algebraically, graphically, numerically in tables, or by verbal descriptions). *For example, given a graph of one quadratic function and an algebraic expression for another, say which has the larger maximum.*	**Lessons 15-1, 16-4**
Functions: Building Functions	
Build a function that models a relationship between two quantities.	
MCC9-12.F.BF.1 Write a function that describes a relationship between two quantities.*	**Lessons 15-1, 15-2, 15-3, 16-1, 16-2, 16-3, 16-4, 17-2, 17-3**
MCC9-12.F.BF.1a **a.** Determine an explicit expression, a recursive process, or steps for calculation from a context.*	**Lessons 16-2, 16-3**

(+) Advanced   * = Also a Modeling Standard

Standards		Lessons
MCC9-12.F.BF.1b **b.** Combine standard function types using arithmetic operations. *For example, build a function that models the temperature of a cooling body by adding a constant function to a decaying exponential, and relate these functions to the model.*		Lesson 15-1
Build new functions from existing functions.		
MCC9-12.F.BF.3 Identify the effect on the graph of replacing $f(x)$ by $f(x) + k$, $k\,f(x)$, $f(kx)$, and $f(x + k)$ for specific values of k (both positive and negative); find the value of k given the graphs. Experiment with cases and illustrate an explanation of the effects on the graph using technology. Include recognizing even and odd functions from their graphs and algebraic expressions for them.		Lesson 15-1
Functions: Linear, Quadratic, and Exponential*		
Construct and compare linear, quadratic, and exponential models and solve problems.		
MCC9-12.F.LE.3 Observe using graphs and tables that a quantity increasing exponentially eventually exceeds a quantity increasing linearly, quadratically, or (more generally) as a polynomial function.		Lessons 15-2, 16-1, 16-4
Geometry: Congruence		
Understand congruence in terms of rigid motions.		
MCC9-12.G.CO.6 Use geometric descriptions of rigid motions to transform figures and to predict the effect of a given rigid motion on a given figure; given two figures, use the definition of congruence in terms of rigid motions to decide if they are congruent.		Lesson 4-1
MCC9-12.G.CO.7 Use the definition of congruence in terms of rigid motions to show that two triangles are congruent if and only if corresponding pairs of sides and corresponding pairs of angles are congruent.		Lessons 4-3, 5-1
MCC9-12.G.CO.8 Explain how the criteria for triangle congruence (ASA, SAS, and SSS) follow from the definition of congruence in terms of rigid motions.		Lessons 5-1, 5-2

(+) Advanced   * = Also a Modeling Standard

Standards	Lessons
Prove geometric theorems.	
MCC9-12.G.CO.9 Prove theorems about lines and angles. Theorems include: vertical angles are congruent; when a transversal crosses parallel lines, alternate interior angles are congruent and corresponding angles are congruent; points on a perpendicular bisector of a line segment are exactly those equidistant from the segment's endpoints.	**Lessons 2-3, 2-4, 3-1, 3-2, 3-3**
MCC9-12.G.CO.10 Prove theorems about triangles. Theorems include: measures of interior angles of a triangle sum to 180°; base angles of isosceles triangles are congruent; the segment joining midpoints of two sides of a triangle is parallel to the third side and half the length; the medians of a triangle meet at a point.	**Lessons 4-2, 5-2, 5-9, 6-3, 6-4, 7-1, 7-2**
MCC9-12.G.CO.11 Prove theorems about parallelograms. Theorems include: opposite sides are congruent, opposite angles are congruent, the diagonals of a parallelogram bisect each other, and conversely, rectangles are parallelograms with congruent diagonals.	**Lessons 7-1, 7-2, 7-3**
Make geometric constructions.	
MCC9-12.G.CO.12 Make formal geometric constructions with a variety of tools and methods (compass and straightedge, string, reflective devices, paper folding, dynamic geometric software, etc.). Copying a segment; copying an angle; bisecting a segment; bisecting an angle; constructing perpendicular lines, including the perpendicular bisector of a line segment; and constructing a line parallel to a given line through a point not on the line.	**Lessons 1-1, 1-2, 3-2, 3-3**
MCC9-12.G.CO.13 Construct an equilateral triangle, a square, and a regular hexagon inscribed in a circle.	**Lessons 4-9, 6-2**
Geometry: Similarity, Right Triangles, and Trigonometry	
Understand similarity in terms of similarity transformations.	
MCC9-12.G.SRT.1 Verify experimentally the properties of dilations given by a center and a scale factor.	**Lessons 8-2, 8-5**
MCC9-12.G.SRT.1a **a.** A dilation takes a line not passing through the center of the dilation to a parallel line, and leaves a line passing through the center unchanged.	**Lessons 8-2, 8-5**

(+) Advanced   * = Also a Modeling Standard

Standards	Lessons
MCC9-12.G.SRT.1b b. The dilation of a line segment is longer or shorter in the ratio given by the scale factor.	**Lessons 8-2, 8-5**
MCC9-12.G.SRT.2 Given two figures, use the definition of similarity in terms of similarity transformations to decide if they are similar; explain using similarity transformations the meaning of similarity for triangles as the equality of all corresponding pairs of angles and the proportionality of all corresponding pairs of sides.	**Lessons 8-2, 8-3**
MCC9-12.G.SRT.3 Use the properties of similarity transformations to establish the AA criterion for two triangles to be similar.	**Lesson 8-3**
Prove theorems involving similarity.	
MCC9-12.G.SRT.4 Prove theorems about triangles. Theorems include: a line parallel to one side of a triangle divides the other two proportionally, and conversely; the Pythagorean Theorem proved using triangle similarity.	**Lessons 8-4, 9-1, 9-2**
MCC9-12.G.SRT.5 Use congruence and similarity criteria for triangles to solve problems and to prove relationships in geometric figures.	**Lessons 5-1, 5-2, 7-1, 7-2, 7-3, 8-4**
Define trigonometric ratios and solve problems involving right triangles.	
MCC9-12.G.SRT.6 Understand that by similarity, side ratios in right triangles are properties of the angles in the triangle, leading to definitions of trigonometric ratios for acute angles.	**Lessons 9-2, 10-1**
MCC9-12.G.SRT.7 Explain and use the relationship between the sine and cosine of complementary angles.	**Lesson 10-1**
MCC9-12.G.SRT.8 Use trigonometric ratios and the Pythagorean Theorem to solve right triangles in applied problems.	**Lessons 9-1, 9-2, 10-1, 10-2, 10-3**
Geometry: Circles	
Understand and apply theorems about circles.	
MCC9-12.G.C.1 Prove that all circles are similar.	**Lesson 8-2**
MCC9-12.G.C.2 Identify and describe relationships among inscribed angles, radii, and chords. Include the relationship between central, inscribed, and circumscribed angles; inscribed angles on a diameter are right angles; the radius of a circle is perpendicular to the tangent where the radius intersects the circle.	**Lessons 12-1, 12-2, 12-4**

(+) Advanced   * = Also a Modeling Standard

Standards	Lessons
MCC9-12.G.C.3 Construct the inscribed and circumscribed circles of a triangle, and prove properties of angles for a quadrilateral inscribed in a circle.	**Lessons 6-2, 12-4**
MCC9-12.G.C.4(+) Construct a tangent line from a point outside a given circle to the circle.	**Lesson 12-1**
Find arc lengths and areas of sectors of circles.	
MCC9-12.G.C.5 Derive using similarity the fact that the length of the arc intercepted by an angle is proportional to the radius, and define the radian measure of the angle as the constant of proportionality; derive the formula for the area of a sector.	**Lesson 12-3**
Geometry: Expressing Geometric Properties with Equations	
Translate between the geometric description and the equation for a conic section.	
MCC9-12.G.GPE.1 Derive the equation of a circle of given center and radius using the Pythagorean Theorem; complete the square to find the center and radius of a circle given by an equation.	**Lesson 17-2**
MCC9-12.G.GPE.2 Derive the equation of a parabola given a focus and directrix.	**Lesson 17-3**
Use coordinates to prove simple geometric theorems algebraically.	
MCC9-12.G.GPE.4 Use coordinates to prove simple geometric theorems algebraically. *For example, prove or disprove that a figure defined by four given points in the coordinate plane is a rectangle; prove or disprove that the point* $(1, \sqrt{3})$ *lies on the circle centered at the origin and containing the point (0, 2).*	**Lessons 6-3, 6-4, 7-4, 17-1, 17-2, 17-3**
Geometry: Geometric Measurement and Dimension	
Explain volume formulas and use them to solve problems.	
MCC9-12.G.GMD.1 Give an informal argument for the formulas for the circumference of a circle, area of a circle, volume of a cylinder, pyramid, and cone. Use dissection arguments, Cavalieri's principle, and informal limit arguments.	**Lessons 11-1, 11-2, 11-3**
MCC9-12.G.GMD.2(+) Give an informal argument using Cavalieri's principle for the formulas for the volume of a sphere and other solid figures.	**Lessons 11-2, 11-4**
MCC9-12.G.GMD.3 Use volume formulas for cylinders, pyramids, cones, and spheres to solve problems.*	**Lessons 11-2, 11-3, 11-4**

(+) Advanced   * = Also a Modeling Standard

Standards	Lessons
Statistics and Probability: Interpreting Categorical and Quantitative Data	
Summarize, represent, and interpret data on two categorical and quantitative variables.	
MCC9-12.S.ID.6a Represent data on two quantitative variables on a scatter plot, and describe how the variables are related.* **a.** Fit a function to the data; use functions fitted to data to solve problems in the context of the data. Use given functions or choose a function suggested by the context. Emphasize linear and exponential models.*	Lesson 15-3
Statistics and Probability: Conditional Probability and the Rules of Probability	
Understand independence and conditional probability and use them to interpret data.	
MCC9-12.S.CP.1 Describe events as subsets of a sample space (the set of outcomes) using characteristics (or categories) of the outcomes, or as unions, intersections, or complements of other events ("or," "and," "not").	Lessons 18-1, 18-3
MCC9-12.S.CP.2 Understand that two events A and B are independent if the probability of A and B occurring together is the product of their probabilities, and use this characterization to determine if they are independent.*	Lesson 19-1
MCC9-12.S.CP.3 Understand the conditional probability of A given B as $\frac{P(A \text{ and } B)}{P(B)}$, and interpret independence of A and B as saying that the conditional probability of A given B is the same as the probability of A, and the conditional probability of B given A is the same as the probability of B.*	Lessons 19-1, 19-2
MCC9-12.S.CP.4 Construct and interpret two-way frequency tables of data when two categories are associated with each object being classified. Use the two-way table as a sample space to decide if events are independent and to approximate conditional probabilities. *For example, collect data from a random sample of students in your school on their favorite subject among math, science, and English. Estimate the probability that a randomly selected student from your school will favor science given that the student is in tenth grade. Do the same for other subjects and compare the results.**	Lesson 19-1, 19-2
MCC9-12.S.CP.5 Recognize and explain the concepts of conditional probability and independence in everyday language and everyday situations. *For example, compare the chance of having lung cancer if you are a smoker with the chance of being a smoker if you have lung cancer.**	Lesson 19-1, 19-2, 19-3
Use the rules of probability to compute probabilities of compound events in a uniform probability model.	
MCC9-12.S.CP.6 Find the conditional probability of A given B as the fraction of B's outcomes that also belong to A, and interpret the answer in terms of the model.*	Lessons 19-2, 19-3
MCC9-12.S.CP.7 Apply the Addition Rule, $P(A \text{ or } B) = P(A) + P(B) - P(A \text{ and } B)$, and interpret the answer in terms of the model.*	Lesson 19-3

(+) Advanced   * = Also a Modeling Standard

Learning the Standards for Mathematical Practice

The Common Core Georgia Performance Standards include eight Standards for Mathematical Practice. Here's how *Explorations in Core Math* helps you learn those standards as you master the Standards for Mathematical Content.

1 Make sense of problems and persevere in solving them.

In *Explorations in Core Math*, you will work through Explores and Examples that present a solution pathway for you to follow. You will be asked questions along the way so that you gain an understanding of the solution process, and then you will apply what you've learned in the Practice for the lesson.

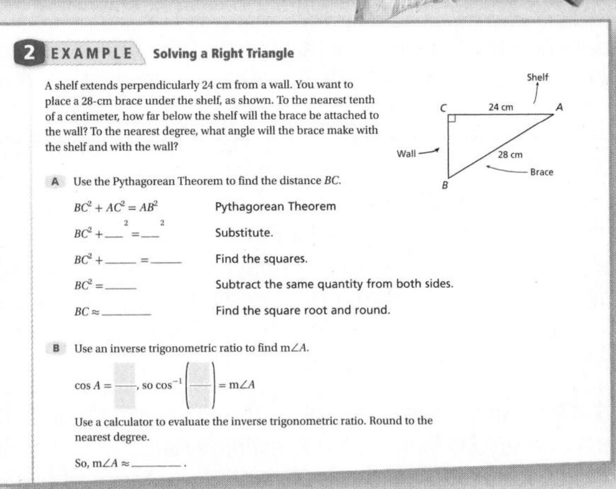

2 EXAMPLE Solving a Right Triangle

A shelf extends perpendicularly 24 cm from a wall. You want to place a 28-cm brace under the shelf, as shown. To the nearest tenth of a centimeter, how far below the shelf will the brace be attached to the wall? To the nearest degree, what angle will the brace make with the shelf and with the wall?

A Use the Pythagorean Theorem to find the distance BC.

$BC^2 + AC^2 = AB^2$	Pythagorean Theorem
$BC^2 + \_\_^2 = \_\_^2$	Substitute.
$BC^2 + \_\_\_ = \_\_\_$	Find the squares.
$BC^2 = \_\_\_$	Subtract the same quantity from both sides.
$BC \approx \_\_\_$	Find the square root and round.

B Use an inverse trigonometric ratio to find $m\angle A$.

$\cos A = \frac{\square}{\square}$, so $\cos^{-1}\left(\frac{\square}{\square}\right) = m\angle A$

Use a calculator to evaluate the inverse trigonometric ratio. Round to the nearest degree.

So, $m\angle A \approx$ ______.

2 Reason abstractly and quantitatively.

When you solve a real-world problem in *Explorations in Core Math*, you will learn to represent the situation symbolically by translating the problem into a mathematical expression or equation. You will use these mathematical models to solve the problem and then state your answer in terms of the problem context. You will reflect on the solution process in order to check your answer for reasonableness and to draw conclusions.

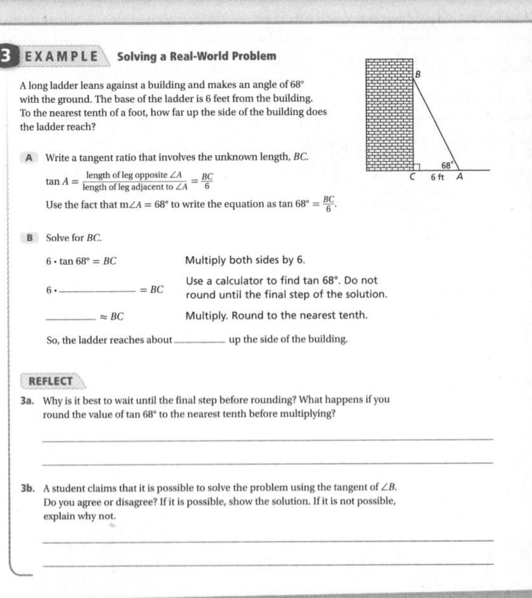

3 EXAMPLE Solving a Real-World Problem

A long ladder leans against a building and makes an angle of 68° with the ground. The base of the ladder is 6 feet from the building. To the nearest tenth of a foot, how far up the side of the building does the ladder reach?

A Write a tangent ratio that involves the unknown length, BC.

$\tan A = \frac{\text{length of leg opposite } \angle A}{\text{length of leg adjacent to } \angle A} = \frac{BC}{6}$

Use the fact that $m\angle A = 68°$ to write the equation as $\tan 68° = \frac{BC}{6}$.

B Solve for BC.

$6 \cdot \tan 68° = BC$	Multiply both sides by 6.
$6 \cdot \_\_\_\_\_\_ = BC$	Use a calculator to find tan 68°. Do not round until the final step of the solution.
$\_\_\_\_\_\_ \approx BC$	Multiply. Round to the nearest tenth.

So, the ladder reaches about ______ up the side of the building.

REFLECT

3a. Why is it best to wait until the final step before rounding? What happens if you round the value of tan 68° to the nearest tenth before multiplying?

3b. A student claims that it is possible to solve the problem using the tangent of $\angle B$. Do you agree or disagree? If it is possible, show the solution. If it is not possible, explain why not.

3 Construct viable arguments and critique the reasoning of others.

Throughout *Explorations in Core Math*, you will be asked to make conjectures, construct a mathematical argument, explain your reasoning, and justify your conclusions. Reflect questions offer opportunities for cooperative learning and class discussion. You will have additional opportunities to critique reasoning in Error Analysis problems.

REFLECT

2a. Given that $\triangle PQR \cong \triangle STU$, $PQ = 2.7$ ft, and $PR = 3.4$ ft, is it possible to determine the length of $\overline{TU}$? If so, find the length. If not, explain why not.

2b. A student claims that any two congruent triangles must have the same perimeter. Do you agree or disagree? Why?

3. Error Analysis A student who is 72 inches tall wants to find the height of a flagpole. He measures the length of the flagpole's shadow and the length of his own shadow at the same time of day, as shown in his sketch below. Explain the error in the student's work.

The triangles are similar by the AA Similarity Criterion, so corresponding sides are proportional.

$\frac{x}{72} = \frac{48}{128}$

$x = 72 \cdot \frac{48}{128}$, so $x = 27$ in.

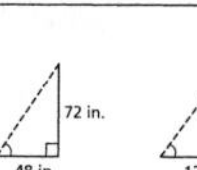

4 Model with mathematics.

Explorations in Core Math presents problems in a variety of contexts such as science, business, and everyday life. You will use models such as equations, tables, diagrams, and graphs to represent the information in the problem and to solve the problem. Then you will interpret your results in context.

4 EXAMPLE Solving a Real-World Problem

Police want to set up a camera to identify drivers who run the red light at point C on Mason Street. The camera must be mounted on a fence that intersects Mason Street at a 40° angle, as shown, and the camera should ideally be 120 feet from point C. What points along the fence, if any, are suitable locations for the camera?

Mason Street, C, 170 ft, A, 40°, Fence

A Because the side opposite $\angle A$ is shorter than $\overline{AC}$, it may be possible to form two triangles. Use the Law of Sines to find possible values for $m\angle B$.

$\frac{\sin A}{a} = \frac{\sin B}{b}$ Law of Sines

$\frac{\sin 40°}{120} = \frac{\sin B}{170}$ Substitute.

$\frac{170 \sin 40°}{120} = \sin B$ Solve for sin B.

_______ $\approx \sin B$ Use a calculator. Round to 4 decimal places.

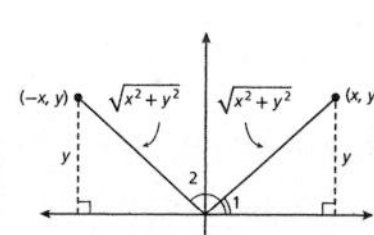

There is an acute angle and an obtuse angle that have this value as their sine. To find the acute angle, use a calculator and round to the nearest tenth.

$\sin^{-1}$(______) ≈ ______

To find the obtuse angle, note that ∠1 and ∠2 have the same sine, $\frac{y}{\sqrt{x^2 + y^2}}$, and notice that these angles are supplementary. Thus, the obtuse angle is supplementary to the acute angle you found above.

(−x, y), $\sqrt{x^2 + y^2}$, $\sqrt{x^2 + y^2}$, (x, y), y, 2, 1, y

So, $m\angle B \approx$ ________ or ________.

REFLECT

4a. How you can check your answers?

4b. Suppose the camera needs to be *at most* 120 feet from point C. In this case, where should the camera be mounted along the fence?

4c. What is the minimum distance at which the camera can be located from point C if it is to be mounted on the fence? Explain your answer.

5 Use appropriate tools strategically.

You will use a variety of tools in *Explorations in Core Math*, including manipulatives, paper and pencil, and technology. You might use manipulatives to develop concepts, paper and pencil to practice skills, and technology (such as graphing calculators, spreadsheets, or geometry software) to investigate more complicated mathematical ideas.

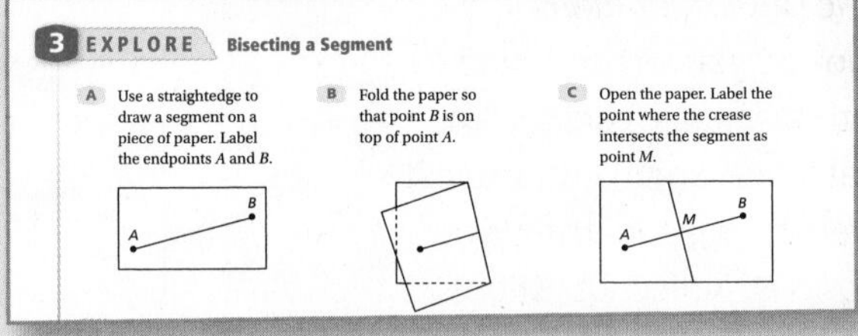

3 EXPLORE **Bisecting a Segment**

A Use a straightedge to draw a segment on a piece of paper. Label the endpoints A and B.

B Fold the paper so that point B is on top of point A.

C Open the paper. Label the point where the crease intersects the segment as point M.

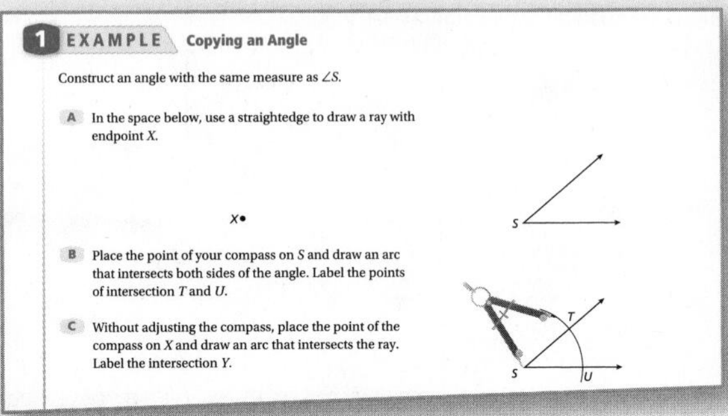

1 EXAMPLE **Copying an Angle**

Construct an angle with the same measure as $\angle S$.

A In the space below, use a straightedge to draw a ray with endpoint X.

B Place the point of your compass on S and draw an arc that intersects both sides of the angle. Label the points of intersection T and U.

C Without adjusting the compass, place the point of the compass on X and draw an arc that intersects the ray. Label the intersection Y.

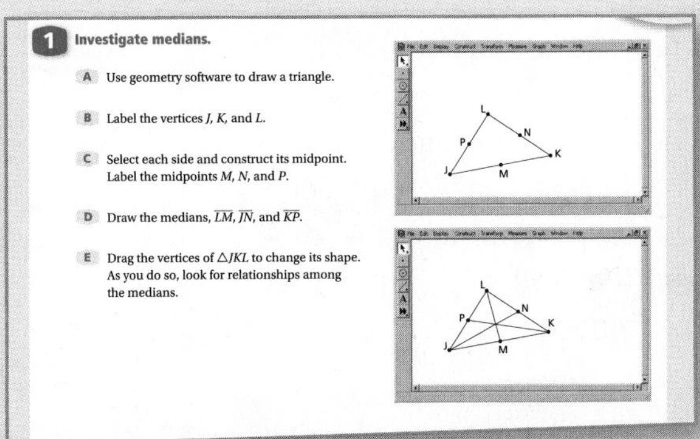

1 Investigate medians.

A Use geometry software to draw a triangle.

B Label the vertices J, K, and L.

C Select each side and construct its midpoint. Label the midpoints M, N, and P.

D Draw the medians, $\overline{LM}$, $\overline{JN}$, and $\overline{KP}$.

E Drag the vertices of $\triangle JKL$ to change its shape. As you do so, look for relationships among the medians.

6 Attend to precision.

Precision refers not only to the correctness of arithmetic calculations, algebraic manipulations, and geometric reasoning but also to the proper use of mathematical language, symbols, and units to communicate mathematical ideas. Throughout *Explorations in Core Math* you will demonstrate your skills in these areas when you are asked to calculate, describe, show, explain, prove, and predict.

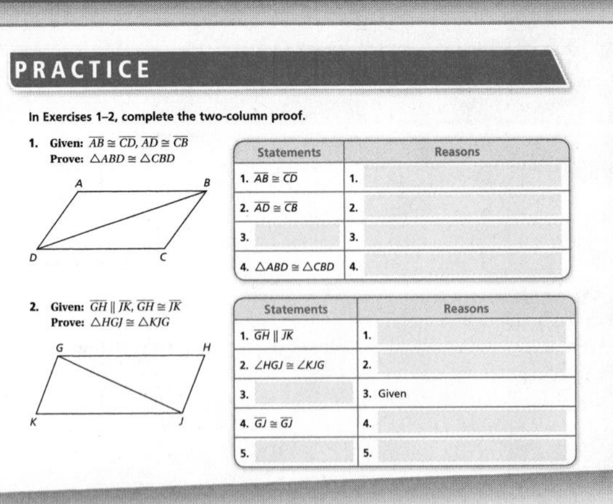

PRACTICE

In Exercises 1–2, complete the two-column proof.

1. Given: $\overline{AB} \cong \overline{CD}$, $\overline{AD} \cong \overline{CB}$
Prove: $\triangle ABD \cong \triangle CBD$

Statements	Reasons
1. $\overline{AB} \cong \overline{CD}$	1.
2. $\overline{AD} \cong \overline{CB}$	2.
3.	3.
4. $\triangle ABD \cong \triangle CBD$	4.

2. Given: $\overline{GH} \parallel \overline{JK}$, $\overline{GH} \cong \overline{JK}$
Prove: $\triangle HGJ \cong \triangle KJG$

Statements	Reasons
1. $\overline{GH} \parallel \overline{JK}$	1.
2. $\angle HGJ \cong \angle KJG$	2.
3.	3. Given
4. $\overline{GJ} \cong \overline{GJ}$	4.
5.	5.

7 Look for and make use of structure.

In *Explorations in Core Math*, you will look for patterns or regularity in mathematical structures such as expressions, equations, geometric figures, and graphs. Becoming familiar with underlying structures will help you build your understanding of more complicated mathematical ideas.

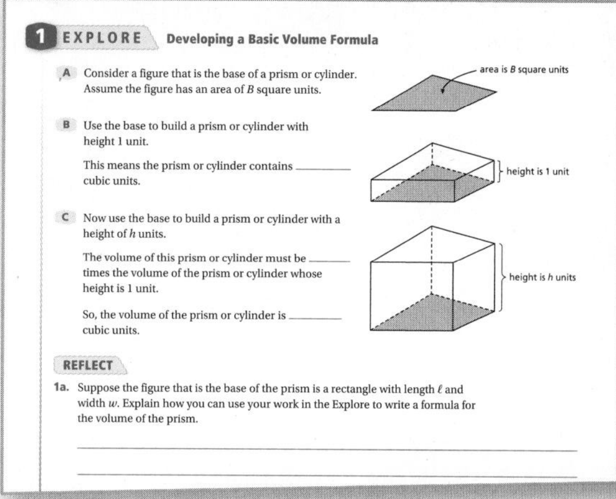

1 EXPLORE **Developing a Basic Volume Formula**

A Consider a figure that is the base of a prism or cylinder. Assume the figure has an area of B square units.

B Use the base to build a prism or cylinder with height 1 unit.

This means the prism or cylinder contains ______ cubic units.

C Now use the base to build a prism or cylinder with a height of h units.

The volume of this prism or cylinder must be ______ times the volume of the prism or cylinder whose height is 1 unit.

So, the volume of the prism or cylinder is ______ cubic units.

REFLECT

1a. Suppose the figure that is the base of the prism is a rectangle with length ℓ and width w. Explain how you can use your work in the Explore to write a formula for the volume of the prism.

8 Look for and express regularity in repeated reasoning.

In *Explorations in Core Math*, you will have the opportunity to explore and reflect on mathematical processes in order to come up with general methods for performing calculations and solving problems.

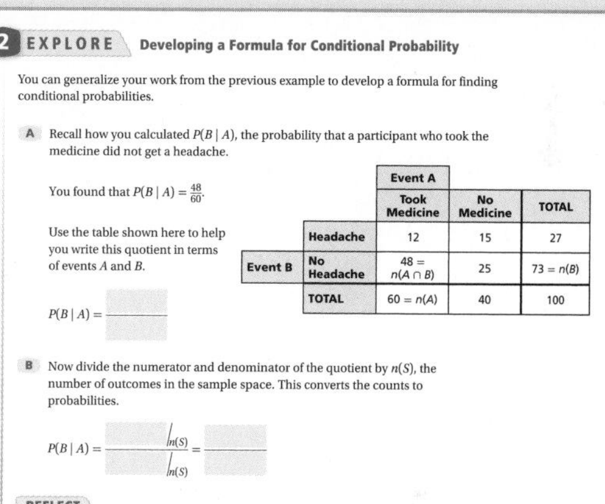

2 EXPLORE **Developing a Formula for Conditional Probability**

You can generalize your work from the previous example to develop a formula for finding conditional probabilities.

A Recall how you calculated $P(B \mid A)$, the probability that a participant who took the medicine did not get a headache.

You found that $P(B \mid A) = \frac{48}{60}$.

Use the table shown here to help you write this quotient in terms of events A and B.

		Event A: Took Medicine	No Medicine	TOTAL
	Headache	12	15	27
Event B	No Headache	48 = $n(A \cap B)$	25	73 = $n(B)$
	TOTAL	60 = $n(A)$	40	100

$P(B \mid A) =$ ______

B Now divide the numerator and denominator of the quotient by $n(S)$, the number of outcomes in the sample space. This converts the counts to probabilities.

$P(B \mid A) = \frac{\;\;/n(S)}{\;\;/n(S)} =$ ______

REFLECT

2a. Write a formula for $P(A \mid B)$ in terms of $n(A \cap B)$ and $n(B)$.

2b. Write a formula for $P(A \mid B)$ in terms of $P(A \cap B)$ and $P(B)$.

Similarity, Congruence, and Proofs

GPS COMMON CORE

Unpacking the Standards

Understanding the standards and the vocabulary terms in the standards will help you know exactly what you are expected to learn in this unit.

MCC912.G.CO.6

Use geometric descriptions of rigid motions to transform figures and to predict the effect of a given rigid motion on a given figure; …

Key Vocabulary

transformation *(transformación)* A change in the position, size, or shape of a figure or graph.

rigid motion *(movimiento rígido)* A transformation that does not change the size or shape of a figure.

What It Means For You

In geometry, when you reposition a figure but don't change its size or shape in the process, you have performed what is called a ***rigid motion.***

EXAMPLE

You can create the pattern on the grid by a series of rigid motions—in this case reflections and rotations—of one of the red crescent shapes.

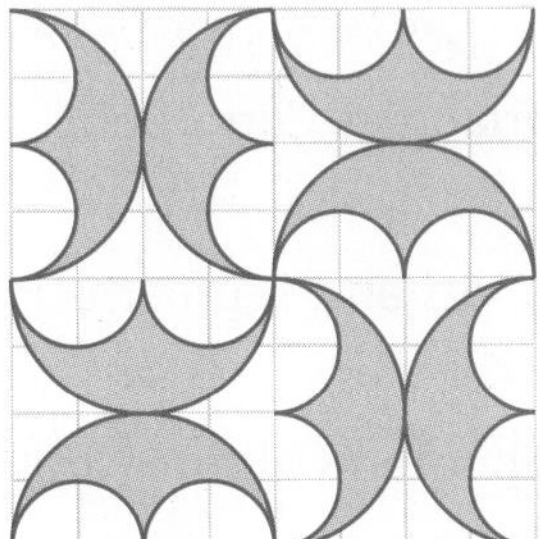

MCC912.G.SRT.5

Use congruence … criteria for triangles to solve problems and to prove relationships in geometric figures.

Key Vocabulary

congruent *(congruente)* Having the same size and shape, denoted by ≅.

triangle *(triángulo)* A three-sided polygon.

What It Means For You

When two triangles are *congruent*, it means that matching sides have the same measure and matching angles have the same measure. You can use this fact to help you solve problems.

EXAMPLE

You can use congruent triangles to find the distance across a canyon by measuring distances on only one side of the canyon.

Walk from D perpendicular to $\overline{BD}$ until you are in line with C and A. Call this point E. The distance DE is the same as the distance AB across the canyon.

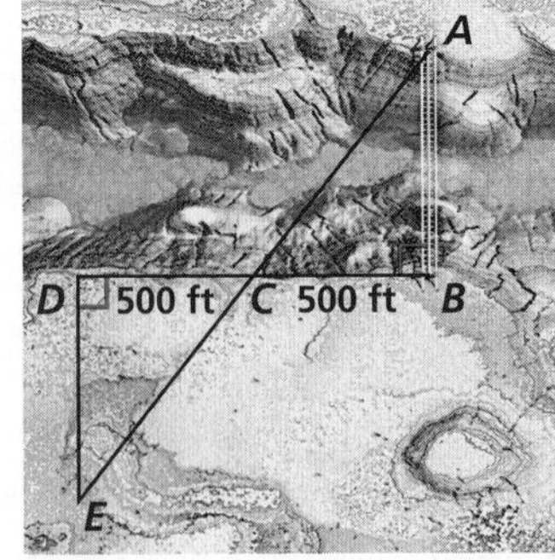

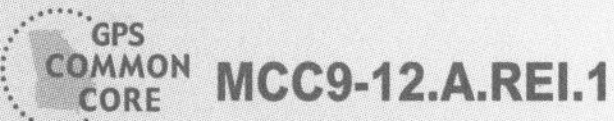

MCC9-12.A.REI.1

Explain each step in solving a simple equation as following from the equality of numbers asserted at the previous step, starting from the assumption that the original equation has a solution. Construct a viable argument to justify a solution method.

Key Vocabulary

equation *(ecuación)* A mathematical statement that two expressions are equivalent.

What It Means For You

You use properties of equality to justify, or prove, that each step is valid when you solve equations. This type of reasoning prepares you to write geometric proofs.

EXAMPLE

A family took out a loan to buy a new car that cost \$22,000. The down payment was \$4,000. The loan was interest free for a period of 5 years. The equation $5(12)p + 4{,}000 = 22{,}000$ represents this situation, where p is the monthly loan payment.

$5(12)p + 4{,}000 = 22{,}000$	*Given*
$60p + 4{,}000 = 22{,}000$	*Simplify.*
$60p = 18{,}000$	*Subtraction Property of Equality*
$p = 300$	*Division Property of Equality*

MCC9-12.G.CO.9

Prove theorems about lines and angles.

Key Vocabulary

proof *(demostración)* An argument that uses logic to show that a conclusion is true.

theorem *(teorema)* A statement that has been proven.

line *(línea)* An undefined term in geometry, a line is a straight path that has no thickness and extends forever.

angle *(ángulo)* A figure formed by two rays with a common endpoint.

What It Means For You

With just a few definitions, properties, and postulates, you can begin to prove simple theorems about line segments, linear pairs, right angles, vertical angles, and complementary or supplementary angles.

EXAMPLE

Given: $\angle 1$ and $\angle 3$ are vertical angles.

Prove: $\angle 1 \cong \angle 3$

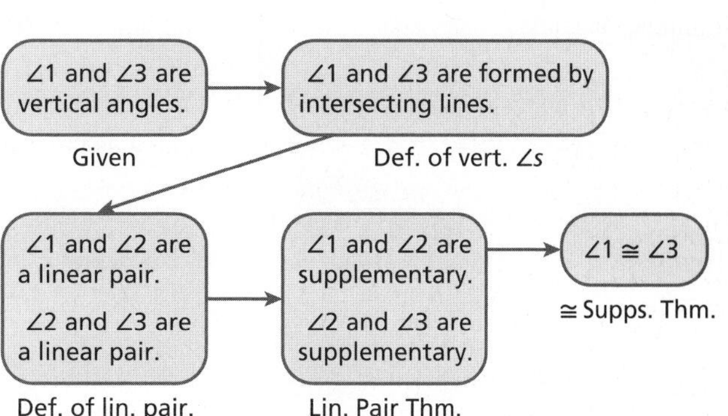

UNIT 1

Key Vocabulary

angle *(ángulo)* A figure formed by two rays with a common endpoint.

alternate exterior angles *(ángulos alternos externos)* For two lines intersected by a transversal, a pair of angles that lie on opposite sides of the transversal and outside the other two lines.

alternate interior angles *(ángulos alternos internos)* For two lines intersected by a transversal, a pair of nonadjacent angles that lie on opposite sides of the transversal and between the other two lines.

conditional statement *(enunciado condicional)* A statement that can be written in the form "if *p*, then *q*," where *p* is the hypothesis and *q* is the conclusion.

corresponding angles of lines intersected by a transversal *(ángulos correspondientes de líneas cortadas por una transversal)* For two lines intersected by a transversal, a pair of angles that lie on the same side of the transversal and on the same sides of the other two lines.

median of a triangle *(mediana de un triángulo)* A segment whose endpoints are a vertex of the triangle and the midpoint of the opposite side.

perpendicular lines *(líneas perpendiculars)* Lines that intersect at 90° angles.

parallel lines *(líneas paralelas)* Lines in the same plane that do not intersect.

parallelogram *(paralelogramo)* A quadrilateral with two pairs of parallel sides.

rectangle *(rectángulo)* A quadrilateral with four right angles.

rhombus *(rombo)* A quadrilateral with four congruent sides.

scale factor *(factor de escala)* The multiplier used on each dimension to change one figure into a similar figure.

similarity ratio *(razón de semejanza)* The ratio of linear measurements in the preimage to corresponding measurements in the image in a pair of similar figures.

square *(cuadrado)* A quadrilateral with four congruent sides and four right angles.

theorem *(teorema)* A statement that has been proven.

vertical angles *(ángulos opuestos por el vértice)* The nonadjacent angles formed by two intersecting lines.

Name ____________________ Class ____________ Date ________

1-1

Measuring and Constructing Segments

Going Deeper

Essential question: *What tools and methods can you use to copy a segment, bisect a segment, and construct a circle?*

Video Tutor

The **distance along a line** is undefined until a unit distance, such as 1 inch or 1 centimeter, is chosen. By placing a ruler alongside the line, you can associate a number from the ruler with each of two points on the line and then take the absolute value of the difference of the numbers to find the distance between the points. This distance is the **length** of the segment determined by the points.

In the figure, the length of $\overline{RS}$, written RS, is the distance between R and S. $RS = |4 - 1| = |3| = 3$ cm.

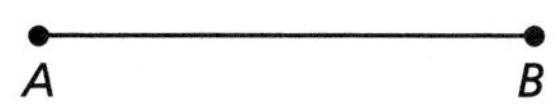

A *construction* is a geometric drawing that uses only a compass and a straightedge. You can construct a line segment whose length is equal to that of a given segment by using only these tools.

MCC9–12.G.CO.12

1 EXAMPLE Copying a Segment

Construct a segment with the same length as $\overline{AB}$.

A B

A In the space below, draw a line segment that is longer than $\overline{AB}$. Choose an endpoint of the segment and label it C.

B Set the opening of your compass to the distance AB, as shown.

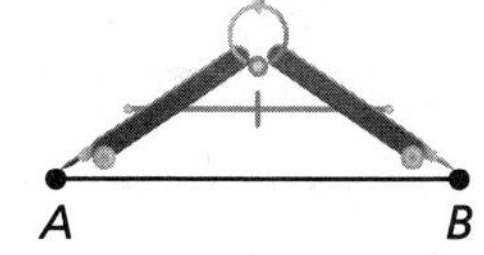

C Place the point of the compass on C. Make a small arc that intersects your line segment. Label the point D where the arc intersects the segment. $\overline{CD}$ is the required line segment.

REFLECT

1a. Why does this construction result in a line segment with the same length as $\overline{AB}$?

____

____

1b. What must you assume about the compass for this construction to work?

____

____

The **midpoint** of a line segment is the point that divides the segment into two segments that have the same length. The midpoint is said to **bisect** the segment. In the figure, the tick marks show that $PM = MQ$. Therefore, M is the midpoint of $\overline{PQ}$ and M bisects $\overline{PQ}$.

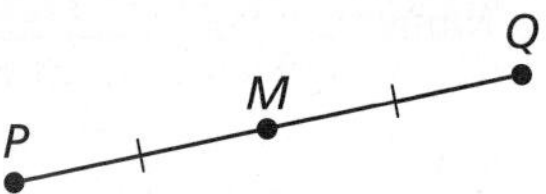

MCC9–12.G.CO.12

2 EXPLORE Bisecting a Segment

A Use a straightedge to draw a segment on a piece of paper. Label the endpoints A and B.

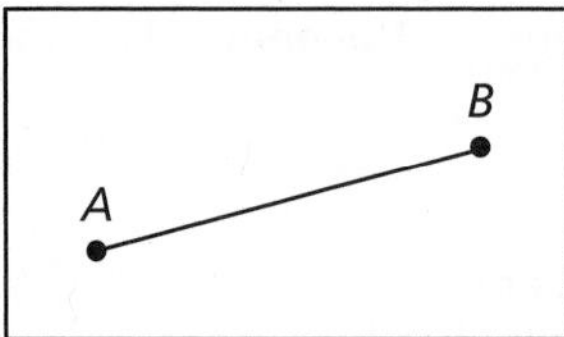

B Fold the paper so that point B is on top of point A.

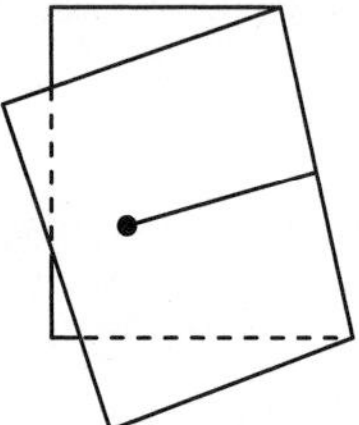

C Open the paper. Label the point where the crease intersects the segment as point M.

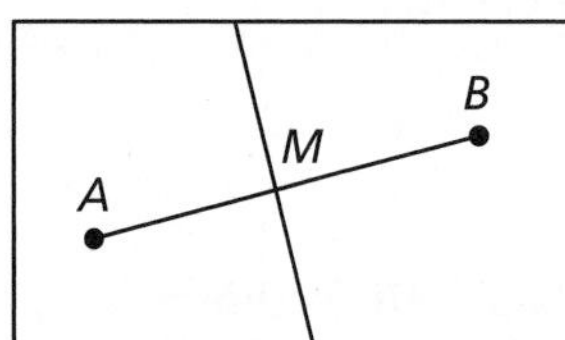

REFLECT

2a. How can you use a ruler to check the construction?

2b. Fold your paper along the segment. What happens to the crease that bisects the segment? What can you say about the four angles formed at point M?

2c. Explain how you could use paper folding to divide a line segment into four segments of equal length.

A **circle** is the set of all points in a plane that are a fixed distance from a point called the **center** of the circle. A **radius** is a line segment whose endpoints are the center of the circle and any point on the circle. The length of such a segment is also called the radius.

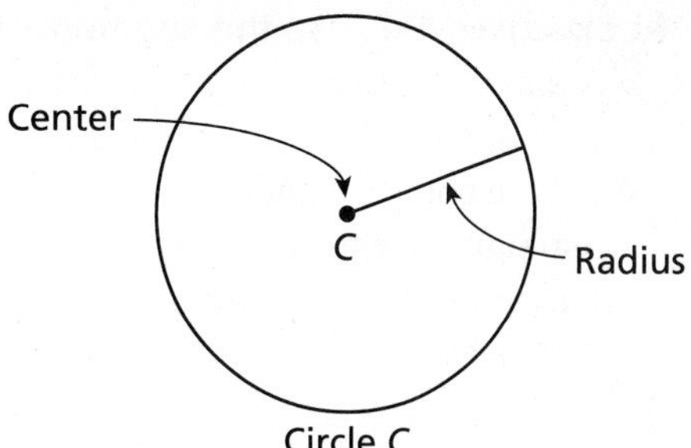

MCC9–12.G.CO.12

3 EXAMPLE Constructing a Circle

Construct a circle with radius *AB*.

A In the space at right, draw a point and label it *C*. This will be the center of the circle.

B Set the opening of your compass to the distance *AB*.

C Place the point of the compass on *C* and draw a circle.

REFLECT

3a. How could you use a piece of string, a thumbtack, and a pencil to construct a circle with radius *AB*?

PRACTICE

Use the figure to construct each figure in the space provided.

1. a segment with the same length as $\overline{KJ}$

2. a circle with radius *KL*

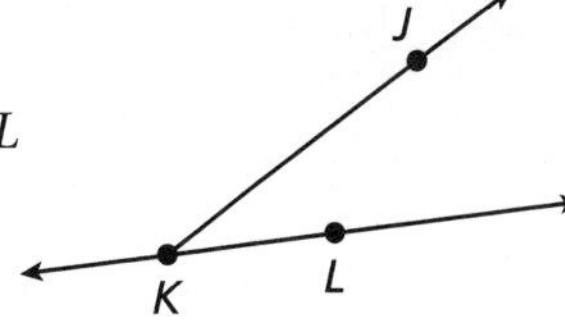

3. Is it possible to construct the midpoint of a ray? Why or why not?

In Exercises 4–7, use the segments shown.

A •——• B
C •————• D

4. Use a compass and straightedge to construct a segment whose length is $AB + CD$.

5. Use a compass and straightedge to construct a segment whose length is $CD - AB$.

6. Use a compass and straightedge to construct a triangle that has two sides of length AB and one side of length CD.

7. Use a compass and straightedge to construct a triangle that has two sides of length CD and one side of length AB.

Additional Practice

For Exercises 1–4, use the segment shown below. Draw your answers in the space provided.

1. Use a compass and straightedge to construct $\overline{XY}$ with the same length as $\overline{UV}$.

2. Use a compass and straightedge to construct a segment whose length is $2 \cdot UV$.

3. Use a compass and straightedge to construct a triangle with sides of length *UV*.

4. Copy $\overline{UV}$. Then bisect $\overline{UV}$ and label the midpoint *M*. Construct a circle with center *M* and radius *MU*. Construct a second circle with center *V* and radius *MU*.

Problem Solving

For Exercises 1–3, use the circle shown.

1. Copy the circle.

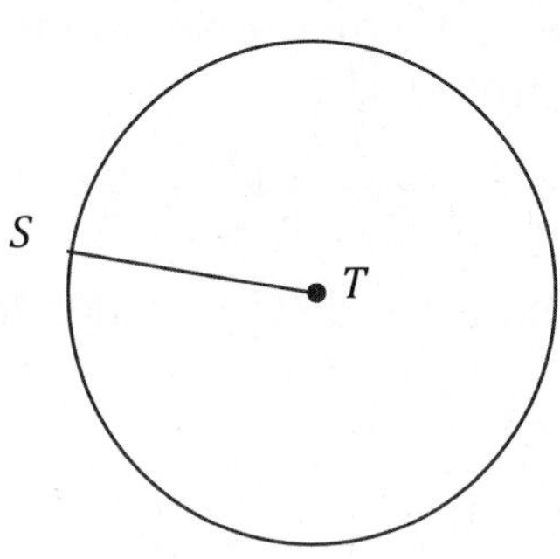

2. Explain how you can use your construction from Exercise 1 to construct two half circles with radius *ST*. Then construct the two half circles.

____

____

____

3. Construct a segment *MN* that is the same length as $\overline{ST}$. Then construct a triangle that has exactly two sides with length *MN*. How does the length of the third side compare with 2 • *MN*?

Choose the best answer.

4. Julia drew $\overline{PQ}$ on a piece of paper. She folded the paper so that point *P* was on top of point *Q*, forming a crease through $\overline{PQ}$. She labeled the intersection of this crease and $\overline{PQ}$ point *S*. If $PQ = 2.4$ centimeters, then what is the length of $\overline{QS}$?

   A 0.6 cm C 2.4 cm

   B 1.2 cm D 4.8 cm

5. Points *J*, *K*, and *L* lie on the same line, and point *K* is between *J* and *L*. Todd constructs $\overline{SV}$ with the same length as $\overline{JL}$. Then he draws point *T* on $\overline{SV}$ so that $\overline{ST}$ is the same length as $\overline{JK}$. Which statement is *not* true?

   F $JK = ST$

   G $ST = SV - TV$

   H $SV = JK + KL$

   J $TV = ST + KL$

Name________________ Class__________ Date________

1-2

Measuring and Constructing Angles

Going Deeper

Video Tutor

Essential question: *What tools and methods can you use to copy an angle and bisect an angle?*

An **angle** is a figure formed by two rays with the same endpoint. The common endpoint is the **vertex** of the angle. The rays are the **sides** of the angle.

Angles may be measured in degrees (°). There are 360° in a circle, so an angle that measures 1° is $\frac{1}{360}$ of a circle. You write $m\angle A$ for the measure of $\angle A$.

Angles may be classified by their measures.

Acute Angle	Right Angle	Obtuse Angle	Straight Angle
A	A	A	A
$0° < m\angle A < 90°$	$m\angle A = 90°$	$90° < m\angle A < 180°$	$m\angle A = 180°$

MCC9-12.G.CO.12

1 EXAMPLE Copying an Angle

Construct an angle with the same measure as $\angle S$.

A In the space below, use a straightedge to draw a ray with endpoint X.

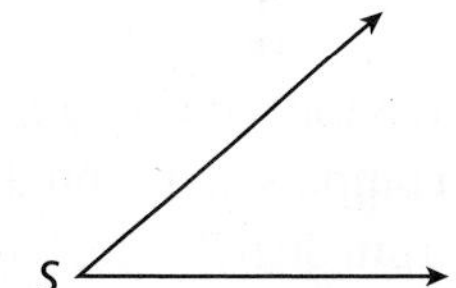

B Place the point of your compass on S and draw an arc that intersects both sides of the angle. Label the points of intersection T and U.

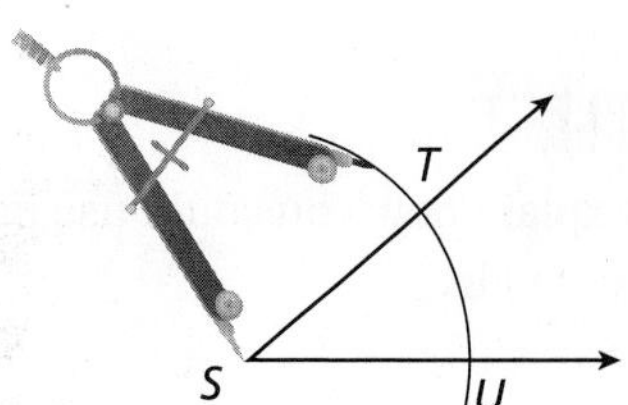

C Without adjusting the compass, place the point of the compass on X and draw an arc that intersects the ray. Label the intersection Y.

D Place the point of the compass on U and open it to the distance TU.

E Without adjusting the compass, place the point of the compass on Y and draw an arc. Label the intersection with the first arc Z.

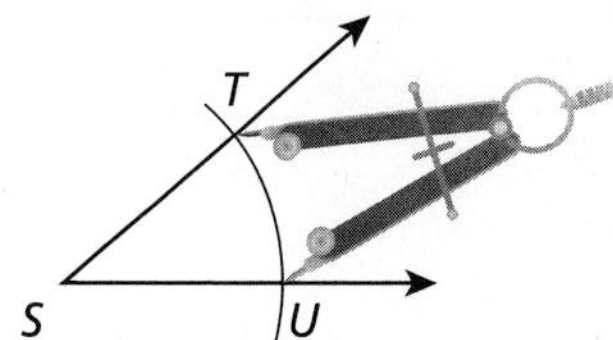

F Use a straightedge to draw $\overrightarrow{XZ}$.

REFLECT

1a. How can you use a protractor to check your construction?

1b. If you draw $\angle X$ so that its sides appear to be longer than the sides shown for $\angle S$, can the two angles have the same measure? Explain.

An **angle bisector** is a ray that divides an angle into two angles that both have the same measure. In the figure, $\overrightarrow{BD}$ bisects $\angle ABC$, so $m\angle ABD = m\angle DBC$. The arcs in the figure show equal angle measures.

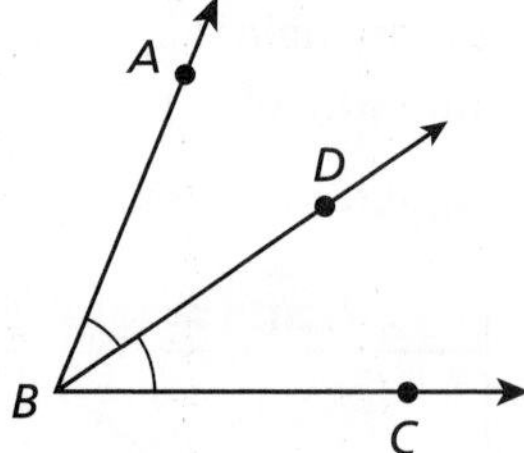

The following example shows how you can use a compass and straightedge to bisect an angle.

MCC9–12.G.CO.12

2 EXAMPLE Constructing the Bisector of an Angle

Construct the bisector of $\angle M$. Work directly on the angle at right.

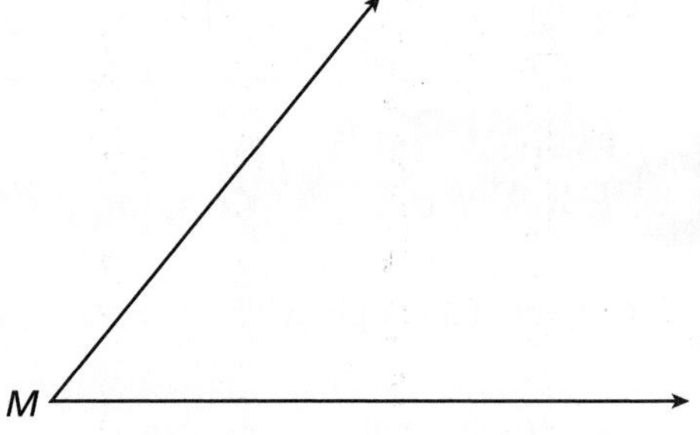

A Place the point of your compass on point M. Draw an arc that intersects both sides of the angle. Label the points of intersection P and Q.

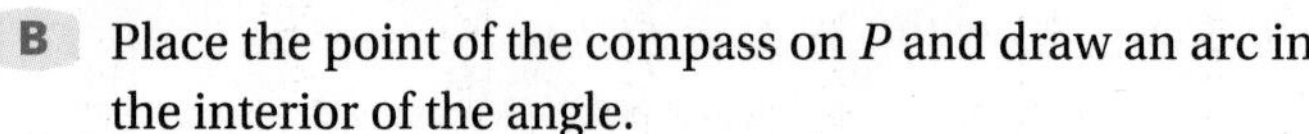

B Place the point of the compass on P and draw an arc in the interior of the angle.

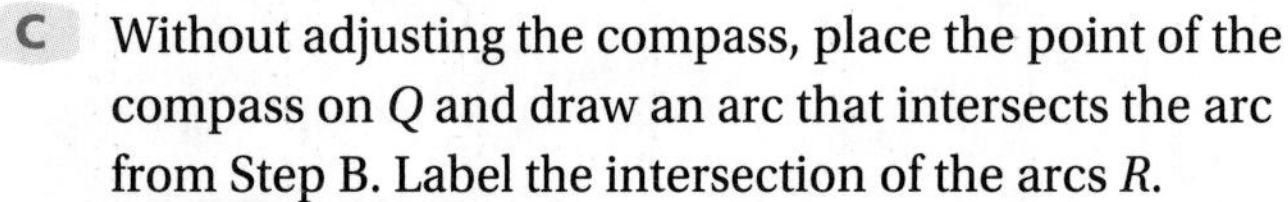

C Without adjusting the compass, place the point of the compass on Q and draw an arc that intersects the arc from Step B. Label the intersection of the arcs R.

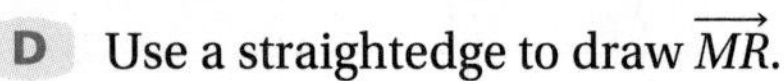

D Use a straightedge to draw $\overrightarrow{MR}$.

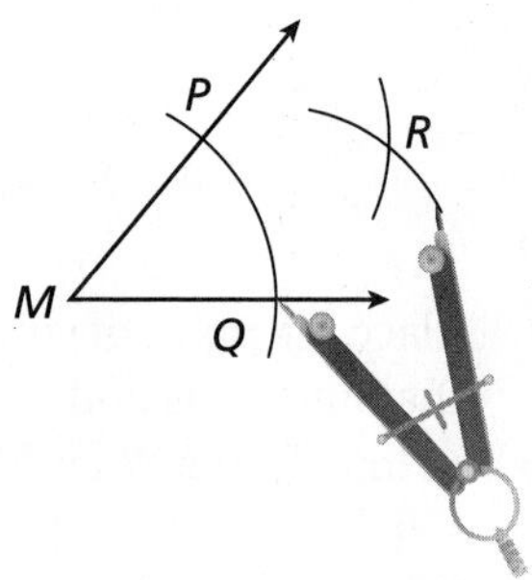

REFLECT

2a. Explain how you could use paper folding to construct the bisector of an angle.

PRACTICE

Construct an angle with the same measure as the given angle.

1.

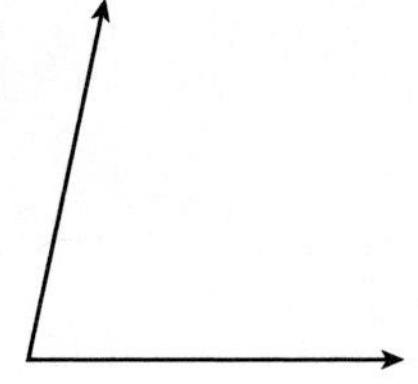

2.

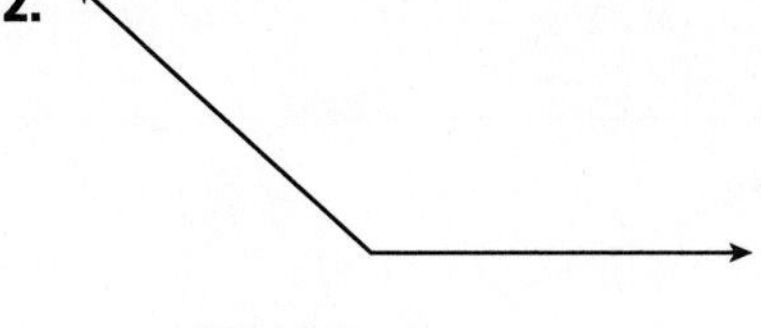

3.

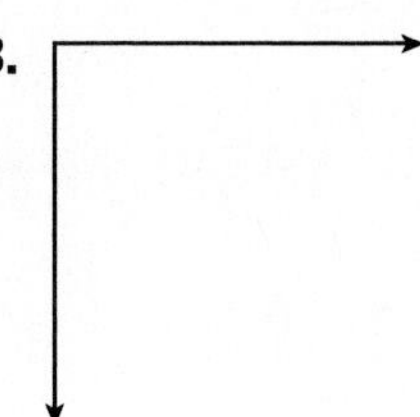

Construct the bisector of the angle.

4.

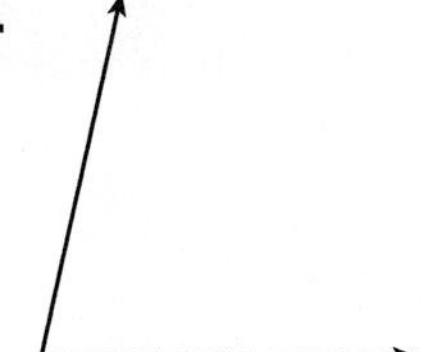

5.

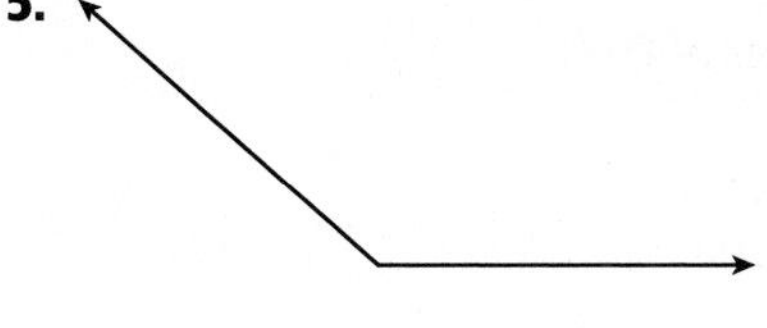

6.

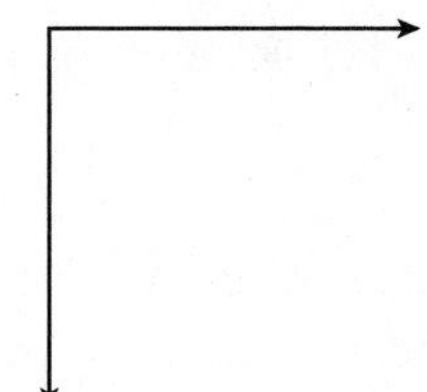

7. Explain how you can use a compass and straightedge to construct an angle that has twice the measure of $\angle A$. Then do the construction in the space provided.

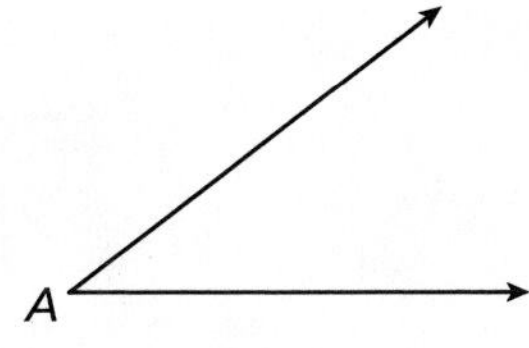

8. Explain how you can use a compass and straightedge to construct an angle that has $\frac{1}{4}$ the measure of $\angle B$. Then do the construction in the space provided.

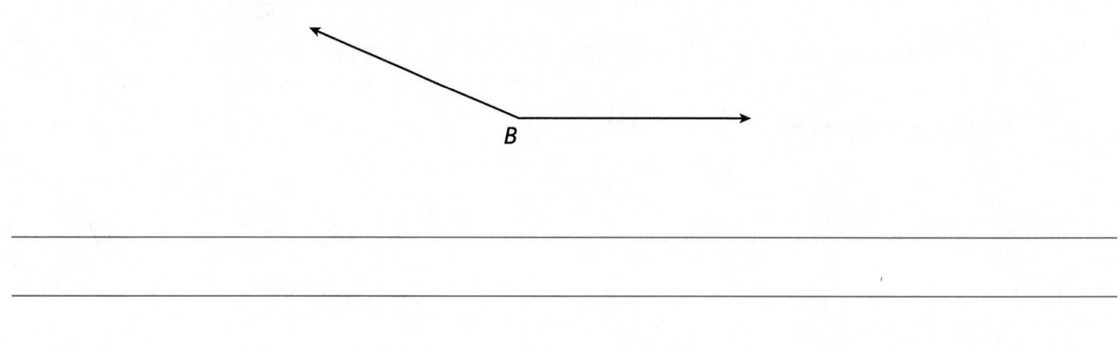

Name__________ Class__________ Date__________

1-2

Additional Practice

For Exercises 1 and 2, use the figure shown.

1. Use a compasss and straightedge to construct angle bisector $\overrightarrow{DG}$. Given that $m\angle EDF = 90°$, find $m\angle EDG$.

   $m\angle EDG =$ __________

2. Use your construction of $\angle EDG$ from Exercise 1. Construct $\angle XYZ$ with the same measure as $\angle EDG$.

3. Use a straightedge to draw an acute angle. Use a compass and straightedge to copy the angle. Then bisect the copy of the angle.

4. Use a straightedge to draw an obtuse angle. Use a compass and straightedge to copy the angle. Then bisect the copy of the angle.

Problem Solving

For Exercises 1–2, use the figure shown.

1. Construct the bisector of $\angle B$ in $\triangle ABC$. Construct the bisectors of $\angle A$ and $\angle C$.

2. What do you notice about the bisectors?

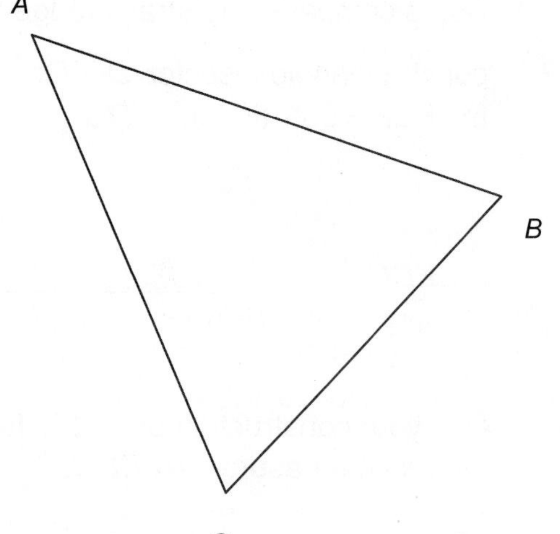

3. Construct an angle whose measure is four times as great as $m\angle K$, shown below.

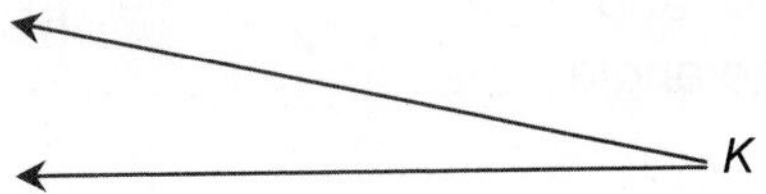

Choose the best answer.

4. Mark drew $\angle PQR$ with measure 168°. He constructed the angle bisector $\overrightarrow{QX}$. Then he bisected $\angle PQX$ by constructing $\overrightarrow{PY}$. What is $m\angle PQY$?

   A 21° B 42° C 84° D 168°

5. Paula bisected $\angle XYZ$, forming angles $\angle XYW$ and $\angle WYZ$. Given that $\angle XYZ$ is an obtuse angle, which statement cannot be true?

   F $m\angle WYZ$ is less than 90°.

   G $m\angle WYZ = m\angle XYW$

   H $m\angle WYZ$ is greater than 90°.

   J $m\angle XYZ = 2 \bullet m\angle XYW$

Name_________________________ Class_______________ Date__________

Using Inductive Reasoning to Make Conjectures

Going Deeper

Essential question: *How can you use examples to support or disprove a conjecture?*

PREP FOR MCC9–12.G.CO.9

1 EXPLORE Making Conjectures about Bisectors of Obtuse Angles

A Draw several obtuse angles. Recall that an obtuse angle is an angle whose measure is between 90° and 180°. One such angle, $\angle ABC$, is shown in the diagram. Ray $\overrightarrow{BD}$ shows the angle bisector of $\angle ABC$.

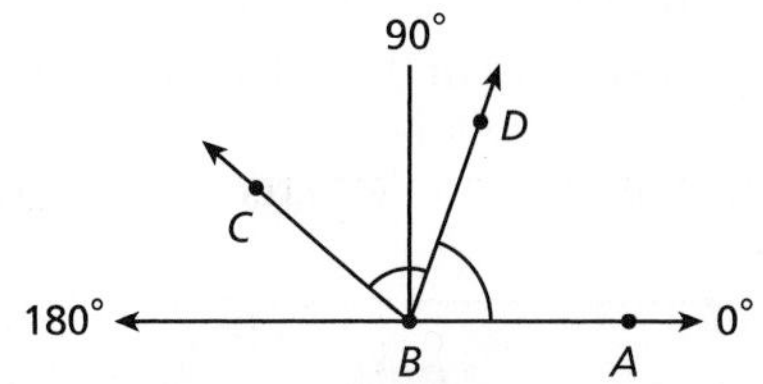

B Using a protractor, measure each angle. Record each measure for each drawing.

C Construct the angle bisector of each angle you drew. Record the measures of the two angles determined by the bisectors on your drawings.

D Fill in the table to record your work. Angle 1 is an example for you.

Angle	1	2	3	4	5	6
Measure	140°					
Measures of Angles Formed by Bisector	70°					
	70°					

REFLECT

1a. Based on your table, make a conjecture about the classification of the angles formed when you bisect an obtuse angle.

____

____

1b. Write a range of angle measures for each of the two angles formed by the angle bisector in each of your diagrams. Justify your range.

____

____

____

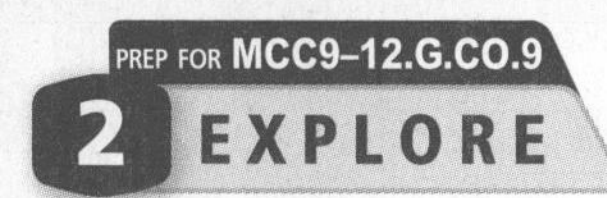

Making Conjectures about Double Angles of Acute Angles

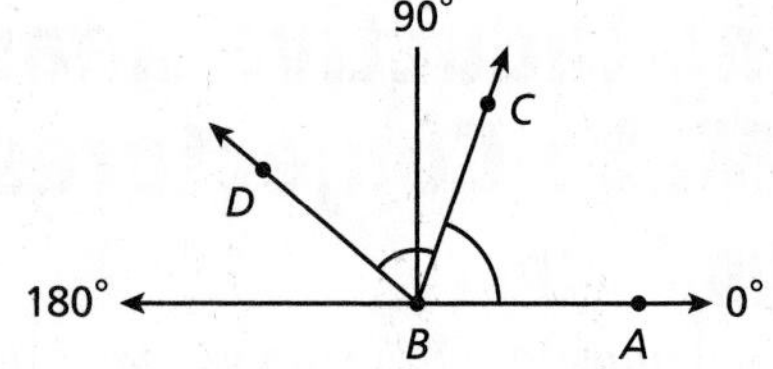

A Draw several acute angles. Recall that an acute angle measures between 0° and 90°. One such angle, $\angle ABC$, is shown in the diagram. Be sure to draw 30° and 60° angles as examples.

B Using a protractor, measure each angle. Record each measure on each angle drawing.

C Using angle construction, draw an adjacent angle for each original angle. In the diagram above, $\angle CBD$ is the congruent adjacent angle. Record the measures of the original angles and the double angles on your drawings.

D Fill in the table to record your work. Angle 1 is an example for you.

Angle	1	2	3	4	5	6
Measure	70°					
Double Angle Measure	140°					

REFLECT

2a. Comment on the following conjecture: When an acute angle is copied so that the new angle is adjacent to the original angle, the resulting double angle is always obtuse.

2b. How many angles must you test in order to determine that the conjecture above is not always true?

2c. For what angle measure will an angle along with its adjacent copy form neither an acute nor an obtuse angle? Explain.

Name________________________ Class______________ Date__________ 1-3

Additional Practice

In each figure, all possible diagonals are drawn from a single vertex. Use the figures in Exercises 1 and 2.

A

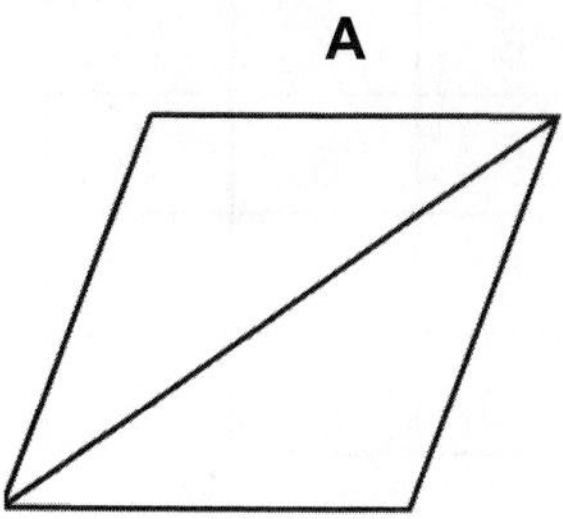

B

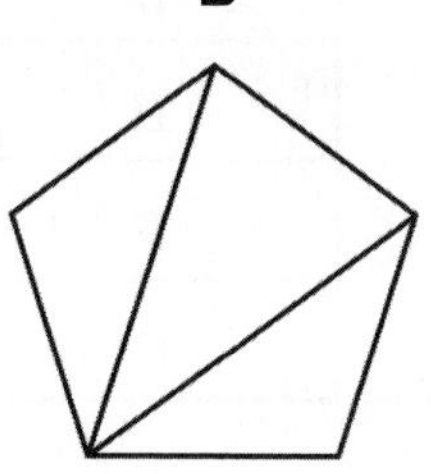

C

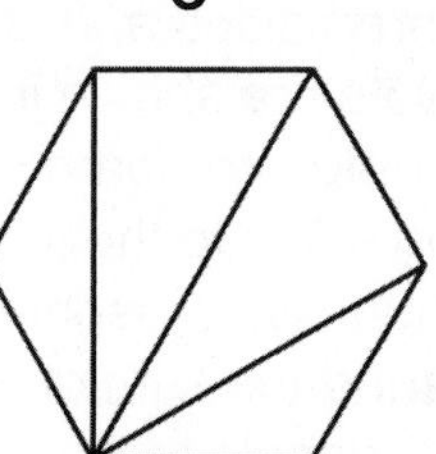

D

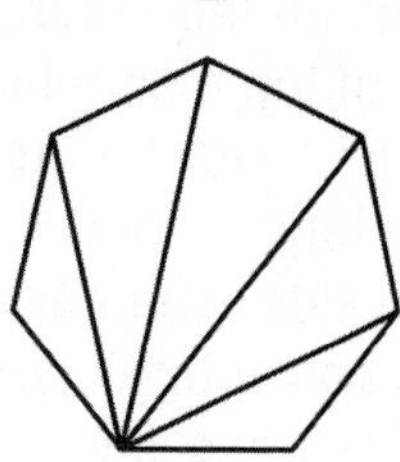

1. Fill in the table.

Figure	A	B	C	D
Number of sides				
Number of triangles formed				

2. Use inductive reasoning to make a conjecture about the number of triangles formed when all possible diagonals are drawn from one vertex of a polygon with *n* sides.

____

Complete each conjecture.

3. The square of any negative number is ______________.
4. The number of segments determined by *n* points is ______________.

Show that each conjecture is false by finding a counterexample.

5. For any integer n, $n^3 > 0$.

____

6. Each angle in a right triangle has a different measure.

____

7. For many years in the United States, each bank printed its own currency. The variety of different bills led to widespread counterfeiting. By the time of the Civil War, a significant fraction of the currency in circulation was counterfeit. If one Civil War soldier had 48 bills, 16 of which were counterfeit, and another soldier had 39 bills, 13 of which were counterfeit, make a conjecture about what fraction of bills were counterfeit at the time of the Civil War.

Problem Solving

1. Residents of an apartment complex were given use of plots of land in a community garden. Some of the plots were shaped like triangles. The lengths (in feet) of the three sides *a*, *b*, and *c* of some of the triangular plots are shown in the table. For each triangular plot, compare the sum of the lengths of any two sides to the length of the third side. Then use inductive reasoning to make a conjecture comparing the sum of the lengths of any two sides of a triangle to the length of the third side.

Triangle	*a*	*b*	*c*
D	6	8	10
E	9	6	5
F	5	7	5
G	10	15	9

____

____

____

The times for the first eight matches of the Santa Barbara Open women's volleyball tournament are shown. Show that each conjecture is false by finding a counterexample.

Match	1	2	3	4	5	6	7	8
Time	0:31	0:56	0:51	0:18	0:50	0:34	1:03	0:36

2. Every one of the first eight matches lasted less than 1 hour.

____

3. These matches were all longer than a half hour.

____

For each of the tiles shown, all of the angles have the same measure. Use a protractor to find the measure of the angles for each tile. Select the best answer.

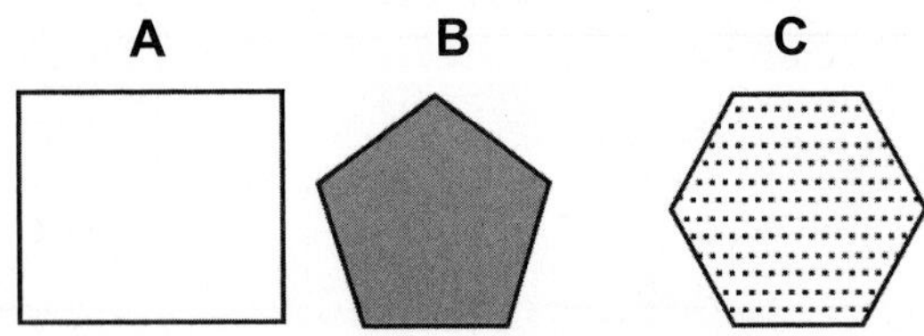

4. Which expressions could you use in the given order to complete the following statement: Figure ▒ has ▒ sides and the sum of the angle measures is ▒ $\times$ 180°.

   A B; 5; 3
   B A; 4; 4
   C C; 6; 3
   D A; 4; 3

5. Which is a reasonable conjecture?

   F The sum of the angle measures of a polygon with n sides is $(4n)°$.
   G The sum of the angle measures of a polygon with n sides is $n(360°)$.
   H The sum of the angle measures of a polygon with n sides is $(n - 2)(180°)$.
   J The sum of the angle measures of a polygon with n sides is $(n - 2)(360°)$.

Name ______________________ Class ______________ Date __________

1-4

Conditional Statements

Extension: Inference Using Venn Diagrams

Video Tutor

Essential question: *How can you use a Venn diagram to interpret conditional statements?*

A conditional statement is one that has the form *If p, then q,* denoted $p \rightarrow q$. The notation $\sim p$ is used to denote "not *p*." You can use Venn diagrams to study conditionals.

MCCMP.3

1 EXPLORE Using Venn Diagrams to Analyze Conditional Statements

Shade the region in the Venn diagram that represents each statement. Part A is already filled in as an example.

All dogs are animals. If an object is a dog, then it is an animal.

p (an object is a dog) q (it is an animal)

A p

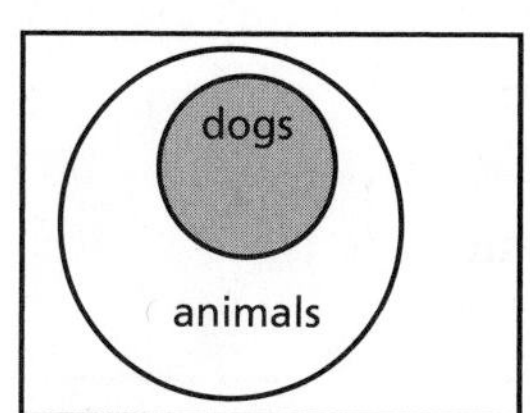

B q

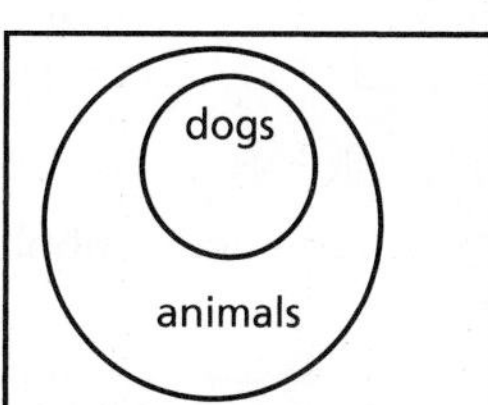

C $\sim p$

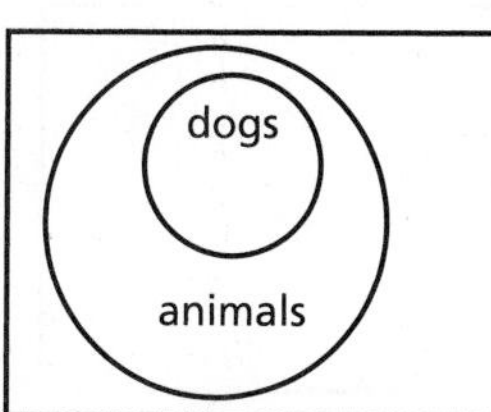

D $\sim q$

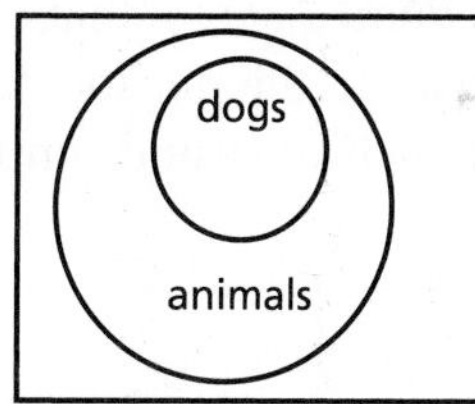

REFLECT

1a. If you know $p \rightarrow q$ and you also know q is true, then can you conclude that p is true or that p is false? Explain how the Venn diagram supports your answer.

____

____

1b. If you know $p \rightarrow q$ and you also know p is false, then can you conclude that q is true or that q is false? Explain how the Venn diagram supports your answer.

____

____

1c. If you know $p \rightarrow q$ and you know $\sim q$, then what can you conclude?

____

PRACTICE

Four Venn diagrams related to $q \rightarrow p$ are shown. Shade the region that represents each statement.

1. q

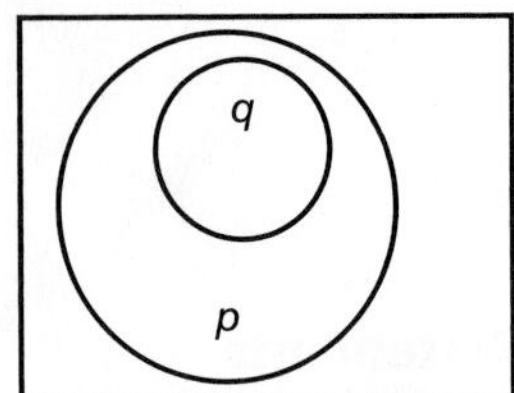

2. p

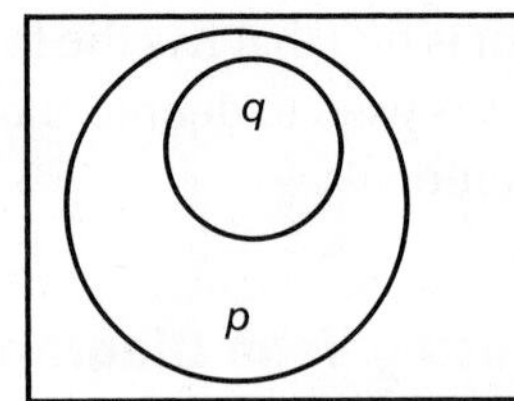

3. $\sim q$

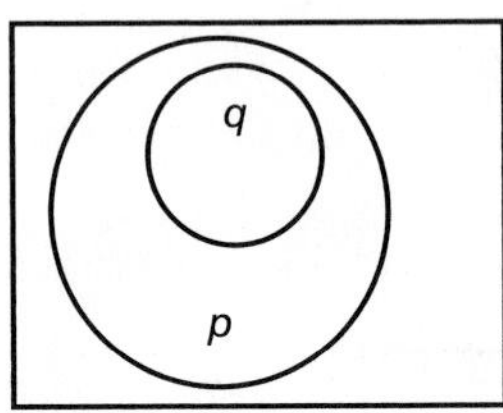

4. $\sim p$

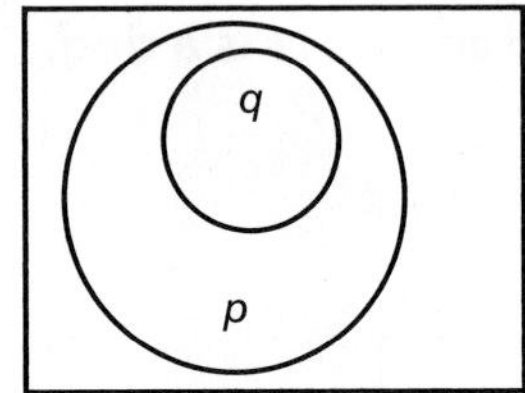

5. If you know $q \rightarrow p$, what other symbolic statement can you make? Explain.

____

____

6. In the box, draw a Venn diagram that conveys $p \rightarrow q$ and $q \rightarrow p$. Describe it. If both a conditional and its converse are true, what can you say about the inverse and contrapositive?

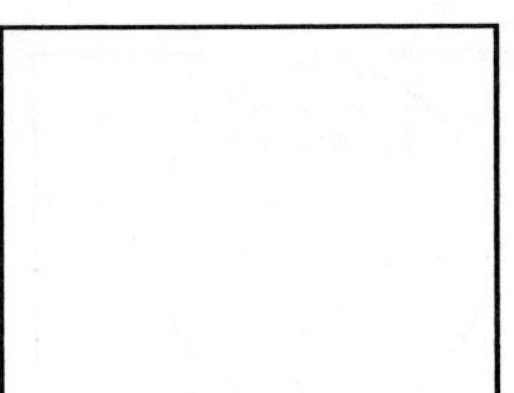

____

____

____

7. In the box, draw a Venn diagram that conveys $p \rightarrow q$ and $q \rightarrow r$. Describe it. Write at least two symbolic statements that you can infer using the diagram.

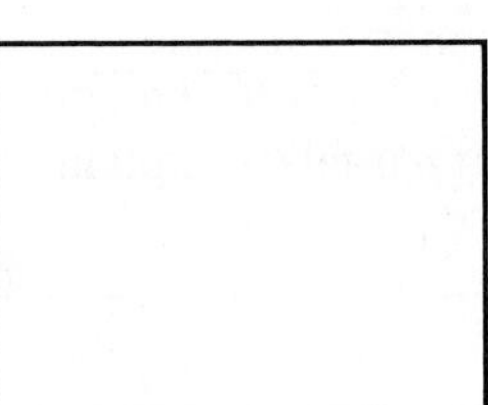

____

____

____

Name ______________________ Class ______________ Date ____________

1-4

Additional Practice

Identify the hypothesis and conclusion of each conditional.

1. If you can see the stars, then it is night.

   Hypothesis: ______________________

   Conclusion: ______________________

2. A pencil writes well if it is sharp.

   Hypothesis: ______________________

   Conclusion: ______________________

Write a conditional statement from each of the following.

3. Three noncollinear points determine a plane.

   ____

4. 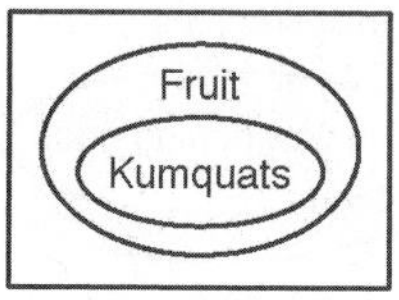

   ____

   ____

   ____

Determine if each conditional is true. If false, give a counterexample.

5. If two points are noncollinear, then a right triangle contains one obtuse angle.

   ____

6. If a liquid is water, then it is composed of hydrogen and oxygen.

   ____

7. If a living thing is green, then it is a plant.

   ____

8. "If G is at 4, then GH is 3." Write the converse, inverse, and contrapositive of this statement. Find the truth value of each.

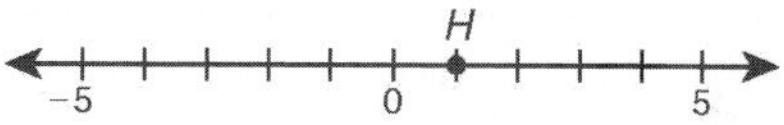

   Converse: ____

   Inverse: ____

   Contrapositive: ____

This chart shows a small part of the *Mammalia* class of animals, the mammals. Write a conditional to describe the relationship between each given pair.

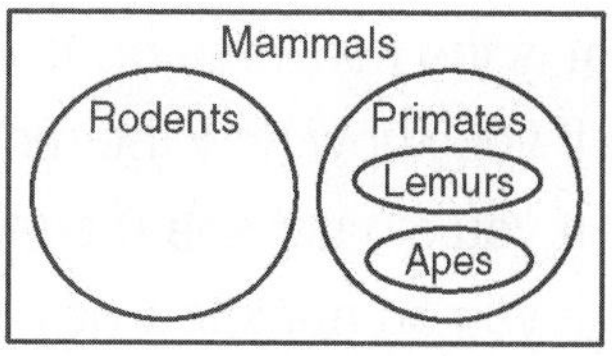

9. primates and mammals ____
10. lemurs and rodents ____
11. rodents and apes ____
12. apes and mammals ____

Problem Solving

1. Write the converse, inverse, and contrapositive of the conditional statement. Find the truth value of each.

If it is April, then there are 30 days in the month.

2. Write a conditional statement from the diagram. Then write the converse, inverse, and contrapositive. Find the truth value of each.

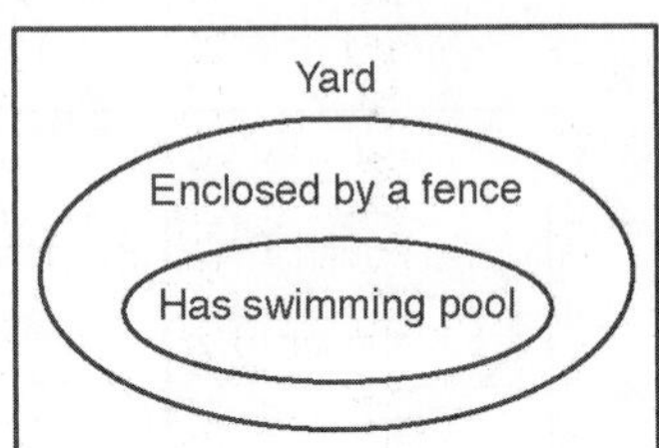

Use the table and the statements listed. Write each conditional and find its truth value.

U.S. Flag	
Year	**Number of Stars**
1777	13
1818	20
1848	30
1959	50

p: 1777 *q*: 30 stars *r*: after 1818 *s*: less than 50 stars

3. $p \rightarrow q$

4. $r \rightarrow s$

5. $q \rightarrow s$

Choose the best answer.

6. What is the converse of "If you saw the movie, then you know how it ends"?
   A If you know how the movie ends, then you saw the movie.
   B If you did not see the movie, then you do not know how it ends.
   C If you do not know how the movie ends, then you did not see the movie.
   D If you do not know how the movie ends, then you saw the movie.

7. What is the inverse of "If you received a text message, then you have a cell phone"?
   F If you have a cell phone, then you received a text message.
   G If you do not have a cell phone, then you did not receive a text message.
   H If you did not receive a text message, then you do not have a cell phone.
   J If you received a text message, then you do not have a cell phone.

Name________________________ Class______________ Date__________

1-5

Using Deductive Reasoning to Verify Conjectures

Going Deeper

Video Tutor

Essential question: *How can you connect statements to visualize a chain of reasoning?*

Deductive reasoning connects true statements to form a valid conclusion. This process can be represented visually by using arrows to show how one true statement follows from a previous true statement. Such a diagram shows the sequence used to link given statements to a final conclusion.

MCCMP.3

1 EXAMPLE Showing Logical Reasoning

Draw arrows to show the logical reasoning used to prove the statement. Some arrows are already drawn to help you.

A **Given:** *m*, and the conditional statements in the boxes

Prove: *c*

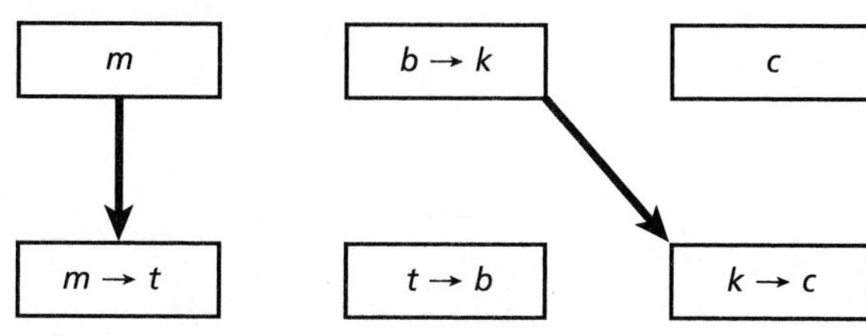

B **Given:** *c*, *d*, and the conditional statements in the boxes

Prove: *z*

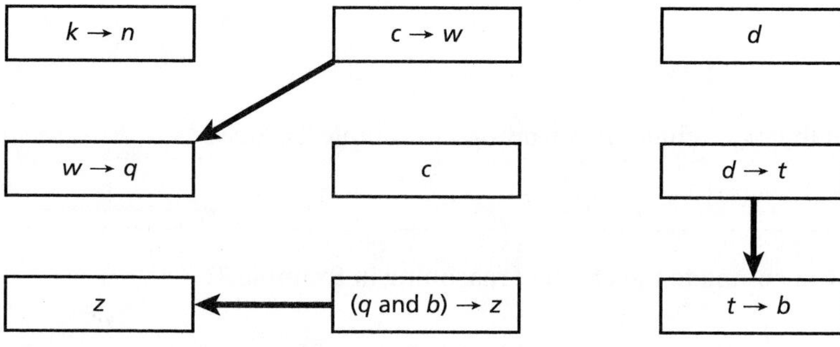

REFLECT

1a. Write a symbolic statement that the chain of reasoning in each part proves.

Part A: ____________ Part B: ____________

1b. In a chain of reasoning, what do you call the statements that have arrows only pointing *away* from them? What do you call the statements that have arrows only pointing *toward* them?

____

1c. Are there any statements in Part B that are not used in the chain of reasoning? Explain.

1d. In the space below, arrange the statements from Part B and draw arrows connecting them in a way that makes the order of the reasoning clearer.

MCCMP.3

2 EXAMPLE Completing a Chain of Logical Reasoning

Draw arrows to show the logical reasoning used to prove the statement. Provide any missing information.

Given: k, and the conditional statements in the boxes

Prove: b

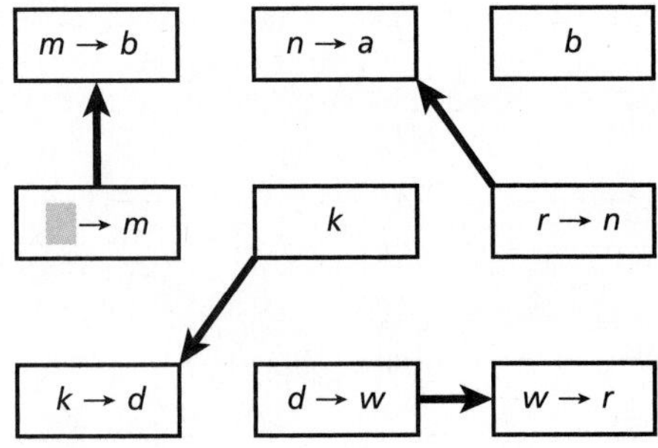

REFLECT

2a. Write a symbolic statement that your chain of reasoning in Example 2 proves.

2b. Is there more than one way to complete the chain of reasoning in Example 2? Explain.

2c. In Example 2, suppose the box with the missing information is completely blank. Is there more than one way to complete the chain of reasoning? Explain.

PRACTICE

Draw arrows to show the logical reasoning used to prove the statement.

1. Given: *z*, and statements in boxes

Prove: *c*

c	$a \to p$	$z \to m$
$p \to c$	$m \to a$	z

2. Given: *j*, and statements in boxes

Prove: *x*

$b \to k$	$w \to b$	$j \to w$
$k \to x$	j	x

3. Given: *t*, *y*, and statements in boxes

Prove: *q*

q	y	$t \to d$
$y \to k$	$n \to s$	t
(s and k) $\to q$	$d \to n$	

4. Given: *h*, *m*, and statements in boxes

Prove: *r*

r	(p and z) $\to r$	
$m \to p$	$b \to z$	h
m	$g \to w$	$h \to b$

Draw arrows to show the logical reasoning used to prove the statement. Provide any missing information.

5. Given: *b*, and statements in boxes

Prove: *e*

$j \to n$	$n \to f$	e
$s \to j$	$b \to r$	▒ $\to x$
$r \to s$	b	$x \to e$

6. Given: *g*, and statements in boxes

Prove: *a*

$e \to t$	$k \to d$	$t \to$ ▒
g	$c \to e$	$n \to a$
$g \to c$	a	$m \to z$

7. Write a symbolic statement for each conditional statement. Then represent the chain of reasoning using symbolic statements linked by arrows.

Band members must stay after school on Wednesday.

If the marching band performs at halftime, then the band practices on Wednesday.

If the band practices on Wednesday, then band members must stay after school on Wednesday.

If there is a football game on Friday, then the marching band performs at halftime.

There is a football game on Friday.

Name________________________ Class______________ Date__________

1-5

Additional Practice

Draw arrows to show the logical reasoning used to prove the statement.

1. **Given:** *y*, and statements in boxes.
   Prove: *a*

$y \to t$	a	$p \to a$
$t \to z$	y	$z \to p$

2. **Given:** *m*, and statements in boxes.
   Prove: *j*

m	$n \to j$	$k \to n$
$z \to k$	$m \to z$	j

3. **Given:** *h*, *q*, and statements in boxes.
   Prove: *f*

$r \to u$	$h \to n$	h
$u \to j$	$(n \text{ and } x) \to f$	f
$q \to r$	$j \to x$	q

4. **Given:** *b*, *y*, and statements in boxes.
   Prove: *j*

j	$z \to k$	$(x \text{ and } n) \to j$
$t \to z$	y	$k \to n$
$y \to t$	b	$b \to x$

Draw arrows to show the logical reasoning used to prove the statement. Provide any missing information.

5. **Given:** *a*, and statements in boxes.
   Prove: *w*

$u \to q$	q	$c \to i$
w	$\square \to c$	$i \to k$
$e \to u$	$k \to w$	$a \to e$

6. **Given:** *a*, and statements in boxes.
   Prove: *z*

$s \to k$	$(x \text{ and } k) \to z$	$v \to s$
z	x	$a \to \square$
$g \to x$	a	g

Problem Solving

Write a symbolic statement for each conditional statement. Then represent the chain of reasoning using symbolic statements linked by arrows.

1. Paloma can drive her parents' car. ____________

   Paloma passes her road test. ____________

   Paloma is covered by her parents' motor vehicle insurance. ____________

   If Paloma passes her road test, then she will get her driver's license. ____________

   If Paloma has a driver's license and is covered by insurance, then she can drive her parents car. ____________

Given *t* and *z*, and the conditional statements in the boxes shown, Jeremy drew arrows to complete the chain of reasoning. Select the best answer.

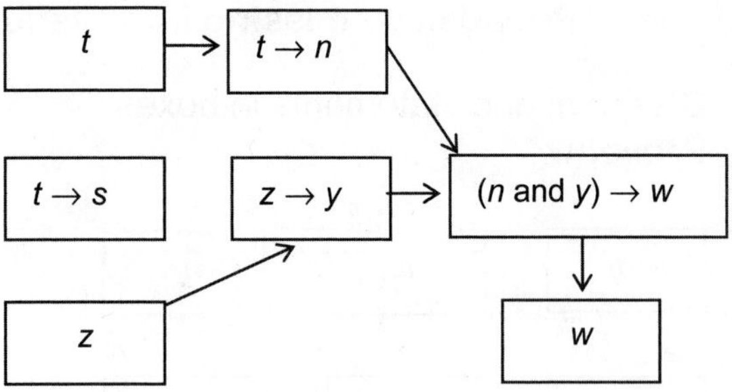

t

$t \to n$

$t \to s$

$z \to y$

$(n \text{ and } y) \to w$

z

w

2. Which statement can you *not* assume to be true from the chain of reasoning?

   A $t \to w$

   B $t \to n$

   C $z \to y$

   D $(n \text{ and } y) \to w$

3. Which symbolic statement did Jeremy prove?

   F $t \to n \to w$

   G $z \to (y \text{ and } w)$

   H $(t \text{ and } z) \to w$

   J $(n \text{ and } y) \to \text{w}$

4. Which statement is *not* necessary in the chain of reasoning?

   A $t \to n$

   B $t \to s$

   C z

   D $\text{z} \to \text{y}$

Name ____________________ Class __________ Date ________

2-1

Biconditional Statements and Definitions

Going Deeper

Video Tutor

Essential question: *How can you analyze the truth of a biconditional statement?*

You have seen *If p, then q* and the notation $p \rightarrow q$. The notation **iff** is shorthand for *if and only if* and means a pair of statements.

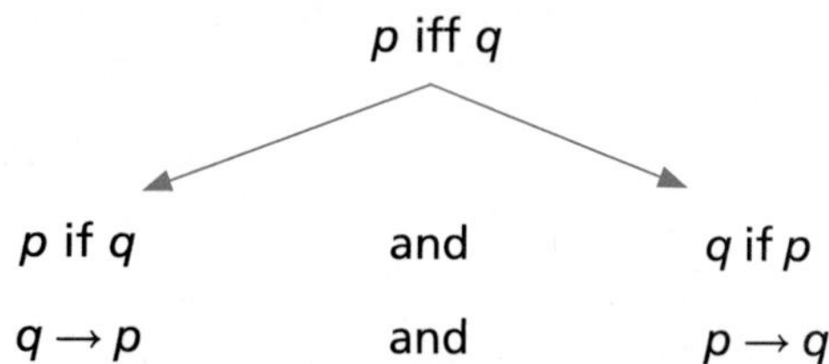

$q \rightarrow p$ and $p \rightarrow q$

The conjunction of these two statements is a biconditional statement. It is true only if both parts are true. It is false if either part is false.

MCCMP.3

1 EXAMPLE Analyzing Biconditionals and Definitions

A student defined *square* this way:

A polygon is a square if and only if it has four right angles.

A Write the biconditional as a pair of conditional statements.

If a polygon ____________________, then the polygon has four right angles.

If a polygon ____________________, then the polygon is a square.

B Analyze each part and tell whether it is true or false. If false, give a counterexample. Explain your thinking.

square → four right angles

____

four right angles → square

____

C Tell whether the student's definition of square is a good one. Explain.

____

____

____

REFLECT

1a. Why is it necessary to prove only one of the two parts of a biconditional is false to conclude that the biconditional is false?

1b. Revise the student's definition of a square so that it is a good one.

PRACTICE

1. A student defined a scalene triangle as follows: A triangle is scalene if and only if it is a right triangle. Is the biconditional true or false? Justify your claim.

2. A student defined a rectangle as a parallelogram with opposite sides the same length. Describe what is wrong with this definition. Then write a correct definition of a rectangle.

3. An acute triangle is a triangle whose angles are acute. Find the error in the following statement.

A triangle is acute if and only if it has one or more acute angles.

Name ______________________ Class ______________ Date ______________

2-1

Additional Practice

Write the conditional statement and converse within each biconditional.

1. The tea kettle is whistling if and only if the water is boiling.

   Conditional: ______________________

   Converse: ______________________

2. A biconditional is true if and only if the conditional and converse are both true.

   Conditional: ______________________

   Converse: ______________________

For each conditional, write the converse and a biconditional statement.

3. Conditional: If n is an odd number, then $n - 1$ is divisible by 2.

   Converse: ______________________

   Biconditional: ______________________

4. Conditional: An angle is obtuse when it measures between 90° and 180°.

   Converse: ______________________

   Biconditional: ______________________

Determine whether a true biconditional can be written from each conditional statement. If not, give a counterexample.

5. If the lamp is unplugged, then the bulb does not shine.

   ____

6. The date can be the 29th if and only if it is not February.

   ____

Write each definition as a biconditional.

7. A cube is a three-dimensional solid with six square faces.

   ____

   ____

8. Tanya claims that the definition of *doofus* is "her younger brother."

   ____

   ____

Problem Solving

Use the table for Exercises 1–4. Determine if a true biconditional statement can be written from each conditional. If so, then write a biconditional. If not, then explain why not.

Mountain Bike Races	Characteristics
Cross-country	A massed-start race. Riders must carry their own tools to make repairs.
Downhill	Riders start at intervals. The rider with the lowest time wins.
Freeride	Courses contain cliffs, drops, and ramps. Scoring depends on the style and the time.
Marathon	A massed-start race that covers more than 250 kilometers.

1. If a mountain bike race is mass-started, then it is a cross-country race.

____

____

____

2. If a mountain bike race is downhill, then time is a factor in who wins.

____

____

____

3. If a mountain bike race covers more than 250 kilometers, then it is a marathon race.

____

____

____

4. If a race course contains cliffs, drops, and ramps, then it is not a marathon race.

____

____

____

Choose the best answer.

5. The cat is the only species that can hold its tail vertically while it walks.
   - A The converse of this statement is false.
   - B The biconditional of this statement is false.
   - C The biconditional of this statement is true.
   - D This statement cannot be written as a biconditional.

6. Which conditional statement can be used to write a true biconditional?
   - F If you travel 2 miles in 4 minutes, then distance is a function of time.
   - G If the distance depends on the time, then distance is a function of time.
   - H If y increases as x increases, then y is a function of x.
   - J If y is not a function of x, then y does not increase as x increases.

Name________________ Class__________ Date________

2-2

Algebraic Proof

Going Deeper

Essential question: *What kinds of justifications can you use in writing algebraic and geometric proofs?*

Video Tutor

PREP FOR MCC9–12.G.CO.9

1 ENGAGE Introducing Proofs

In mathematics, a **proof** is a logical argument that uses a sequence of statements to prove a conjecture. Once the conjecture is proved, it is called a **theorem**.

Each statement in a proof must follow logically from what has come before and must have a reason to support it. The reason may be a piece of given information, a definition, a previously proven theorem, or a mathematical property.

The table states some properties of equality that you have seen in earlier courses. You have used these properties to solve algebraic equations and you will often use these properties as reasons in a proof.

Properties of Equality	
Addition Property of Equality	If $a = b$, then $a + c = b + c$.
Subtraction Property of Equality	If $a = b$, then $a - c = b - c$.
Multiplication Property of Equality	If $a = b$, then $ac = bc$.
Division Property of Equality	If $a = b$ and $c \neq 0$, then $\frac{a}{c} = \frac{b}{c}$.
Reflexive Property of Equality	$a = a$
Symmetric Property of Equality	If $a = b$, then $b = a$.
Transitive Property of Equality	If $a = b$ and $b = c$, then $a = c$.
Substitution Property of Equality	If $a = b$, then b can be substituted for a in any expression.

REFLECT

1a. Given the equation $3 = x - 2$, you quickly write the solution as $x = 5$. Which property or properties of equality are you using? Explain.

____

____

1b. Give an example of an equation that you can solve using the Division Property of Equality. Explain how you would use this property to solve the equation.

____

____

A **postulate** (or *axiom*) is a statement that is accepted as true without proof. Like undefined terms, postulates are basic building blocks of geometry. The following postulate states that the lengths of segments "add up" in a natural way.

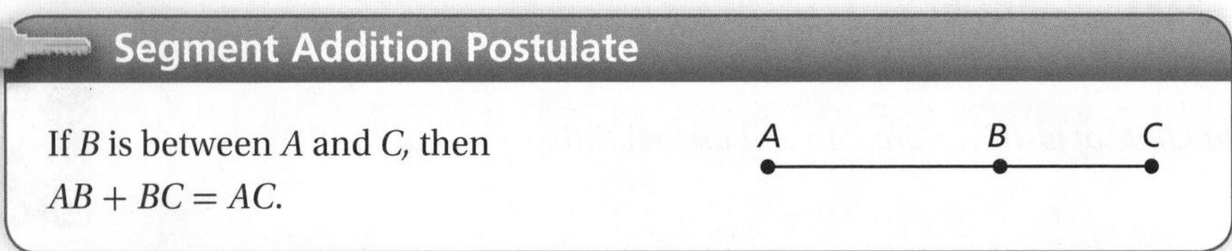

The Angle Addition Postulate is similar to the Segment Addition Postulate.

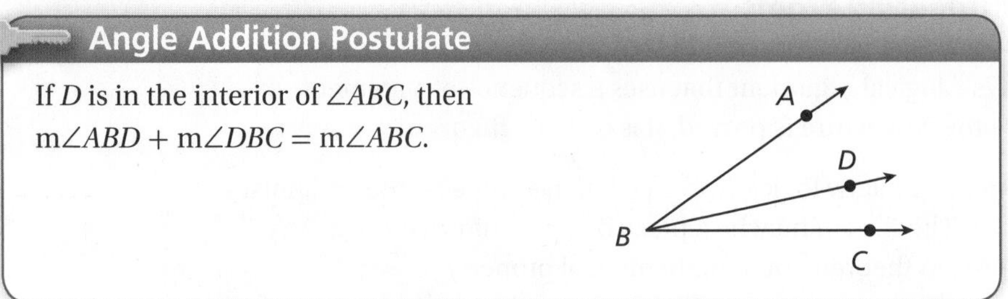

Properties of equality and postulates can be used as reasons in proofs. Note how the proof shown below in Exercise 1 is arranged in a two-column format so that it is easy to see the logical sequence of the statements and their corresponding reasons.

PRACTICE

1. If A, B, C, and D are collinear, as shown in the figure, with $AC = BD$, then $AB = CD$. Complete the proof by writing the missing statements or reasons.

Given: $AC = BD$
Prove: $AB = CD$

Statements	Reasons
1.	1. Given
2. $AC = AB + BC$; $BD = BC + CD$	2.
3.	3. Substitution Property of Equality
4. $AB = CD$	4.

2. In the figure, X is the midpoint of $\overline{WY}$, and Y is the midpoint of $\overline{XZ}$. Explain how to prove $WX = YZ$.

Name ______________________ Class ____________ Date __________ **2-2**

Additional Practice

Solve each equation. Show all your steps and write a justification for each step.

1. $\frac{1}{5}(a + 10) = -3$

2. $t + 6.5 = 3t - 1.3$

3. The formula for the perimeter P of a rectangle with length ℓ and width w is $P = 2(\ell + w)$. Find the length of the rectangle shown here if the perimeter is $9\frac{1}{2}$ feet. Solve the equation for ℓ and justify each step.

$1\frac{1}{4}$ ft

ℓ

Write a justification for each step.

4.

$7x - 3$

H $2x + 6$ I $3x - 3$ J

$HJ = HI + IJ$ ______________

$7x - 3 = (2x + 6) + (3x - 3)$ ______________

$7x - 3 = 5x + 3$ ______________

$7x = 5x + 6$ ______________

$2x = 6$ ______________

$x = 3$ ______________

Identify the property that justifies each statement.

5. $m = n$, so $n = m$.

____

6. $\angle ABC \cong \angle ABC$

____

7. $\overline{KL} \cong \overline{LK}$

____

8. $p = q$ and $q = -1$, so $p = -1$.

____

Problem Solving

1. Because of a recent computer glitch, an airline mistakenly sold tickets for round-trip flights at a discounted price. The equation $n(p + t) = 3298.75$ relates the number of discounted tickets sold n, the price of each ticket p, and the tax per ticket t. What was the discounted price of each ticket if 1015 tickets were sold and the tax per ticket was \$1.39? Solve the equation for p. Justify each step.

2. The equation $C = 7.25s + 15.95a$ describes the total cost of admission C to the aquarium. How many student tickets were sold if the total cost for the entire class and 6 adults was \$298.70? Solve the equation for s. Justify each step.

s = number of student tickets
a = number of adult tickets
C = total cost of admission

Refer to the figure. Choose the best answer.

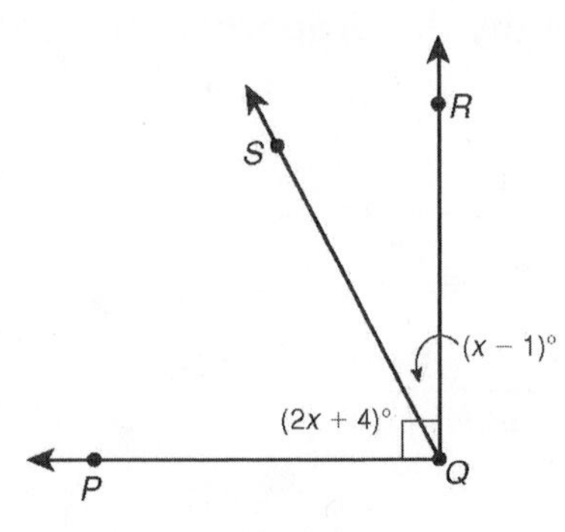

3. Which could be used to find the value of x?
   A Segment Addition Postulate
   B Angle Addition Postulate
   C Transitive Property of Congruence
   D Definition of supplementary angles

4. What is $m\angle SQR$?
   F 28°
   G 29°
   H 61°
   J 62°

Name ______________________ Class ______________ Date __________

2-3

Geometric Proof

Going Deeper

Essential question: *How can you organize the deductive reasoning of a geometric proof?*

You will use the Angle Addition Postulate and the following definitions to prove an important theorem about angles.

Opposite rays are two rays that have a common endpoint and form a straight line. A **linear pair** of angles is a pair of adjacent angles whose noncommon sides are opposite rays.

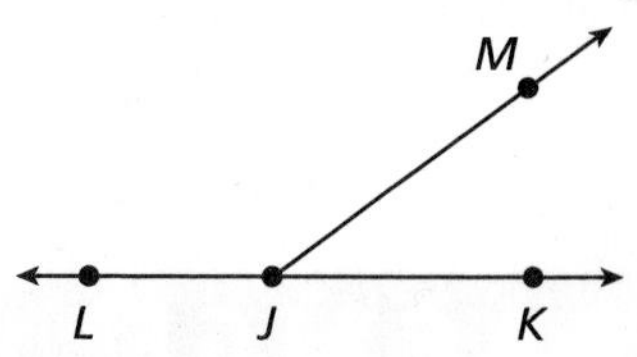

In the figure, $\overrightarrow{JK}$ and $\overrightarrow{JL}$ are opposite rays; $\angle MJK$ and $\angle MJL$ are a linear pair of angles.

Recall that two angles are *complementary* if the sum of their measures is 90°. Two angles are *supplementary* if the sum of their measures is 180°. The following theorem ties together some of the preceding ideas.

MCC9–12.G.CO.9

1 PROOF **Linear Pair Theorem**

If two angles form a linear pair, then they are supplementary.

Given: $\angle MJK$ and $\angle MJL$ are a linear pair of angles.
Prove: $\angle MJK$ and $\angle MJL$ are supplementary.

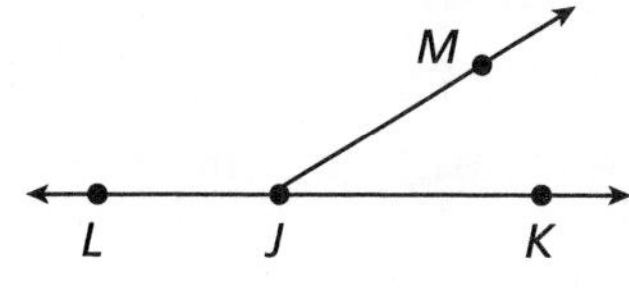

A Develop a plan for the proof.

Since it is given that $\angle MJK$ and $\angle MJL$ are a linear pair of angles, $\overrightarrow{JL}$ and $\overrightarrow{JK}$ are opposite rays. They form a straight angle. Explain why $m\angle MJK + m\angle MJL$ must equal 180°.

____

B Complete the proof by writing the missing reasons. Choose from the following reasons.

Angle Addition Postulate | Definition of opposite rays | Substitution Property of Equality | Given

Statements	Reasons
1. $\angle MJK$ and $\angle MJL$ are a linear pair.	1.
2. $\overrightarrow{JL}$ and $\overrightarrow{JK}$ are opposite rays.	2. Definition of linear pair
3. $\overrightarrow{JL}$ and $\overrightarrow{JK}$ form a straight line.	3.
4. $m\angle LJK = 180°$	4. Definition of straight angle
5. $m\angle MJK + m\angle MJL = m\angle LJK$	5.
6. $m\angle MJK + m\angle MJL = 180°$	6.
7. $\angle MJK$ and $\angle MJL$ are supplementary.	7. Definition of supplementary angles

REFLECT

1a. Is it possible to prove the theorem by measuring $\angle MJK$ and $\angle MJL$ in the figure and showing that the sum of the angle measures is 180°? Explain.

1b. The proof shows that if two angles form a linear pair, then they are supplementary. Is this statement true in the other direction? That is, if two angles are supplementary, must they be a linear pair? Why or why not?

PRACTICE

1. You can use the Linear Pair Theorem to prove a result about vertical angles. Complete the proof by writing the missing statements or reasons.

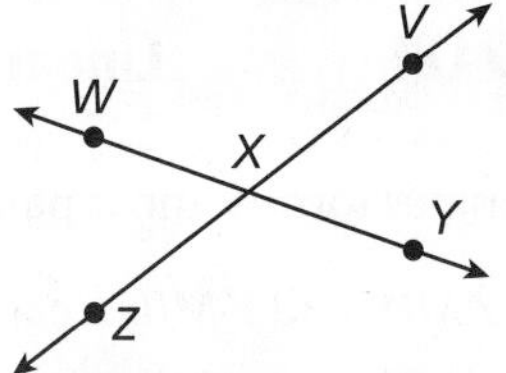

Given: $\angle VXW$ and $\angle ZXY$ are vertical angles, as shown.

Prove: $m\angle VXW = m\angle ZXY$

Statements	Reasons
1. $\angle VXW$ and $\angle ZXY$ are vertical angles.	1.
2. $\angle VXW$ and $\angle ZXY$ are formed by intersecting lines.	2. Definition of vertical angles
3. $\angle VXW$ and $\angle WXZ$ are a linear pair. $\angle WXZ$ and $\angle ZXY$ are a linear pair.	3. Definition of linear pair
4. $\angle VXW$ and $\angle WXZ$ are supplementary.	4.
5. $m\angle VXW + m\angle WXZ = 180°$	5.
6.	6. Linear Pair Theorem
7.	7. Definition of supplementary angles
8. $m\angle VXW + m\angle WXZ = m\angle WXZ + m\angle ZXY$	8. Transitive Property of Equality
9. $m\angle VXW = m\angle ZXY$	9.

Name ________________ Class ________ Date ________

Additional Practice

Write a justification for each step.

Given: $AB = EF$, B is the midpoint of $\overline{AC}$, and E is the midpoint of $\overline{DF}$.

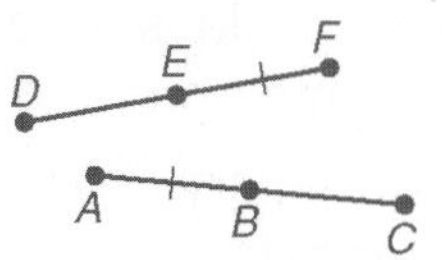

1. B is the midpoint of $\overline{AC}$, and E is the midpoint of $\overline{DF}$. ________________
2. $\overline{AB} \cong \overline{BC}$, and $\overline{DE} \cong \overline{EF}$. ________________
3. $AB = BC$, and $DE = EF$. ________________
4. $AB + BC = AC$, and $DE + EF = DF$. ________________
5. $2AB = AC$, and $2EF = DF$. ________________
6. $AB = EF$ ________________
7. $2AB = 2EF$ ________________
8. $AC = DF$ ________________
9. $\overline{AC} \cong \overline{DF}$ ________________

Fill in the blanks to complete the two-column proof.

10. **Given:** $\angle HKJ$ is a straight angle. $\overrightarrow{KI}$ bisects $\angle HKJ$.
    Prove: $\angle IKJ$ is a right angle.
    Proof:

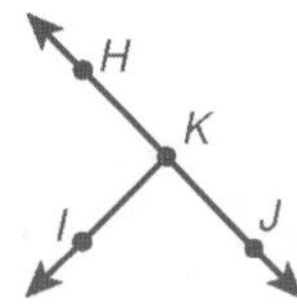

Statements	Reasons
1. a. ________________	1. Given
2. $m\angle HKJ = 180°$	2. b. ________________
3. c. ________________	3. Given
4. $\angle IKJ \cong \angle IKH$	4. Def. of $\angle$ bisector
5. $m\angle IKJ = m\angle IKH$	5. Def. of $\cong$ $\angle$s
6. d. ________________	6. $\angle$ Add. Post.
7. $2m\angle IKJ = 180°$	7. e. Subst. (Steps ________)
8. $m\angle IKJ = 90°$	8. Div. Prop. of $=$
9. $\angle IKJ$ is a right angle.	9. f. ________________

Problem Solving

1. Refer to the diagram of the stained-glass window and use the given plan to write a two-column proof.

   Given: $\angle 1$ and $\angle 3$ are supplementary.
   $\angle 2$ and $\angle 4$ are supplementary.
   $\angle 3 \cong \angle 4$

   Prove: $\angle 1 \cong \angle 2$

   Plan: Use the definition of supplementary angles to write the given information in terms of angle measures. Then use the Substitution Property of Equality and the Subtraction Property of Equality to conclude that $\angle 1 \cong \angle 2$.

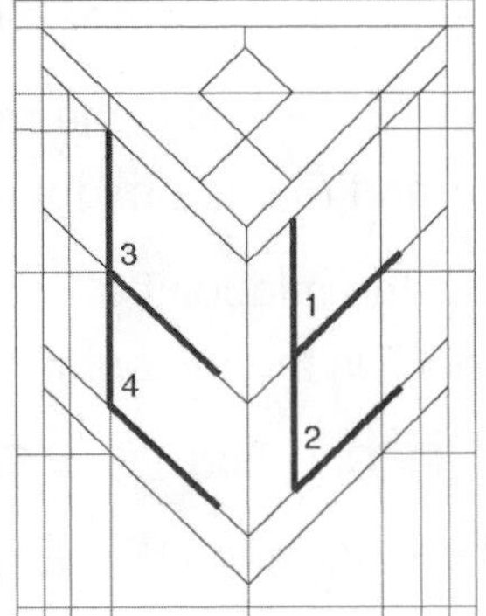

The position of a sprinter at the starting blocks is shown in the diagram. Which statement can be proved using the given information? Choose the best answer.

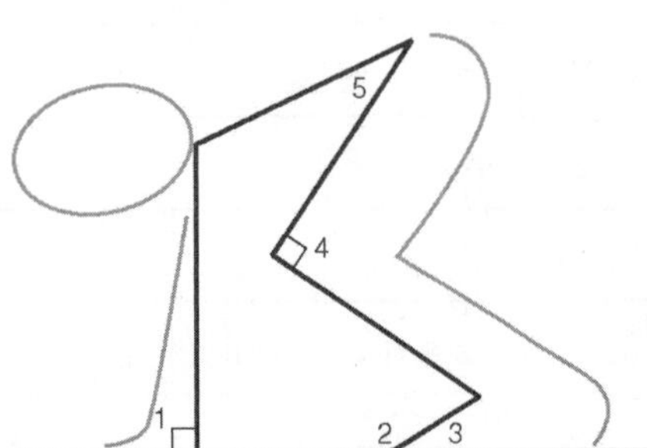

2. **Given:** $\angle 1$ and $\angle 4$ are right angles.

   A $\angle 3 \cong \angle 5$ C $m\angle 1 + m\angle 4 = 90°$

   B $\angle 1 \cong \angle 4$ D $m\angle 3 + m\angle 5 = 180°$

3. **Given:** $\angle 2$ and $\angle 3$ are supplementary.
   $\angle 2$ and $\angle 5$ are supplementary.

   F $\angle 3 \cong \angle 5$ H $\angle 3$ and $\angle 5$ are complementary.

   G $\angle 2 \cong \angle 5$ J $\angle 1$ and $\angle 2$ are supplementary.

Name________________________ Class________________ Date____________

2-4

Flowchart and Paragraph Proofs
Going Deeper

Essential question: *What are some formats you can use to organize geometric proofs?*

Video Tutor

MCC9–12.G.CO.9

1 PROOF Vertical Angles Theorem

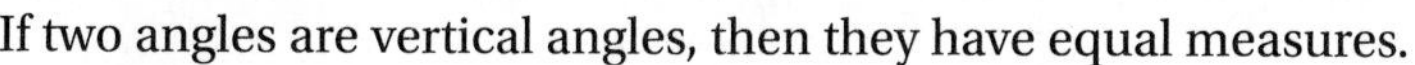

If two angles are vertical angles, then they have equal measures.

Given: $\angle 1$ and $\angle 3$ are vertical angles.
Prove: $m\angle 1 = m\angle 3$

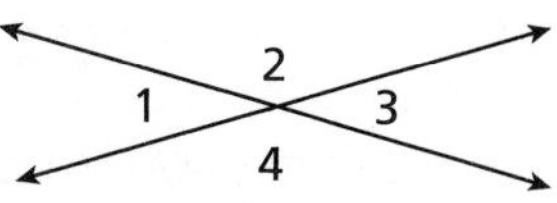

A Develop a plan for the proof.

Since $\angle 1$ and $\angle 2$ are a linear pair, and $\angle 2$ and $\angle 3$ are a linear pair, these pairs of angles are supplementary. This means $m\angle 1 + m\angle 2 = 180°$ and $m\angle 2 + m\angle 3 = 180°$. By substitution, $m\angle 1 + m\angle 2 = m\angle 2 + m\angle 3$. What is the final step in the plan?

____

B Complete a flowchart proof of the Vertical Angles Theorem by supplying the missing statements and reasons.

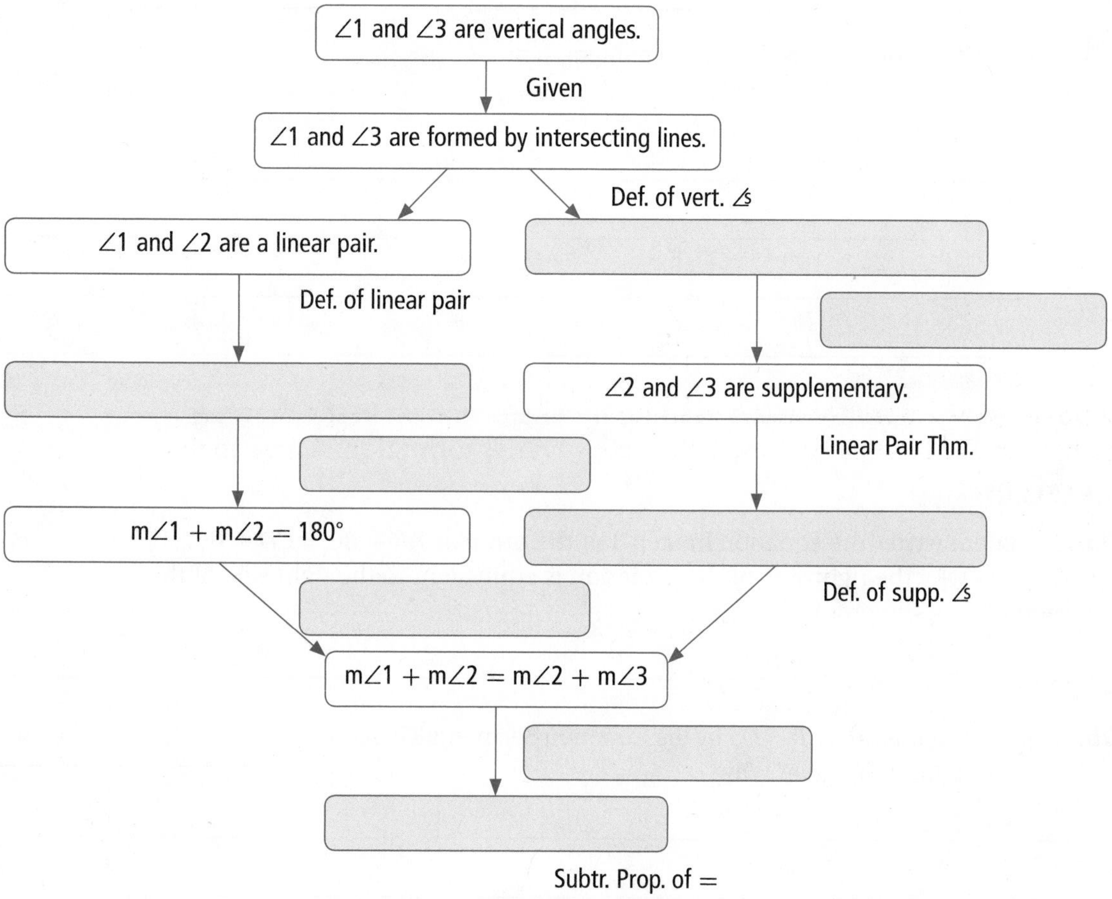

$\angle 1$ and $\angle 3$ are vertical angles.

Given

$\angle 1$ and $\angle 3$ are formed by intersecting lines.

$\angle 1$ and $\angle 2$ are a linear pair.

Def. of vert. $\angle$s

Def. of linear pair

$\angle 2$ and $\angle 3$ are supplementary.

Linear Pair Thm.

$m\angle 1 + m\angle 2 = 180°$

Def. of supp. $\angle$s

$m\angle 1 + m\angle 2 = m\angle 2 + m\angle 3$

Subtr. Prop. of =

REFLECT

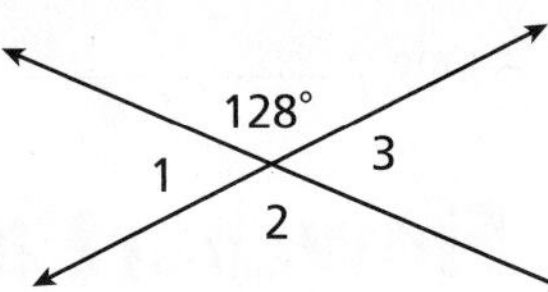

1a. Explain how to find m∠1, m∠2, and m∠3 in the figure.

MCC9–12.G.CO.9

2 PROOF Common Segments Theorem

If *A, B, C,* and *D* are collinear, as shown in the figure, with $AB = CD$, then $AC = BD$.

Given: $AB = CD$
Prove: $AC = BD$

A Complete the two-column proof.

Statements	Reasons
1. $AB = CD$	1.
2. $BC = BC$	2.
3. $AB + BC = BC + CD$	3.
4. $AB + BC = AC$; $BC + CD = BD$	4.
5. $AC = BD$	5.

B Use the two-column proof to write a paragraph proof.

REFLECT

2a. A student writes the equation in Step 3 of the proof as $AB + BC = CD + BC$. Explain why the right side of this equation is equivalent to the right side of the equation in the proof.

2b. A student claims that $PR = QS$ by the Common Segments Theorem. Do you agree or disagree? Why?

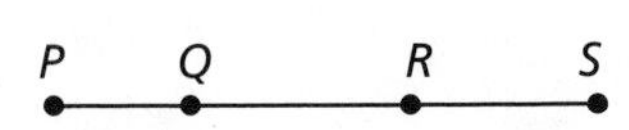

Name ______________________ Class ______________ Date ____________

2-4

Additional Practice

1. Use the given two-column proof to write a flowchart proof.

Given: $\angle 4 \cong \angle 3$

Prove: $m\angle 1 = m\angle 2$

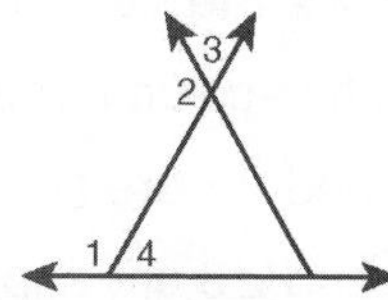

Statements	Reasons
1. $\angle 1$ and $\angle 4$ are supplementary, $\angle 2$ and $\angle 3$ are supplementary.	1. Linear Pair Thm.
2. $\angle 4 \cong \angle 3$	2. Given
3. $\angle 1 \cong \angle 2$	3. $\cong$ Supps. Thm.
4. $m\angle 1 = m\angle 2$	4. Def. of $\cong$ $\angle$s

2. Use the given two-column proof to write a paragraph proof.

Given: $AB = CD$, $BC = DE$

Prove: C is the midpoint of $\overline{AE}$.

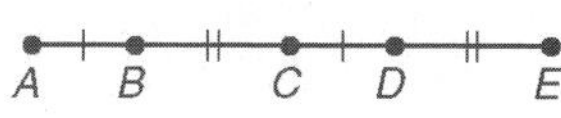

Statements	Reasons
1. $AB = CD$, $BC = DE$	1. Given
2. $AB + BC = CD + DE$	2. Add. Prop. of =
3. $AB + BC = AC$, $CD + DE = CE$	3. Seg. Add. Post.
4. $AC = CE$	4. Subst.
5. $\overline{AC} \cong \overline{CE}$	5. Def. of $\cong$ segs.
6. C is the midpoint of $\overline{AE}$.	6. Def. of mdpt.

Problem Solving

The diagram shows the second-floor glass railing at a mall.

1. Use the given two-column proof to write a flowchart proof.

   Given: $\angle 2$ and $\angle 3$ are supplementary.

   Prove: $\angle 1$ and $\angle 3$ are supplementary.

   Two-Column Proof:

Statements	Reasons
1. $\angle 2$ and $\angle 3$ are supplementary.	1. Given
2. $m\angle 2 + m\angle 3 = 180°$	2. Def. of supp. ∠s
3. $\angle 2 \cong \angle 1$	3. Vert. ∠s Thm.
4. $m\angle 2 = m\angle 1$	4. Def. of ≅ ∠s
5. $m\angle 1 + m\angle 3 = 180°$	5. Subst.
6. $\angle 1$ and $\angle 3$ are supplementary.	6. Def. of supp. ∠s

Choose the best answer.

2. Which would NOT be included in a paragraph proof of the two-column proof above?

   A Since $\angle 2$ and $\angle 3$ are supplementary, $m\angle 2 = m\angle 3$.

   B $\angle 2 \cong \angle 1$ by the Vertical Angles Theorem.

   C Using substitution, $m\angle 1 + m\angle 3 = 180°$.

   D $m\angle 2 = m\angle 1$ by the definition of congruent angles.

Name________________________ Class______________ Date__________

3-1

Angles Formed by Parallel Lines and Transversals

Going Deeper

Essential question: *How can you prove and use theorems about angles formed by transversals that intersect parallel lines?*

MCC9–12.G.CO.9

1 ENGAGE Introducing Transversals

Recall that a *transversal* is a line that intersects two coplanar lines at two different points. In the figure, line t is a transversal. The table summarizes the names of angle pairs formed by a transversal.

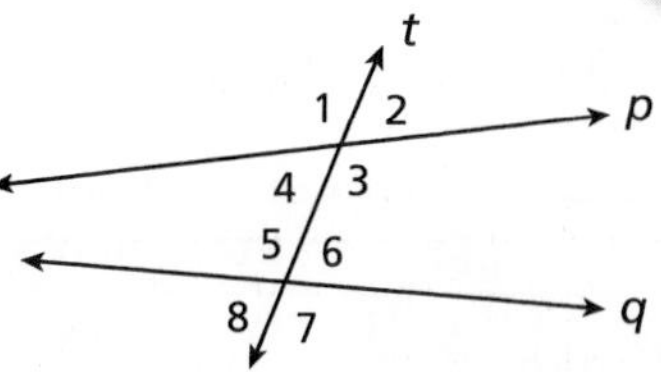

Angle Pair	Example
Corresponding angles lie on the same side of the transversal and on the same sides of the intersected lines.	$\angle 1$ and $\angle 5$
Same-side interior angles lie on the same side of the transversal and between the intersected lines.	$\angle 3$ and $\angle 6$
Alternate interior angles are nonadjacent angles that lie on opposite sides of the transversal between the intersected lines.	$\angle 3$ and $\angle 5$
Alternate exterior angles are angles that lie on opposite sides of the transversal outside the intersected lines.	$\angle 2$ and $\angle 8$

The following postulate is the starting point for proving theorems about parallel lines that are intersected by a transversal.

Same-Side Interior Angles Postulate

If two parallel lines are cut by a transversal, then the pairs of same-side interior angles are supplementary.

Given $p \parallel q$, $\angle 4$ and $\angle 5$ are supplementary.
Given $p \parallel q$, $\angle 3$ and $\angle 6$ are supplementary.

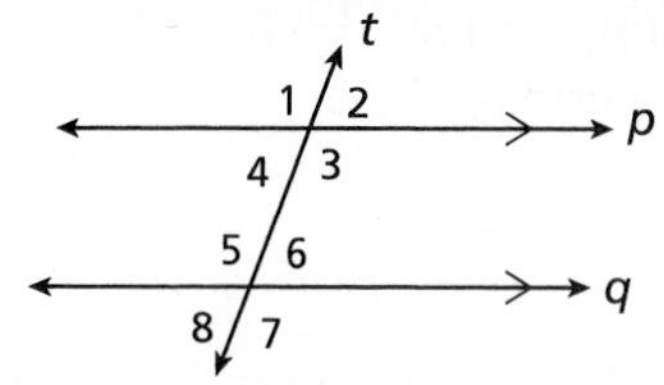

REFLECT

1a. Explain how you can find $m\angle 3$ in the postulate diagram if $p \parallel q$ and $m\angle 6 = 61°$.

____

____

1b. In the postulate diagram, suppose $p \parallel q$ and line t is perpendicular to line p. Can you conclude that line t is perpendicular to line q? Explain.

____

____

MCC9–12.G.CO.9

2 PROOF Alternate Interior Angles Theorem

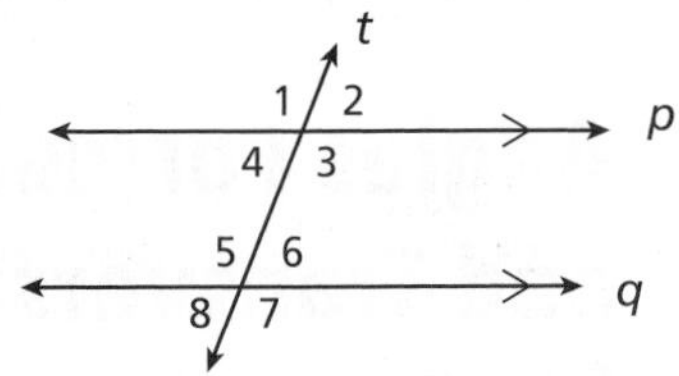

If two parallel lines are cut by a transversal, then the pairs of alternate interior angles have the same measure.

Given: $p \parallel q$
Prove: $m\angle 3 = m\angle 5$

Complete the proof by writing the missing reasons. Choose from the following reasons. You may use a reason more than once.

Same-Side Interior Angles Postulate	Given	Definition of supplementary angles
Subtraction Property of Equality	Substitution Property of Equality	Linear Pair Theorem

Statements	Reasons
1. $p \parallel q$	1.
2. $\angle 3$ and $\angle 6$ are supplementary.	2.
3. $m\angle 3 + m\angle 6 = 180°$	3.
4. $\angle 5$ and $\angle 6$ are a linear pair.	4.
5. $\angle 5$ and $\angle 6$ are supplementary.	5.
6. $m\angle 5 + m\angle 6 = 180°$	6.
7. $m\angle 3 + m\angle 6 = m\angle 5 + m\angle 6$	7.
8. $m\angle 3 = m\angle 5$	8.

REFLECT

2a. Suppose $m\angle 4 = 57°$ in the above figure. Describe two different ways to determine $m\angle 6$.

2b. In the above figure, explain why $\angle 1$, $\angle 3$, $\angle 5$, and $\angle 7$ all have the same measure.

2c. In the above figure, is it possible for all eight angles to have the same measure? If so, what is that measure?

MCC9-12.G.CO.9

3 PROOF Corresponding Angles Theorem

If two parallel lines are cut by a transversal, then the pairs of corresponding angles have the same measure.

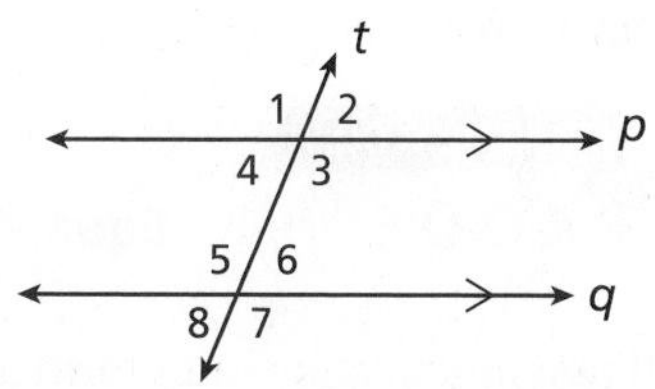

Given: $p \parallel q$
Prove: $m\angle 1 = m\angle 5$

Complete the proof by writing the missing reasons.

Statements	Reasons
1. $p \parallel q$	1.
2. $m\angle 3 = m\angle 5$	2.
3. $m\angle 1 = m\angle 3$	3.
4. $m\angle 1 = m\angle 5$	4.

REFLECT

3a. Explain how you can you prove the Corresponding Angles Theorem using the Same-Side Interior Angles Postulate and a linear pair of angles.

____

____

____

Many postulates and theorems are written in the form "If p, then q." The **converse** of such a statement has the form "If q, then p." The converse of a postulate or theorem may or may not be true. The converse of the Same-Side Interior Angles Postulate is accepted as true, and this makes it possible to prove that the converses of the previous theorems are true.

Converse of the Same-Side Interior Angles Postulate

If two lines are cut by a transversal so that a pair of same-side interior angles are supplementary, then the lines are parallel.

Converse of the Alternate Interior Angles Theorem

If two lines are cut by a transversal so that a pair of alternate interior angles have the same measure, then the lines are parallel.

Converse of the Corresponding Angles Theorem

If two lines are cut by a transversal so that a pair of corresponding angles have the same measure, then the lines are parallel.

A *paragraph proof* is another way of presenting a mathematical argument. As in a two-column proof, the argument must flow logically and every statement should have a reason.

MCC9–12.G.CO.9

4 PROOF Equal-Measure Linear Pair Theorem

If two intersecting lines form a linear pair of angles with equal measures, then the lines are perpendicular.

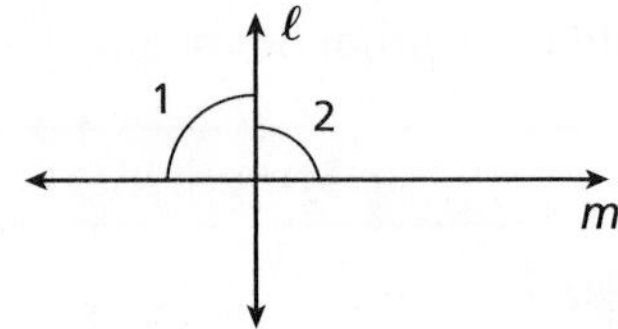

Given: $m\angle 1 = m\angle 2$
Prove: $\ell \perp m$

Complete the following paragraph proof.

It is given that $\angle 1$ and $\angle 2$ form a linear pair. Therefore, $\angle 1$ and $\angle 2$ are supplementary by the ______________________. By the definition of supplementary angles, $m\angle 1 + m\angle 2 = 180°$. It is also given that $m\angle 1 = m\angle 2$. So, $m\angle 1 + m\angle 1 = 180°$ by the ______________________. Simplifying gives $2m\angle 1 = 180°$ and $m\angle 1 = 90°$ by the Division Property of Equality. Therefore, $\angle 1$ is a right angle and $\ell \perp m$ by the ______________________.

REFLECT

4a. State the converse of the Equal-Measure Linear Pair Theorem shown above. Is the converse true?

____

____

PRACTICE

In Exercises 1–2, complete each proof by writing the missing statements or reasons.

1. If two parallel lines are cut by a transversal, then the pairs of alternate exterior angles have the same measure.

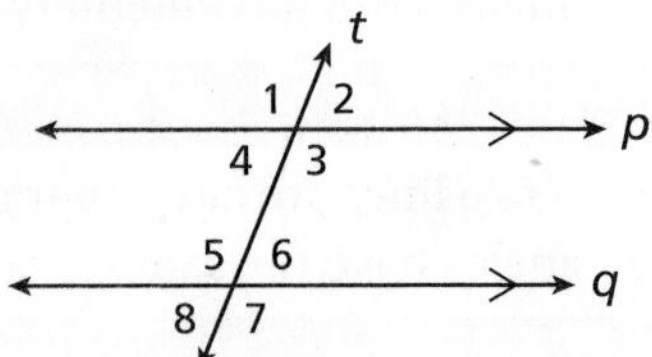

Given: $p \parallel q$
Prove: $m\angle 1 = m\angle 7$

Statements	Reasons
1. $p \parallel q$	1.
2. $m\angle 1 = m\angle 5$	2.
3. $m\angle 5 = m\angle 7$	3.
4. $m\angle 1 = m\angle 7$	4.

2. Prove the Converse of the Alternate Interior Angles Theorem.

Given: $m\angle 3 = m\angle 5$
Prove: $p \parallel q$

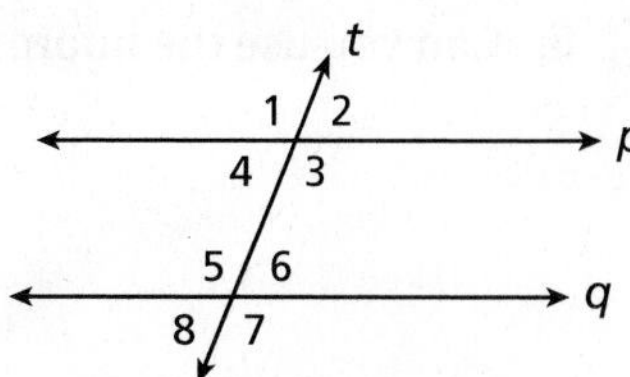

Statements	Reasons
1. $m\angle 3 = m\angle 5$	1.
2. $\angle 5$ and $\angle 6$ are a linear pair.	2. Definition of linear pair
3.	3. Linear Pair Theorem
4. $m\angle 5 + m\angle 6 = 180°$	4.
5. $m\angle 3 + m\angle 6 = 180°$	5.
6. $\angle 3$ and $\angle 6$ are supplementary.	6.
7. $p \parallel q$	7.

3. Complete the paragraph proof.

Given: $\ell \parallel m$ and $p \parallel q$
Prove: $m\angle 1 = m\angle 2$

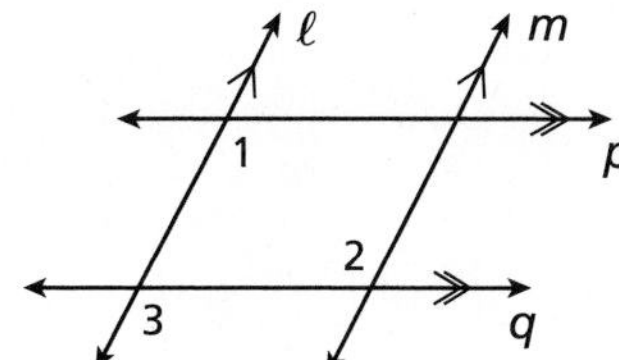

It is given that $p \parallel q$, so $m\angle 1 = m\angle 3$ by the ______________________________.

It is also given that $\ell \parallel m$, so $m\angle 3 = m\angle 2$ by the ______________________________.

Therefore, $m\angle 1 = m\angle 2$ by the ______________________________.

4. The figure shows a given line m, a given point P, and the construction of a line ℓ that is parallel to line m. Explain why line ℓ is parallel to line m.

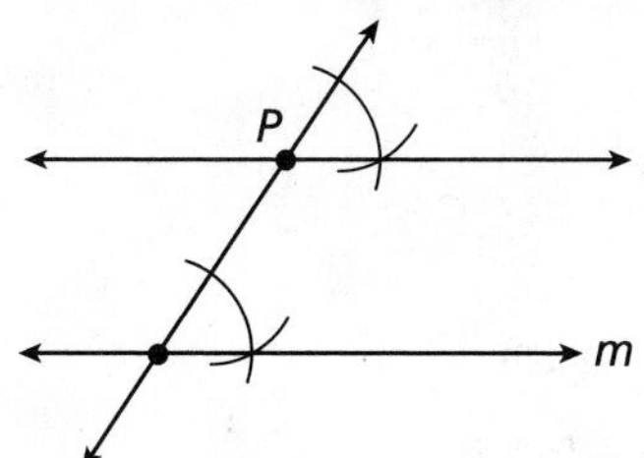

____

____

____

____

5. Can you use the information in the figure to conclude that $p \parallel q$? Why or why not?

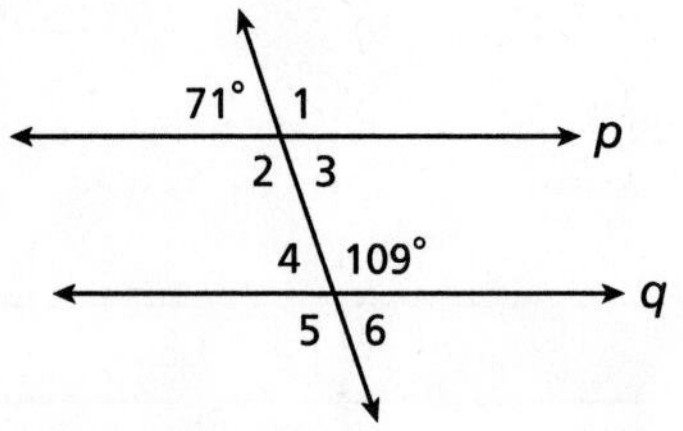

Name ______________________ Class ______________ Date ____________

3-1

Additional Practice

Find each angle measure.

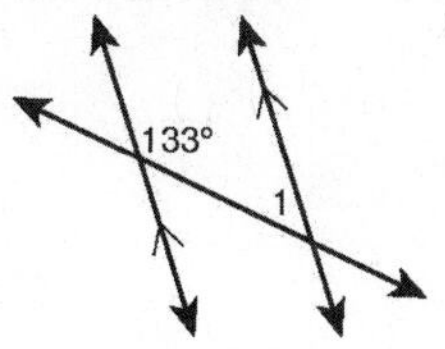

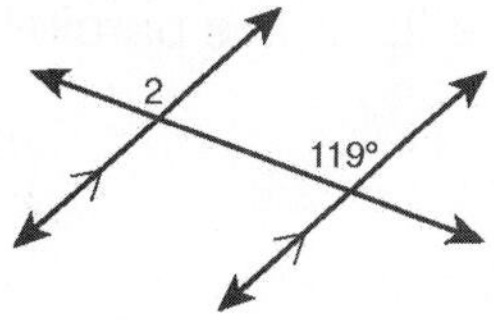

1. m∠1 ______________________

2. m∠2 ______________________

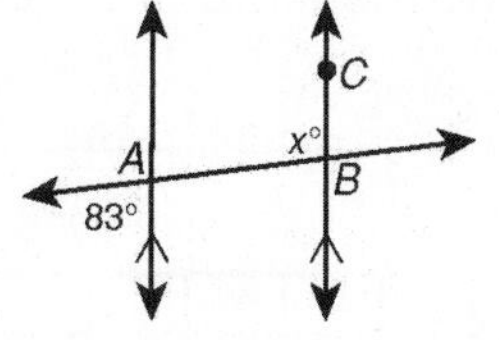

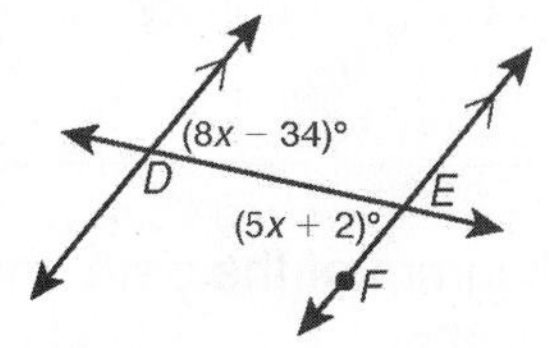

3. m∠*ABC* ______________________

4. m∠*DEF* ______________________

Complete the two-column proof to show that same-side exterior angles are supplementary.

5. **Given:** $p \parallel q$

   Prove: m∠1 + m∠3 = 180°

   Proof:

Statements	Reasons
1. $p \parallel q$	1. Given
2. a. ______________	2. Lin. Pair Thm.
3. ∠1 ≅ ∠2	3. b. ______________
4. c. ______________	4. Def. of ≅ ∠s
5. d. ______________	5. e. ______________

6. Ocean waves move in parallel lines toward the shore. The figure shows Sandy Beaches windsurfing across several waves. For this exercise, think of Sandy's wake as a line. m∠1 = $(2x + 2y)°$ and m∠2 = $(2x + y)°$. Find x and y.

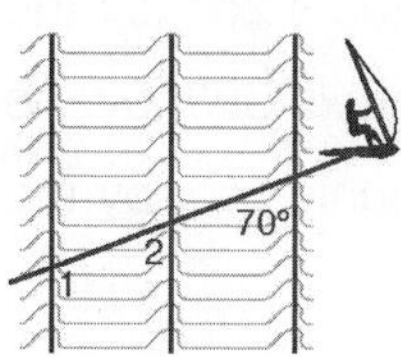

x = __________

y = __________

Problem Solving

Find each value. Name the postulate or theorem that you used to find the values.

1. In the diagram of movie theater seats, the incline of the floor, f, is parallel to the seats, s.

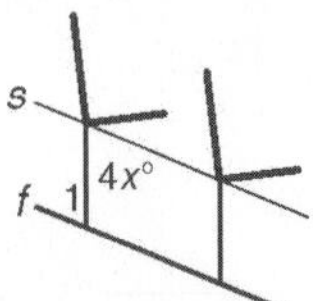

If $m\angle 1 = 68°$, what is x?

____

2. In the diagram, roads a and b are parallel.

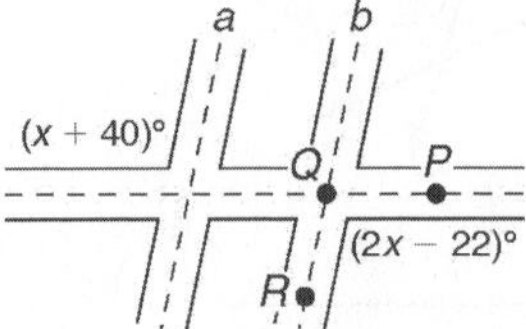

What is the measure of $\angle PQR$?

____

3. In the diagram of the gate, the horizontal bars are parallel and the vertical bars are parallel. Find x and y.

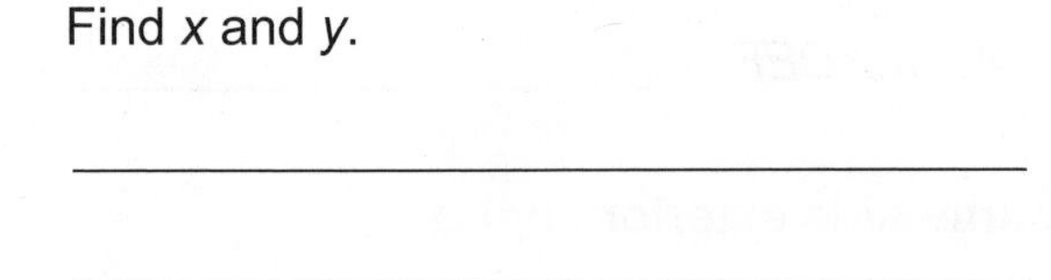

____

____

____

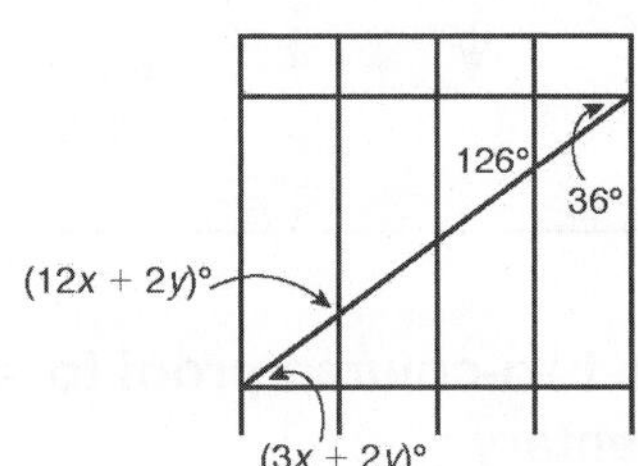

Use the diagram of a staircase railing for Exercises 4 and 5. $\overline{AG} \parallel \overline{CJ}$ and $\overline{AD} \parallel \overline{FJ}$. Choose the best answer.

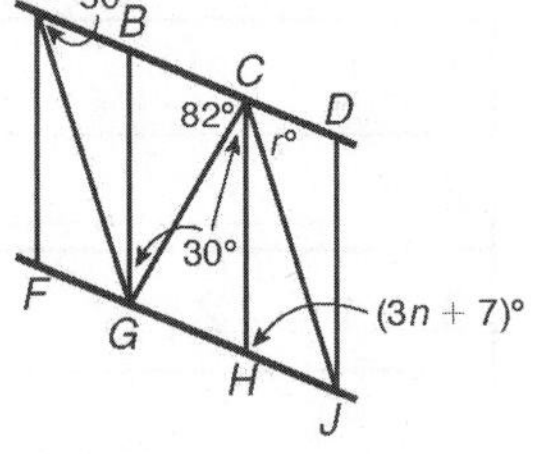

4. Which is a true statement about the measure of $\angle DCJ$?
   - A It equals 30°, by the Alternate Interior Angles Theorem.
   - B It equals 30°, by the Corresponding Angles Postulate.
   - C It equals 50°, by the Alternate Interior Angles Theorem.
   - D It equals 50°, by the Corresponding Angles Postulate.

5. Which is a true statement about the value of n?
   - F It equals 25°, by the Alternate Interior Angles Theorem.
   - G It equals 25°, by the Same-Side Interior Angles Theorem.
   - H It equals 35°, by the Alternate Interior Angles Theorem.
   - J It equals 35°, by the Same-Side Interior Angles Theorem.

Name ____________________ Class ____________ Date ________

3-2

Proving Lines Parallel

Connection: Constructing Parallel Lines

Essential question: *How can you construct a line parallel to another line that passes through a given point?*

Parallel lines lie in the same plane and do not intersect. In the figure, line ℓ is parallel to line m and you write $\ell \parallel m$. The arrows on the lines also indicate that the lines are parallel.

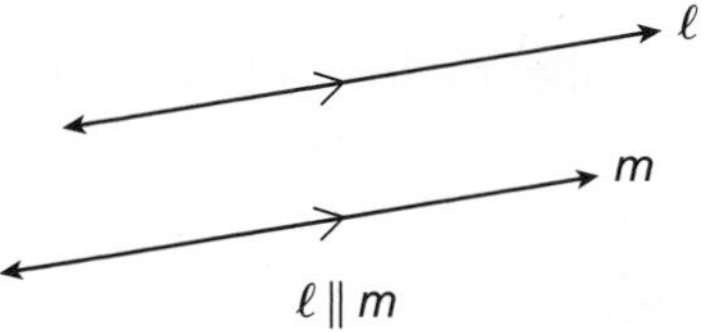

MCC9–12.G.CO.12

1 EXAMPLE Constructing Parallel Lines

Construct a line parallel to line m that passes through point P. Work directly on the figure below.

A Choose points Q and R on line m.

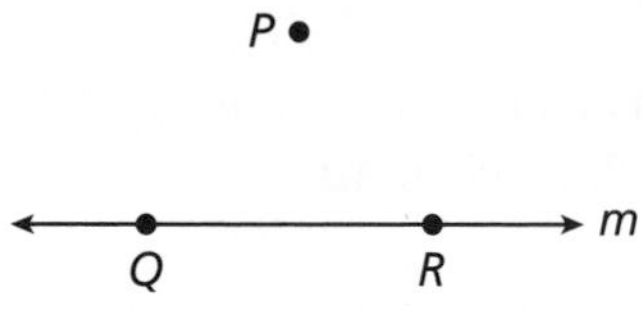

B Use a straightedge to draw $\overleftrightarrow{PQ}$.

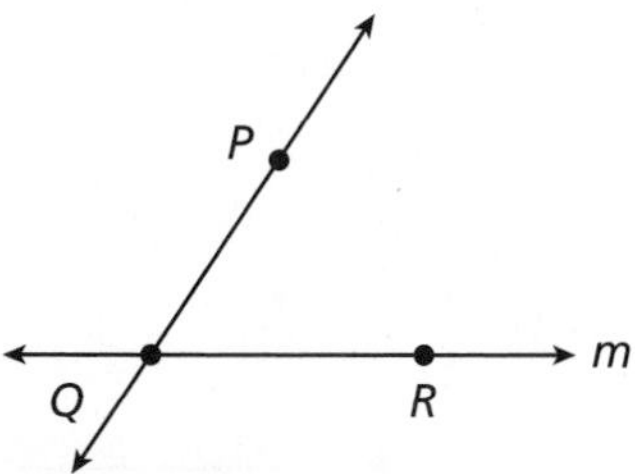

C Copy $\angle PQR$ at point P, as shown. Label line ℓ. Line ℓ is the required line.

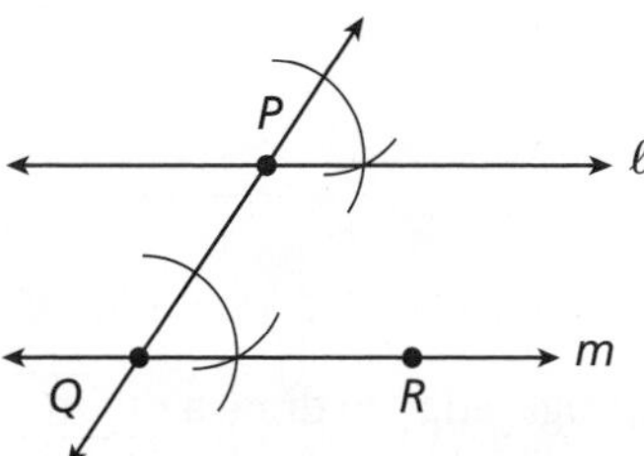

REFLECT

1a. Why does it make sense to copy $\angle PQR$ to get a line parallel to line m?

____

____

1b. Is it possible to construct a line parallel to a given line m that passes through a point P that is *on* line m? Why or why not?

____

____

1c. Write an if-then statement that justifies the method used in the construction of parallel lines.

____

____

PRACTICE

Construct a line parallel to line *m* that passes through point *P*.

1.

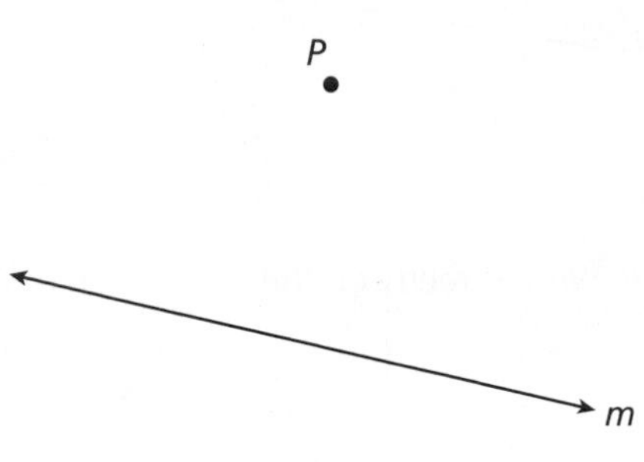

2.

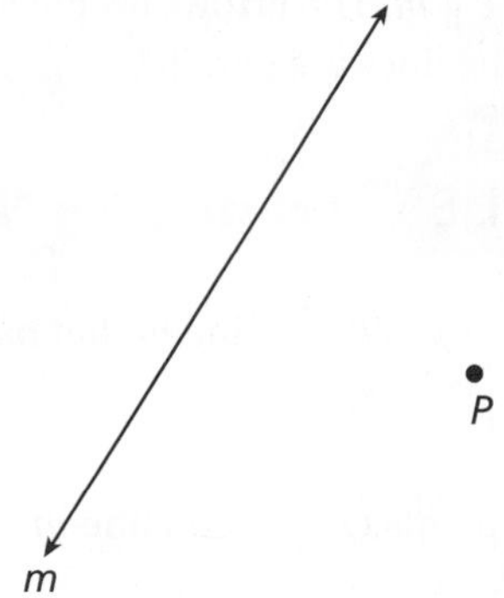

3. You can use what you know about constructing parallel lines to divide a given line segment into three equal parts. Follow the directions and work directly on $\overline{AB}$ in the space below.

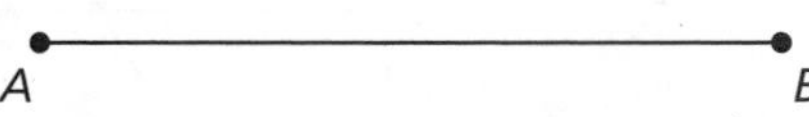

a. Use a straightedge to draw a ray $\overrightarrow{AC}$ as shown.

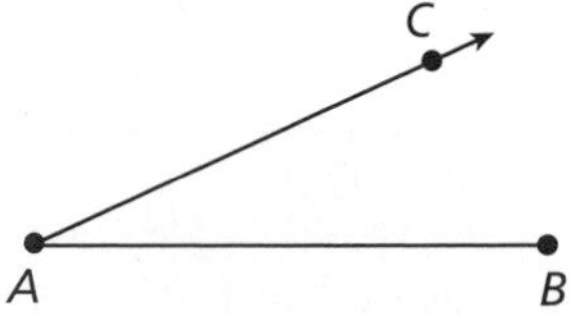

b. Place the point of your compass on A and make an arc that intersects $\overrightarrow{AC}$. Without adjusting the compass, place the point on the intersection of the arc with $\overrightarrow{AC}$ and make another arc. Place the point on the intersection of the new arc with $\overrightarrow{AC}$ and make a third arc. Label the points of intersection with $\overrightarrow{AC}$ as shown.

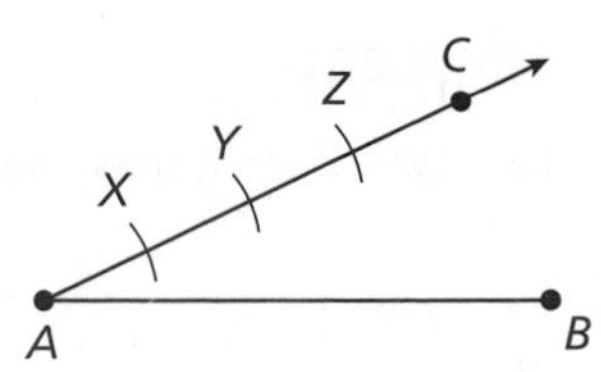

c. Use the straightedge to draw $\overleftrightarrow{ZB}$. Then construct lines parallel to $\overline{ZB}$ that pass through X and Y. These lines divide $\overline{AB}$ into three equal parts.

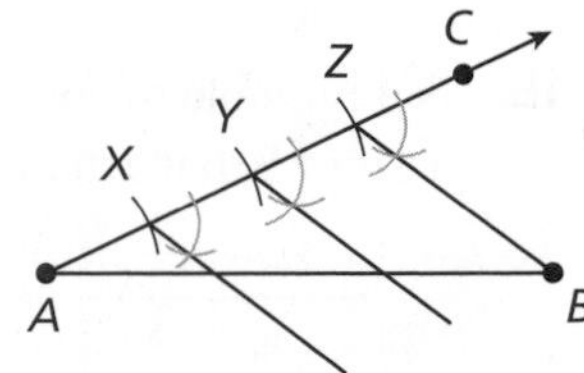

d. Use a ruler to check that you have divided $\overline{AB}$ into three equal parts.

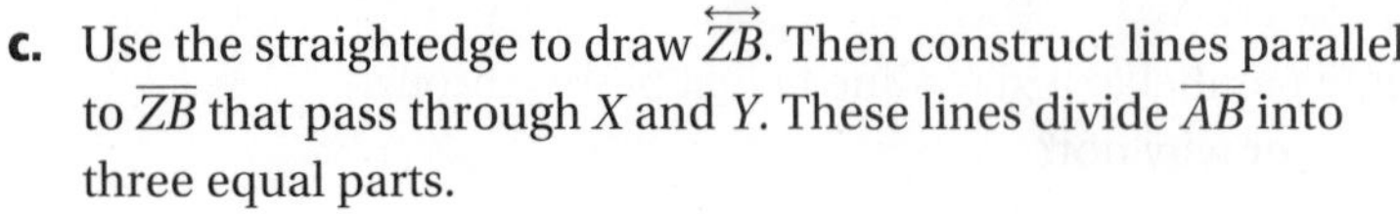

Name ______________________ Class ______________ Date ______________ **3-2**

Additional Practice

Construct a line parallel to line *r* that passes through point *P*.

1. 2.

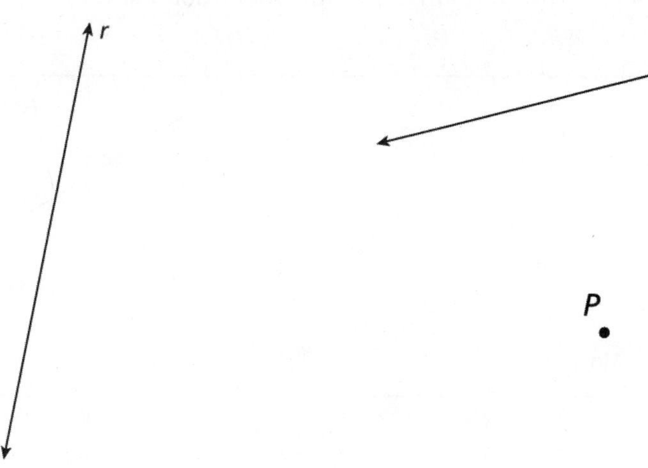

3. Use the parallel line construction to divide $\overleftrightarrow{CD}$ into four congruent parts.

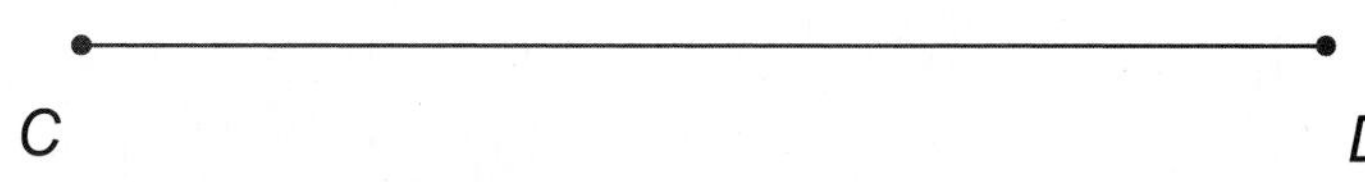

4. Construct a line parallel to $\overline{AB}$ through a point that is a distance *XY* away from $\overline{AB}$ as measured along line *m*.

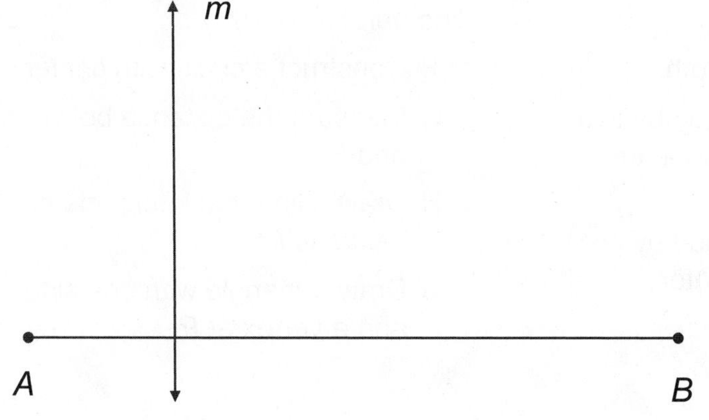

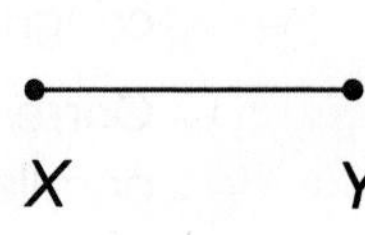

Problem Solving

1. A cartographer is creating a map of the city center, as shown below. Pine Street is parallel to Main Street and passes through the intersection of Elm Street and Route 30. Construct a line to represent Pine Street.

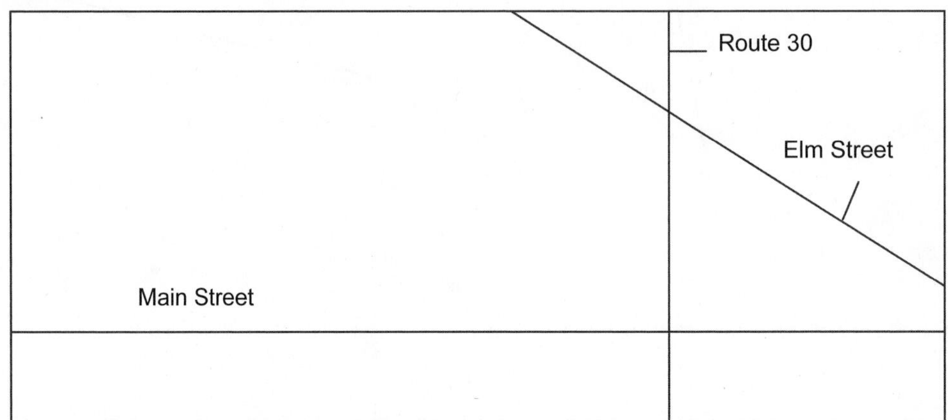

2. A graphic designer is drawing a logo, as shown below. In the logo, $AB = BC = DE = EF$. Construct another line so that the logo is divided into four rectangles that all have the same area.

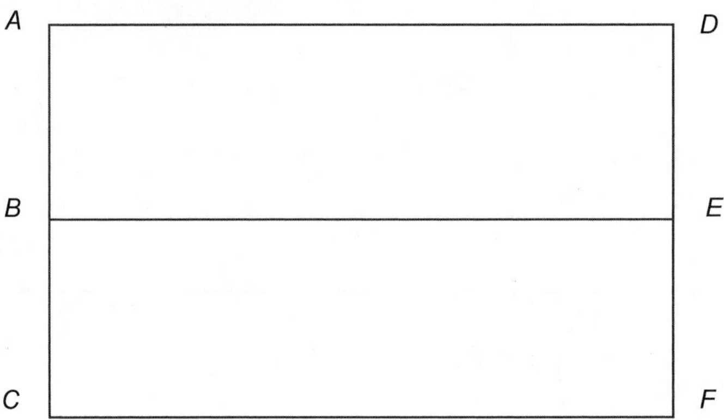

Select the best answer.

3. Which of the following facts do you use when constructing parallel lines?
   - A A transversal that intersects two parallel lines is parallel to both.
   - B Corresponding angles formed by two parallel lines and a transversal are congruent.
   - C Corresponding angles formed by two parallel lines are supplementary.
   - D All right angles are congruent.

4. When given a line *m* and a point *P* not on *m*, what is the first step in constructing a line parallel to *m*?
   - F Construct a circle with center *P*.
   - G Measure the distance between *m* and *P*.
   - H Draw a line that intersects *m* and contains *P*.
   - J Draw a triangle with one side on *m* and a vertex at *P*.

Name ______________________ Class ______________ Date ________

3-3

Perpendicular Lines
Going Deeper

Essential question: *How can you construct perpendicular lines and prove theorems about perpendicular bisectors?*

Video Tutor

Perpendicular lines are lines that intersect at right angles. In the figure, line ℓ is perpendicular to line m and you write $\ell \perp m$. The right angle mark in the figure indicates that the lines are perpendicular.

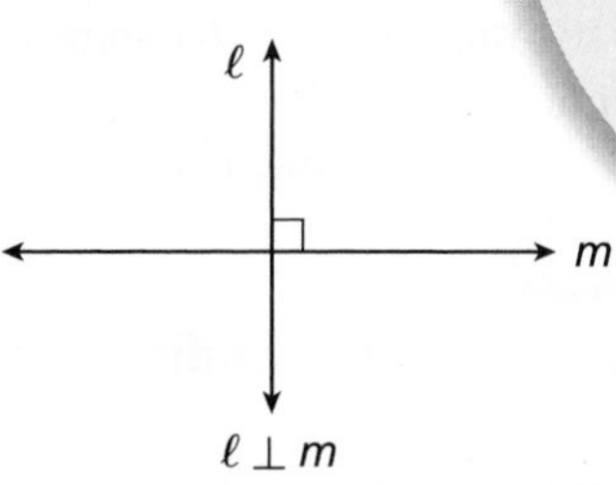

The **perpendicular bisector** of a line segment is a line perpendicular to the segment at the segment's midpoint.

MCC9–12.G.CO.12

1 EXAMPLE Constructing a Perpendicular Bisector

Construct the perpendicular bisector of $\overline{AB}$. Work directly on the figure below.

A Place the point of your compass at A. Using a compass setting that is greater than half the length of $\overline{AB}$, draw an arc.

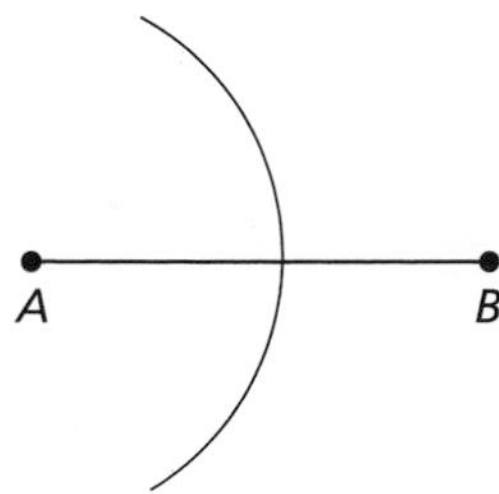

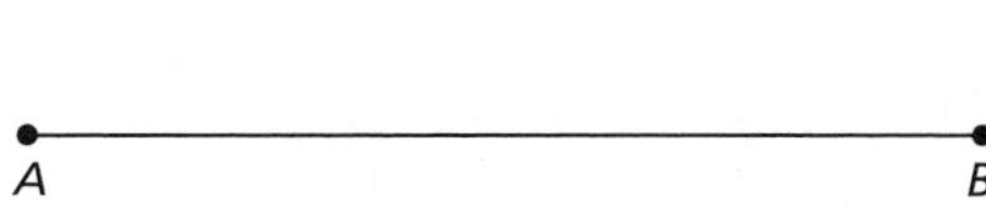

B Without adjusting the compass, place the point of the compass at B and draw an arc intersecting the first arc at C and D.

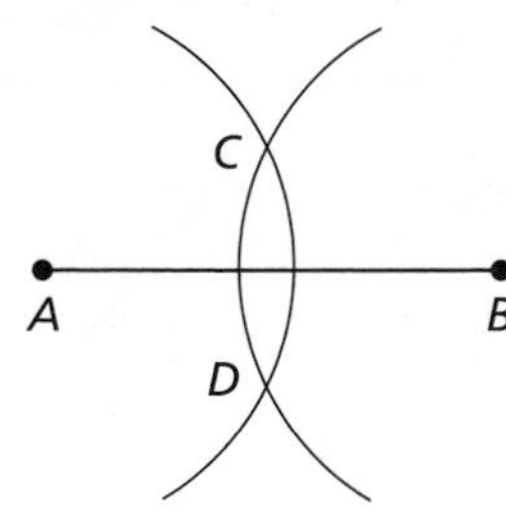

C Use a straightedge to draw $\overleftrightarrow{CD}$. $\overleftrightarrow{CD}$ is the perpendicular bisector of $\overline{AB}$.

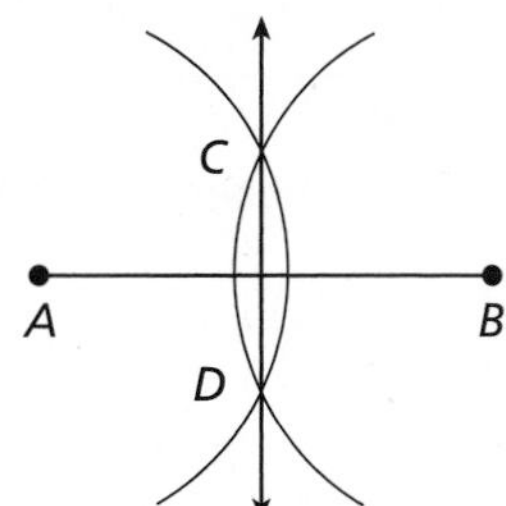

REFLECT

1a. How can you use a ruler and protractor to check the construction?

____

____

You can use reflections and their properties to prove a theorem about perpendicular bisectors. Refer to the diagram in the Proof below as you read this definition of reflection.

A **reflection** across line m maps a point A to its image B as follows.

- Line m is the perpendicular bisector of $\overline{AB}$ if and only if A is not on line m.
- The image of P is P if and only if P is on line m.

The notation $r_m(A) = B$ means that the image of point A after a reflection across line m is point B. The notation $r_m(P) = P$ means that the image of point P is point P, which implies that P is on line m.

MCC9–12.G.CO.9

2 PROOF Perpendicular Bisector Theorem

If a point is on the perpendicular bisector of a segment, then it is equidistant from the endpoints of the segment.

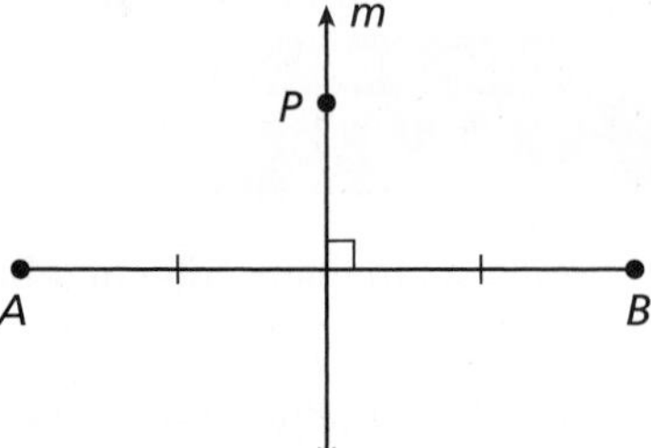

Given: P is on the perpendicular bisector m of $\overline{AB}$.

Prove: $PA = PB$

Complete the following proof.

Consider the reflection across line m. Then $r_m(P) = P$ because

____

Also, $r_m(A) = B$ by the definition of reflection.

Therefore, $PA = PB$ because _______________________

REFLECT

2a. Suppose you use a compass and straightedge to construct the perpendicular bisector of a segment, $\overline{AB}$. If you choose a point P on the perpendicular bisector, how can you use your compass to check that P is equidistant from A and B?

____

____

____

2b. What conclusion can you make about $\triangle KLJ$ in the figure? Explain.

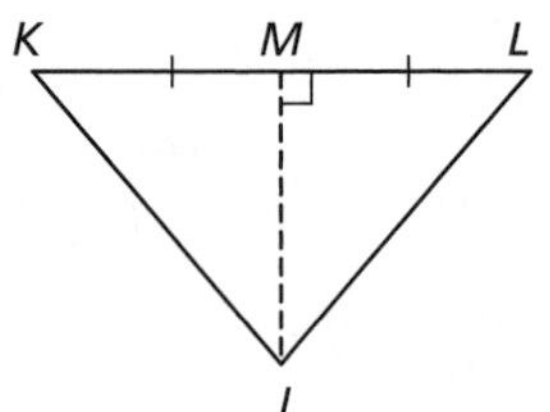

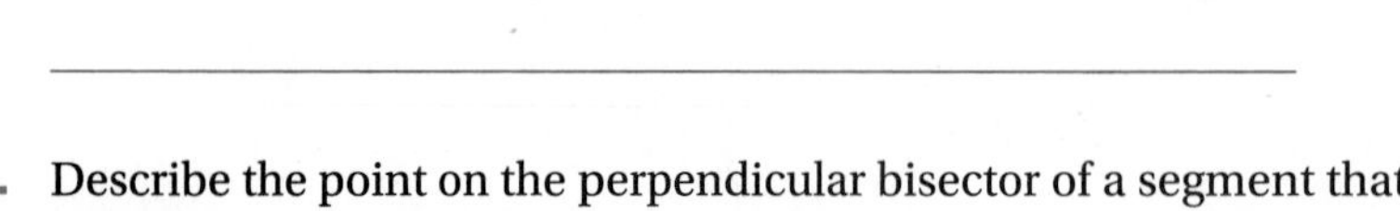

2c. Describe the point on the perpendicular bisector of a segment that is closest to the endpoints of the segment.

____

____

The converse of the Perpendicular Bisector Theorem is also true. In order to prove the converse, you will use the Pythagorean Theorem.

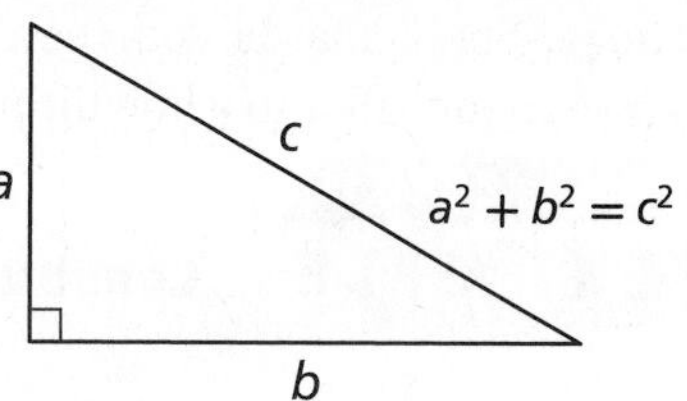

Recall that the Pythagorean Theorem states that in a right triangle with legs of length a and b and hypotenuse of length c, $a^2 + b^2 = c^2$.

MCC9–12.G.CO.9

3 PROOF Converse of the Perpendicular Bisector Theorem

If a point is equidistant from the endpoints of a segment, then it lies on the perpendicular bisector of the segment.

Given: $PA = PB$

Prove: P is on the perpendicular bisector m of $\overline{AB}$.

A Use the method of *indirect proof.* Assume the *opposite* of what you want to prove and show this leads to a contradiction.

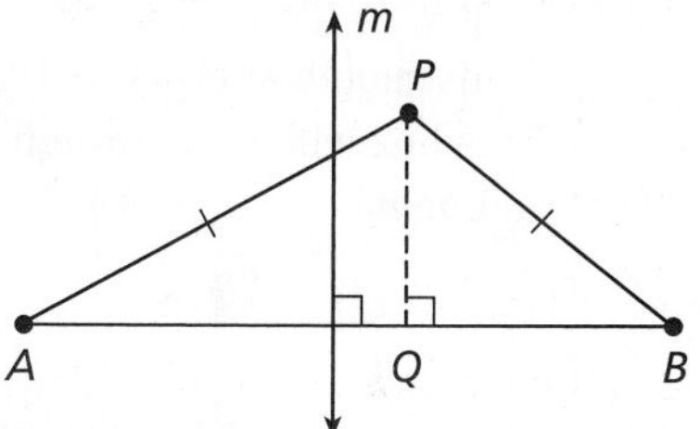

Assume that point P is *not* on the perpendicular bisector m of $\overline{AB}$. Then when you draw a perpendicular from P to the line containing A and B, the perpendicular intersects this line at a point Q, which is not the midpoint of $\overline{AB}$.

B Complete the following to show that this assumption leads to a contradiction.

$\overline{PQ}$ forms two right triangles, $\triangle AQP$ and $\triangle BQP$.

$AQ^2 + QP^2 = PA^2$ and $BQ^2 + QP^2 = PB^2$ by ______________________

Subtract these equations:

$$\begin{aligned} AQ^2 + QP^2 &= PA^2 \\ BQ^2 + QP^2 &= PB^2 \\ \hline AQ^2 - BQ^2 &= PA^2 - PB^2 \end{aligned}$$

However, $PA^2 - PB^2 = 0$ because ______________________

Therefore, $AQ^2 - BQ^2 = 0$. This means $AQ^2 = BQ^2$ and $AQ = BQ$. This contradicts the fact that Q is not the midpoint of $\overline{AB}$. Thus, the initial assumption must be incorrect, and P must lie on the perpendicular bisector of $\overline{AB}$.

REFLECT

3a. In the proof, once you know $AQ^2 = BQ^2$, why can you conclude $AQ = BQ$?

____

3b. Explain how the converse of the Perpendicular Bisector Theorem justifies the compass-and-straightedge construction of the perpendicular bisector of a segment.

____

____

____

____

The perpendicular bisector construction can be used as part of the method for drawing the perpendicular to a line through a given point not on the line.

MCC9-12.G.CO.12

4 EXAMPLE Constructing a Perpendicular to a Line

Construct a line perpendicular to line *m* that passes through point *P*. Work directly on the figure at right.

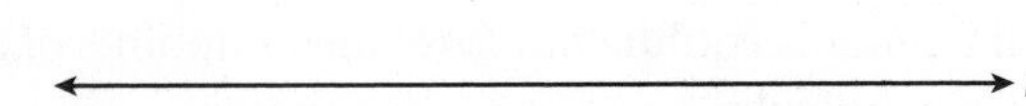

A Place the point of your compass at *P*. Draw an arc that intersects line *m* at two points, *A* and *B*.

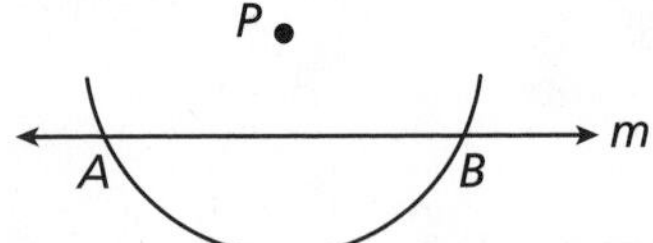

B Construct the perpendicular bisector of $\overline{AB}$. This line will pass through *P* and be perpendicular to line *m*.

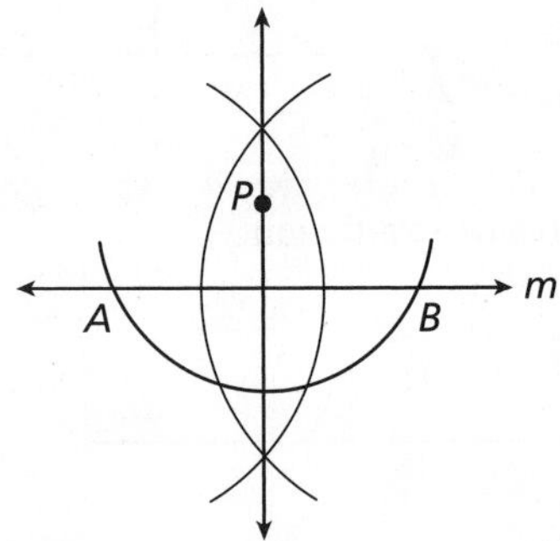

REFLECT

4a. Does the construction still work if point *P* is on line *m*? Why or why not?

____

____

PRACTICE

1. Construct the perpendicular bisector of the segment shown below.

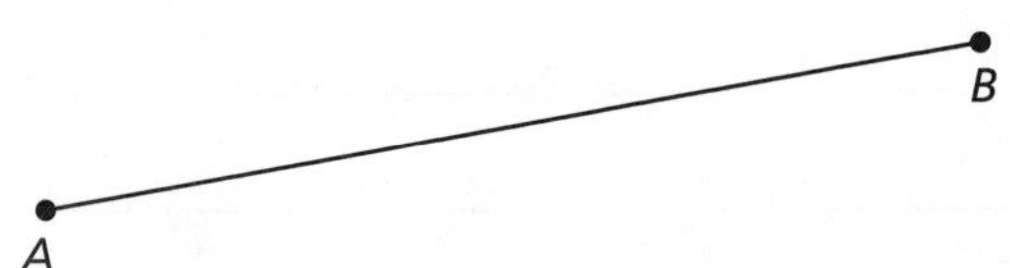

2. Construct a line perpendicular to line *m* that passes through point *P*.

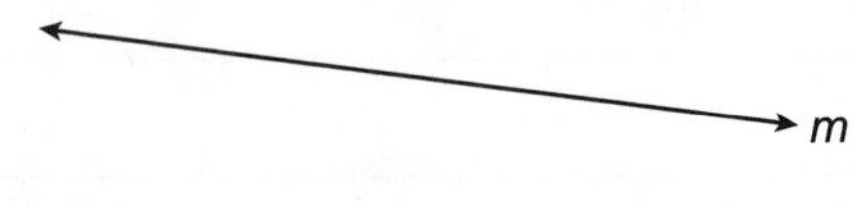

P

Name__________ Class__________ Date__________ **3-3**

Additional Practice

1. Construct a line perpendicular to line *r*.

2. Construct the perpendicular bisector of $\overline{CD}$.

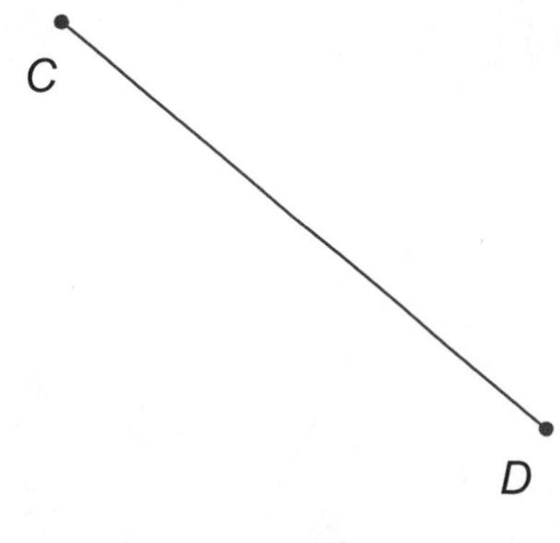

3. Construct a line perpendicular to *m* through *P*. Then, using your two perpendicular lines, construct a right triangle that has *P* as a vertex and a hypotenuse with length *XY*.

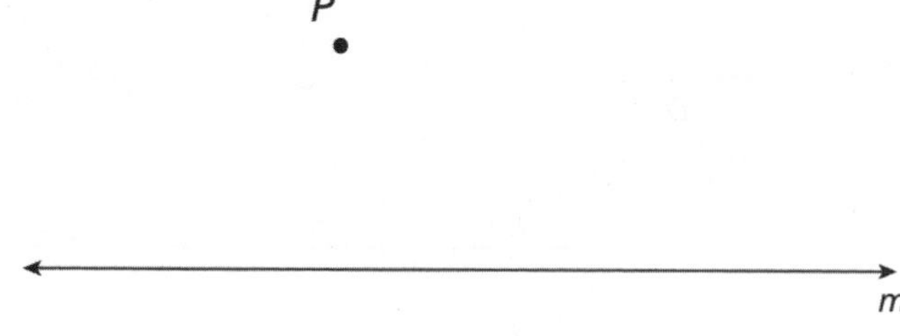

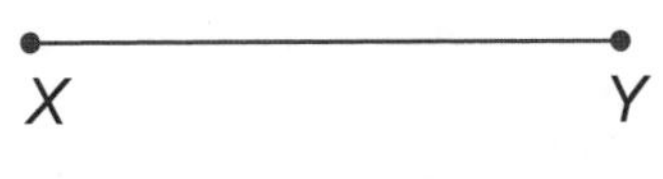

Use the diagram to find the given quantity.

4.

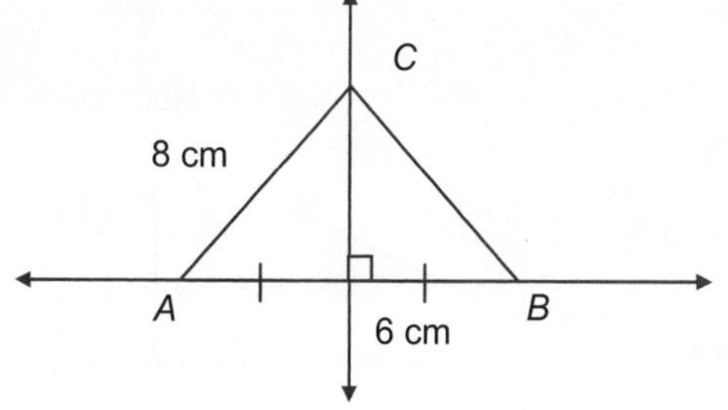

CB = __________

5.

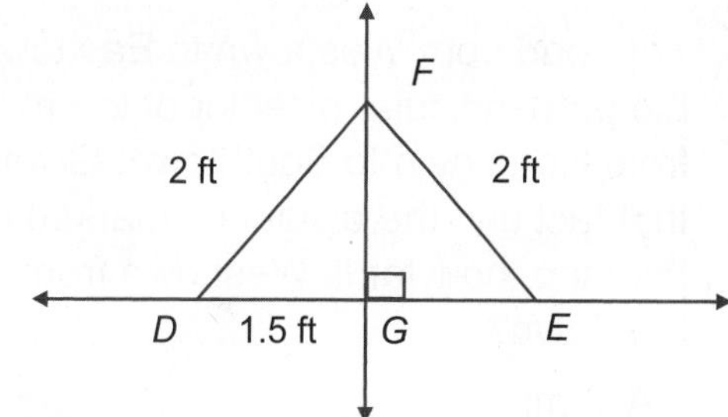

GE = __________

Problem Solving

1. Use geometric constructions to find a single point that is equidistant from *A* and *B*, and also equidistant from *C* and *D*. (*Note*: The distance from the point to *A* does not have to be the same as the distance from the point to *C*. It only matters that the point is equidistant from each pair.)

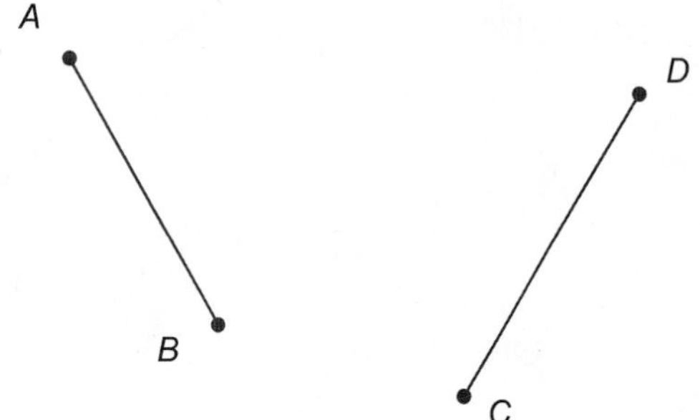

2. If the two segments from Exercise 1 were arranged so that they were both part of the same line, as shown below, could you still find a point that is equidistant from A and B, and also equidistant from C and D? Explain why or why not.

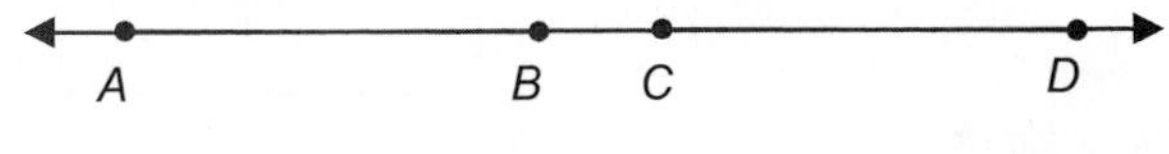

____

____

____

Select the best answer.

3. The road from Westtown to Easttown is the perpendicular bisector of the road from Northtown to Southtown. Given that fact and the distances marked on the map, how far is Westtown from Easttown?

   A 3 mi

   B 4 mi

   C 5 mi

   D 6 mi

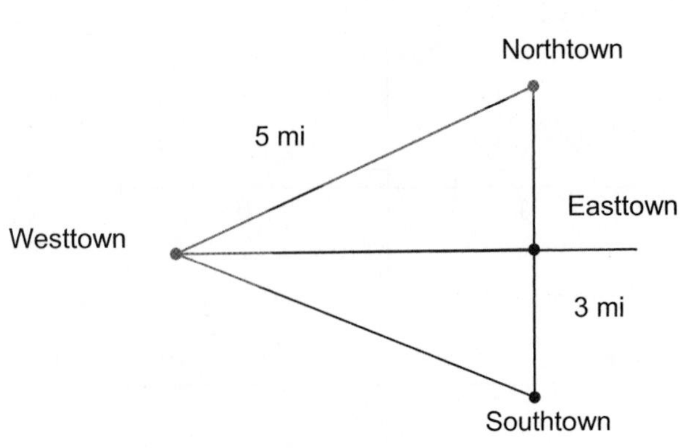

Name________________________ Class______________ Date__________

4-1

Congruence and Transformations

Going Deeper

Video Tutor

Essential question: *How can you use transformations to determine whether figures are congruent?*

Two figures are *congruent* if they have the same size and shape. A more formal mathematical definition of congruence depends on the notion of rigid motions.

Two plane figures are **congruent** if and only if one can be obtained from the other by rigid motions (that is, by a sequence of reflections, translations, and/or rotations.)

MCC9–12.G.CO.6

1 EXAMPLE Determining If Figures are Congruent

Use the definition of congruence in terms of rigid motions to determine whether the two figures are congruent and explain your answer.

A $\triangle ABC$ and $\triangle DEF$ have different sizes.

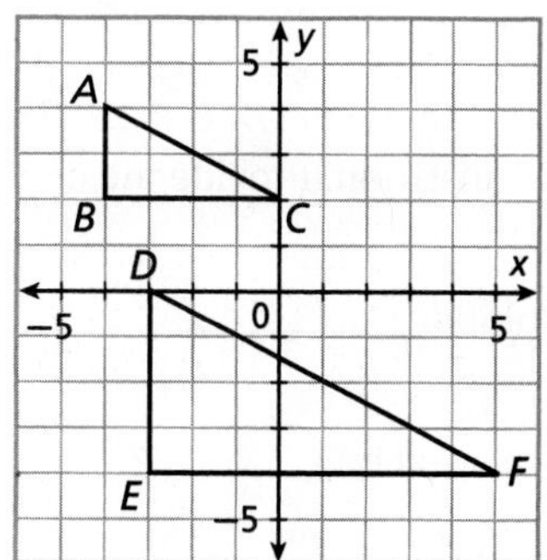

Since rigid motions preserve distance, there is no sequence of rigid motions that will map $\triangle ABC$ to $\triangle DEF$.

Therefore, ______________________

B You can map *JKLM* to *PQRS* by the translation that has the following coordinate notation:

____

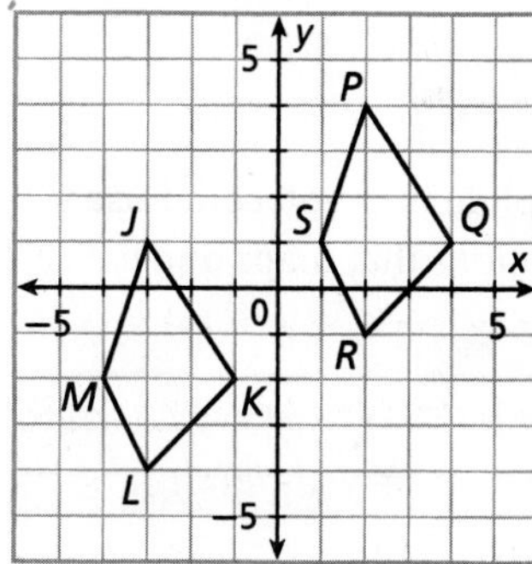

A translation is a rigid motion.

Therefore, ______________________

REFLECT

1a. Why does the fact that $\triangle ABC$ and $\triangle DEF$ have different sizes lead to the conclusion that there is no sequence of rigid motions that maps $\triangle ABC$ to $\triangle DEF$?

____

____

____

The definition of congruence tells you that when two figures are known to be congruent, there must be some sequence of rigid motions that maps one to the other. You will investigate this idea in the next example.

MCC9-12.G.CO.5

2 EXAMPLE Finding a Sequence of Rigid Motions

For each pair of congruent figures, find a sequence of rigid motions that maps one figure to the other.

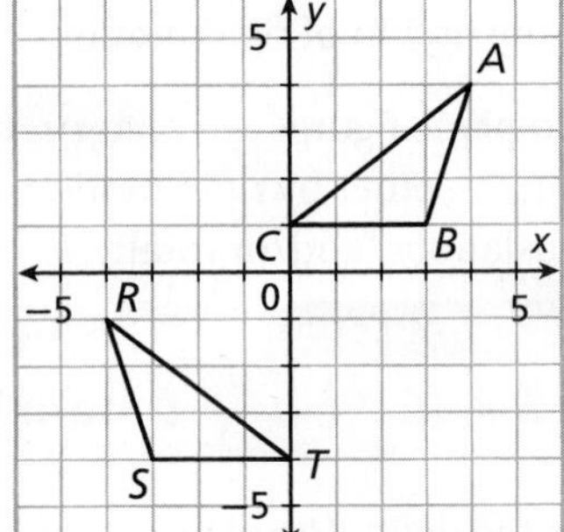

A You can map $\triangle ABC$ to $\triangle RST$ by a reflection followed by a translation. Provide the coordinate notation for each.

Reflection: ______________________

Followed by...

Translation: ______________________

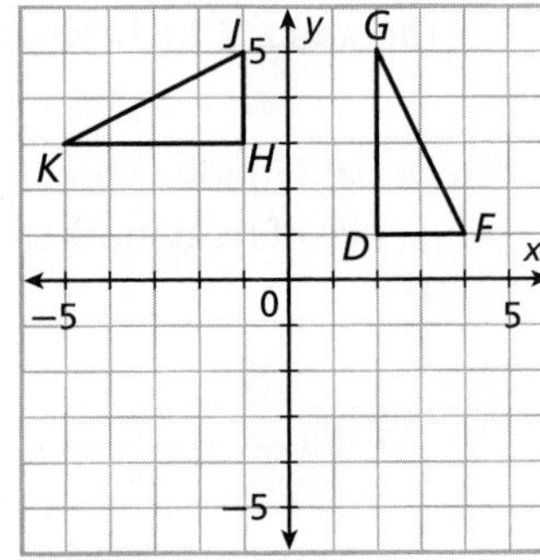

B You can map $\triangle DFG$ to $\triangle HJK$ by a rotation followed by a translation. Provide the coordinate notation for each.

Rotation: ______________________

Followed by...

Translation: ______________________

REFLECT

2a. Explain how you could use tracing paper to help you find a sequence of rigid motions that maps one figure to another congruent figure.

____

____

____

2b. Given two congruent figures, is there a *unique* sequence of rigid motions that maps one figure to the other? Use one or more of the above examples to explain your answer.

____

____

Name ______________________ Class ______________ Date ________

4-2

Angle Relationships in Triangles

Focus on Reasoning

Essential question: *What are some theorems about angle measures in triangles?*

Video Tutor

1 Investigate the angle measures of a triangle.

A Use a straightedge to draw a large triangle on a sheet of paper.

B Cut out the triangle.

C Tear off the angles of the triangle.

D Place the angles together so their sides are adjacent and their vertices meet at a point. Take note of how the angles come together.

E Repeat the process by drawing different triangles. Be sure you try an acute triangle, a right triangle, and an obtuse triangle. In each case, note how the angles come together.

REFLECT

1a. Compare your work with that of other students. What always seems to be true about the three angles of a triangle when they are placed together?

____

1b. Make a conjecture: What can you say about the sum of the angle measures in a triangle?

____

1c. An equiangular triangle has three congruent angles. What do you think is true about the angles of an equiangular triangle? Why?

____

1d. In a right triangle, what is the relationship of the measures of the two acute angles?

____

The relationship you investigated above is known as the Triangle Sum Theorem.

The Triangle Sum Theorem

The sum of the angle measures in a triangle is 180°.

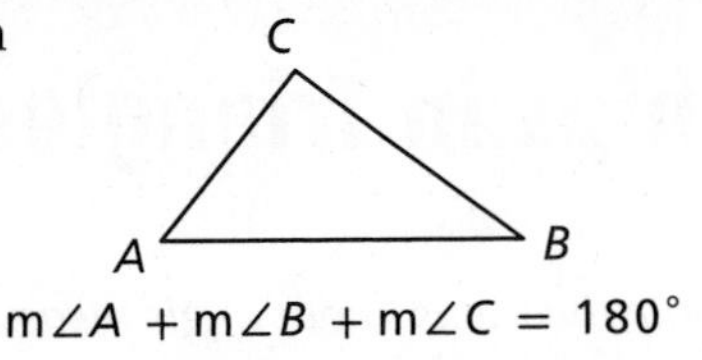

$m\angle A + m\angle B + m\angle C = 180°$

The proof of the Triangle Sum Theorem depends upon a postulate known as the Parallel Postulate.

The Parallel Postulate

Through a point P not on a line ℓ, there is exactly one line parallel to ℓ.

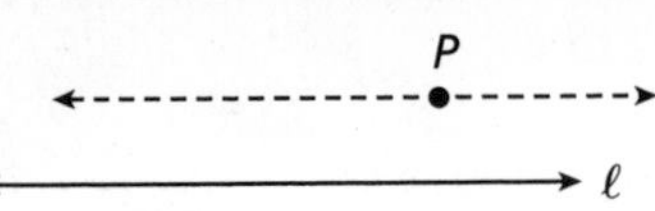

2 Prove the Triangle Sum Theorem.

The sum of the angle measures in a triangle is 180°.

Given: $\triangle ABC$

Prove: $m\angle 1 + m\angle 2 + m\angle 3 = 180°$

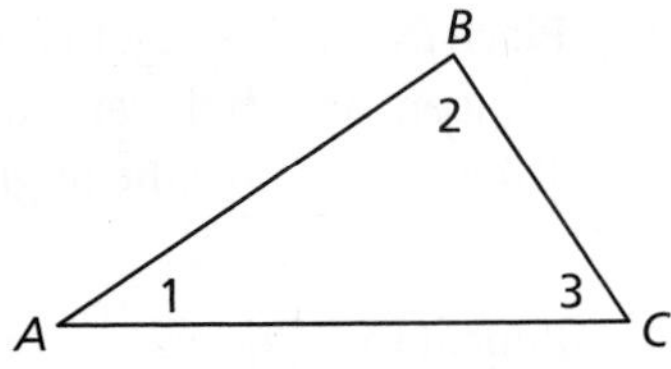

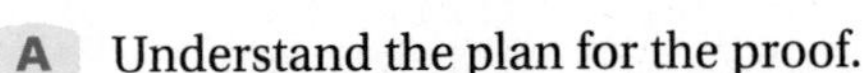

A Understand the plan for the proof.

Draw a line through B that is parallel to $\overline{AC}$. This creates three angles that form a straight angle, so the sum of their measures is 180°. Use the fact that alternate interior angles have the same measure to conclude that the sum of the measures of the angles in a triangle is 180°.

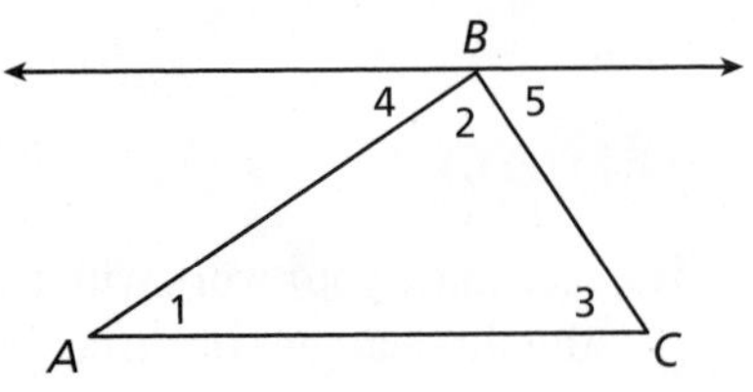

B Complete the proof.

Statements	Reasons
1. Draw ℓ through point B parallel to $\overline{AC}$.	1.
2. $m\angle 4 = m\angle 1$ and $m\angle 5 = m\angle 3$	2.
3. $m\angle 4 + m\angle 2 + m\angle 5 = 180°$	3. Angle Addition Postulate and definition of straight angle
4.	4.

REFLECT

2a. Give an indirect proof to show why it is not possible for a triangle to have two right angles.

___

___

___

A **corollary** to a theorem is a statement that can be proved easily by using the theorem. A useful corollary to the Triangle Sum Theorem involves exterior angles of a triangle.

When you extend the sides of a polygon, the original angles may be called **interior angles** and the angles that form linear pairs with the interior angles are the **exterior angles**.

Each exterior angle of a triangle has two remote interior angles. A **remote interior angle** is an interior angle that is not adjacent to the exterior angle.

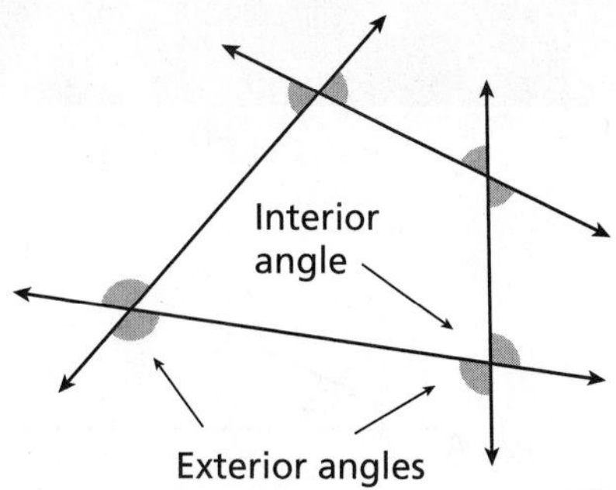

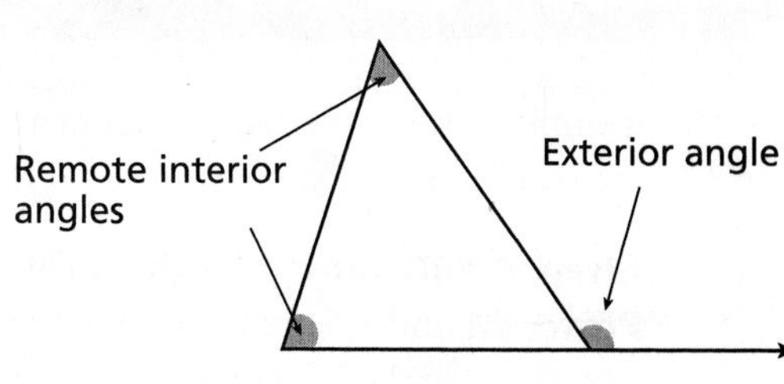

3 Prove the Exterior Angle Theorem.

The measure of an exterior angle of a triangle is equal to the sum of the measures of its remote interior angles.

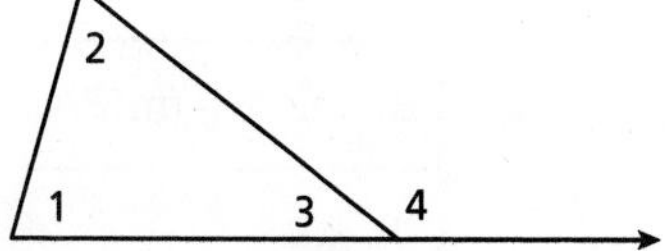

Given: $\triangle ABC$
Prove: $m\angle 4 = m\angle 1 + m\angle 2$

Complete the proof.

Statements	Reasons
1. $\angle 3$ and $\angle 4$ are supplementary.	1.
2. $m\angle 3 + m\angle 4 = 180°$	2.
3.	3. Triangle Sum Theorem
4. $m\angle 3 + m\angle 4 = m\angle 1 + m\angle 2 + m\angle 3$	4.
5. $m\angle 4 = m\angle 1 + m\angle 2$	5.

REFLECT

3a. Explain how you could verify the Exterior Angle Theorem using a method similar to that of the Explore.

Another important corollary of the Triangle Sum Theorem is the Quadrilateral Sum Theorem. You will prove the theorem as an exercise.

Quadrilateral Sum Theorem

The sum of the angle measures in a quadrilateral is 360°.

PRACTICE

1. Complete the proof that the acute angles of a right triangle are complementary.

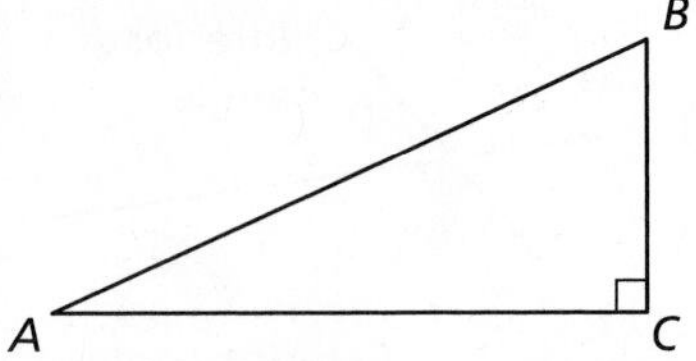

Given: $\triangle ABC$ with $\angle C$ a right angle
Prove: $\angle A$ and $\angle B$ are complementary.

Statements	Reasons
1. $\angle C$ is a right angle.	1.
2. $m\angle C = 90°$	2.
3. $m\angle A + m\angle B + m\angle C = 180°$	3.
4.	4. Substitution Property of Equality
5.	5. Subtraction Property of Equality
6. $\angle A$ and $\angle B$ are complementary.	6.

2. Write a paragraph proof of the Quadrilateral Sum Theorem.

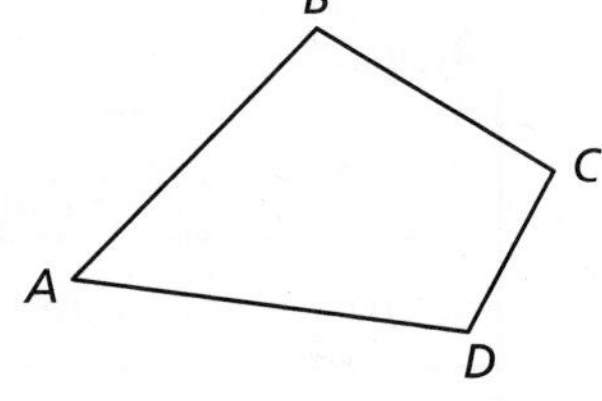

Given: Quadrilateral *ABCD*
Prove: $m\angle A + m\angle B + m\angle C + m\angle D = 360°$
(*Hint:* Draw diagonal $\overline{AC}$ and number the angles formed.)

3. If two angles of one triangle are congruent to two angles of another triangle, must the third angles of the triangles also be congruent? Why or why not?

Name ____________ Class ________ Date ________

4-2

Additional Practice

1. An area in central North Carolina is known as the Research Triangle because of the relatively large number of high-tech companies and research universities located there. Duke University, the University of North Carolina at Chapel Hill, and North Carolina State University are all within this area. The Research Triangle is roughly bounded by the cities of Chapel Hill, Durham, and Raleigh. From Chapel Hill, the angle between Durham and Raleigh measures 54.8°. From Raleigh, the angle between Chapel Hill and Durham measures 24.1°. Find the angle between Chapel Hill and Raleigh from Durham. ____________

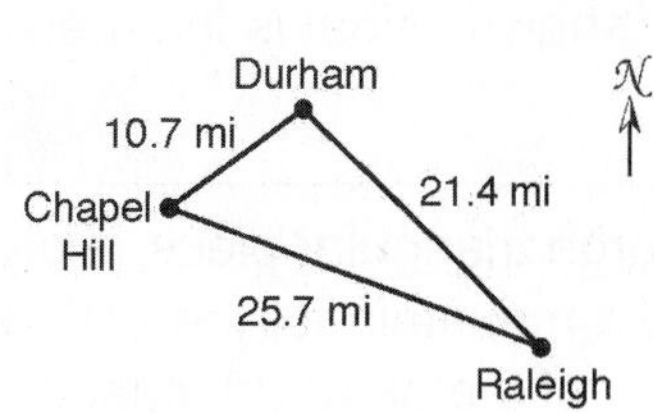

2. The acute angles of right triangle ABC are congruent. Find their measures. ____________

The measure of one of the acute angles in a right triangle is given. Find the measure of the other acute angle.

3. 44.9° ____________
4. $(90 - z)°$ ____________
5. 0.3° ____________

Find each angle measure.

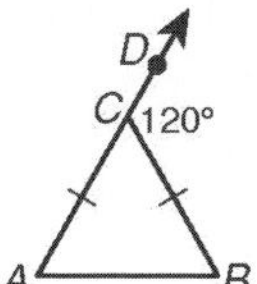

P
23°
(5x − 1)°
(9x + 2)°
S
R
Q

6. m∠B ____________

7. m∠PRS ____________

8. In △LMN, the measure of an exterior angle at N measures 99°. $m\angle L = \frac{1}{3}x°$ and $m\angle M = \frac{2}{3}x°$. Find m∠$L$, m∠$M$, and m∠$LNM$. ____________

9. m∠E and m∠G ____________

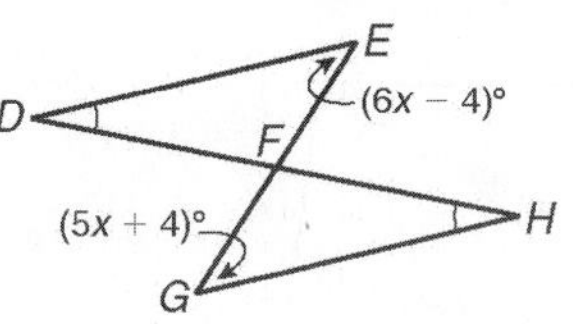

10. m∠T and m∠V ____________

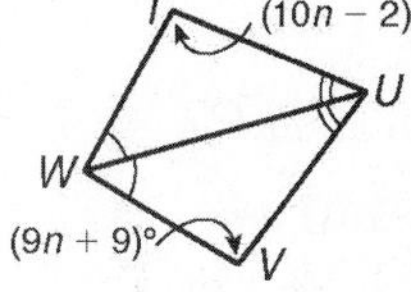

11. In △ABC and △DEF, m∠A = m∠D and m∠B = m∠E. Find m∠F if an exterior angle at A measures 107°, m∠$B = (5x + 2)$ °, and m∠$C = (5x + 5)$ °. ____________

12. The angle measures of a triangle are in the ratio 3 : 4 : 3. Find the angle measures of the triangle. ____________

Problem Solving

1. The locations of three food stands on a fair's midway are shown. What is the measure of the angle labeled $x°$?

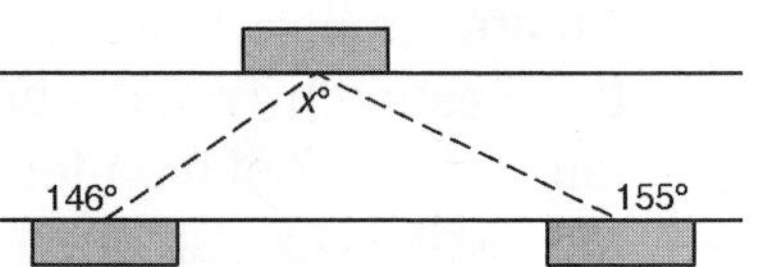

2. A large triangular piece of plywood is to be painted to look like a mountain for the spring musical. The angles at the base of the plywood measure 76° and 45°. What is the measure of the top angle that represents the mountain peak?

Use the figure of the banner for Exercises 3 and 4.

3. What is the value of n?

4. What is the measure of each angle in the banner?

Use the figure of the athlete pole vaulting for Exercises 5 and 6.

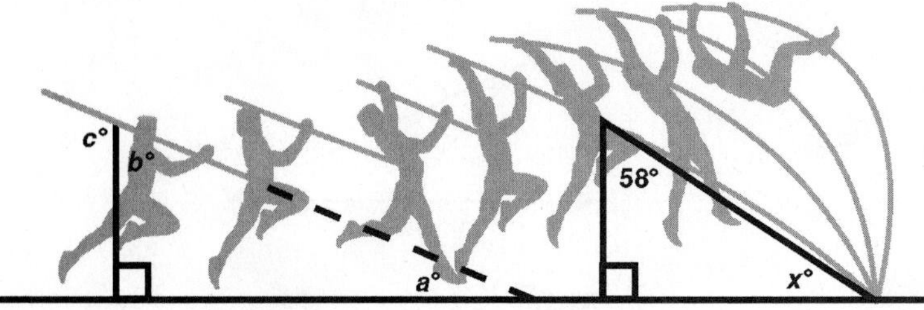

5. What is $x°$, the measure of the angle that the pole makes when it first touches the ground?

6. At takeoff, $a° = 23°$. What is $c°$, the measure of the angle the pole makes with the athlete's body?

The figure shows a path through a garden. Choose the best answer.

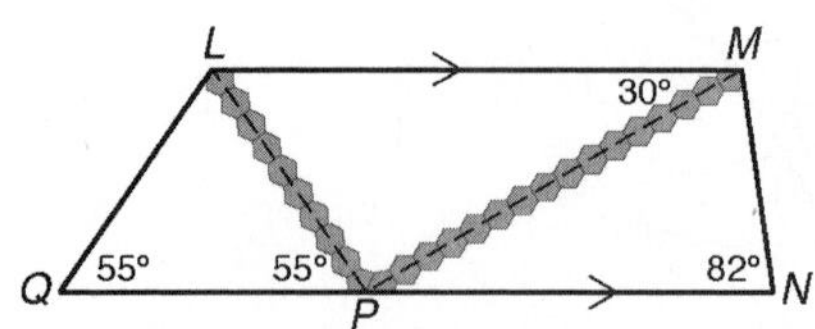

7. What is the measure of $\angle QLP$?

A 20° C 110°

B 70° D 125°

8. What is the measure of $\angle LPM$?

F 85° H 95°

G 90° J 125°

9. What is the measure of $\angle PMN$?

A 98° C 60°

B 68° D 55°

Name ____________________ Class ____________ Date ________

4-3

Congruent Triangles

Connection: Using Rigid Motions

Video Tutor

Essential question: *How can you use properties of rigid motions to draw conclusions about corresponding sides and corresponding angles in congruent triangles?*

When you know that two triangles are congruent, you can make conclusions about the sides and angles of the triangles.

MCC9–12.G.CO.7

1 EXAMPLE Finding an Unknown Dimension

$\triangle ABC \cong \triangle DEF$. Find DE and $m\angle B$. Explain your reasoning.

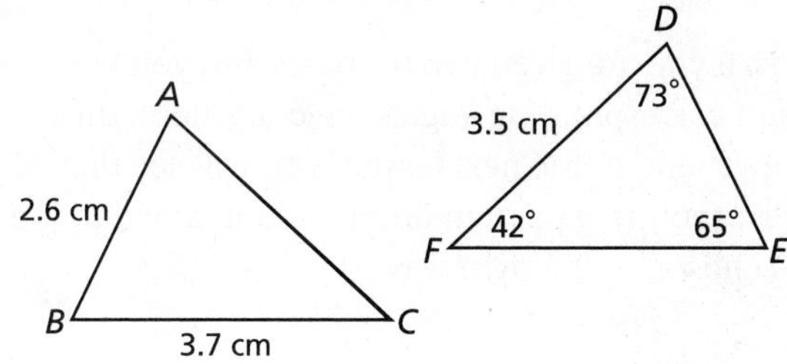

A Complete the following to find DE.

Because $\triangle ABC \cong \triangle DEF$, there is a sequence of rigid motions that maps $\triangle ABC$ to $\triangle DEF$.

This same sequence of rigid motions maps $\overline{AB}$ to ________.

This means $\overline{AB} \cong$ ________.

Congruent segments have the same length, so $AB =$ ________.

$AB =$ ________, so $DE =$ ________.

B To find $m\angle B$, use similar reasoning to show that $\angle B \cong$ ________.

So, $m\angle B =$ ________.

REFLECT

1a. If you know $\triangle ABC \cong \triangle DEF$, what six congruence statements about segments and angles can you write? Why?

____

____

____

When two triangles are congruent, the **corresponding parts** are the sides and angles that are images of each other. You write a congruence statement for two figures by matching the corresponding parts. In other words, the statement $\triangle ABC \cong \triangle DEF$ contains the information that $\overline{AB}$ corresponds to $\overline{DE}$ (and $\overline{AB} \cong \overline{DE}$), $\angle A$ corresponds to $\angle D$ (and $\angle A \cong \angle D$), and so on.

The following theorem is often abbreviated CPCTC. The proof of the theorem is similar to the argument presented in the previous example.

Corresponding Parts of Congruent Triangles are Congruent Theorem (CPCTC)

If two triangles are congruent, then corresponding sides are congruent and corresponding angles are congruent.

The converse of CPCTC is also true. That is, if you are given two triangles and you know that the six pairs of corresponding sides and corresponding angles are congruent, then you can conclude that the triangles are congruent. In the next lesson, you will see that you need only three pairs of congruent corresponding parts in order to conclude that the triangles are congruent, provided they are chosen in the right way.

MCC9–12.G.CO.7

2 EXAMPLE Using CPCTC

$\triangle RGK \cong \triangle MQB$. Write six congruence statements about corresponding parts.

A Identify corresponding sides.

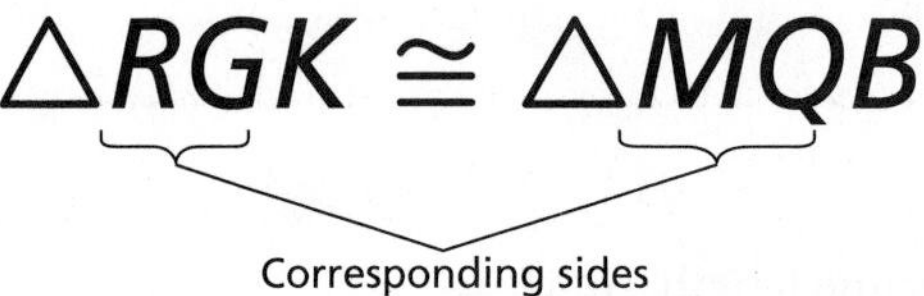

Corresponding sides are named using pairs of letters in the same position on either side of the congruence statement.

$\overline{RG} \cong \overline{MQ}$; $\overline{GK} \cong$ __________; __________ $\cong$ __________

B Identify corresponding angles.

Corresponding angles are named using letters in the same position on either side of the congruence statement.

$\angle R \cong \angle M$; $\angle G \cong$ __________; __________ $\cong$ __________

REFLECT

2a. Given that $\triangle PQR \cong \triangle STU$, $PQ = 2.7$ ft, and $PR = 3.4$ ft, is it possible to determine the length of $\overline{TU}$? If so, find the length. If not, explain why not.

____

____

2b. A student claims that any two congruent triangles must have the same perimeter. Do you agree or disagree? Why?

____

____

PRACTICE

1. $\triangle ABC \cong \triangle DEF$. Find AB and $m\angle E$.

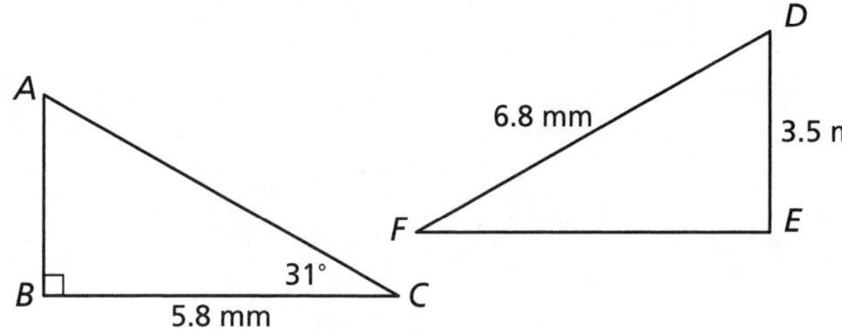

____

2. $\triangle MNP \cong \triangle QRS$. Find NP and $m\angle P$.

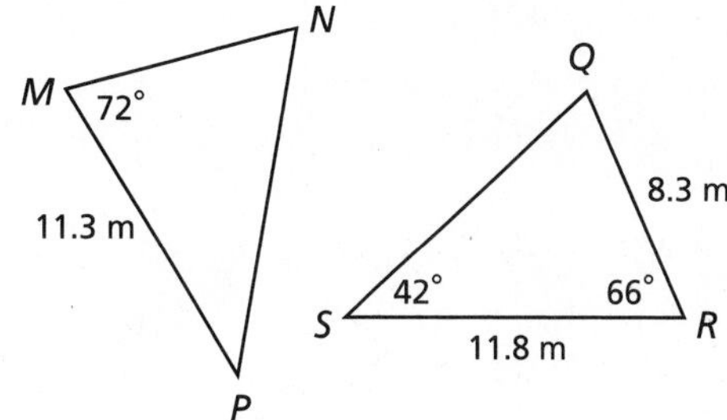

____

3. $\triangle JKL \cong \triangle LMJ$. Find JK and $m\angle JLM$.

____

4. $\triangle ABC \cong \triangle DEF$. Find DF and $m\angle EDC$.

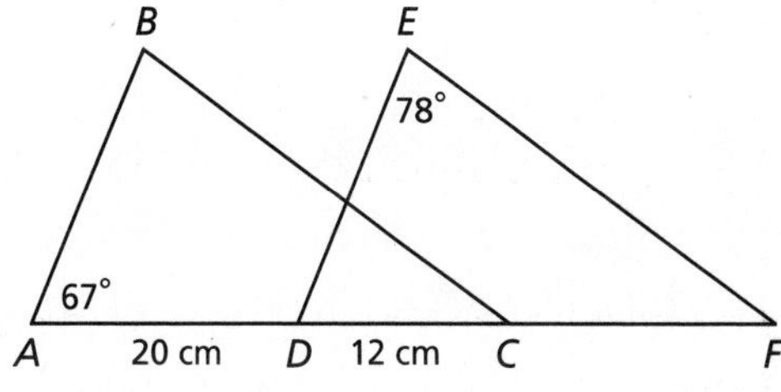

____

For each given congruence statement, write six congruence statements about corresponding parts.

5. $\triangle JWT \cong \triangle GKH$

6. $\triangle PQL \cong \triangle KYU$

7. $\triangle HTJ \cong \triangle NRZ$

____

____

____

8. The figure shows a portion of the truss of a bridge. $\triangle ABG \cong \triangle BCH \cong \triangle HGB$.

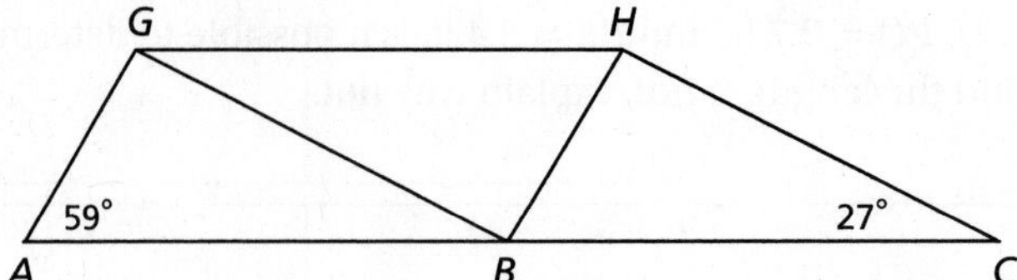

a. Is it possible to determine $m\angle GBH$? If so, how? If not, why not?

b. A student claims that B is the midpoint of $\overline{AC}$. Do you agree? Explain.

Name ________________ Class ________________ Date ________________

4-3

Additional Practice

In baseball, home plate is a pentagon. Pentagon *ABCDE* is a diagram of a regulation home plate. The baseball rules are very specific about the exact dimensions of this pentagon so that every home plate is congruent to every other home plate. If pentagon *PQRST* is another home plate, identify each congruent corresponding part.

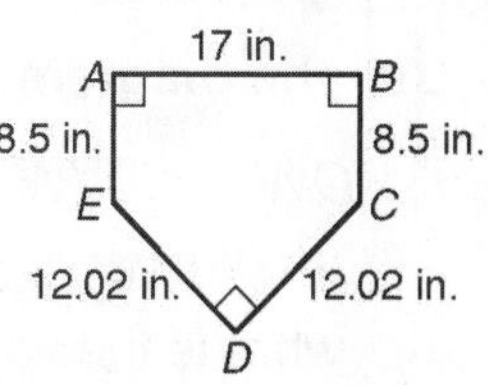

1. $\angle S \cong$ ________
2. $\angle B \cong$ ________
3. $\overline{EA} \cong$ ________
4. $\angle E \cong$ ________
5. $\overline{PQ} \cong$ ________
6. $\overline{TS} \cong$ ________

Given: $\triangle DEF \cong \triangle LMN$. Find each value.

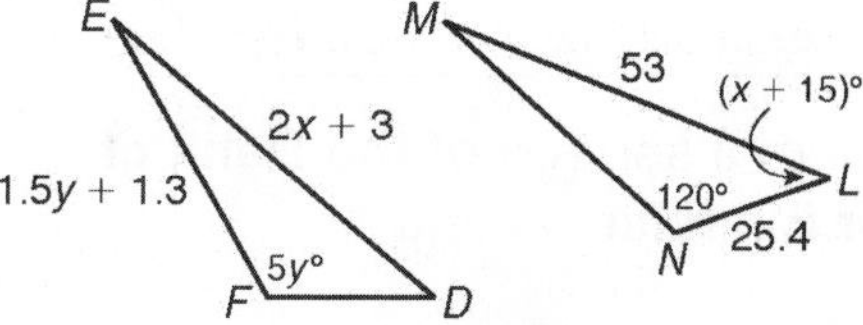

7. $m\angle L =$ ________
8. $EF =$ ________
9. Write a two-column proof.

   Given: $\angle U \cong \angle UWV \cong \angle ZXY \cong \angle Z$, $\overline{UV} \cong \overline{WV}$, $\overline{XY} \cong \overline{ZY}$, $\overline{UX} \cong \angle \overline{WZ}$

   Prove: $\Delta UVW \cong \Delta XYZ$

   Proof:

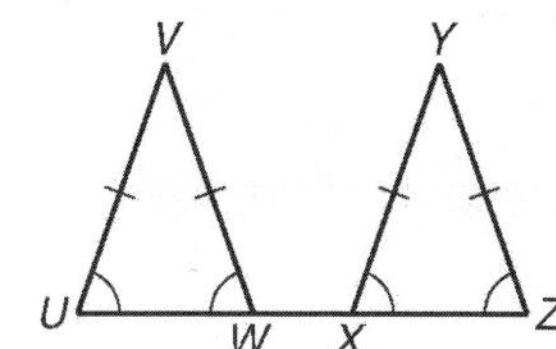

10. **Given:** $\triangle CDE \cong \triangle HIJ$, $DE = 9x$, and $IJ = 7x + 3$. Find x and DE.

____

11. **Given:** $\triangle CDE \cong \triangle HIJ$, $m\angle D = (5y + 1)°$, and $m\angle I = (6y - 25)°$. Find y and $m\angle D$.

____

Problem Solving

Use the diagram of the fence for Exercises 1 and 2.

$\triangle RQW \cong \triangle TVW$

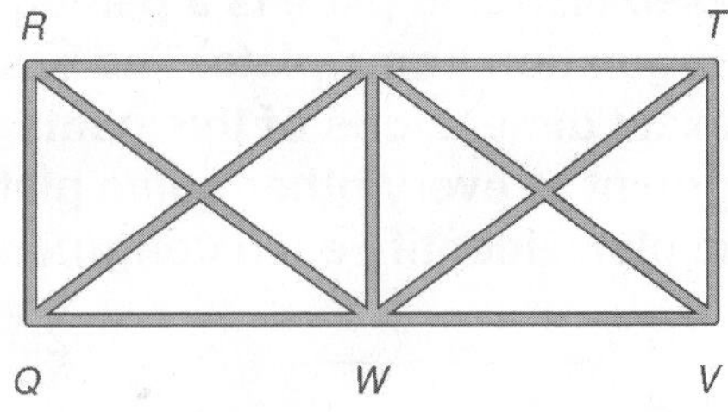

1. If $m\angle RWQ = 36°$ and $m\angle TWV = (2x + 5)°$, what is the value of x?

____

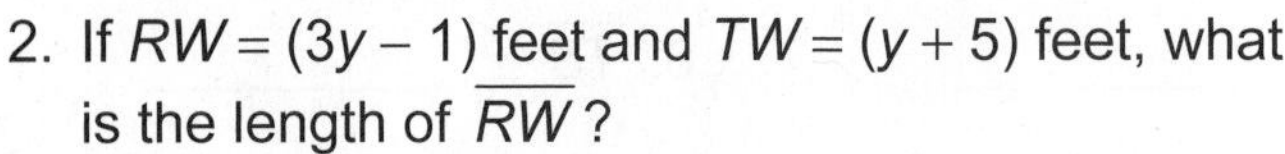

2. If $RW = (3y - 1)$ feet and $TW = (y + 5)$ feet, what is the length of $\overline{RW}$?

____

Use the diagram of a section of the Bank of China Tower for Exercises 3 and 4.

$\triangle JKL \cong \triangle LHJ$

3. What is the value of x?

____

4. Find $m\angle JHL$.

____

Choose the best answer.

5. Chairs with triangular seats were popular in the Middle Ages. Suppose a chair has a seat that is an isosceles triangle and the congruent sides measure $1\frac{1}{2}$ feet. A second chair has a triangular seat with a perimeter of $5\frac{1}{10}$ feet, and it is congruent to the first seat. What is a side length of the second seat?

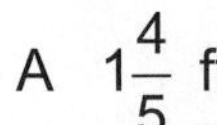

A $1\frac{4}{5}$ ft C 3 ft

B $2\frac{1}{10}$ ft D $3\frac{3}{5}$ ft

Use the diagram for Exercises 6 and 7.

6. C is the midpoint of $\overline{EB}$ and $\overline{AD}$. What additional information would allow you to prove $\triangle ABC \cong \triangle DEC$ by the definition of congruent triangles?

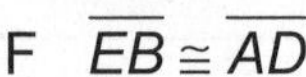

F $\overline{EB} \cong \overline{AD}$ H $\angle ECD \cong \angle ACB$

G $\overline{DE} \cong \overline{AB}$ J $\angle A \cong \angle D$, $\angle B \cong \angle E$

7. If $\triangle ABC \cong \triangle DEC$, $ED = 4y + 2$, and $AB = 6y - 4$, what is the length of $\overline{AB}$?

A 3 C 14

B 12 D 18

Name ______________________ Class ______________ Date __________

Triangle Congruence: SSS and SAS

Going Deeper

Essential question: *How can you establish the SSS and SAS triangle congruence criteria using properties of rigid motions?*

You have seen that when two triangles are congruent, the corresponding sides and corresponding angles are congruent. Conversely, if all six pairs of corresponding sides and corresponding angles of two triangles are congruent, then the triangles are congruent.

The proofs of the SSS and SAS congruence criteria that follow serve as proof of this converse. In each case, the proof demonstrates a "shortcut," in which only three pairs of congruent corresponding parts are needed in order to conclude that the triangles are congruent.

MCC9–12.G.CO.8

1 PROOF SSS Congruence Criterion

If three sides of one triangle are congruent to three sides of another triangle, then the triangles are congruent.

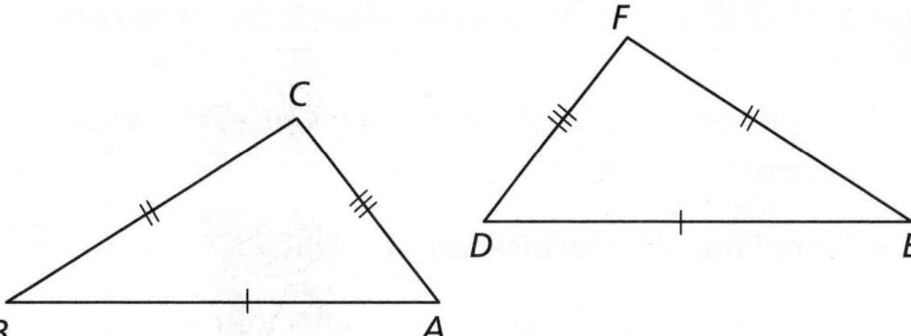

Given: $\overline{AB} \cong \overline{DE}$, $\overline{BC} \cong \overline{EF}$, and $\overline{AC} \cong \overline{DF}$.

Prove: $\triangle ABC \cong \triangle DEF$

To prove the triangles are congruent, you will find a sequence of rigid motions that maps $\triangle ABC$ to $\triangle DEF$. Complete the following steps of the proof.

A Since $\overline{AB} \cong \overline{DE}$, there is a sequence of rigid motions that maps $\overline{AB}$ to ________.

Apply this sequence of rigid motions to $\triangle ABC$ to get $\triangle A'B'C'$, which shares a side with $\triangle DEF$.

If C' lies on the same side of $\overline{DE}$ as F, reflect $\triangle A'B'C'$ across $\overline{DE}$. This results in the figure at right.

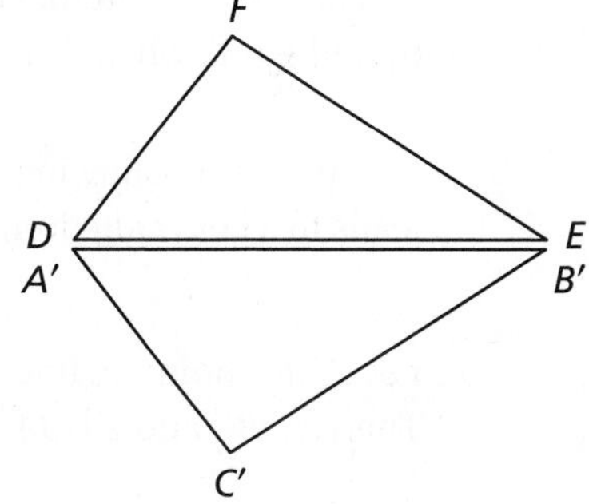

B $\overline{A'C'} \cong \overline{AC}$ because ________________________________.

It is also given that $\overline{AC} \cong \overline{DF}$.

Therefore, $\overline{A'C'} \cong \overline{DF}$ because of the ____________ Property of Congruence.

By a similar argument, $\overline{B'C'} \cong$ ____________.

C Because $\overline{A'C'} \cong \overline{DF}$, D lies on the perpendicular bisector of $\overline{FC'}$, by the Converse of the Perpendicular Bisector Theorem. Similarly, because $\overline{B'C'} \cong \overline{EF}$, E lies on the perpendicular bisector of $\overline{FC'}$. So, $\overline{DE}$ is the perpendicular bisector of $\overline{FC'}$.

By the definition of reflection, the reflection across $\overline{DE}$ maps C' to ________.

The proof shows that there is a sequence of rigid motions that maps $\triangle ABC$ to $\triangle DEF$. Therefore, $\triangle ABC \cong \triangle DEF$.

REFLECT

1a. The proof uses the fact that congruence is transitive. That is, if you know figure $A \cong$ figure B, and figure $B \cong$ figure C, you can conclude that figure $A \cong$ figure C. Why is this true?

____

____

____

You can use reflections and their properties to prove theorems about angle bisectors. These theorems will be very useful in proofs later on.

The first proof is an indirect proof (or a *proof by contradiction*). To write such a proof, you assume that what you are trying to prove is false and you show that this assumption leads to a contradiction.

MCC9–12.G.CO.9

2 PROOF Angle Bisection Theorem

If a line bisects an angle, then each side of the angle is the image of the other under a reflection across the line.

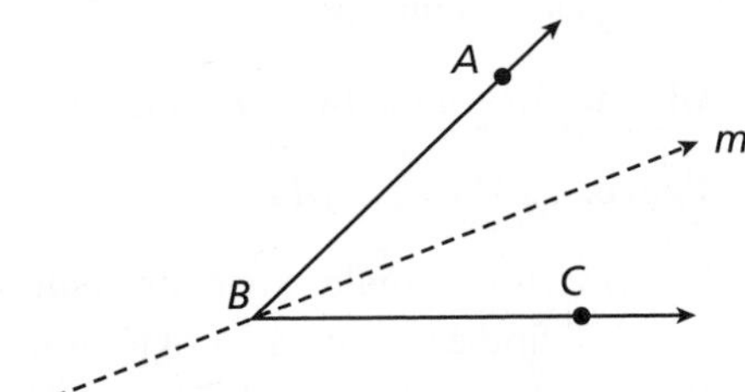

Given: Line m is the bisector of $\angle ABC$.

Prove: The image of $\overrightarrow{BA}$ under a reflection across line m is $\overrightarrow{BC}$.

A Assume what you are trying to prove is false.

Assume that the image of $\overrightarrow{BA}$ under a reflection across line m is *not* $\overrightarrow{BC}$. In that case, let the reflection image of $\overrightarrow{BA}$ be $\overrightarrow{BA'}$, which is not the same ray as $\overrightarrow{BC}$.

B Complete the following to show that this assumption leads to a contradiction.

Let D be a point on line m in the interior of $\angle ABC$. Then $\angle DBC$ and $\angle DBA'$ must have different measures.

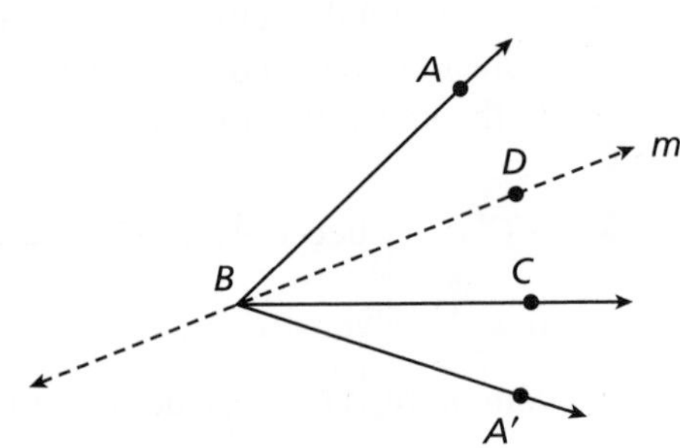

However, $m\angle DBA = m\angle DBC$ since line m is

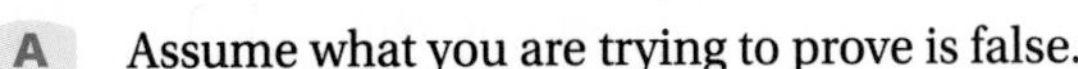

That means $\angle DBA$ and $\angle DBA'$ must have different measures.

This is a contradiction because reflections preserve ______________________

Therefore, the initial assumption must be incorrect, and the image of $\overrightarrow{BA}$ under a reflection across line m is $\overrightarrow{BC}$.

REFLECT

2a. Explain how you can use paper folding to explain why the Angle Bisection Theorem makes sense.

MCC9-12.G.CO.9

3 PROOF Reflected Points on an Angle Theorem

If two points of an angle are located the same distance from the vertex but on different sides of the angle, then the points are images of each other under a reflection across the line that bisects the angle.

Given: Line m is the bisector of $\angle ABC$ and $BA = BC$.

Prove: $r_m(A) = C$ and $r_m(C) = A$.

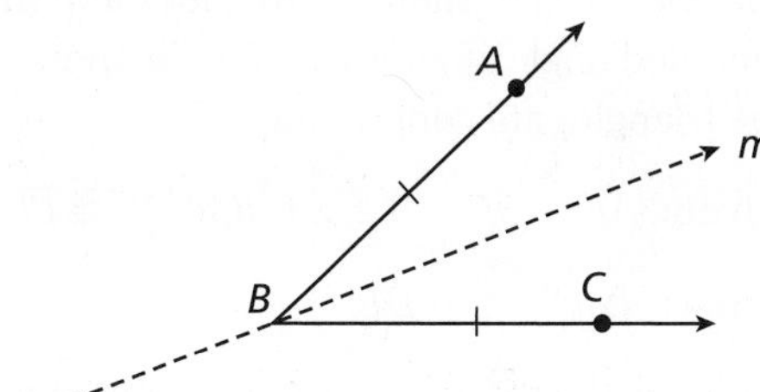

Complete the following proof.

It is given that line m is the bisector of $\angle ABC$. Therefore, when $\overrightarrow{BA}$ is reflected across line m, its image is $\overrightarrow{BC}$.

This is justified by ________________

This means that $r_m(A)$ lies on $\overrightarrow{BC}$. Let $r_m(A) = A'$.

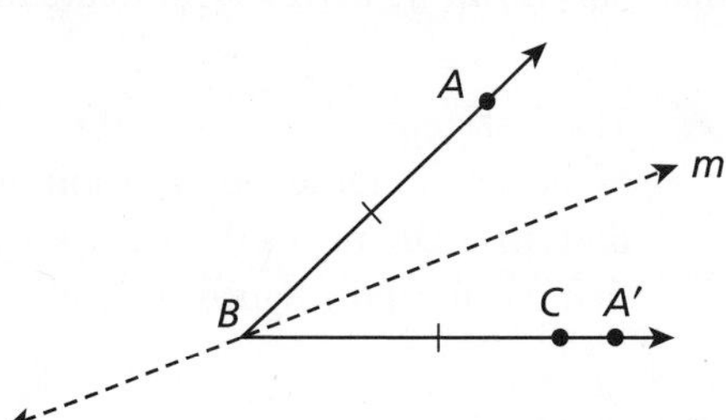

Since point B is on the line of reflection, $r_m(B) = B$, and since reflections preserve distance, $BA = BA'$.

However, it is given that $BA = BC$. By the Substitution Property of Equality, you can conclude that

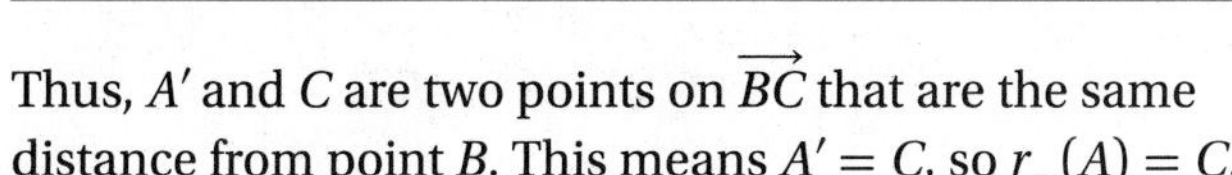

Thus, A' and C are two points on $\overrightarrow{BC}$ that are the same distance from point B. This means $A' = C$, so $r_m(A) = C$.

A similar argument shows that $r_m(C) = A$.

REFLECT

3a. Using the above argument as a model, write out a similar argument that shows that $r_m(C) = A$.

REFLECT

3b. In the figure on the previous page, suppose you reflect point A across line m. Then you reflect the image of point A across line m. What is the final location of the point? Why?

____

____

____

MCC9–12.G.CO.8

4 PROOF SAS Congruence Criterion

If two sides and the included angle of one triangle are congruent to two sides and the included angle of another triangle, then the triangles are congruent.

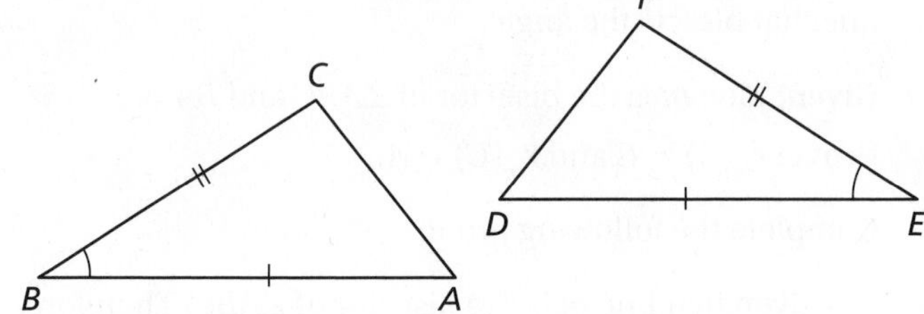

Given: $\overline{AB} \cong \overline{DE}$, $\angle B \cong \angle E$, and $\overline{BC} \cong \overline{EF}$.

Prove: $\triangle ABC \cong \triangle DEF$

To prove the triangles are congruent, you will find a sequence of rigid motions that maps $\triangle ABC$ to $\triangle DEF$. Complete the following steps of the proof.

A The first step is the same as the first step in the proof of the SSS Congruence Criterion. In particular, the fact that $\overline{AB} \cong \overline{DE}$ means there is a sequence of rigid motions that results in the figure at right.

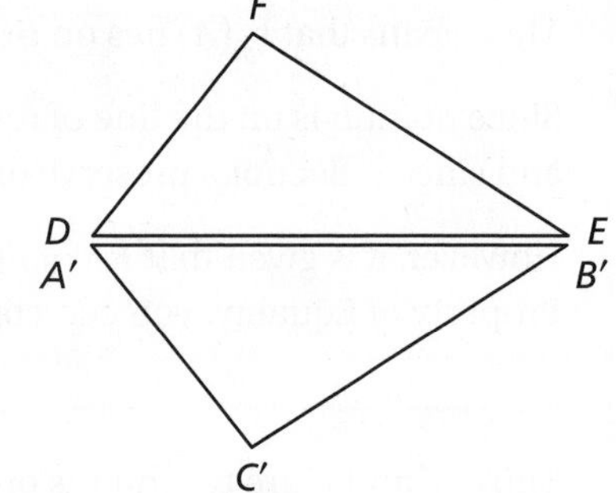

B Rigid motions preserve distance, so $\overline{B'C'} \cong \overline{BC}$. Also, it is given that $\overline{BC} \cong \overline{EF}$.

So, ______________ because congruence is transitive.

It is given that $\angle DEF \cong \angle B$. Also, $\angle B \cong$ ______________ because rigid motions preserve angle measure.

Therefore, $\angle DEF \cong$ ______________ because congruence is transitive. You can use this to conclude that $\overline{DE}$ is the bisector of $\angle FEC'$.

C Now consider the reflection across $\overline{DE}$.

Under this reflection, the image of C' is ______________ by the Reflected Points on an Angle Theorem.

The proof shows that there is a sequence of rigid motions that maps $\triangle ABC$ to $\triangle DEF$. Therefore, $\triangle ABC \cong \triangle DEF$.

REFLECT

4a. Explain how the Reflected Points on an Angle Theorem lets you conclude that the image of C' under a reflection across $\overline{DE}$ is F.

MCC9–12.G.SRT.5

5 EXAMPLE Using the SSS Congruence Criterion

Complete the proof.

Given: M is the midpoint of $\overline{RT}$; $\overline{SR} \cong \overline{ST}$

Prove: $\triangle RSM \cong \triangle TSM$

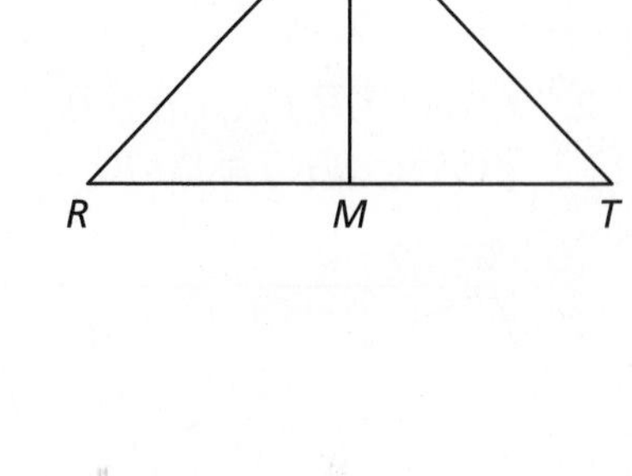

A Use a colored pen or pencil to mark the figure using the given information.

B Write a statement in each cell to complete the proof. The reason for each statement is provided.

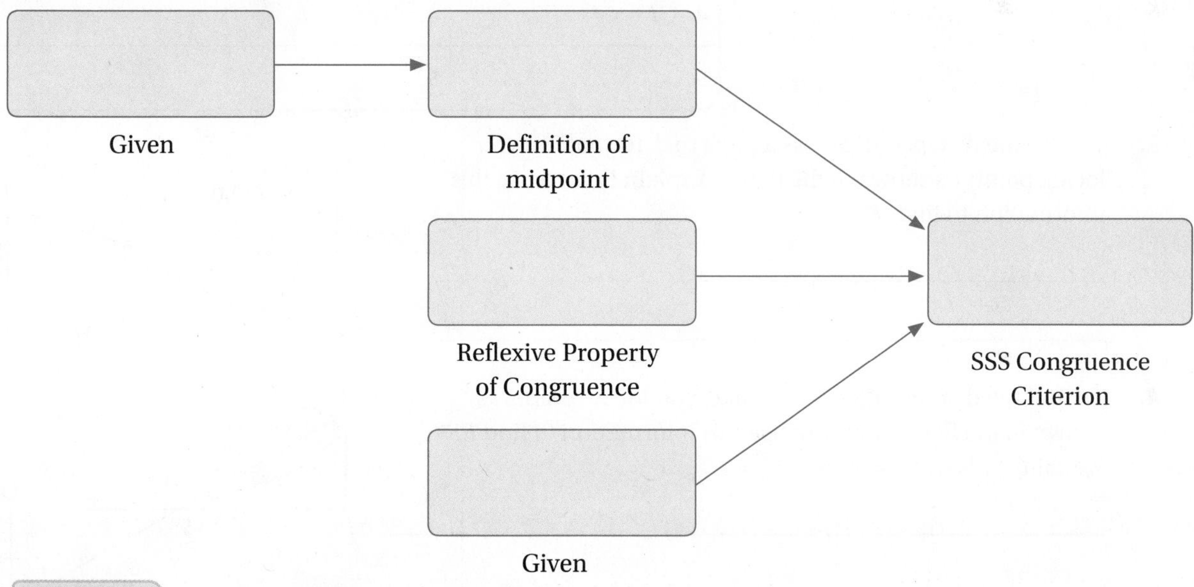

REFLECT

5a. What piece of additional given information in the above example would allow you to use the SAS Congruence Criterion to prove that $\triangle RSM \cong \triangle TSM$?

5b. Suppose the given information had been that M is the midpoint of $\overline{RT}$ and $\angle R \cong \angle T$. Would it have been possible to prove $\triangle RSM \cong \triangle TSM$? Explain.

PRACTICE

Complete the two-column proof.

1. **Given:** $\overline{AB} \cong \overline{CD}$, $\overline{AD} \cong \overline{CB}$
   Prove: $\triangle ABD \cong \triangle CBD$

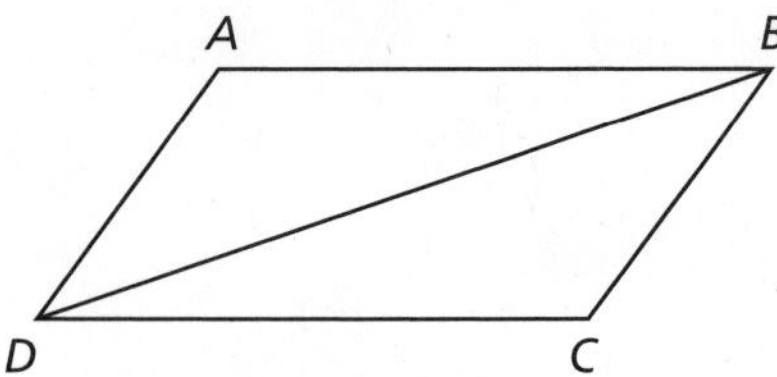

Statements	Reasons
1. $\overline{AB} \cong \overline{CD}$	1.
2. $\overline{AD} \cong \overline{CB}$	2.
3.	3.
4. $\triangle ABD \cong \triangle CBD$	4.

2. **Given:** $\overline{GH} \parallel \overline{JK}$, $\overline{GH} \cong \overline{JK}$
   Prove: $\triangle HGJ \cong \triangle KJG$

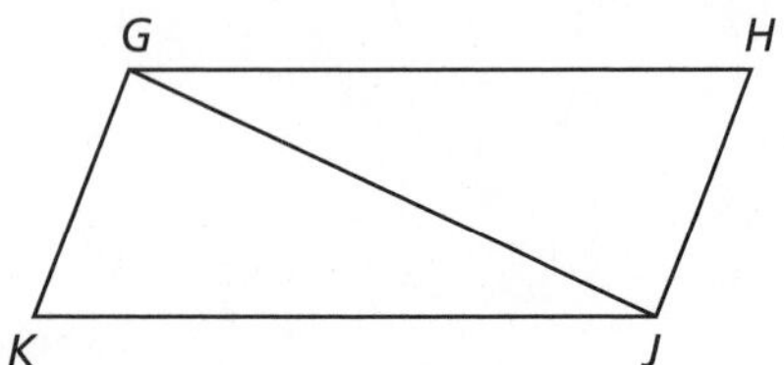

Statements	Reasons
1. $\overline{GH} \parallel \overline{JK}$	1.
2. $\angle HGJ \cong \angle KJG$	2.
3.	3. Given
4. $\overline{GJ} \cong \overline{GJ}$	4.
5.	5.

3. To find the distance *JK* across a large rock formation, you locate points as shown in the figure. Explain how to use this information to find *JK*.

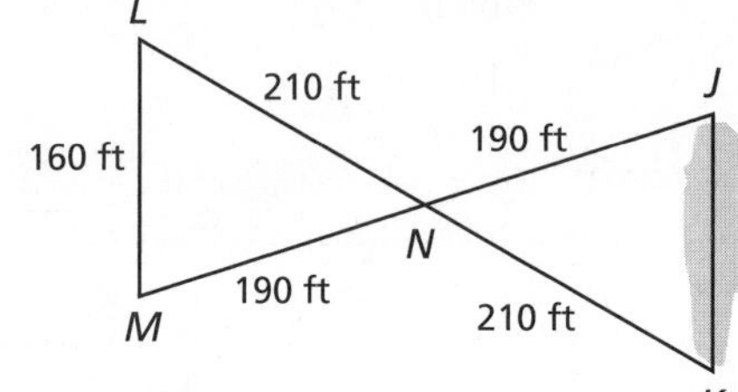

4. To find the distance *RS* across a lake, you locate points as shown in the figure. Can you use this information to find *RS*? Explain.

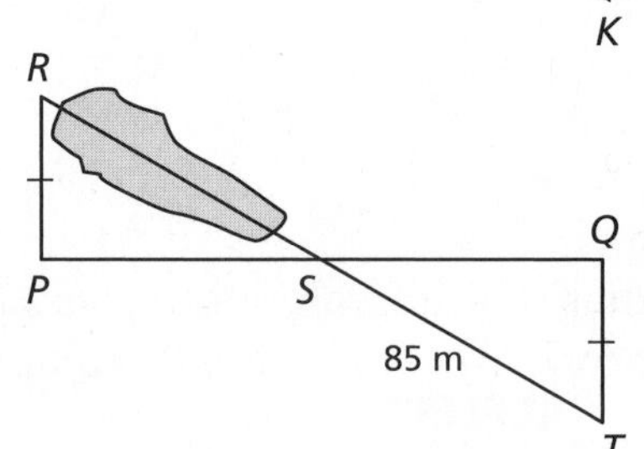

5. $\triangle DEF \cong \triangle GHJ$, $DF = 3x + 2$, $GJ = 6x - 13$, and $HJ = 5x$. Find *HJ*.

6. In the figure, $\overleftrightarrow{MC}$ is the perpendicular bisector of $\overline{AB}$. Is it possible to prove that $\triangle AMC \cong \triangle BMC$? Why or why not?

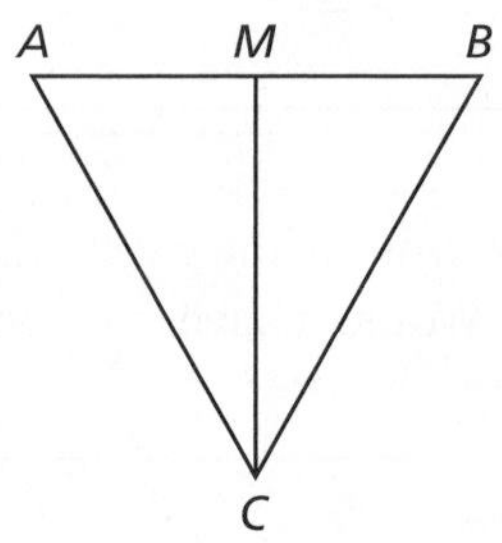

Name________________________________ Class__________________ Date______________ **5-1**

Additional Practice

Write whether SSS or SAS, if either, can be used to prove the triangles congruent. If no triangles can be proved congruent, write *neither*.

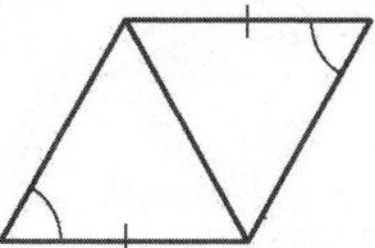

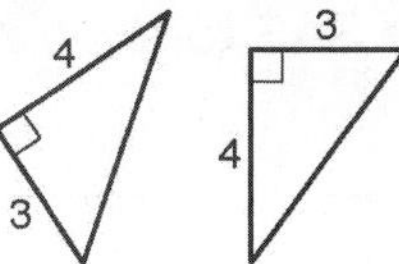

1. ______________________________

2. ______________________________

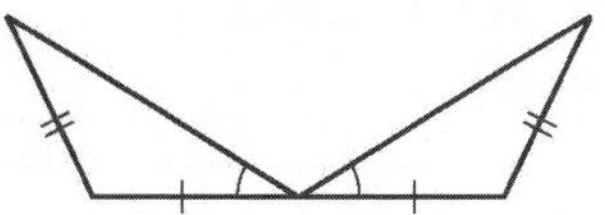

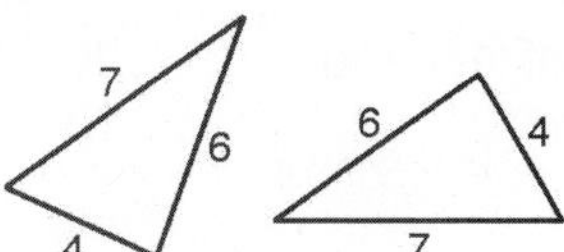

3. ______________________________

4. ______________________________

Find the value of *x* so that the triangles are congruent.

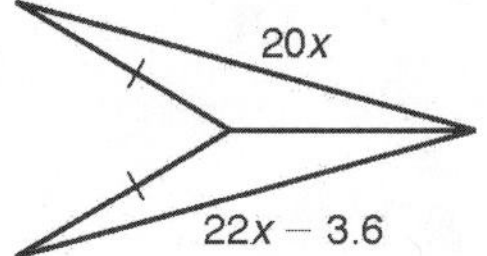

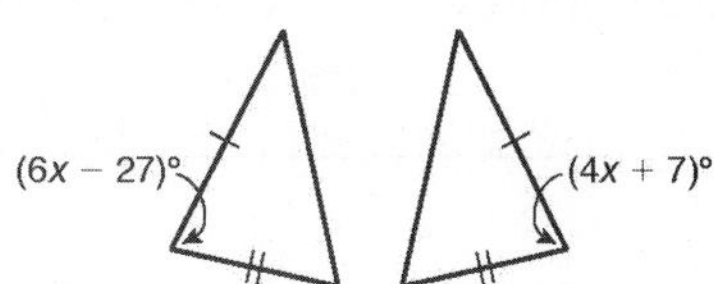

5. $x =$ ______________________________

6. $x =$ ______________________________

The Hatfield and McCoy families are feuding over some land. Neither family will be satisfied unless the two triangular fields are exactly the same size. You know that *C* is the midpoint of each of the intersecting segments. Write a two-column proof that will settle the dispute.

7. **Given:** *C* is the midpoint of $\overline{AD}$ and $\overline{BE}$.

   Prove: $\triangle ABC \cong \triangle DEC$

   Proof:

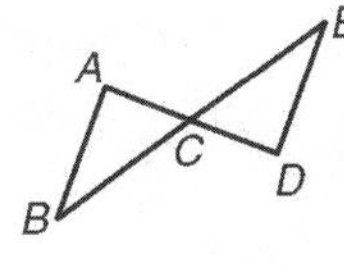

Problem Solving

Use the diagram for Exercises 1 and 2.

A shed door appears to be divided into congruent right triangles.

1. Suppose $\overline{AB} \cong \overline{CD}$. Use SAS to show $\triangle ABD \cong \triangle DCA$.

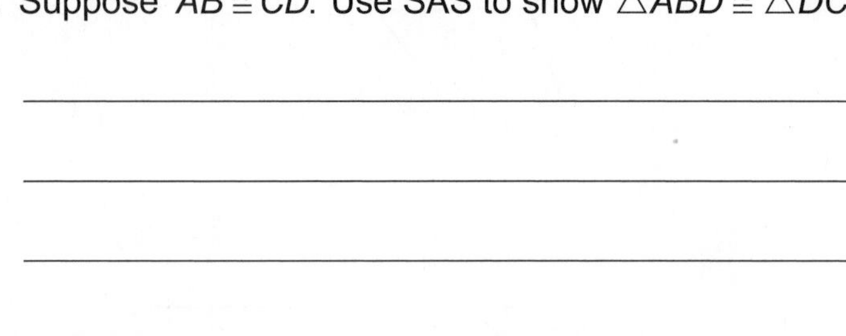

2. J is the midpoint of AB and $\overline{AK} \cong \overline{BK}$. Use SSS to explain why $\triangle AKJ \cong \triangle BKJ$.

3. A *balalaika* is a Russian stringed instrument. Show that the triangular parts of the two balalaikas are congruent for $x = 6$.

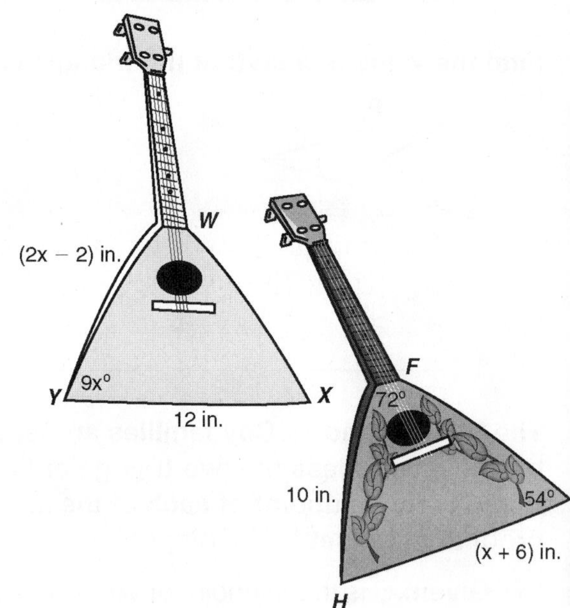

A quilt pattern of a dog is shown. Choose the best answer.

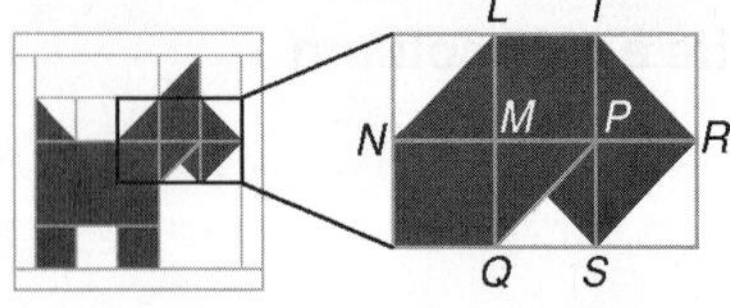

4. $ML = MP = MN = MQ = 1$ inch. Which statement is correct?

   A $\triangle LMN \cong \triangle QMP$ by SAS.

   B $\triangle LMN \cong \triangle QMP$ by SSS.

   C $\triangle LMN \cong \triangle MQP$ by SAS.

   D $\triangle LMN \cong \triangle MQP$ by SSS.

5. P is the midpoint of $\overline{TS}$ and $TR = SR = 1.4$ inches. What can you conclude about ΔTRP and ΔSRP?

   F $\triangle TRP \cong \triangle SRP$ by SAS.

   G $\triangle TRP \cong \triangle SRP$ by SSS.

   H $\triangle TRP \cong \triangle SPR$ by SAS.

   J $\triangle TRP \cong \triangle SPR$ by SSS.

Name______________________ Class______________ Date__________

5-2

Triangle Congruence: ASA, AAS, and HL

Going Deeper

Essential question: *How can you establish and use the ASA and AAS triangle congruence criteria?*

MCC9–12.G.CO.8

1 PROOF — ASA Congruence Criterion

If two angles and the included side of one triangle are congruent to two angles and the included side of another triangle, then the triangles are congruent.

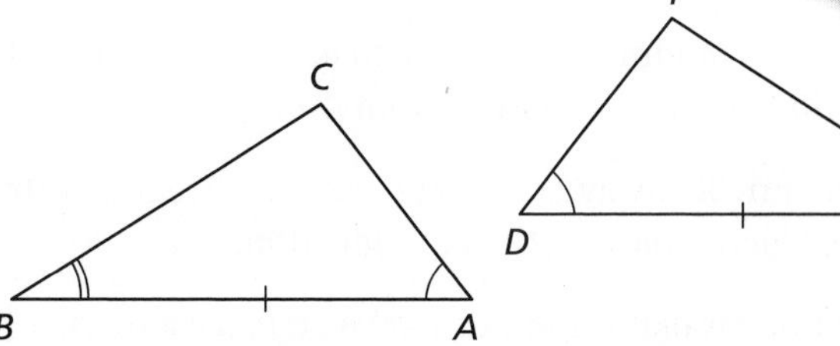

Given: $\overline{AB} \cong \overline{DE}$, $\angle A \cong \angle D$, and $\angle B \cong \angle E$.

Prove: $\triangle ABC \cong \triangle DEF$

To prove the triangles are congruent, you will find a sequence of rigid motions that maps $\triangle ABC$ to $\triangle DEF$. Complete the following steps of the proof.

A The first step is the same as the first step in the proof of the SSS Congruence Criterion. In particular the fact that $\overline{AB} \cong \overline{DE}$, means there is a sequence of rigid motions that results in the figure at right.

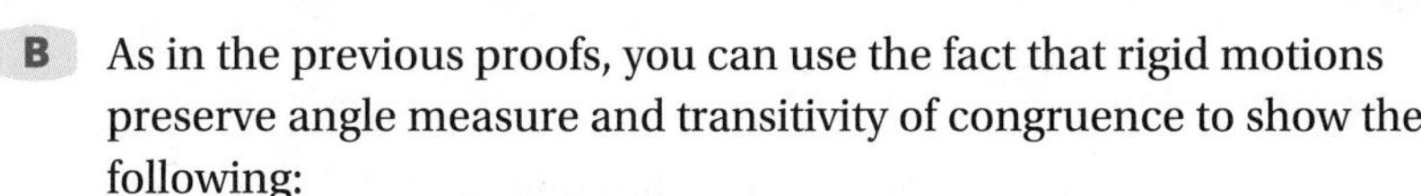

B As in the previous proofs, you can use the fact that rigid motions preserve angle measure and transitivity of congruence to show the following:

$\angle C'A'B' \cong$ ____________ and $\angle C'B'A' \cong$ ____________.

This means $\overline{DE}$ bisects both $\angle FDC'$ and ____________.

By the Angle Bisection Theorem, under a reflection across $\overline{DE}$, $\overrightarrow{A'C'}$ maps to $\overrightarrow{DF}$, and $\overrightarrow{B'C'}$ maps to $\overrightarrow{EF}$. Since the image of C' lies on both $\overrightarrow{DF}$ and $\overrightarrow{EF}$, the image of C' must be F.

The proof shows that there is a sequence of rigid motions that maps $\triangle ABC$ to $\triangle DEF$. Therefore, $\triangle ABC \cong \triangle DEF$.

REFLECT

1a. Explain how knowing that the image of C' lies on both $\overrightarrow{DF}$ and $\overrightarrow{EF}$ allows you to conclude that the image of C' is F.

____

Once you have shown that two triangles are congruent, you can use the fact that corresponding parts of congruent triangles are congruent (CPCTC) to draw conclusions about side lengths and angle measures.

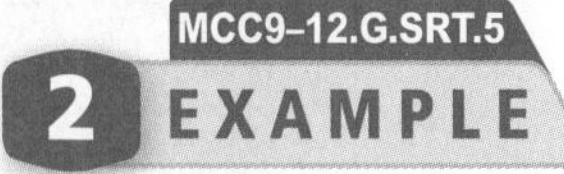

Using the ASA Congruence Criterion

Solve the following problem.

You want to find the distance across a river. In order to find the distance *AB*, you locate points as described below. Explain how to use this information and the figure to find *AB*.

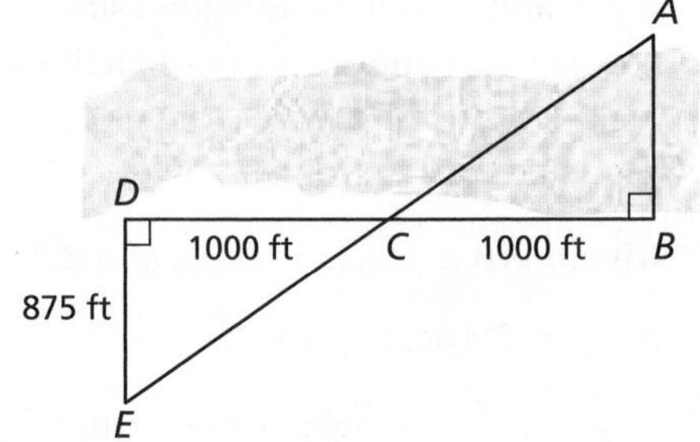

1. Identify a landmark, such as a tree, at *A*. Place a marker (*B*) directly across the river from *A*.
2. At *B*, turn 90° away from *A* and walk 1000 feet in a straight line. Place a marker (*C*) at this location.
3. Continue walking another 1000 feet. Place a marker (*D*) at this location.
4. Turn 90° away from the river and walk until the marker *C* aligns with *A*. Place a marker (*E*) at this location. Measure $\overline{DE}$.

A Show $\triangle ABC \cong \triangle EDC$.

- Based on the information marked in the figure, which pairs of sides or pairs of angles do you know to be congruent?

____

- What additional pair of sides or pair of angles do you know to be congruent? Why?

____

- How can you conclude that $\triangle ABC \cong \triangle EDC$?

____

B Use corresponding parts of congruent triangles.

- Which side of $\triangle EDC$ corresponds to $\overline{AB}$? _______________
- What is the length of $\overline{AB}$? Why?

____

REFLECT

2a. Suppose you had walked 500 feet from *B* to *C* and then walked another 500 feet from *C* to *D*. Would that have changed the distance *ED*? Explain.

____

____

You have already used three triangle congruence criteria: SSS, SAS, and ASA. There is another criterion that is useful in proofs, the AAS Congruence Criterion.

AAS Congruence Criterion

If two angles and a non-included side of one triangle are congruent to two angles and the corresponding non-included side of another triangle, then the triangles are congruent.

MCC9–12.G.CO.10

3 PROOF ASA Congruence Criterion

Given: $\angle B \cong \angle E$, $\angle C \cong \angle F$, $\overline{AC} \cong \overline{DF}$

Prove: $\triangle ABC \cong \triangle DEF$

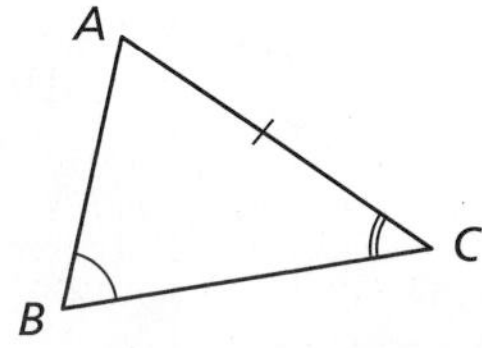

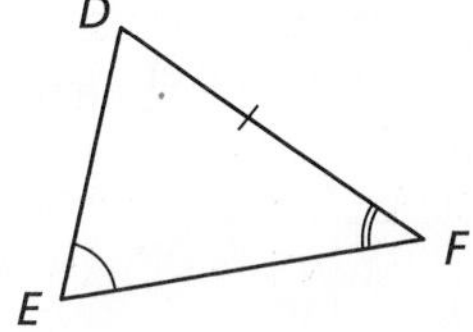

To prove the triangles are congruent, you can use the Triangle Sum Theorem and reasoning about the angles of the triangles to show that $\angle A \cong \angle D$. Then you can show the triangles are congruent by using ASA.

Complete the proof by filling in the missing statements and reasons.

Statements	Reasons
1. $\angle B \cong \angle E$, $\angle C \cong \angle F$	1. Given
2. $m\angle A + m\angle B + m\angle C = 180°$	2. Triangle Sum Theorem
3. $m\angle A = 180° - m\angle B - m\angle C$	3.
4. $m\angle D + m\angle E + m\angle F = 180°$	4.
5.	5. Subtraction Property of Equality
6. $m\angle B = m\angle E$, $m\angle C = m\angle F$	6. Definition of congruent angles
7. $m\angle D = 180° - m\angle B - m\angle C$	7.
8. $m\angle A = m\angle D$	8. Transitive Property of Equality
9. $\angle A \cong \angle D$	9.
10. $\overline{AC} \cong \overline{DF}$	10. Given
11.	11. ASA Congruence Criterion

REFLECT

3a. Which prior steps of the proof are used in step 8?

____

3b. Which prior steps of the proof are used in the last step? Explain.

____

____

PRACTICE

1. Complete the proof.

   Given: $\overline{GE}$ bisects $\angle DGF$ and $\angle DEF$.

   Prove: $\triangle GDE \cong \triangle GFE$

[ ] Given	→ [ ] Definition of bisector	→
[ ] Given	→ [ ] Definition of bisector	→ [ ] ______ ______
	[ ] ______ ______	→

2. **a.** Write a two-column proof in the table provided at right. You may not need to use all the rows of the table for your proof.

   Given: $\angle QMP \cong \angle PNQ$, $\angle MPQ \cong \angle NQP$

   Prove: $\triangle MQP \cong \triangle NPQ$

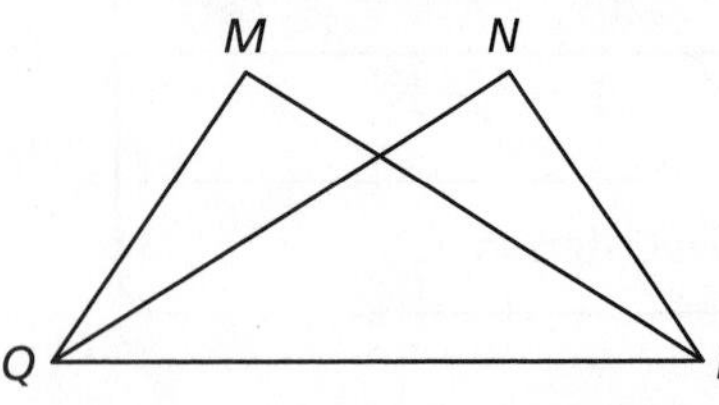

Statements	Reasons
1.	1.
2.	2.
3.	3.
4.	4.
5.	5.
6.	6.

   b. What additional congruence statements can you write using CPCTC?

   ______

Name ______________________ Class ______________ Date ____________

5-2

Additional Practice

Students in Mrs. Marquez's class are watching a film on the uses of geometry in architecture. The film projector casts the image on a flat screen as shown in the figure. The dotted line is the bisector of $\angle ABC$. Tell whether you can use each congruence theorem to prove that $\triangle ABD \cong \triangle CBD$. If not, tell what else you need to know.

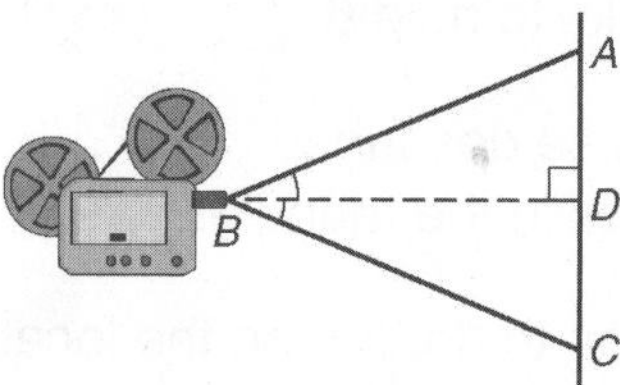

1. Hypotenuse-Leg

____

2. Angle-Side-Angle

____

3. Angle-Angle-Side

____

Write which postulate, if any, can be used to prove the pair of triangles congruent.

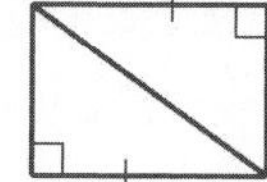

4. ______________________

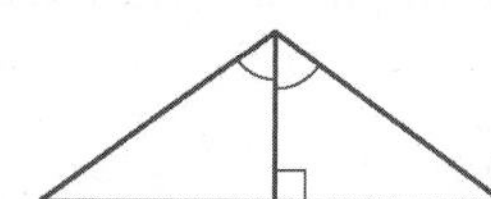

5. ______________________

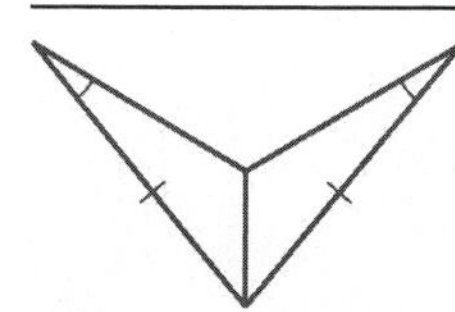

6. ______________________

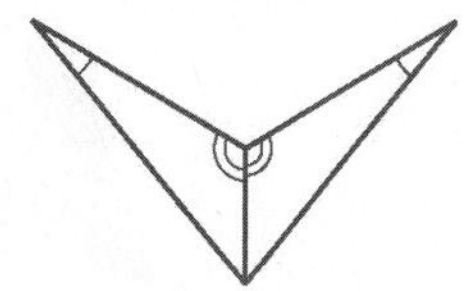

7. ______________________

Write a paragraph proof.

8. **Given:** $\angle PQU \cong \angle TSU$,
$\angle QUR$ and $\angle SUR$ are right angles.

Prove: $\triangle RUQ \cong \triangle RUS$

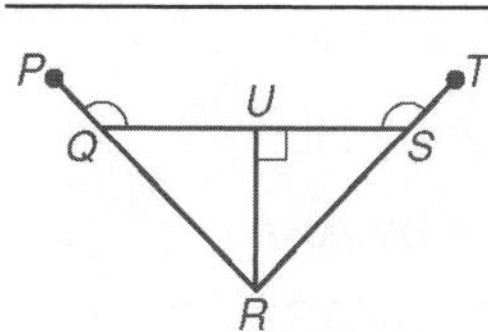

Problem Solving

Use the following information for Exercises 1 and 2.

Melanie is at hole 6 on a miniature golf course. She walks east 7.5 meters to hole 7. She then faces south, turns 67° west, and walks to hole 8. From hole 8, she faces north, turns 35° west, and walks to hole 6.

1. Draw the section of the golf course described. Label the measures of the angles in the triangle.

2. Is there enough information given to determine the location of holes 6, 7, and 8? Explain.

3. A section of the front of an English Tudor home is shown in the diagram. If you know that $\overline{KN} \cong \overline{LN}$ and $\overline{JN} \cong \overline{MN}$, can you use HL to conclude that $\triangle JKN \cong \triangle MLN$? Explain.

Use the diagram of a kite for Exercises 4 and 5.

$\overline{AE}$ is the angle bisector of $\angle DAF$ and $\angle DEF$.

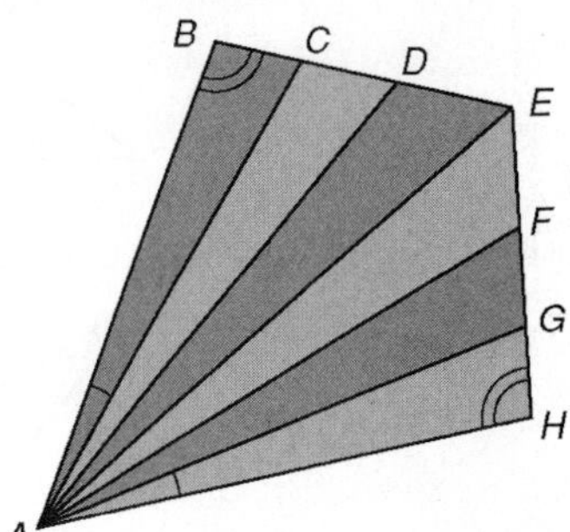

4. What can you conclude about $\triangle DEA$ and $\triangle FEA$?
   - A $\triangle DEA \cong \triangle FEA$ by HL.
   - B $\triangle DEA \cong \triangle FEA$ by AAA.
   - C $\triangle DEA \cong \triangle FEA$ by ASA.
   - D $\triangle DEA \cong \triangle FEA$ by SAS.

5. Based on the diagram, what can you conclude about $\triangle BCA$ and $\triangle HGA$?
   - F $\triangle BCA \cong \triangle HGA$ by HL.
   - G $\triangle BCA \cong \triangle HGA$ by AAS.
   - H $\triangle BCA \cong \triangle HGA$ by ASA.
   - J It cannot be shown using the given information that $\triangle BCA \cong \triangle HGA$.

Name________________________ Class________________ Date__________

5-3

Triangle Congruence: CPCTC

Connection: Proving Slope Criteria

Essential question: *How can CPCTC be used in proving slope criteria for parallel and perpendicular lines?*

Slope is useful for determining whether two lines are parallel.

Slope Criterion for Parallel Lines

Two non-vertical lines are parallel if and only if they have the same slope.

Because the theorem is stated as a biconditional (*if and only if*), the proof has two parts, one for each "direction" of the theorem.

MCC9–12.G.GPE.5

1 PROOF Parallel Lines Have the Same Slope

Given: Non-vertical lines m and n, $m \parallel n$

Prove: Line m and line n have the same slope.

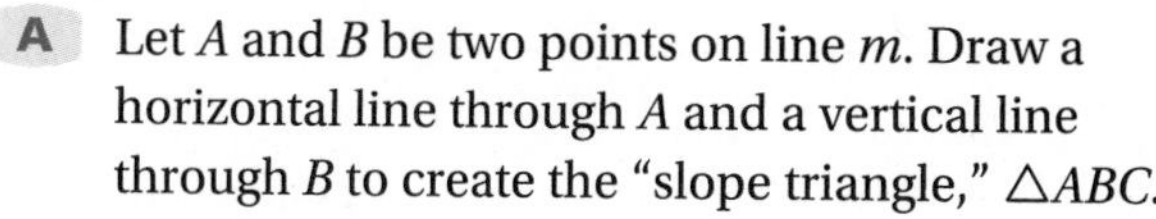
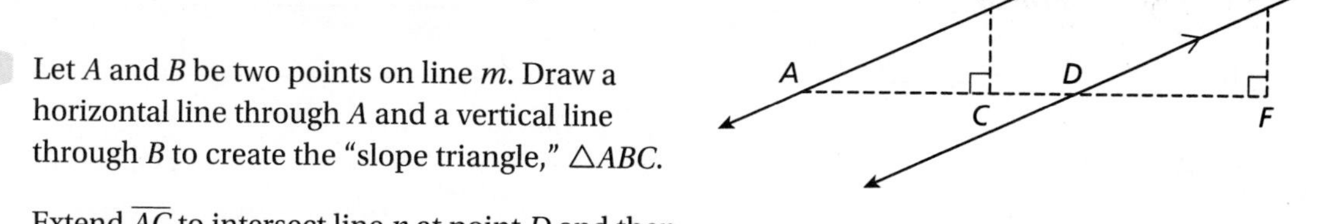

A Let A and B be two points on line m. Draw a horizontal line through A and a vertical line through B to create the "slope triangle," $\triangle ABC$.

Extend $\overline{AC}$ to intersect line n at point D and then extend it to point F so that $AC = DF$. Draw a vertical line through F intersecting line n at point E.

B Since $m \parallel n$, $\angle BAC \cong \angle EDF$ by ________________________.

$\triangle BAC \cong \triangle EDF$ by ________________________.

So, $\overline{BC} \cong \overline{EF}$ by ________________________.

This means $BC = EF$, so $\frac{BC}{AC} = \frac{EF}{DF}$ by ________________________.

This shows that the slope of m equals the slope of n by the definition of slope.

REFLECT

1a. Does the above proof work if the lines are horizontal? If not, does the theorem still hold? Explain.

____

____

1b. How can you estimate the slope of lines m and n in the above figure?

____

MCC9–12.G.GPE.5

2 PROOF Lines with the Same Slope Are Parallel

Given: Line m and line n have the same slope.

Prove: $m \parallel n$

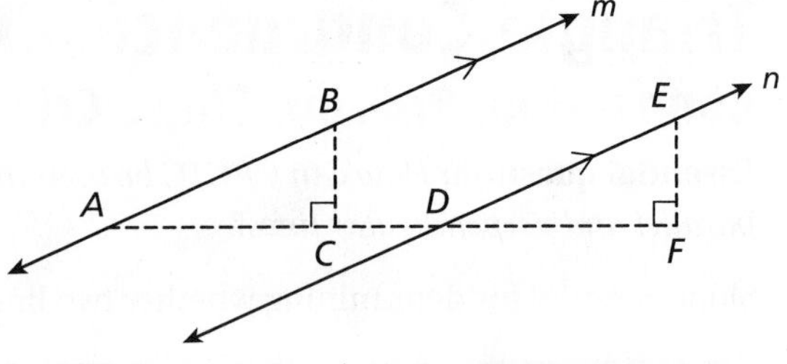

A Let A and B be two points on line m. Draw a horizontal line through A and a vertical line through B to create the "slope triangle," $\triangle ABC$.

Extend $\overline{AC}$ to intersect line n at point D and then extend it to point F so that $DF = AC$. Draw a vertical line through F intersecting line n at point E.

B Since line m and line n have the same slope, $\frac{BC}{AC} = \frac{\square}{\square}$.

But $DF = AC$, so by substitution, $\frac{BC}{AC} = \frac{\square}{\square}$.

Multiplying both sides by AC shows that $BC =$ ______.

C Now $\triangle BAC \cong \triangle EDF$ by ______________________________.

So, $\angle BAC \cong \angle EDF$ by ______________________________.

This shows $m \parallel n$ by ______________________________.

REFLECT

2a. In the proof above, what are the names of the corresponding angles in the two triangles that are used to show that the triangles are congruent? How do you know they are congruent?

____

____

____

2b. In the proof above, what are the names of the corresponding angles in the two triangles that are used to show that line m and line n are parallel? What transversal is involved in the reasoning?

____

____

Slope is useful for determining whether two lines are perpendicular.

Slope Criterion for Perpendicular Lines

Two non-vertical lines are perpendicular if and only if the product of their slopes is -1.

Like the Slope Criterion for Parallel Lines, the theorem is stated as a biconditional. Therefore, the proof has two parts, one for each "direction" of the theorem.

MCC9–12.G.GPE.5

3 PROOF Perpendicular Lines Have Slopes Whose Product Is -1

Given: Non-vertical lines m and n, $m \perp n$

Prove: The product of the slope of line m and the slope of line n is -1.

A Assume the lines intersect at point P, and assume the slope of line m is positive. (You can write a similar proof in the case that the slope of line m is negative.)

Let Q be a point on line m, and draw the "slope triangle," $\triangle PQR$, as shown.

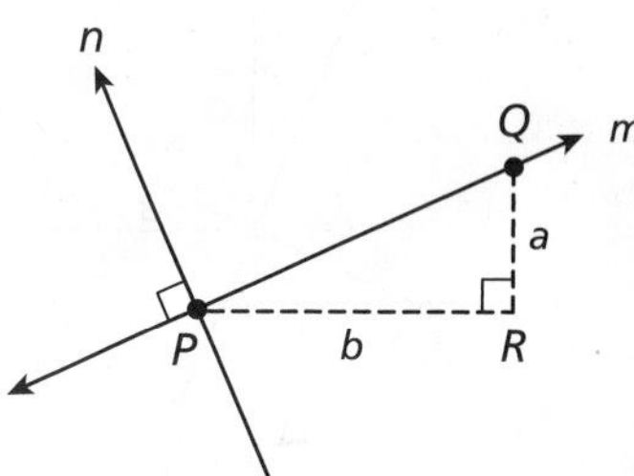

The slope of line m is ________, where a and b are both positive.

B Rotate $\triangle PQR$ 90° around point P. This gives $\triangle PQ'R'$, as shown.

$\triangle PQ'R'$ is a slope triangle for line n.

Let the coordinates of P be (x_1, y_1) and let the coordinates of Q' be (x_2, y_2).

Then the slope of line n is $\frac{y_2 - y_1}{x_2 - x_1} = \frac{b}{\square} = -\frac{\square}{\square}$.

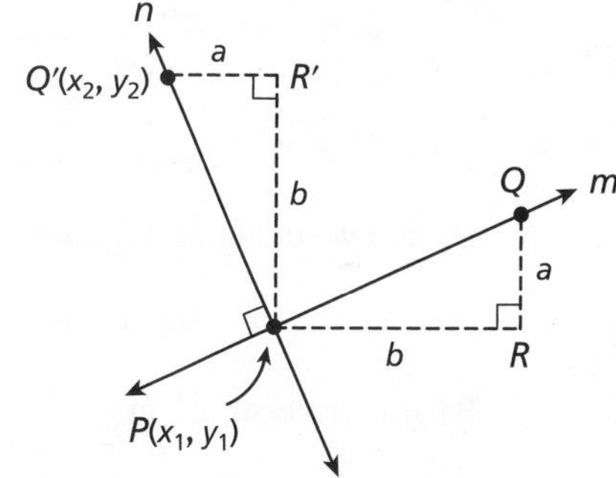

C Find the product of the slope of line m and the slope of line n.

The product of the slopes is ______ • ______ = ______.

So, the product of the slope of line m and the slope of line n is ________ .

REFLECT

3a. When you calculate the slope of line n, why is $x_2 - x_1$ negative?

____

3b. Does the theorem apply when one of the lines is horizontal? Explain.

____

Lines with Slopes Whose Product Is −1 Are Perpendicular

Given: The product of the slope of line m and the slope of line n is -1.

Prove: $m \perp n$

A Let line m have positive slope $\frac{a}{b}$, where a and b are both positive.

Let line n have slope z. It is given that $z \cdot \frac{a}{b} = -1$.

Solving for z shows that the slope of line n is ________.

B Assume the lines intersect at point P. Set up slope triangles for lines m and n as shown.

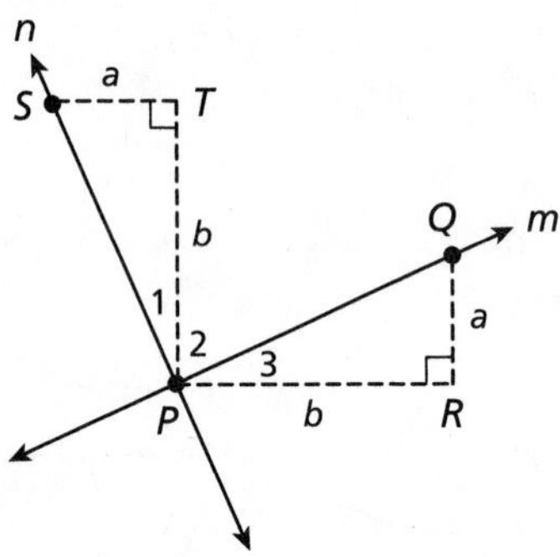

Then $\overline{ST} \cong$ ________ and $\overline{PT} \cong$ ________.

Also, $\angle T \cong \angle R$ because ________________________________.

So, $\triangle STP \cong \triangle QRP$ by ________________________________.

C Now $\angle 1 \cong \angle 3$ by ________________________________.

$\overline{PT}$ is a vertical line segment and $\overline{PR}$ is a horizontal line segment, so $\angle TPR$

is a right angle. This means $\angle 2$ and $\angle 3$ are ________________________________.

By substitution, $\angle 2$ and $\angle 1$ are ________________________________.

But $m\angle 1 + m\angle 2 = m\angle SPQ$ by the Angle Addition Postulate.

So, $m\angle SPQ =$ ________ and line m is perpendicular to line n.

REFLECT

4a. The proof begins by assuming that line m has a positive slope. If the product of the slopes of two lines is -1, how do you know that one of the lines must have a positive slope?

____

____

Name________________________ Class______________ Date____________

5-3

Additional Practice

1. Heike Dreschler set the Woman's World Junior Record for the long jump in 1983. She jumped about 23.4 feet. The diagram shows two triangles and a pond. Explain whether Heike could have jumped the pond along path *BA* or along path *CA*.

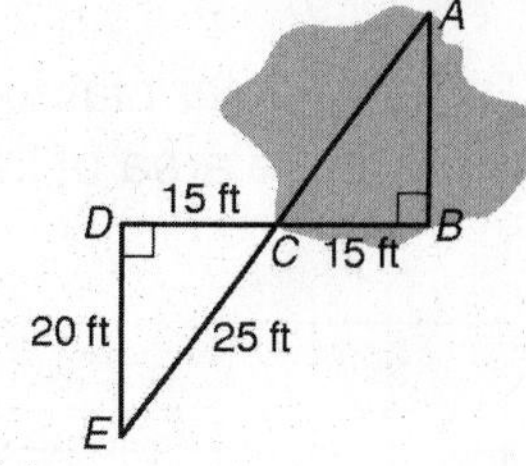

____

____

____

____

____

Write a flowchart proof.

2. **Given:** $\angle L \cong \angle J$, $\overline{KJ} \parallel \overline{LM}$

   Prove: $\angle LKM \cong \angle JMK$

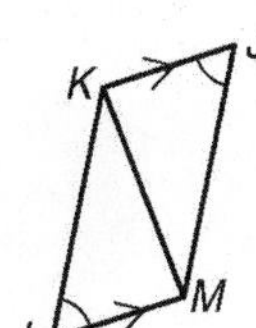

Write a two-column proof.

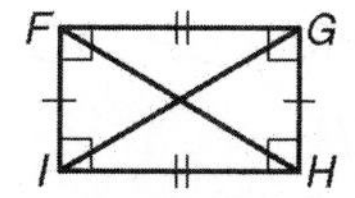

3. **Given:** *FGHI* is a rectangle.

   Prove: The diagonals of a rectangle have equal lengths.

Problem Solving

1. Two triangular plates are congruent. The area of one of the plates is 60 square inches. What is the area of the other plate? Explain.

____

____

2. An archaeologist draws the triangles to find the distance *XY* across a ravine. What is *XY*? Explain.

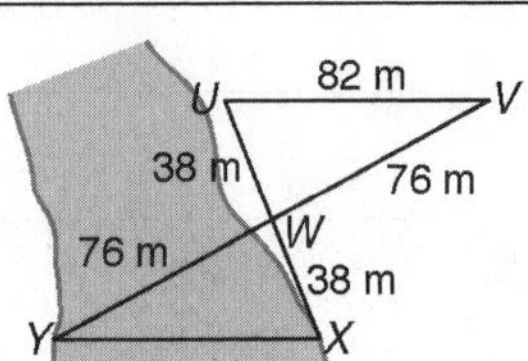

____

____

3. A city planner sets up the triangles to find the distance *RS* across a river. Describe the steps that she can use to find *RS*.

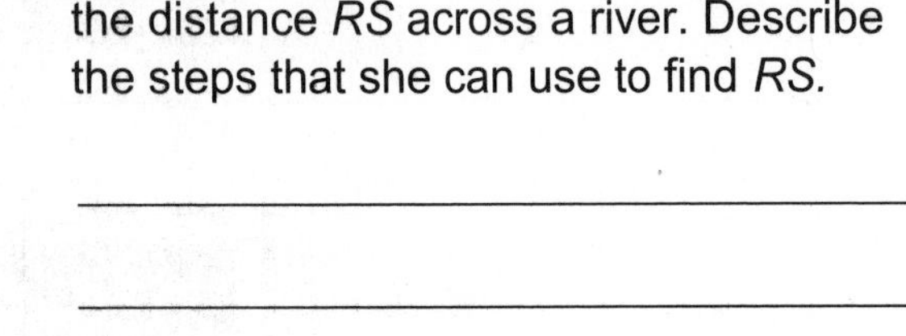

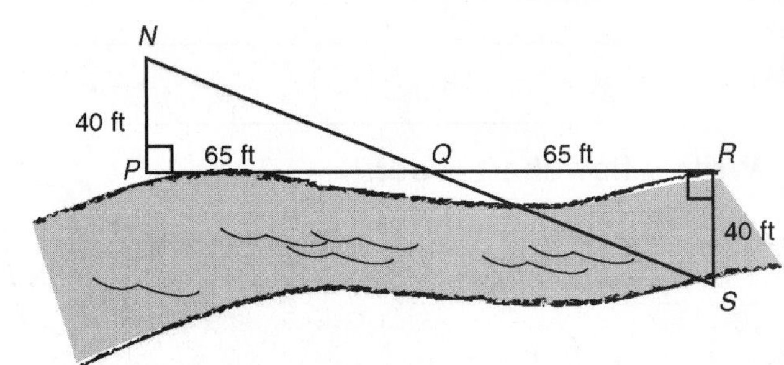

____

____

____

____

____

Choose the best answer.

4. A lighthouse and the range of its shining light are shown. What can you conclude?

   A $x = y$ by CPCTC C $\angle AED \cong \angle ADE$ by CPCTC

   B $x = 2y$ D $\angle AED \cong \angle ACB$

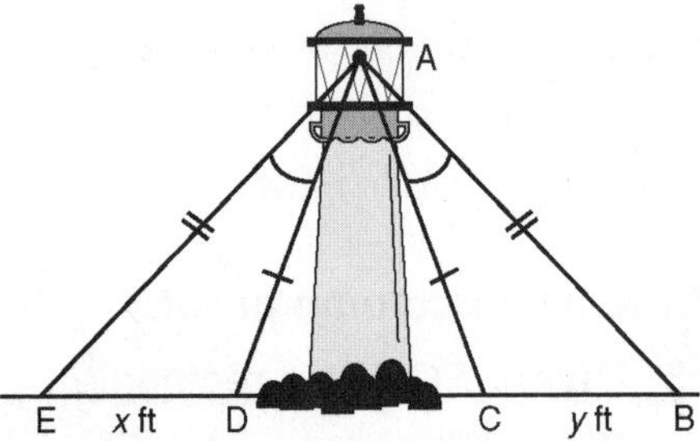

5. A rectangular piece of cloth 15 centimeters long is cut along a diagonal to form two triangles. One of the triangles has a side length of 9 centimeters. Which is a true statement?

   F The second triangle has an angle measure of 15° by CPCTC.

   G The second triangle has a side length of 9 centimeters by CPCTC.

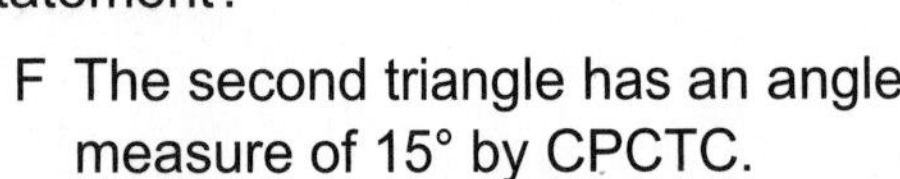

   H You cannot make a conclusion about the side length of the second triangle.

   J The triangles are not congruent.

6. Small sandwiches are cut in the shape of right triangles. The longest sides of all the sandwiches are 3 inches. One sandwich has a side length of 2 inches. Which is a true statement?

   A All the sandwiches have a side length of 2 inches by CPCTC.

   B All the sandwiches are isosceles triangles with side lengths of 2 inches.

   C None of the other sandwiches have side lengths of 2 inches.

   D You cannot make a conclusion using CPCTC.

Name ______________________ Class ____________ Date ________

5-4

Video Tutor

Isosceles and Equilateral Triangles

Focus on Reasoning

Essential question: *What special relationships exist among the sides and angles of isosceles triangles?*

Recall that an *isosceles* triangle is a triangle with at least two congruent sides. The congruent sides are called the **legs** of the triangle. The angle formed by the legs is the **vertex angle**. The side of the triangle opposite the vertex angle is the **base**. The angles that have the base as a side are the **base angles**.

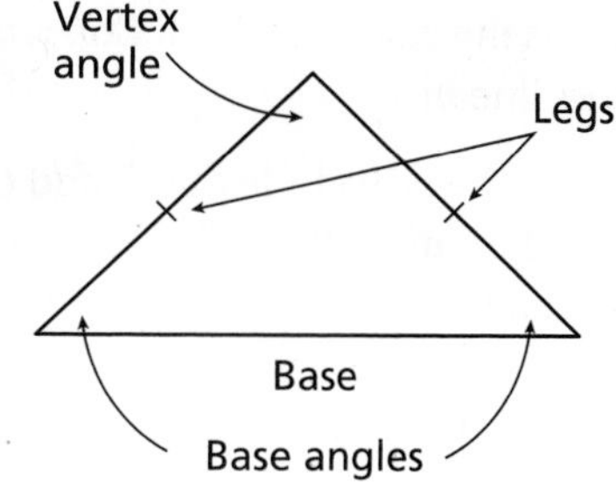

1 Investigate isosceles triangles.

A Work on a separate sheet of paper. Use a straightedge to draw an angle. Label it $\angle A$.

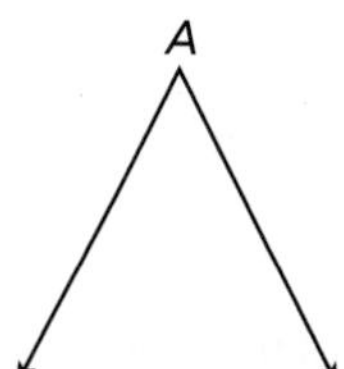

B Place the point of your compass on the vertex of the angle and draw an arc that intersects the sides of the angle at *B* and *C*.

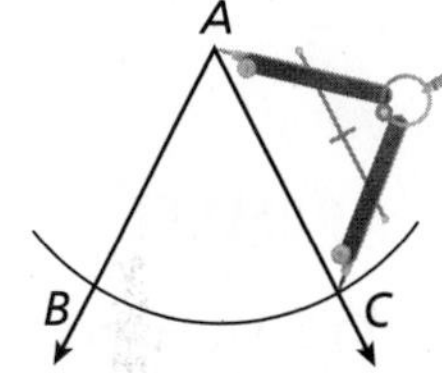

C Use the straightedge to draw $\overline{BC}$.

D Use a protractor to measure $\angle B$ and $\angle C$. Record the measures in the table under the column for Triangle 1.

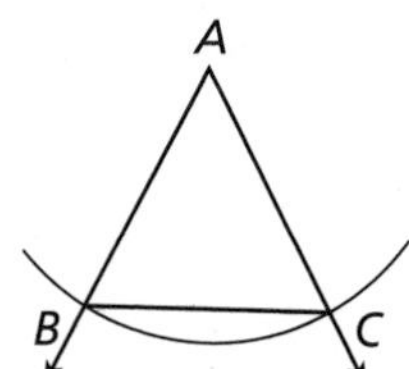

E Repeat the process two more times, drawing different angles and using different compass settings. In each case, note $m\angle B$ and $m\angle C$ in the table.

	Triangle 1	Triangle 2	Triangle 3
$m\angle B$			
$m\angle C$			

REFLECT

1a. How do you know the triangles you constructed were isosceles triangles?

____

____

1b. Compare your work with that of other students. Then make a conjecture about isosceles triangles.

____

2 Prove the Isosceles Triangle Theorem.

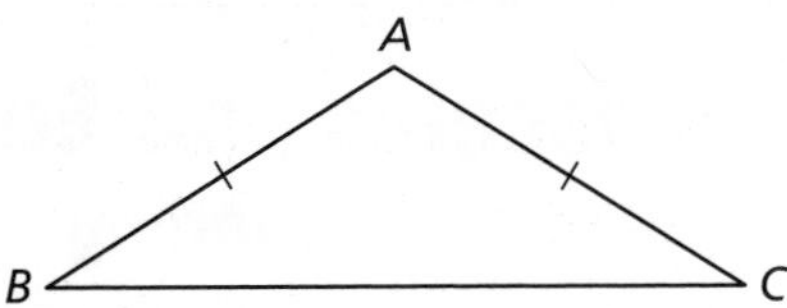

The base angles of an isosceles triangle are congruent.

Given: $\overline{AB} \cong \overline{AC}$
Prove: $\angle B \cong \angle C$

Complete the proof.

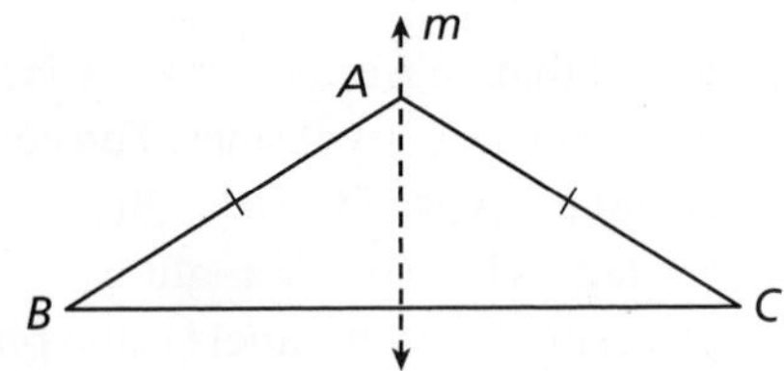

Draw line m, which is the bisector of $\angle A$. Consider the reflection across line m.

Because $AB = AC$, you can conclude that B and C are images of each other under the reflection across line m. This is justified by

____

So, $\angle B$ and $\angle C$ are images of each other and therefore $\angle B \cong \angle C$, because

____

REFLECT

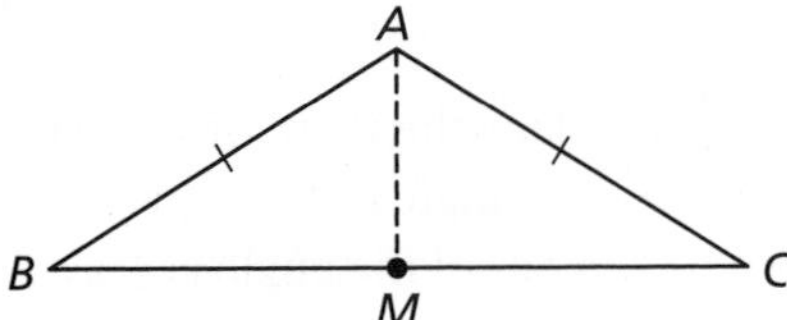

2a. A different proof of the Isosceles Triangle Theorem is based on letting point M be the midpoint of $\overline{BC}$ and drawing $\overline{AM}$. Explain the steps of this proof.

____

____

____

3 Prove the Converse of the Isosceles Triangle Theorem.

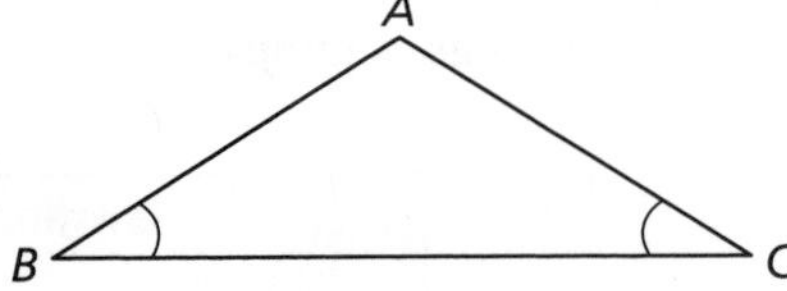

If two angles of a triangle are congruent, then the sides opposite them are congruent.

Given: $\angle B \cong \angle C$
Prove: $\overline{AB} \cong \overline{AC}$

Complete the proof.

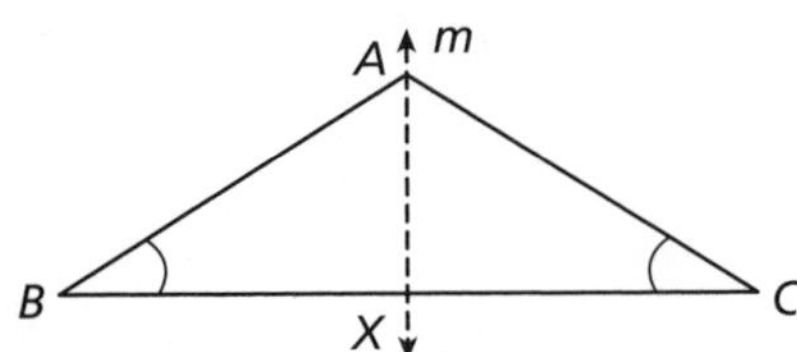

Draw line m, which is the bisector of $\angle A$. Let point X be the point where line m intersects $\overline{BC}$.

Then, by the definition of angle bisector,

____

Also, $\overline{AX} \cong \overline{AX}$ by the Reflexive Property of Congruence. Therefore, $\triangle BAX \cong \triangle CAX$ by the AAS Congruence Criterion.

So, $\overline{AB} \cong \overline{AC}$ by ____

REFLECT

3a. An equiangular triangle has three congruent angles. An equilateral triangle has three congruent sides. Use the figure to help you explain why an equiangular triangle must also be an equilateral triangle.

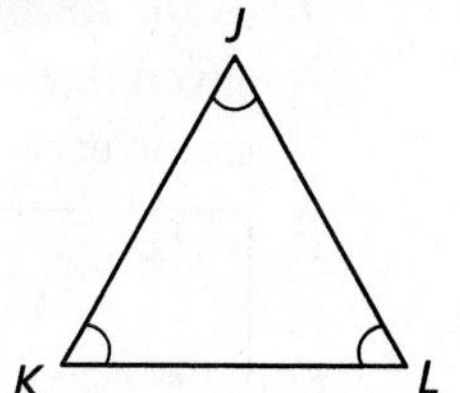

PRACTICE

Find the measure of the indicated angle.

1. m∠B

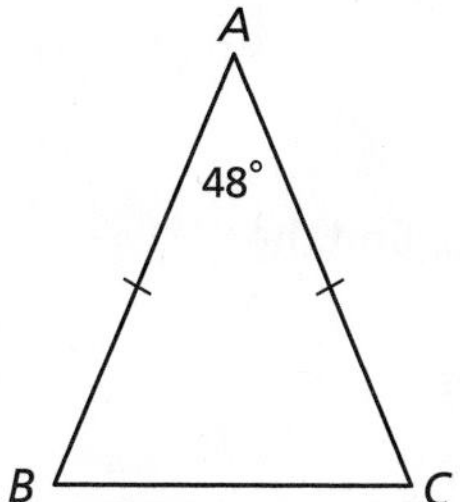

2. m∠J

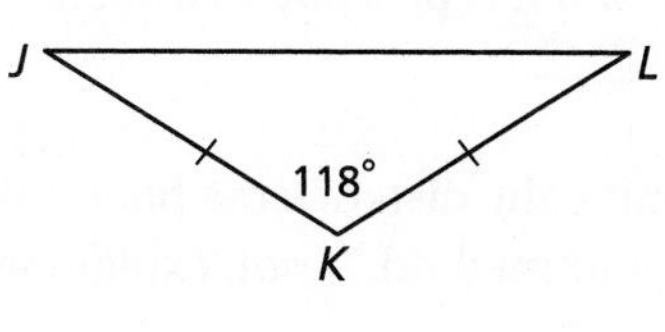

3. m∠R

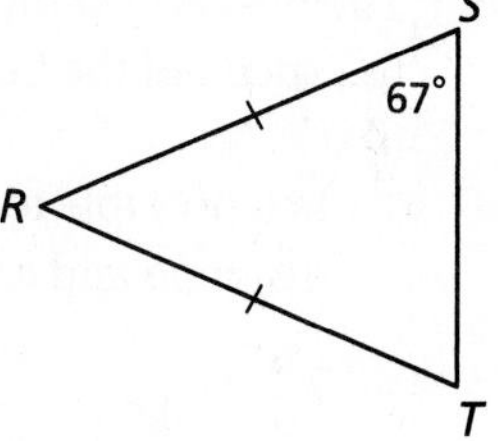

Find the length of the indicated side.

4. $\overline{DF}$

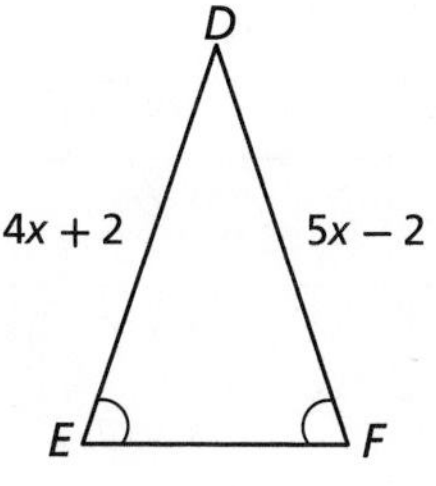

5. $\overline{LM}$

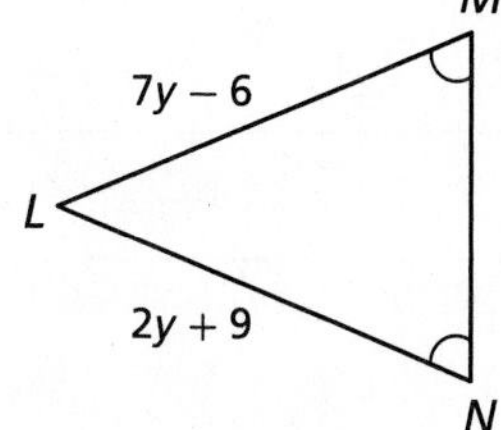

6. $\overline{RS}$

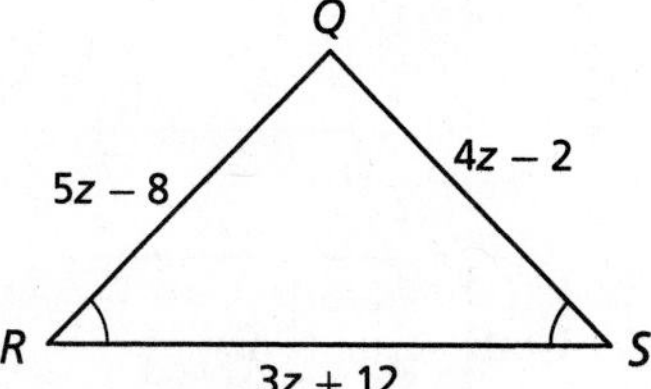

7. Error Analysis Two students are asked to find the angle measures of $\triangle XYZ$, given that $\triangle XYZ$ is isosceles. Their work is shown below. Is either answer incorrect? Explain.

Lee's Answer	Skyler's Answer
$m\angle Z = 70°$. Since an isosceles triangle has two congruent angles, $m\angle X = m\angle Y = 55°$.	$m\angle Z = 70°$. Since base angles are congruent, $m\angle Y = 70°$ also. This leaves 40° for $m\angle X$.

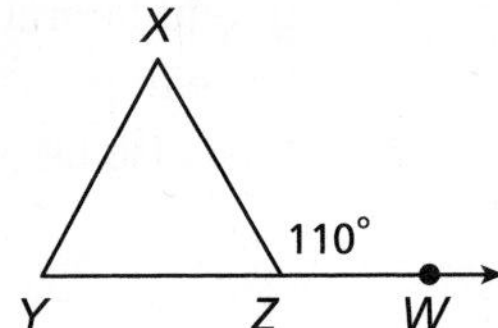

8. A boat travels at a constant speed parallel to a coastline that is approximately a straight line. An observer on the coast at point P uses radar to find the distance to the boat when the boat makes an angle of 35° with the coastline. Then, 5 seconds later, the observer finds the distance to the boat when it makes an angle of 70° with the coastline. The observer wants to know if it is possible to calculate the speed of the boat.

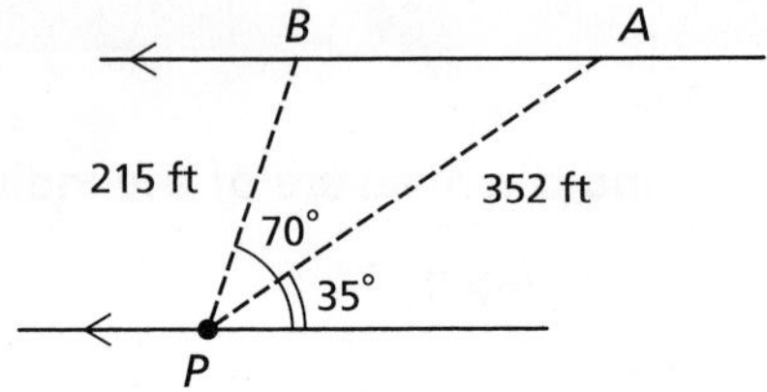

a. Is it possible to determine the distance the boat traveled, AB? If so, find the distance and explain your method. If not, explain why not.

b. Is it possible to determine the speed of the boat? If so, find the speed and explain your method. If not, explain why not.

Name______________________ Class______________ Date__________ 5-4

Additional Practice

An altitude of a triangle is a perpendicular segment from a vertex to the line containing the opposite side. Write a paragraph proof that the altitude to the base of an isosceles triangle bisects the base.

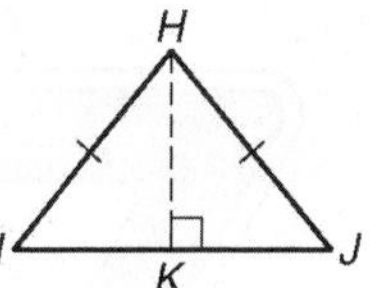

1. **Given:** $\overline{HI} \cong \overline{HJ}, \overline{HK} \perp \overline{IJ}$

   Prove: $\overline{HK}$ bisects $\overline{IJ}$.

2. An *obelisk* is a tall, thin, four-sided monument that tapers to a pyramidal top. The most well-known obelisk to Americans is the Washington Monument on the National Mall in Washington, D.C. Each face of the pyramidal top of the Washington Monument is an isosceles triangle. The height of each triangle is 55.5 feet, and the base of each triangle measures 34.4 feet. Find the length, to the nearest tenth of a foot, of one of the two equal legs of the triangle. __________

Find each value.

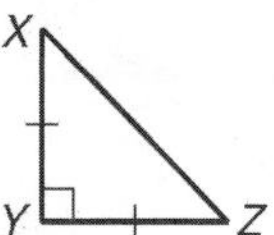

3. m∠X = __________

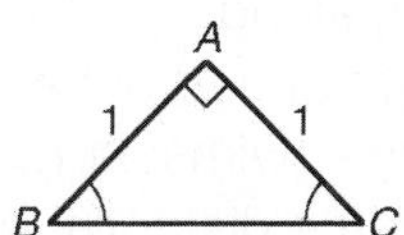

4. BC = __________

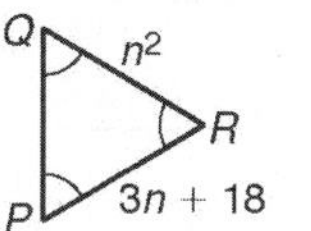

5. PQ = __________

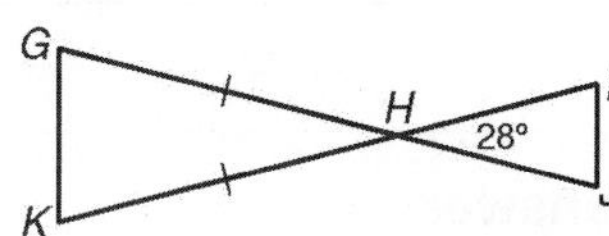

6. m∠K = __________

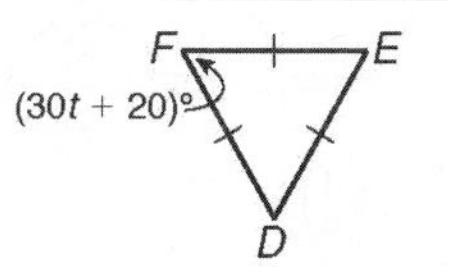

7. t = __________

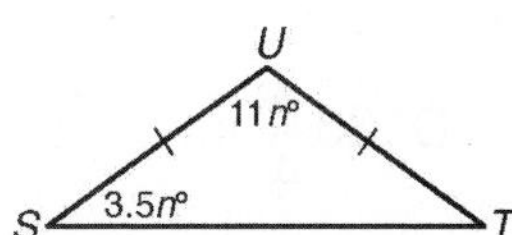

8. n = __________

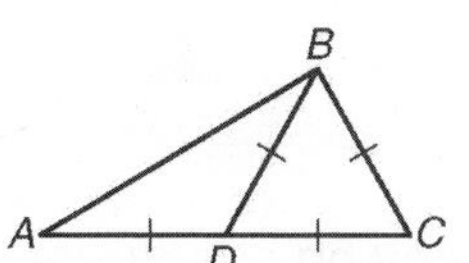

9. m∠A = __________

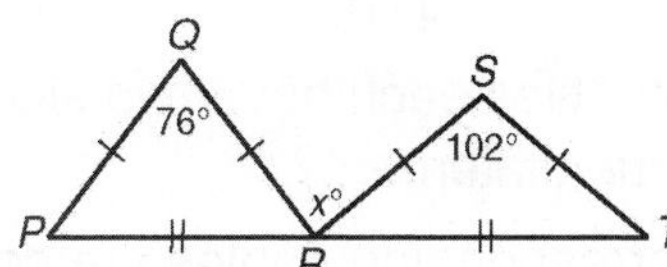

10. x = __________

Problem Solving

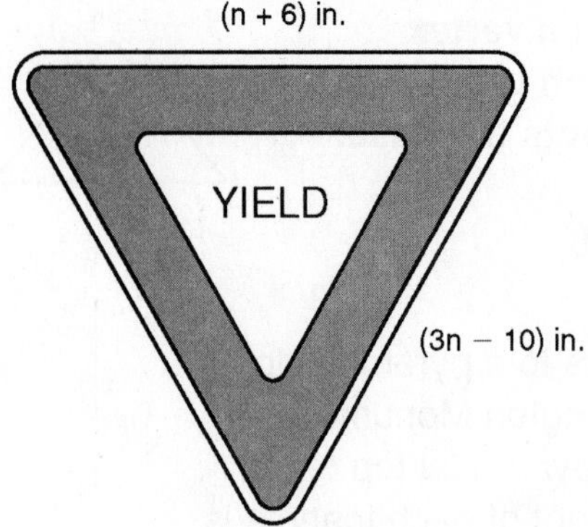

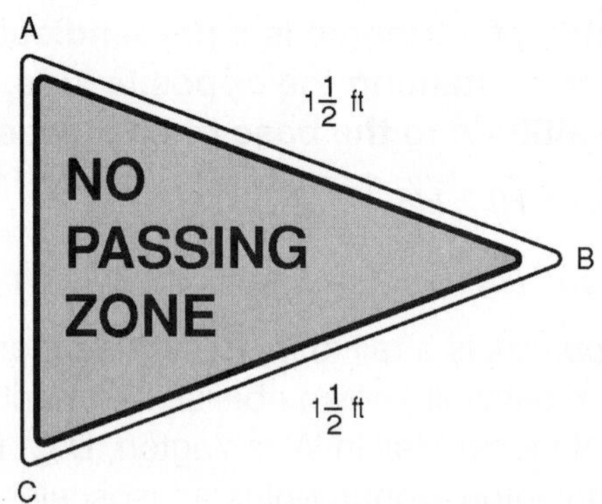

1. A "Yield" sign is an equiangular triangle. What are the lengths of the sides?

2. The measure of $\angle C$ is 70°. What is the measure of $\angle B$?

3. Samantha is swimming along $\overrightarrow{HF}$. When she is at point *H*, she sees a necklace straight ahead of her but on the bottom of the pool at point *J*. Then she swims 11 more feet to point *G*. Use the diagram to find *GJ*, the distance Samantha is from the necklace. Explain.

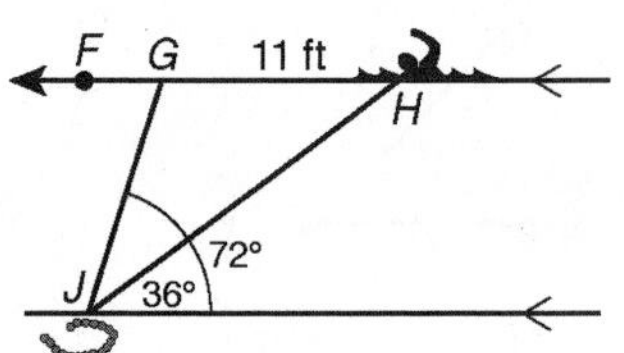

Choose the best answer.

4. A billiards triangle is equiangular. What is the perimeter?

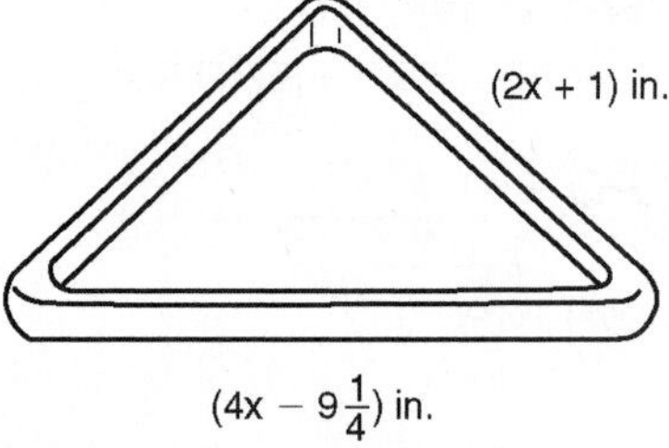

A $5\frac{1}{8}$ in. C $11\frac{1}{4}$ in.

B $10\frac{1}{4}$ in. D $33\frac{3}{4}$ in.

5. A triangular shaped trellis has angles *R*, *S*, and *T* that measure 73°, 73°, and 34°, respectively. If $ST = 4y + 6$ and $TR = 7y - 21$, what is the value of *y*?

F 5 H 11

G 9 J 15

6. Two triangular tiles each have two sides measuring 4 inches. Which is a true statement?

A Their corresponding angles are congruent. C The triangles may be congruent.

B The triangles are congruent. D The triangles cannot be congruent.

7. What is the value of *x* in the figure?

F 42° H 96°

G 90° J 106°

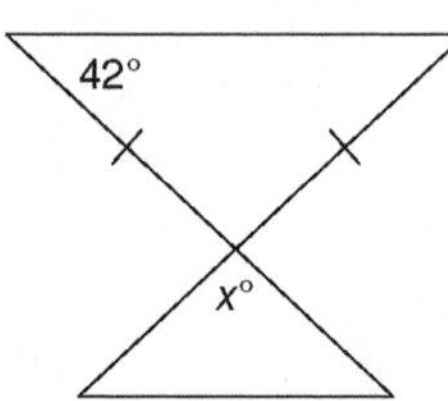

Name ____________________ Class ____________ Date ________

6-1

Perpendicular and Angle Bisectors

Extension: Perpendicular Bisectors and Parabolas

Essential question: *How do you write the equation of a parabola given its focus and directrix?*

The distance from a point to a line is the length of the perpendicular segment from the point to the line. In the figure, the distance from point A to line ℓ is AB.

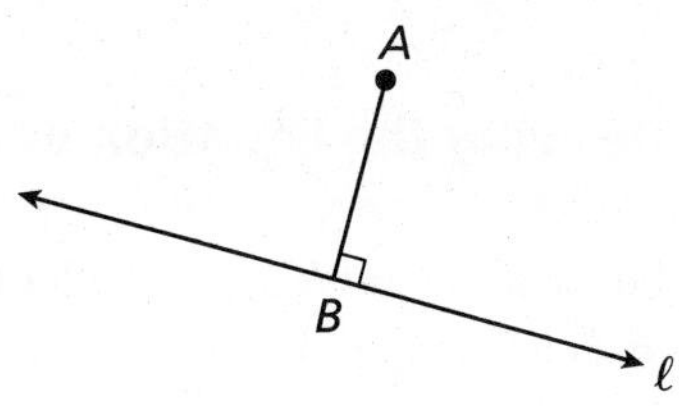

You will use the idea of the distance from a point to a line below.

PREP FOR MCC9–12.G.GPE.2

1 EXPLORE Creating a Parabola

Follow these instructions to plot a point. You will report the approximate coordinates of the point to your teacher, who will create a graph consisting of all points from everyone in the class. Be sure to work as accurately as possible.

A Choose a point on line ℓ. Plot a point Q at this location.

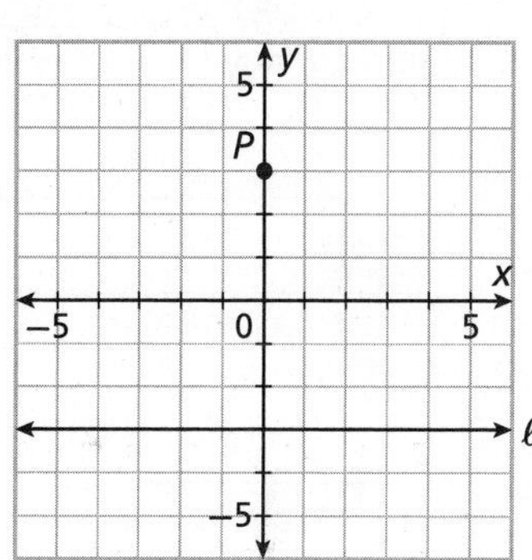

B Using a straightedge, draw a perpendicular to ℓ that passes through point Q. Label this line m.

C Use the straightedge to draw $\overline{PQ}$. Then use a compass and straightedge to construct the perpendicular bisector of $\overline{PQ}$.

D Plot a point X where the perpendicular bisector intersects line m.

E Write the approximate coordinates of point X and report the coordinates to your teacher.

____

REFLECT

1a. Use the figure to help you explain why the point X that you plotted is equidistant from point P and line ℓ.

____

____

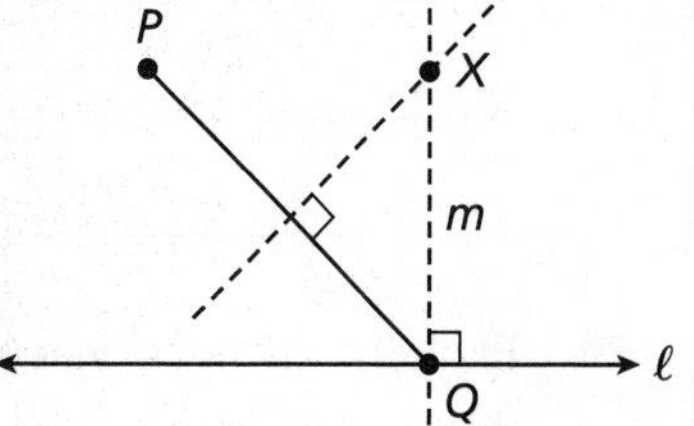

1b. What do you notice about the set of points your teacher plotted?

____

____

A **parabola** is the set of all points P in a plane that are equidistant from a given point, called the **focus**, and a given line, called the **directrix**.

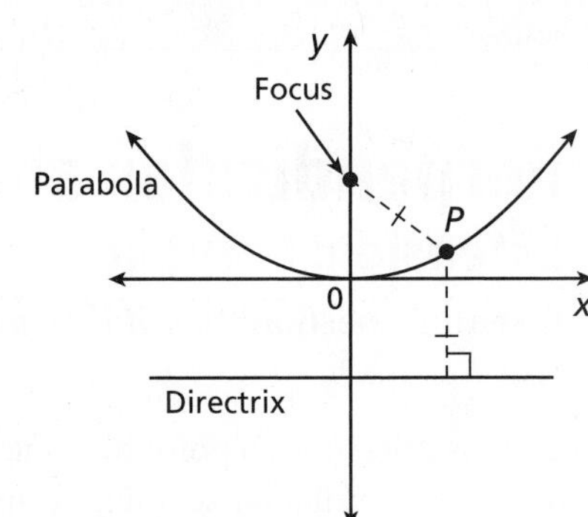

To derive the general equation of a parabola, you can use the above definition, the distance formula, and the idea that the distance from a point to a line is the length of the perpendicular segment from the point to the line.

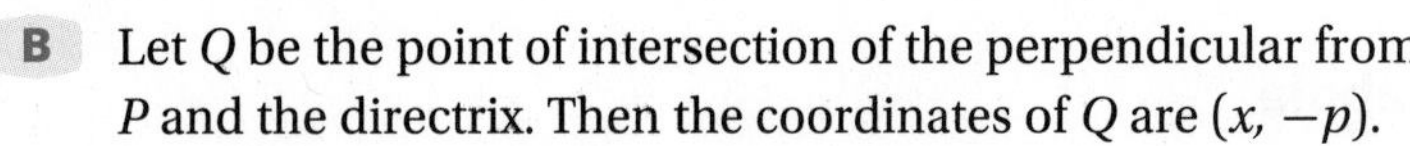

Deriving the Equation of a Parabola

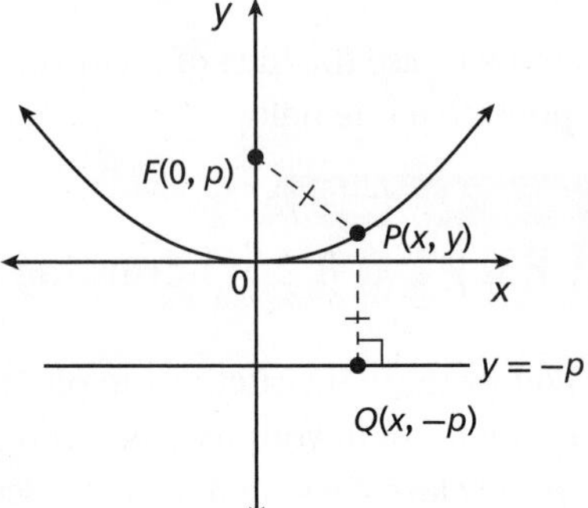

A Let the focus of the parabola be $F(0, p)$ and let the directrix be the line $y = -p$. Let P be a point on the parabola with coordinates (x, y).

B Let Q be the point of intersection of the perpendicular from P and the directrix. Then the coordinates of Q are $(x, -p)$.

C By the definition of a parabola, $FP = QP$.

By the distance formula,

$FP = \sqrt{(x-0)^2 + (y-p)^2} = \sqrt{x^2 + (y-p)^2}$

and $QP = \sqrt{(x-x)^2 + (y-(-p))^2} = \sqrt{0 + (y+p)^2} = |y+p|$.

__________ = __________ Set FP equal to QP.

__________ = __________ Square both sides.

__________ = __________ Expand the squared terms.

__________ = __________ Subtract y^2 and p^2 from both sides.

__________ = __________ Add $2py$ to both sides.

__________ = __________ Solve for y.

REFLECT

2a. Explain how the value of p determines whether the parabola opens up or down.

____

____

____

____

2b. Explain why the origin $(0, 0)$ is always a point on a parabola with focus $F(0, p)$ and directrix $y = -p$.

____

____

MCC9–12.G.GPE.2

3 EXAMPLE Writing the Equation of a Parabola

Write the equation of the parabola with focus $(0, -4)$ and directrix $y = 4$. Then graph the parabola.

A The focus of the parabola is $(0, p)$, so $p =$ ____________________.

The general equation of a parabola is $y = \frac{1}{4p}x^2$.

So, the equation of this parabola is ____________________.

B To graph the parabola, complete the table of values. Then plot points and draw the curve.

x	y
−8	
−4	
0	
4	
8	

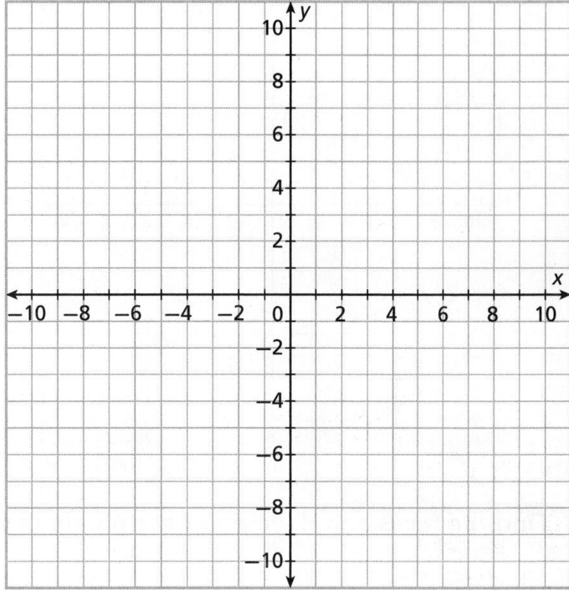

REFLECT

3a. The *vertex* of a parabola is the midpoint of the perpendicular segment from the focus to the directrix. What is the vertex of the parabola you graphed?

____

3b. Does your graph lie above or below the x-axis? Why does this make sense based on the parabola's equation?

____

____

3c. Describe any symmetry your graph has. Why does this make sense based on the parabola's equation?

____

____

____

PRACTICE

Write the equation of the parabola with the given focus and directrix. Then graph the parabola.

1. focus: $(0, 2)$; directrix: $y = -2$

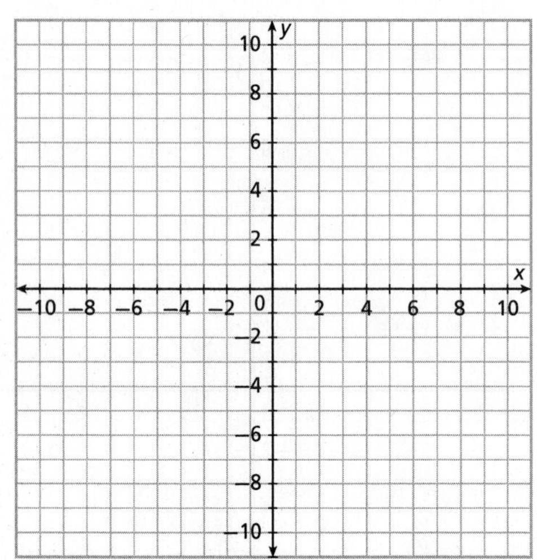

2. focus: $(0, -5)$; directrix: $y = 5$

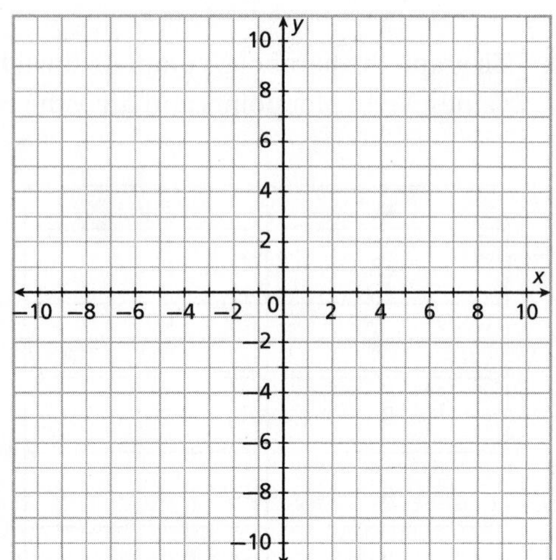

Find the focus and directrix of the parabola with the given equation.

3. $y = -\frac{1}{24}x^2$

4. $y = 2x^2$

5. Complete the table by writing the equation of each parabola. Then use a calculator to graph the equations in the same window to help you make a conjecture: What happens to the graph of a parabola as the focus and directrix move apart?

Focus	(0, 1)	(0, 2)	(0, 3)	(0, 4)
Directrix	$y = -1$	$y = -2$	$y = -3$	$y = -4$
Equation				

6. Find the length of the line segment that is parallel to the directrix of a parabola, that passes through the focus, and that has endpoints on the parabola.

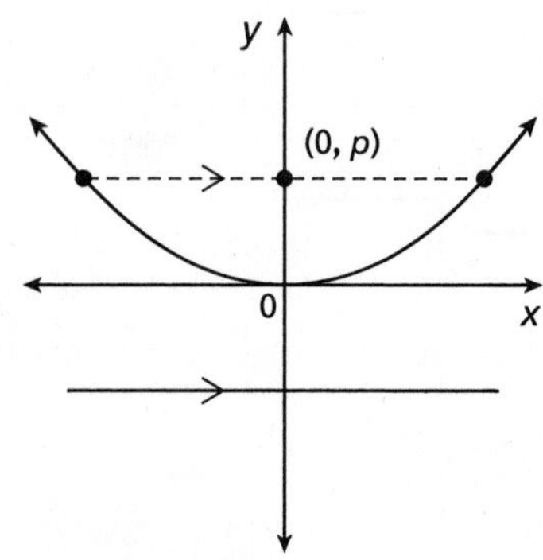

Name____________________ Class__________ Date__________

6-1

Additional Practice

Write the equation of the parabola with the given focus and directrix.

1. focus: (0, 10), directrix: $y = -10$

   ____

2. focus(0, –6), directrix: $y = 6$

   ____

3. focus (0, –13), directrix: $y = 13$

   ____

4. focus (0, 1.5), directrix: $y = -1.5$

   ____

5. focus (0, –3), directrix: $y = 3$

   ____

6. focus (0, –5.5), directrix: $y = 5.5$

   ____

Find the value of *p*, the focus, and the directrix of the parabola with the given equation.

7. $y = -\frac{1}{12}x^2$

   ____

8. $y = \frac{1}{32}x^2$

   ____

9. $y = -\frac{1}{36}x^2$

   ____

10. $y = \frac{1}{8}x^2$

    ____

11. $y = \frac{1}{48}x^2$

    ____

12. $y = -\frac{1}{10}x^2$

    ____

13. Find the value of *p*, the focus, and the directrix of the parabola with equation $y = -\frac{1}{28}x^2$. Then graph the parabola.

    ____

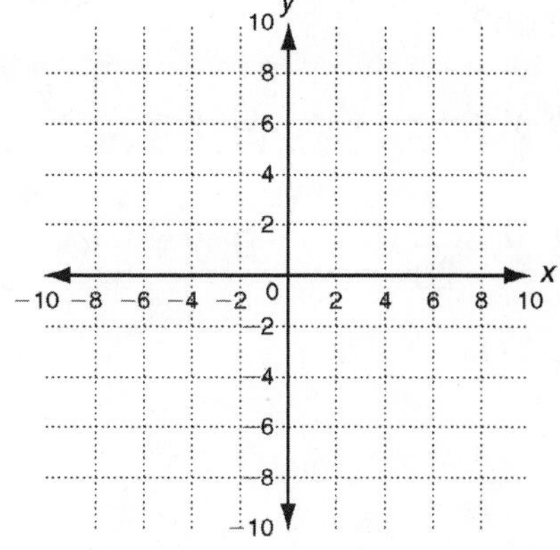

Problem Solving

A model of a parabolic mirror has a cross section that can be modeled by the equation $y = \frac{1}{96}x^2$.

1. You want to graph the equation of the cross section of the model.

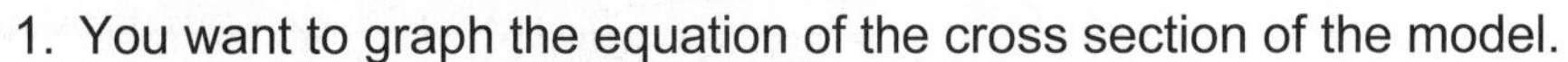

   a. What are the coordinates of the vertex of the parabola?

   ____

   b. Find the distance, p, from the vertex to both the focus and the directrix of the parabola.

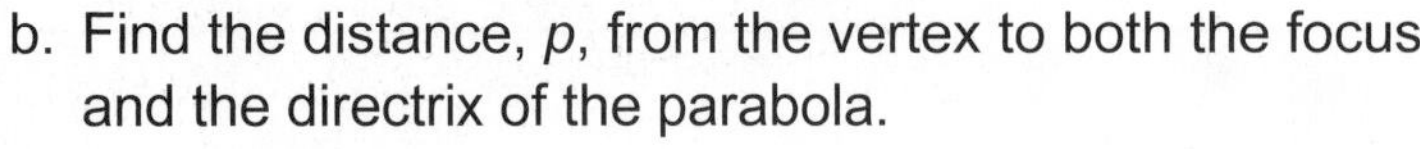

   ____

   c. Find the coordinates of the focus.

   ____

   d. Write the equation of the directrix.

   ____

   e. Sketch a graph of the cross section of the model including the focus and the directrix.

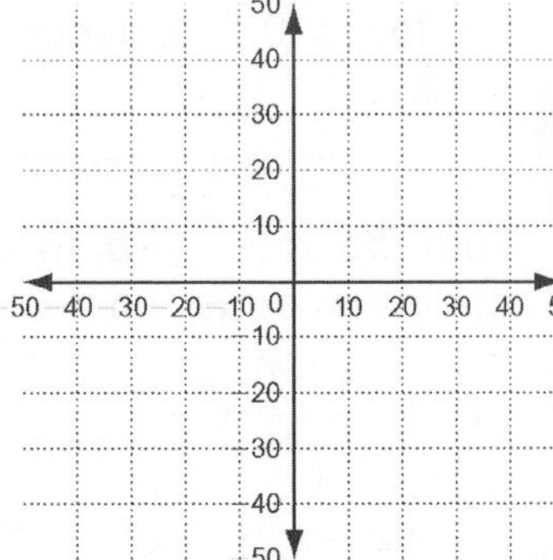

2. You want to construct a model of a different parabolic mirror. For this model, you want the focus to be (0, 18) and the directrix to be $y = -18$. Write the equation of the new parabola.

____

Choose the letter for the best answer.

3. Melissa wrote the equation of a parabola with focus (0, –5) and directrix $y = 5$. Which equation should Melissa have written?

   A $y = -\frac{1}{20}x^2$ C $y = -\frac{1}{5}x^2$

   B $y = \frac{1}{20}x^2$ D $y = \frac{1}{5}x^2$

4. A solar trough used to collect solar energy has a reflective surface. The surface has a cross section that is a parabola with equation $y = \frac{1}{24}x^2$. What is the focus of the parabola?

   F (0, –6)

   G (–6, 0)

   H (6, 0)

   J (0, 6)

Name ______________________ Class ______________ Date __________

Bisectors of Triangles

Going Deeper

Essential question: *How do you construct the circle that circumscribes a triangle, and how do you inscribe a circle in a triangle?*

Video Tutor

A circle is said to **circumscribe** a polygon if the circle passes through all of the polygon's vertices. In the figure, circle C circumscribes $\triangle XYZ$ and this circle is called the **circumcircle** of $\triangle XYZ$.

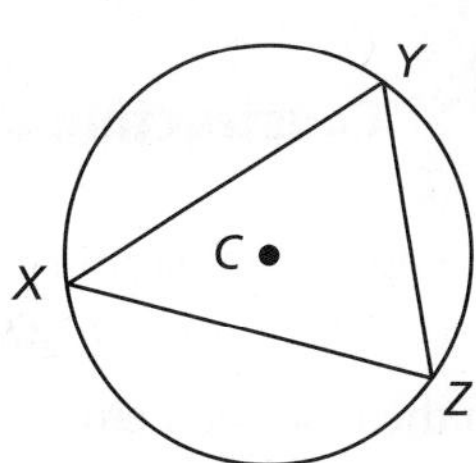

In order to construct the circumcircle of a triangle, you need to find the center of the circle. This point is called the **circumcenter** of the triangle. The following example will guide you through the reasoning process to do this.

MCC9–12.G.C.3

1 EXAMPLE Constructing a Circumscribed Circle

Work directly on the figure to construct the circumcircle of $\triangle PQR$.

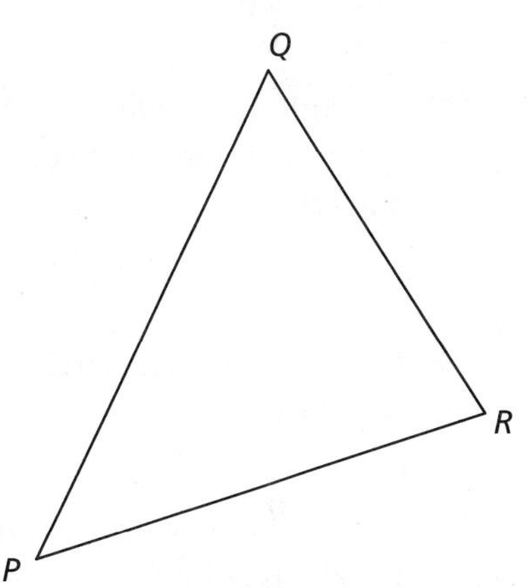

A The circumcircle will pass through P, Q, and R. So, the center of the circle must be equidistant from all three points. In particular, the center must be equidistant from P and R. What is the set of points equidistant from P and R?

____

Use a compass and straightedge to construct this set of points.

B Similarly, the center must be equidistant from Q and R. What is the set of points equidistant from Q and R?

____

Use a compass and straightedge to construct this set of points.

C The center must lie at the intersection of the two sets of points you constructed. Label this point C.

D Place the point of your compass at C and open it to the distance CP. Then draw the circumcircle.

REFLECT

1a. Suppose you started by constructing the set of points equidistant from P and Q, and then you constructed the set of points equidistant from Q and R. Would you have found the same center point? Check by doing this construction.

____

A circle is **inscribed** in a polygon if each side of the polygon is tangent to the circle. In the figure, circle *C* is inscribed in quadrilateral *WXYZ* and this circle is called the **incircle** of the quadrilateral.

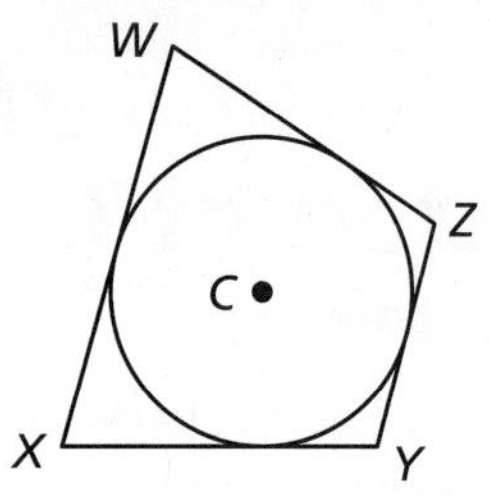

In order to construct the incircle of a triangle, you need to find the center of the circle. This point is called the **incenter** of the triangle. The following example will guide you through the reasoning process for constructing an inscribed circle in a triangle.

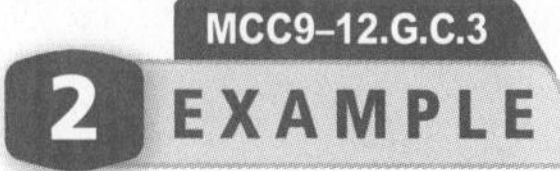

Constructing an Inscribed Circle

Work directly on the figure to inscribe a circle in $\triangle PQR$.

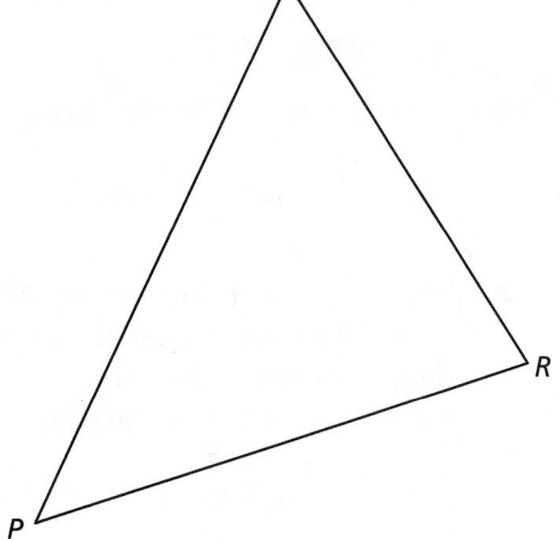

A The center of the inscribed circle must be equidistant from the sides of $\triangle PQR$. In particular, the center must be equidistant from $\overline{PQ}$ and $\overline{PR}$. What is the set of points equidistant from $\overline{PQ}$ and $\overline{PR}$?

____

Use a compass and straightedge to construct this set of points.

B Similarly, the center must be equidistant from $\overline{PR}$ and $\overline{QR}$. What is the set of points equidistant from $\overline{PR}$ and $\overline{QR}$?

____

Use a compass and straightedge to construct this set of points.

C The center must lie at the intersection of the two sets of points you constructed. Label this point *C*.

D Place the point of your compass at *C* and open the compass until the pencil just touches a side of $\triangle PQR$. Then draw the inscribed circle.

REFLECT

2a. Suppose you started by constructing the set of points equidistant from $\overline{PR}$ and $\overline{QR}$, and then constructed the set of points equidistant from $\overline{QR}$ and $\overline{QP}$. Would you have found the same center point? Check by doing this construction.

____

2b. Is it possible for the incenter of a triangle to fall outside the triangle? If so, give an example and describe the triangle.

____

____

PRACTICE

Construct the circumcircle of each triangle.

1.

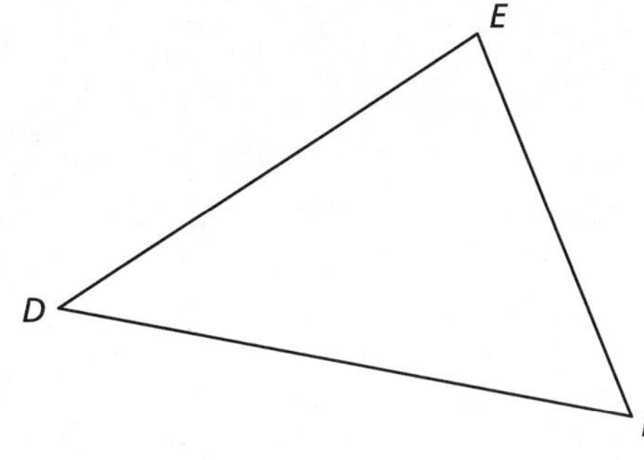

2.

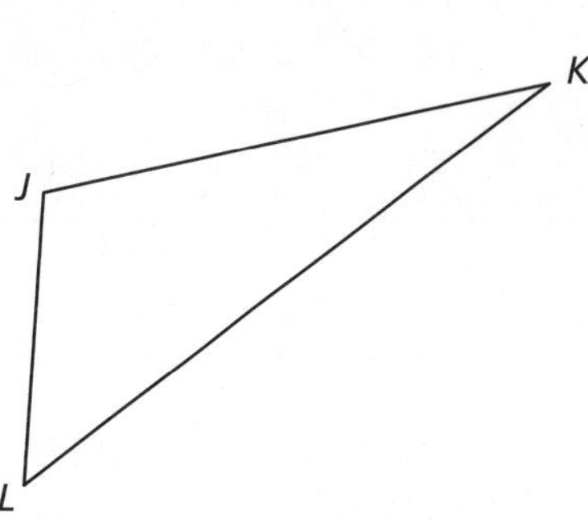

3.

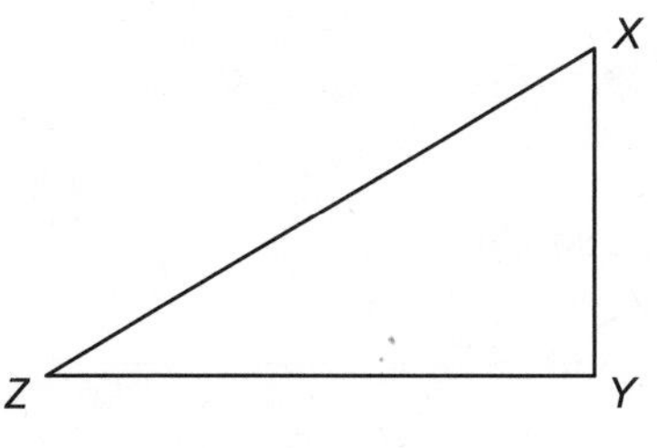

4.

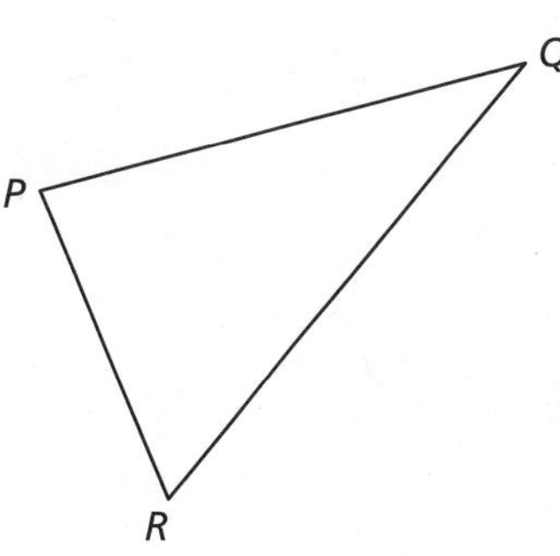

5. Explain how to use a compass and straightedge to locate the center of a circle. (*Hint:* Start by plotting three points on the circle.)

____

____

____

6. Use a compass and straightedge to locate the circumcenter of an acute triangle, a right triangle, and an obtuse triangle. Considering these constructions and the other constructions from this lesson, what can you say about the location of a triangle's circumcenter?

____

____

____

Construct the inscribed circle for each triangle.

7.

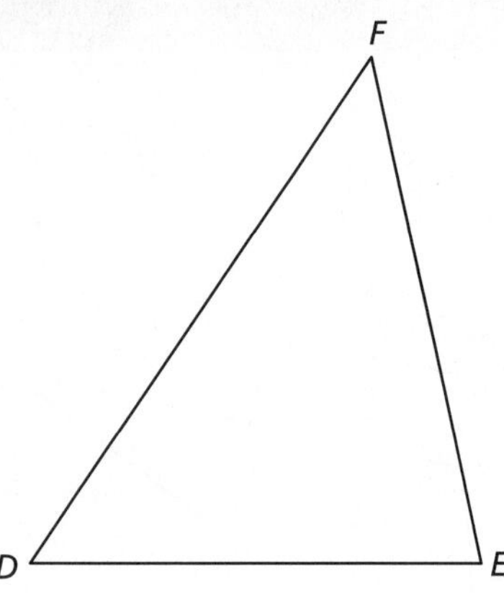

8.

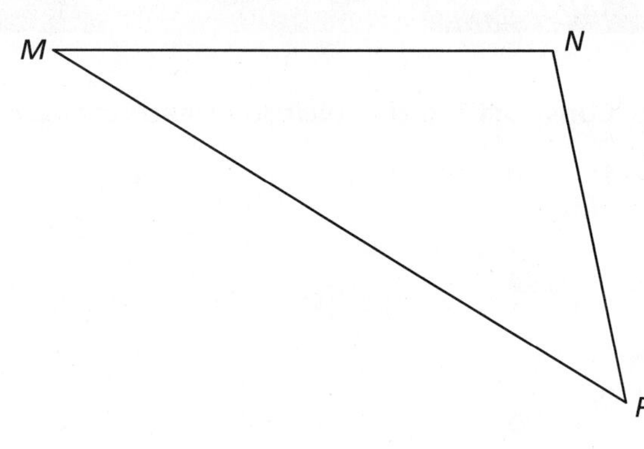

9.

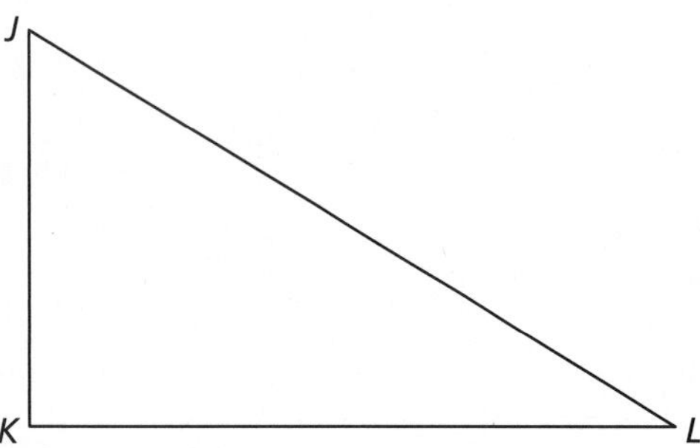

10.

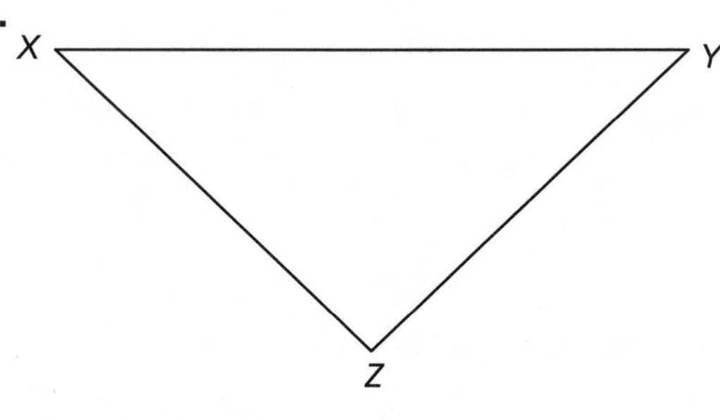

11. Explain how you can use paper folding to find the incenter of a triangle.

____

____

____

12. Is it possible for the incenter and the circumcenter of a triangle to be the same point? If so, describe a triangle for which this is true. If not, explain why not.

____

____

____

Name________________________ Class____________ Date____________

Additional Practice

Construct the circumcircle of each triangle.

1\.

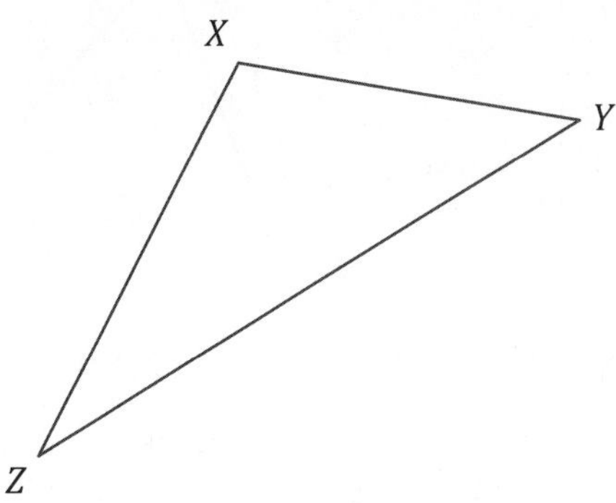

2\.

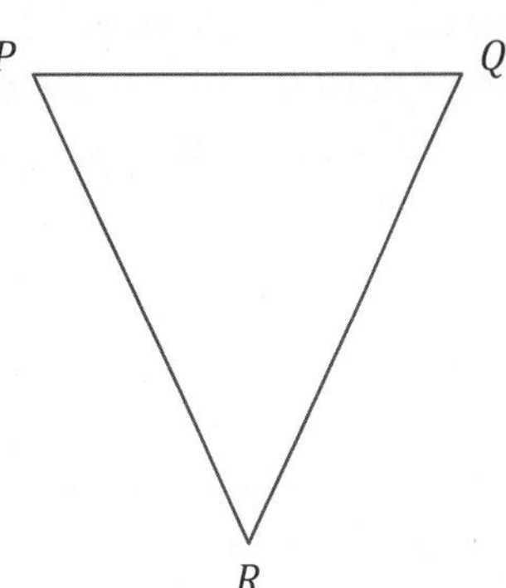

Construct the incircle of each triangle.

3\.

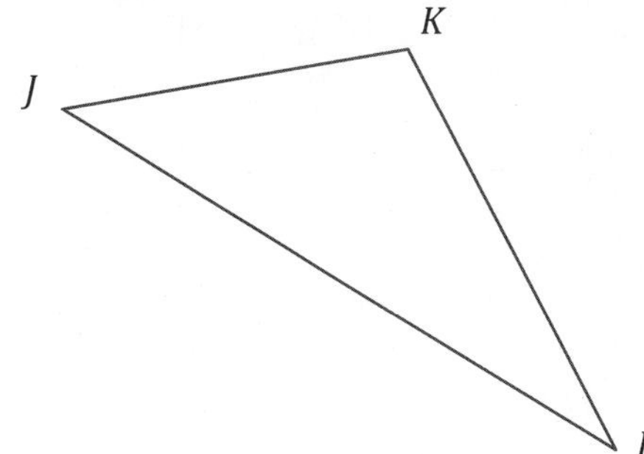

4\.

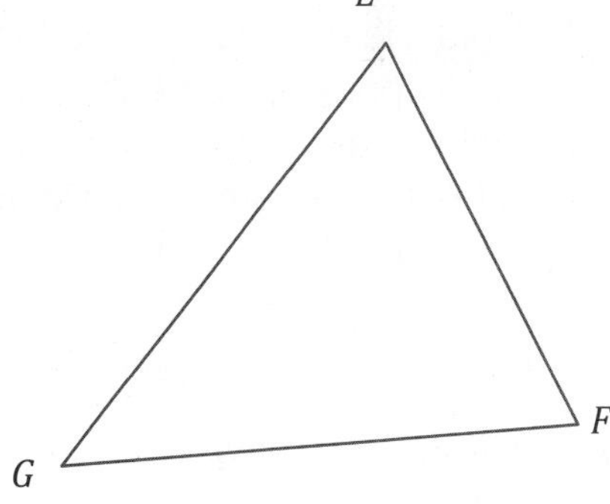

Complete using one of these words: *incenter, circumcenter.*

5. To locate the ____________ of a triangle, you can construct the perpendicular bisector of each side of the triangle.

6. To locate the ____________ of a triangle, you can construct the angle bisector of each angle of the triangle.

7. A car's logo is the triangle shown. Raleigh has to use this logo as the center of the steering wheel. Explain how Raleigh can do this. Sketch his design on the figure.

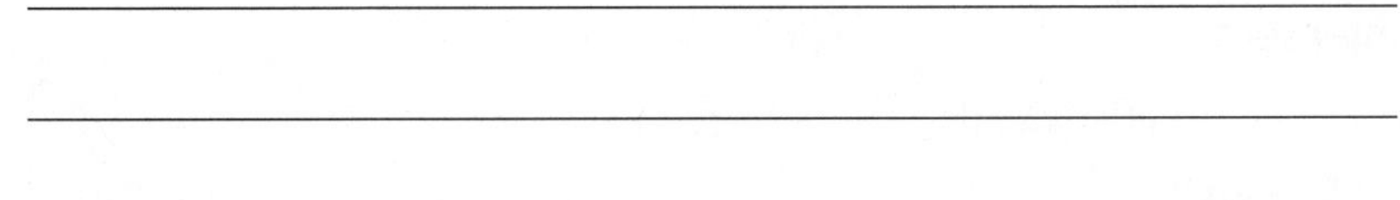

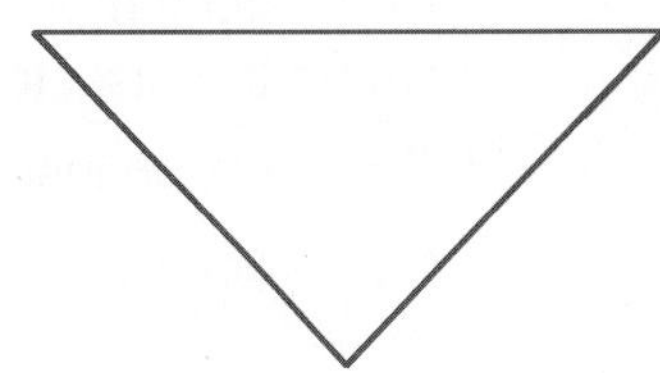

Problem Solving

1. The diagram shows the locations of three cities, labeled *X*, *Y*, and *Z*. Explain how to use a compass and straightedge to mark a location for a new water tower that will be the same distance from each of the three cities. Then perform the construction.

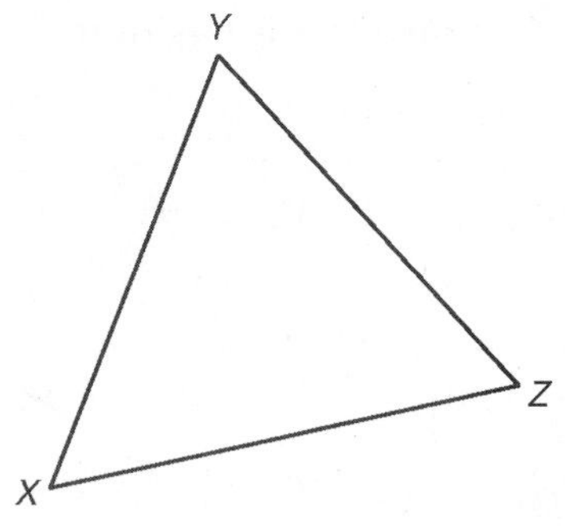

____

____

____

____

2. Paulo drew a right triangle by using a corner of a piece of paper to draw the right angle. Then he constructed the circumcircle of his right triangle. He noticed that the longest side of the triangle appeared to be the diameter of the triangle. Draw your own right triangle. Then construct its circumcircle. Do you get the same result as Paulo?

____

Choose the best answer.

3. An architect draws $\triangle JKL$ to represent a triangular sitting area in a mall. The architect then constructs the angle bisectors of the angles of the triangle and finds that the bisectors intersect at a point 5 centimeters from $\overline{JK}$. On the architect's drawing, what is the distance of this point from $\overline{KL}$?

   A 2.5 cm   B 5 cm   C 7.5 cm   D 10 cm

4. A new gym is to be located the same distance from three schools. You have a compass and straightedge and a map with points *A*, *B*, and *C* representing the three schools. How can you locate the new gym?

   F Construct the perpendicular bisectors of the sides of $\triangle ABC$ and find the point where the perpendicular bisectors intersect.

   G Construct the bisectors of the angles of $\triangle ABC$ and find the point where the bisectors intersect.

   H Construct an inscribed circle inside $\triangle ABC$.

   J Construct the incircle of $\triangle ABC$.

Name ______________________ Class ______________ Date ________

6-3

Medians and Altitudes of Triangles

Focus on Reasoning

Essential question: *What can you conclude about the medians of a triangle?*

A **median** of a triangle is a line segment whose endpoints are a vertex of the triangle and the midpoint of the opposite side. Every triangle has three medians. In the figure, $\overline{LM}$ is a median of $\triangle JKL$.

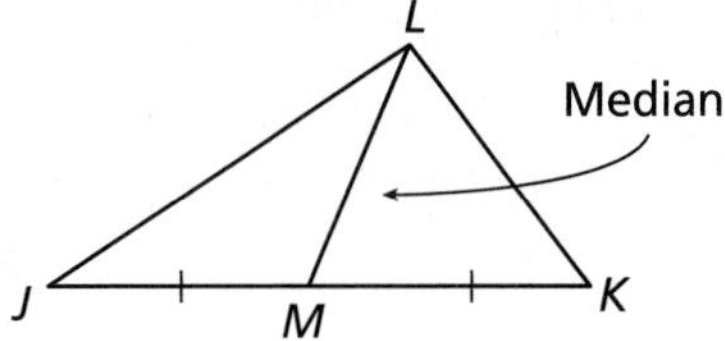

1 Investigate medians.

A Use geometry software to draw a triangle.

B Label the vertices *J, K,* and *L*.

C Select each side and construct its midpoint. Label the midpoints *M, N,* and *P*.

D Draw the medians, $\overline{LM}$, $\overline{JN}$, and $\overline{KP}$.

E Drag the vertices of $\triangle JKL$ to change its shape. As you do so, look for relationships among the medians.

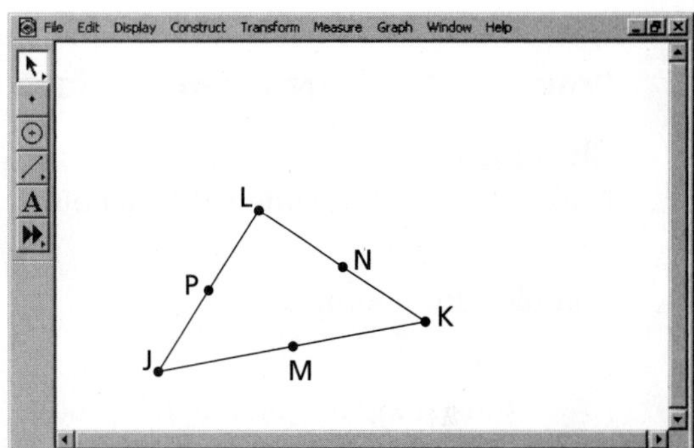

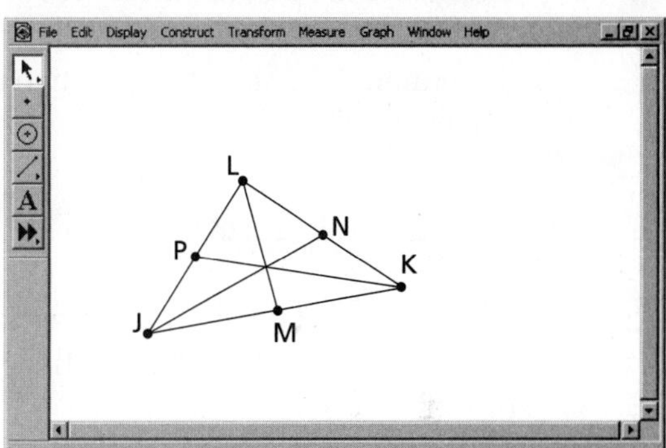

REFLECT

1a. Compare your observations with those of other students. Then make a conjecture. What can you say about the medians of a triangle?

____

____

1b. Paul draws $\triangle ABC$ and the medians from vertices *A* and *B*. He finds that the medians intersect at a point and he labels this point *X*. Paul claims that point *X* lies outside $\triangle ABC$. Do you think this is possible? Explain.

____

____

Three or more lines are said to be **concurrent** when they intersect at a point. The point is called the **point of concurrency**. You have seen that the medians of a triangle are concurrent. The point of concurrency of the medians of a triangle is called the **centroid** of the triangle.

Concurrency of Medians Theorem

The medians of a triangle are concurrent.

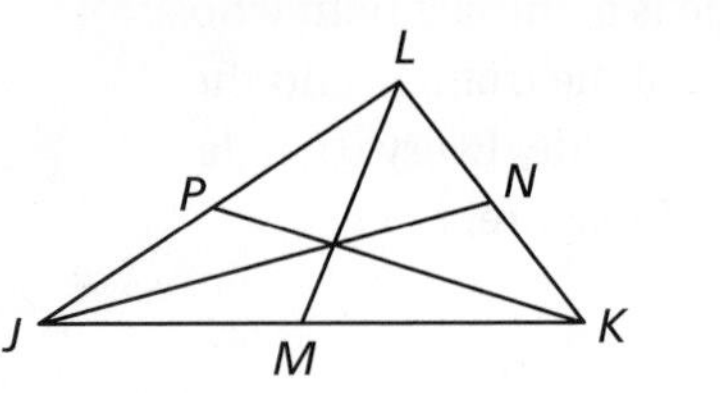

2 Prove the Concurrency of Medians Theorem.

Given: $\triangle JKL$ with medians $\overline{LM}$, $\overline{JN}$, and $\overline{KP}$.
Prove: The medians intersect at a point.

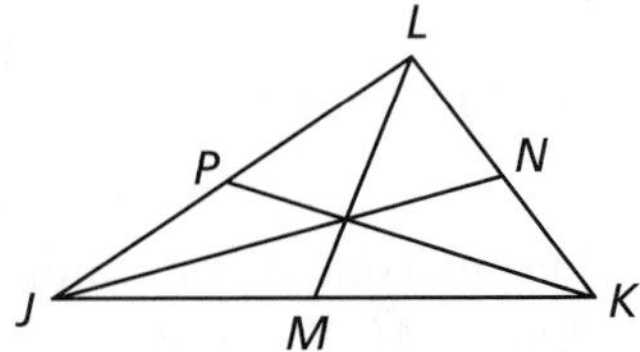

Complete the coordinate proof.

A Understand the plan for the proof.

Assign coordinates to the vertices of the triangle and find the coordinates of the midpoint of each side. Write an equation for the line containing each median. Determine the point of intersection of two of the lines. Show that this point lies on the third line.

B Assign coordinates to the vertices of the triangle.

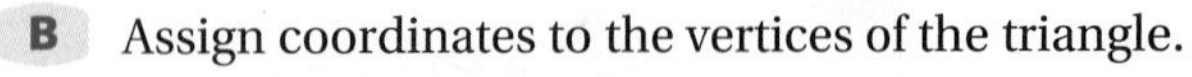

Place J at the origin and $\overline{JK}$ along the x-axis. Assign coordinates to K and L as shown.

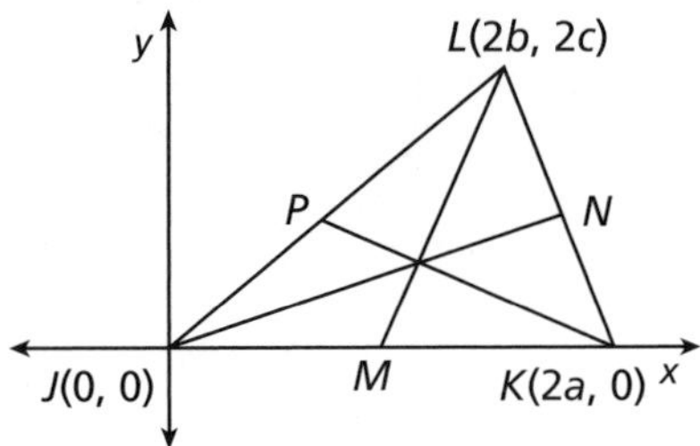

C Find the coordinates of the midpoint of each side. Use the midpoint formula.

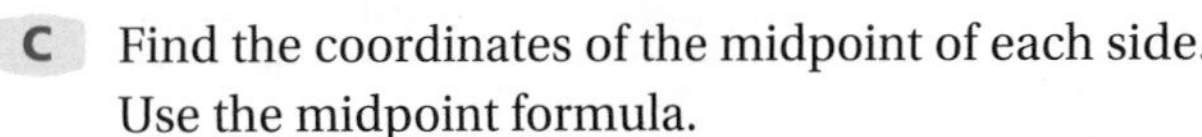

$M\left(\frac{\square + \square}{2}, \frac{\square + \square}{2}\right) = M(\square, \square)$

$N\left(\frac{\square + \square}{2}, \frac{\square + \square}{2}\right) = N(\square, \square)$

$P\left(\frac{\square + \square}{2}, \frac{\square + \square}{2}\right) = P(\square, \square)$

D Write the equation for the line containing $\overline{JN}$. To do so, use the *point-slope form* of the equation of a line: If a line has slope m and passes through (x_0, y_0), then the line's equation is $y - y_0 = m(x - x_0)$.

Slope of $\overline{JN} = \frac{c - 0}{a + b - 0} = \frac{c}{a + b}$

To write the equation of $\overleftrightarrow{JN}$, use the fact that the line passes through (0, 0).

Equation of $\overleftrightarrow{JN}$: $y - 0 = \frac{c}{a + b}(x - 0)$ or $y = \frac{c}{a + b}x$

E Write the equations for the lines containing $\overline{LM}$ and $\overline{PK}$.

Slope of $\overline{LM} = \frac{\_\_ - \_\_}{\_\_ - \_\_} = \frac{\_\_}{\_\_}$

Equation of $\overleftrightarrow{LM}$: $y - \_\_ = \frac{\_\_}{\_\_}(x - \_\_)$ or $y = \frac{\_\_}{\_\_}(x - \_\_)$

Slope of $\overline{PK} = \frac{\_\_ - \_\_}{\_\_ - \_\_} = \frac{\_\_}{\_\_}$

Equation of $\overleftrightarrow{PK}$: $y - \_\_ = \frac{\_\_}{\_\_}(x - \_\_)$ or $y = \frac{\_\_}{\_\_}(x - \_\_)$

F Find the point of intersection of $\overleftrightarrow{JN}$ and $\overleftrightarrow{LM}$. To do so, set the right side of the equation for $\overleftrightarrow{JN}$ equal to the right side of the equation for $\overleftrightarrow{LM}$. Then solve for x, to find the x-coordinate of the point of intersection.

$\frac{c}{a + b}x = \frac{2c}{2b - a}(x - a)$	Write the equation for x.
$cx(2b - a) = 2c(x - a)(a + b)$	Multiply both sides by $(a + b)(2b - a)$.
$2bcx - acx = (2cx - 2ac)(a + b)$	Multiply.
________________	Multiply on right side of equation.
________________	Subtract $2bcx$ from both sides.
________________	Subtract $2acx$ from both sides.
________________	Factor out ac; divide both sides by ac.
________________	Divide both sides by -3.

To find the y-coordinate of the point of intersection, substitute this value of x into the equation for $\overleftrightarrow{JN}$ and solve for y.

$y = \frac{c}{a + b}x = \frac{c}{a + b} \cdot \frac{\_\_}{\_\_} = \frac{\_\_}{\_\_}$

The coordinates of the point of intersection of $\overleftrightarrow{JN}$ and $\overleftrightarrow{LM}$ are ____________.

G Now show that the point you found in Step F lies on $\overleftrightarrow{PK}$. To do so, substitute the x-coordinate of the point into the equation for $\overleftrightarrow{PK}$. Then simplify to show that the corresponding y-value is the same as the y-coordinate you calculated in Step F.

$y = \frac{c}{b - 2a}(x - 2a)$ Write the equation for $\overleftrightarrow{PK}$.

______________________ Substitute the x-coordinate of the point.

______________________ Subtract inside the parentheses.

______________________ Factor the numerator inside the parentheses.

______________________ Divide to remove common factors.

______________________ Simplify.

Because this y-value is the same as the y-coordinate of the point of intersection from Step F, the point also lies on $\overleftrightarrow{PK}$. This shows that the medians are concurrent.

REFLECT

2a. Explain how you can find the coordinates of the centroid of a triangle with vertices $R(0, 0)$, $S(6, 0)$, and $T(3, 9)$.

____

____

____

2b. A student proves the Concurrency of Medians Theorem by first assigning coordinates to the vertices of $\triangle JKL$ as $J(0, 0)$, $K(2a, 0)$, and $L(2a, 2c)$. The students says that this choice of coordinates makes the algebra in the proof a bit easier. Do you agree with the student's choice of coordinates? Explain.

____

____

2c. A student claims that the averages of the x-coordinates and of the y-coordinates of the vertices of a triangle are the x- and y-coordinates of the centroid. Does the coordinate proof of the Concurrency of Medians Theorem support the claim? Explain.

____

____

____

Name________________ Class________ Date________

6-3

Additional Practice

Use the figure for Exercises 1–4. $GB = 12\frac{2}{3}$ and $CD = 10$.

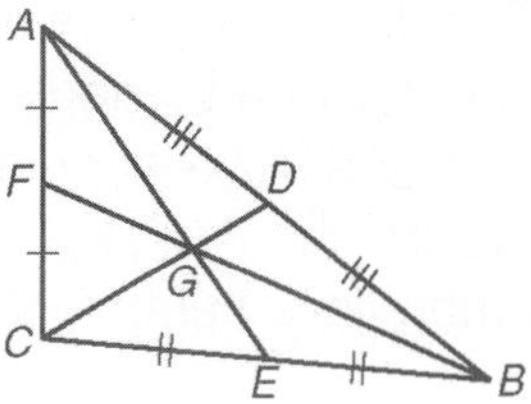

Find each length.

1. *FG* ________________
2. *BF* ________________
3. *GD* ________________
4. *CG* ________________
5. A triangular compass needle will turn most easily if it is attached to the compass face through its centroid. Find the coordinates of the centroid.

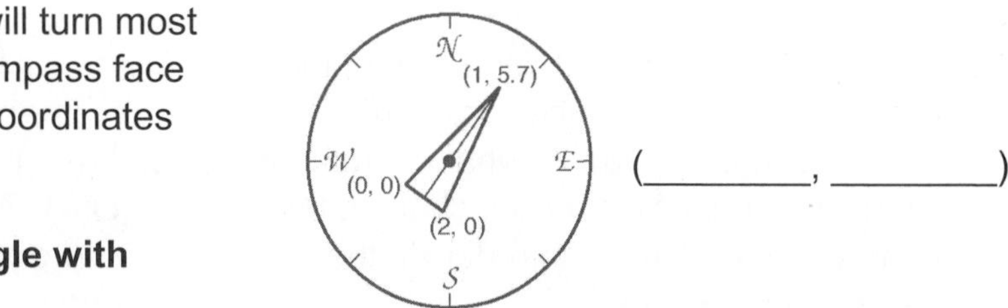

(________, ________)

Find the orthocenter of the triangle with the given vertices.

6. $X(-5, 4)$, $Y(2, -3)$, $Z(1, 4)$

(________, ________)

7. $A(0, -1)$, $B(2, -3)$, $C(4, -1)$

(________, ________)

Use the figure for Exercises 8 and 9. $\overline{HL}$, $\overline{IM}$, and $\overline{JK}$ are medians of $\triangle HIJ$.

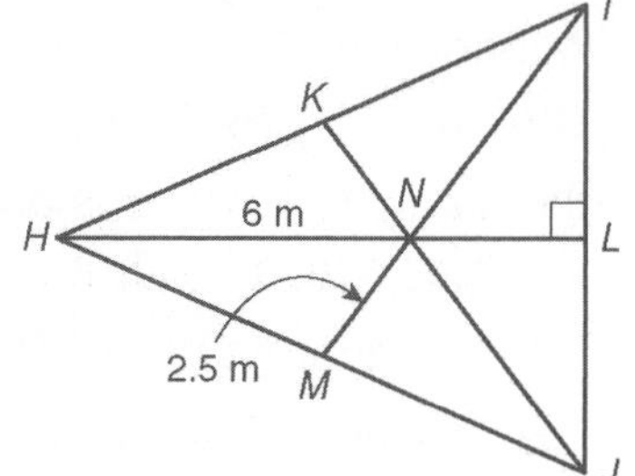

8. Find the area of the triangle. ________________
9. If the perimeter of the triangle is 49 meters, then find the length of $\overline{MH}$. (*Hint:* What kind of a triangle is it?)

____

10. Two medians of a triangle were cut apart at the centroid to make the four segments shown below. Use what you know about the Centroid Theorem to reconstruct the original triangle from the four segments shown. Measure the side lengths of your triangle to check that you constructed medians. (*Note:* There are many possible answers.)

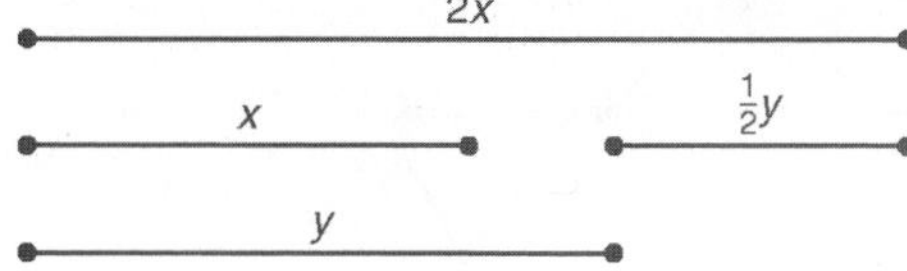

Problem Solving

1. The diagram shows the coordinates of the vertices of a triangular patio umbrella. The umbrella will rest on a pole that will support it. Where should the pole be attached so that the umbrella is balanced?

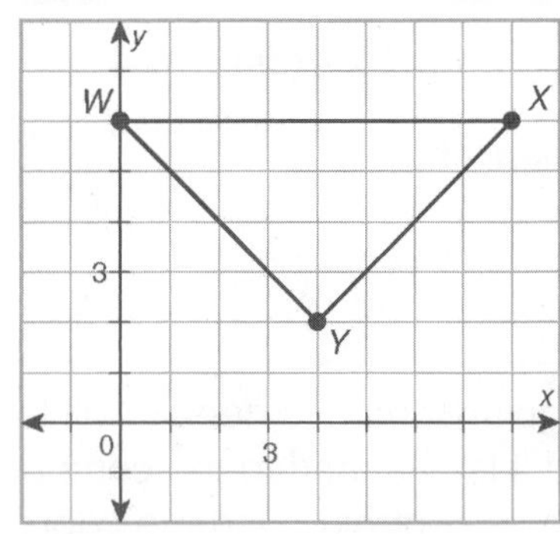

____

2. In a plan for a triangular wind chime, the coordinates of the vertices are $J(10, 2)$, $K(7, 6)$, and $L(12, 10)$. At what coordinates should the manufacturer attach the chain from which it will hang in order for the chime to be balanced?

____

3. Triangle PQR has vertices at $P(-3, 5)$, $Q(-1, 7)$, and $R(3, 1)$. Find the coordinates of the orthocenter and the centroid.

____

Choose the best answer.

4. A triangle has coordinates at $A(0, 6)$, $B(8, 6)$, and $C(5, 0)$. $\overline{CD}$ is a median of the triangle, and $\overline{CE}$ is an altitude of the triangle. Which is a true statement?

   A The coordinates of D and E are the same.

   B The distance between D and E is 1 unit.

   C The distance between D and E is 2 units.

   D D is on the triangle, and E is outside the triangle.

5. Lines j and k contain medians of $\triangle DEF$. Find y and z.

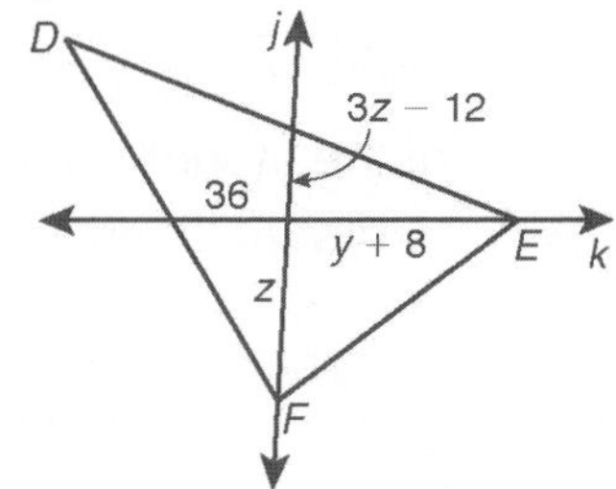

   F $y = 16$; $z = 4$ H $y = 64$; $z = 4.8$

   G $y = 32$; $z = 4$ J $y = 108$; $z = 8$

6. An inflatable triangular raft is towed behind a boat. The raft is an equilateral triangle. To maintain balance, the seat is at the centroid B of the triangle. What is AB, the distance from the seat to the tow rope? Round to the nearest tenth.

   A 18.7 in.

   B 37.4 in.

   C 43.1 in.

   D 56.0 in.

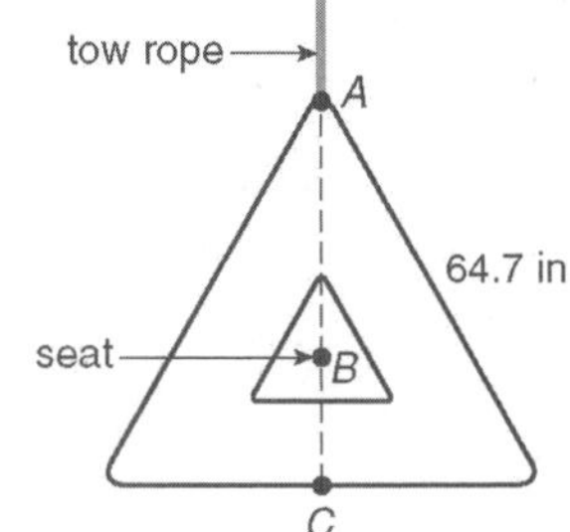

Name ______________________ Class ______________ Date ________

6-4

The Triangle Midsegment Theorem

Focus on Reasoning

Video Tutor

Essential question: *What must be true about the segment that connects the midpoints of two sides of a triangle?*

A **midsegment** of a triangle is a line segment that connects the midpoints of two sides of the triangle.

1 Investigate midsegments.

A Use geometry software to draw a triangle.

B Label the vertices *A*, *B*, and *C*.

C Select $\overline{AB}$ and construct its midpoint.
Select $\overline{AC}$ and construct its midpoint.
Label the midpoints *D* and *E*.

D Draw the midsegment, $\overline{DE}$.

E Measure the lengths of $\overline{DE}$ and $\overline{BC}$.

F Measure $\angle ADE$ and $\angle ABC$.

G Drag the vertices of $\triangle ABC$ to change its shape. As you do so, look for relationships in the measurements.

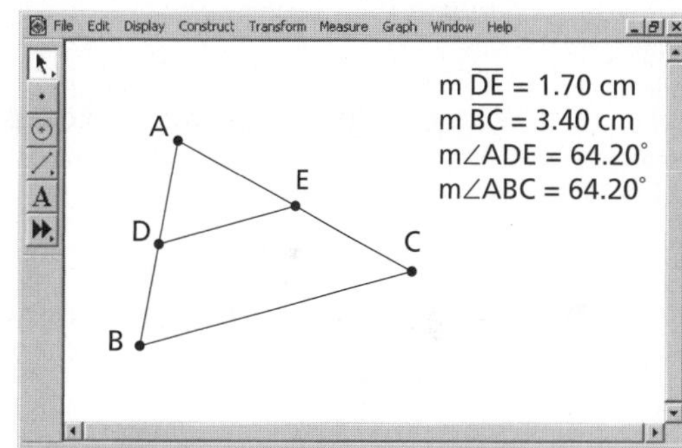

REFLECT

1a. How is the length of $\overline{DE}$ related to the length of $\overline{BC}$?

____

1b. How is m$\angle ADE$ related to m$\angle ABC$? What does this tell you about $\overline{DE}$ and $\overline{BC}$? Explain.

____

1c. Compare your results with those of other students. Then state a conjecture about a midsegment of a triangle.

____

____

2 Prove the Midsegment Theorem.

A midsegment of a triangle is parallel to the third side of the triangle and is half as long as the third side.

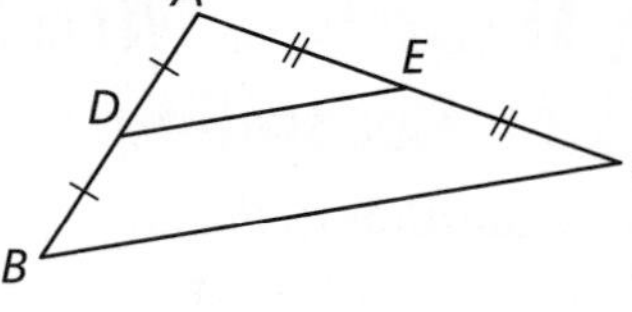

Given: $\overline{DE}$ is a midsegment of $\triangle ABC$.
Prove: $\overline{DE} \parallel \overline{BC}$ and $DE = \frac{1}{2}BC$.

A Use a coordinate proof. Place $\triangle ABC$ on a coordinate plane so that one vertex is at the origin and one side lies on the x-axis, as shown. For convenience, assign vertex C the coordinates $(2p, 0)$ and assign vertex A the coordinates $(2q, 2r)$.

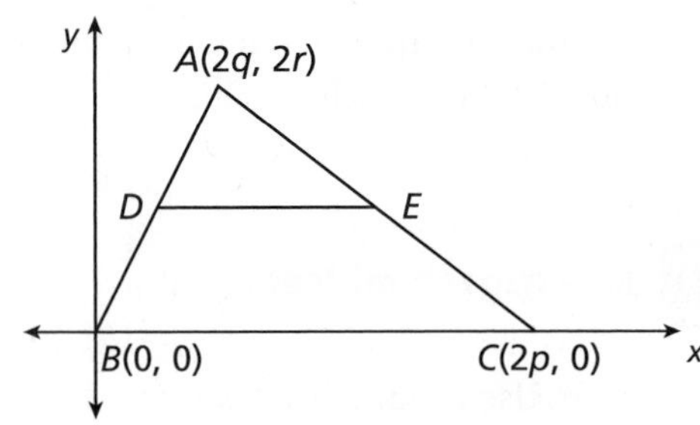

B Use the midpoint formula to find the coordinates of D and E. Complete the calculations.

$D\left(\frac{2q+0}{2}, \frac{2r+0}{2}\right) = D(q, r)$ $\qquad E\left(\frac{\square + \square}{2}, \frac{\square + \square}{2}\right) = E(\square, \square)$

C To prove that $\overline{DE} \parallel \overline{BC}$, first find the slopes of $\overline{DE}$ and $\overline{BC}$.

Slope of $\overline{DE} = \frac{\square - \square}{\square - \square} = \square$

Slope of $\overline{BC} = \frac{\square - \square}{\square - \square} = \square$

What conclusion can you make based on the slopes? Why?

___

D Show how to use the distance formula to prove that $DE = \frac{1}{2}BC$.

___

___

REFLECT

2a. Explain why it is more convenient to assign the coordinates as $C(2p, 0)$ and $A(2q, 2r)$ rather than $C(p, 0)$ and $A(q, r)$.

___

2b. Explain how the perimeter of $\triangle JKL$ compares to that of $\triangle MNP$.

___

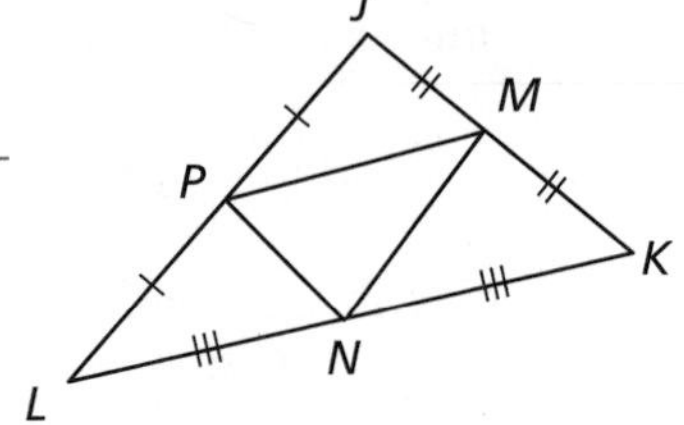

Name ______________________ Class ______________ Date ____________

6-4

Additional Practice

Use the figure for Exercises 1–6. Find each measure.

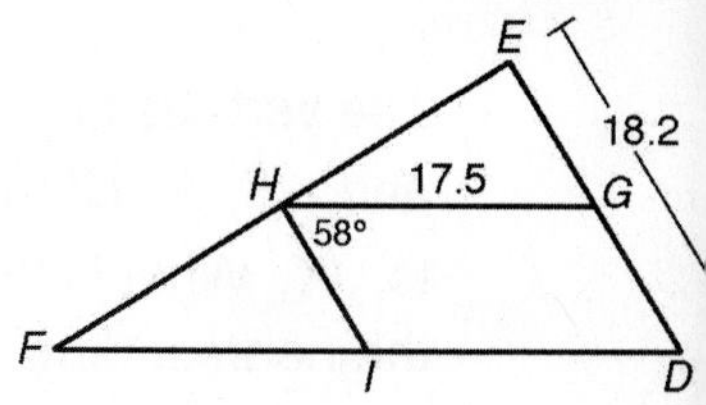

1. *HI* ____________ 2. *DF* ____________

3. *GE* ____________ 4. m∠*HIF* ____________

5. m∠*HGD* ____________ 6. m∠*D* ____________

The Bermuda Triangle is a region in the Atlantic Ocean off the southeast coast of the United States. The triangle is bounded by Miami, Florida; San Juan, Puerto Rico; and Bermuda. In the figure, the dotted lines are midsegments.

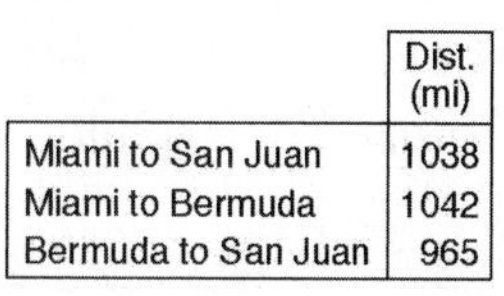

	Dist. (mi)
Miami to San Juan	1038
Miami to Bermuda	1042
Bermuda to San Juan	965

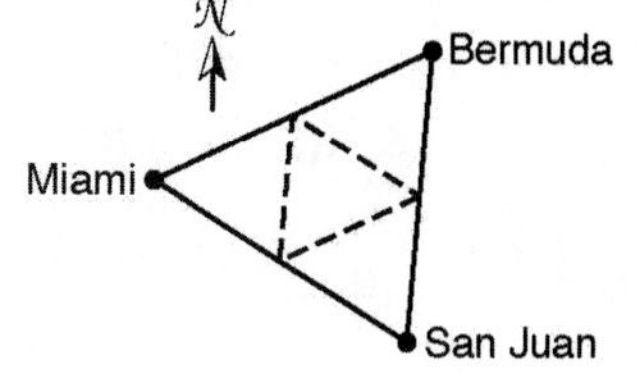

7. Use the distances in the chart to find the perimeter of the Bermuda Triangle. ____________

8. Find the perimeter of the midsegment triangle within the Bermuda Triangle. ____________

9. How does the perimeter of the midsegment triangle compare to the perimeter of the Bermuda Triangle?

____

Write a two-column proof that the perimeter of a midsegment triangle is half the perimeter of the triangle.

10. **Given:** $\overline{US}$, $\overline{ST}$, and $\overline{TU}$ are midsegments of $\triangle PQR$.

Prove: The perimeter of $\triangle STU = \frac{1}{2}(PQ + QR + RP)$.

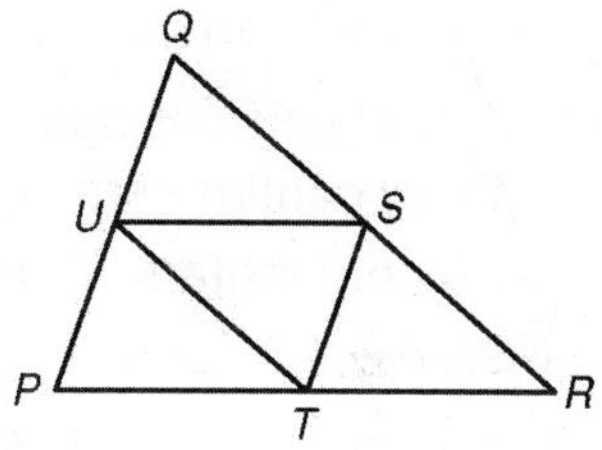

Problem Solving

1. The vertices of $\triangle JKL$ are $J(-9, 2)$, $K(10, 1)$, and $L(5, 6)$. $\overline{CD}$ is the midsegment parallel to $\overline{JK}$. What is the length of $\overline{CD}$? Round to the nearest tenth.

____

2. In $\triangle QRS$, $QR = 2x + 5$, $RS = 3x - 1$, and $SQ = 5x$. What is the perimeter of the midsegment triangle of $\triangle QRS$?

____

3. Is XY a midsegment of $\triangle LMN$ if its endpoints are $X(8, 2.5)$ and $Y(6.5, -2)$? Explain.

____

____

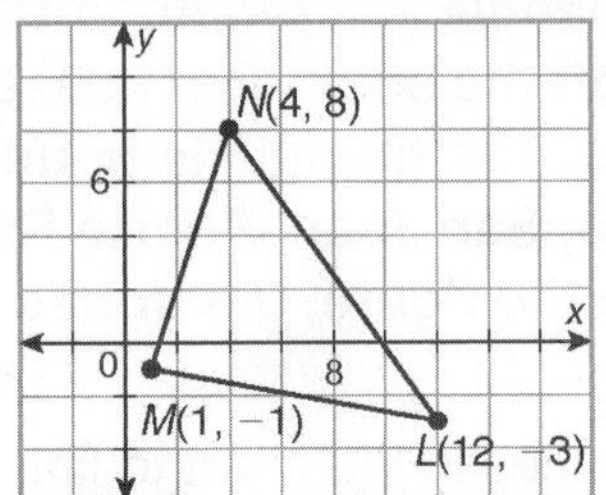

4. The diagram at right shows horseback riding trails. Point B is the halfway point along path $\overline{AC}$. Point D is the halfway point along path $\overline{CE}$. The paths along $\overline{BD}$ and $\overline{AE}$ are parallel. If riders travel from A to B to D to E, and then back to A, how far do they travel?

____

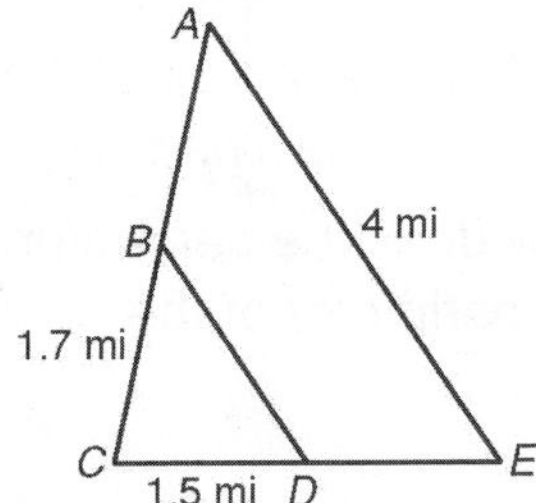

Choose the best answer.

5. Right triangle FGH has midsegments of length 10 centimeters, 24 centimeters, and 26 centimeters. What is the area of $\triangle FGH$?

   A 60 cm^2 C 240 cm^2

   B 120 cm^2 D 480 cm^2

6. In triangle HJK, $m\angle H = 110°$, $m\angle J = 30°$, and $m\angle K = 40°$. If R is the midpoint of $\overline{JK}$, and S is the midpoint of $\overline{HK}$, what is $m\angle JRS$?

   F 150° H 110°

   G 140° J 30°

Use the diagram for Exercises 7 and 8.

On the balance beam, V is the midpoint of $\overline{AB}$, and W is the midpoint of $\overline{YB}$.

7. The length of $\overline{VW}$ is $1\frac{7}{8}$ feet. What is AY?

   A $\frac{7}{8}$ ft C $3\frac{3}{4}$ ft

   B $\frac{15}{16}$ ft D $7\frac{1}{2}$ ft

8. The measure of $\angle AYW$ is 50°. What is the measure of $\angle VWB$?

   F 45° H 90°

   G 50° J 130°

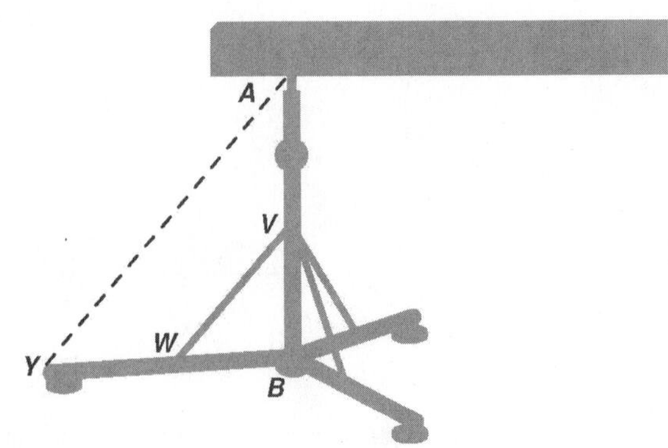

Name ______________________ Class ______________ Date ________

7-1

Video Tutor

Properties of Parallelograms

Focus on Reasoning

Essential question: *What can you conclude about the sides, angles, and diagonals of a parallelogram?*

Recall that a *parallelogram* is a quadrilateral that has two pairs of parallel sides. You use the symbol ▱ to name a parallelogram. For example, the figure shows ▱*ABCD*.

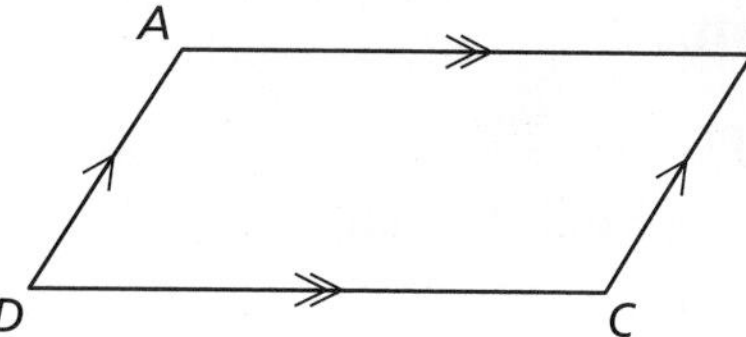

1 Investigate parallelograms.

A Use the straightedge tool of your geometry software to draw a straight line. Then plot a point that is not on the line. Select the point and line, go to the Construct menu, and construct a line through the point that is parallel to the line. This will give you a pair of parallel lines, as shown.

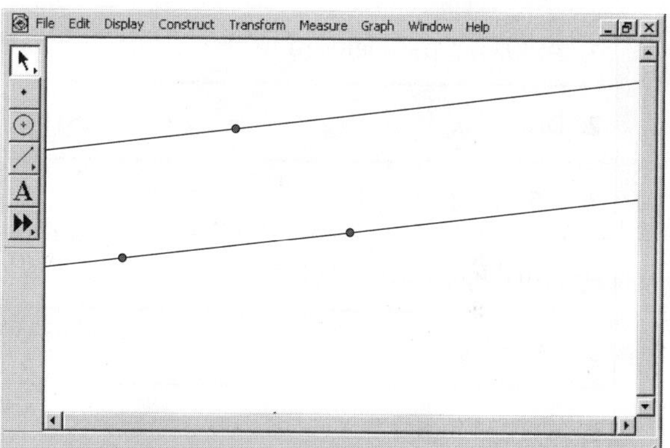

B Repeat Step A to construct a second pair of parallel lines that intersect those from Step A.

C The intersections of the parallel lines create a parallelogram. Plot points at these intersections. Label the points *A*, *B*, *C*, and *D*.

D Use the Measure menu to measure each angle of the parallelogram.

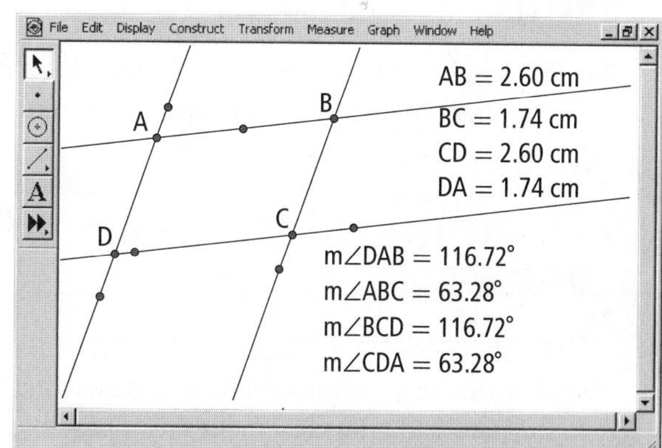

E Use the Measure menu to measure the length of each side of the parallelogram. (You can do this by measuring the distance between consecutive vertices.)

F Drag the points and lines in your construction to change the shape of the parallelogram. As you do so, look for relationships in the measurements.

REFLECT

1a. Make a conjecture about the sides and angles of a parallelogram.

____

____

You may have discovered the following theorem about parallelograms.

Theorem

If a quadrilateral is a parallelogram, then opposite sides are congruent.

2 Prove that opposite sides of a parallelogram are congruent.

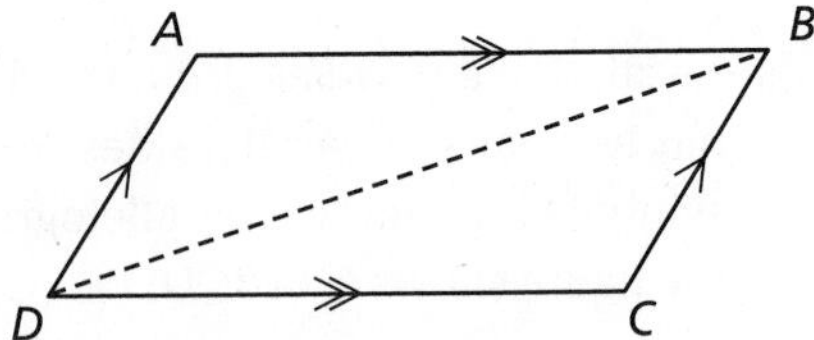

Complete the proof.

Given: *ABCD* is a parallelogram.

Prove: $\overline{AB} \cong \overline{CD}$ and $\overline{AD} \cong \overline{BC}$

Statements	Reasons
1. *ABCD* is a parallelogram.	1.
2. Draw $\overline{DB}$.	2. Through any two points there exists exactly one line.
3. $\overline{AB} \parallel \overline{DC}$; $\overline{AD} \parallel \overline{BC}$	3.
4. $\angle ADB \cong \angle CBD$; $\angle ABD \cong \angle CDB$	4.
5. $\overline{DB} \cong \overline{DB}$	5.
6.	6. ASA Congruence Criterion
7. $AB \cong CD$; $AD \cong BC$	7.

REFLECT

2a. Explain how you can use the rotational symmetry of a parallelogram to give an argument that supports the above theorem.

______

______

______

2b. One side of a parallelogram is twice as long as another side. The perimeter of the parallelogram is 24 inches. Is it possible to find all the side lengths of the parallelogram? If so, find the lengths. If not, explain why not.

______

______

Essential question: *What can you conclude about the diagonals of a parallelogram?*

A segment that connects any two nonconsecutive vertices of a polygon is a **diagonal**. A parallelogram has two diagonals. In the figure, $\overline{AC}$ and $\overline{BD}$ are diagonals of $\square ABCD$.

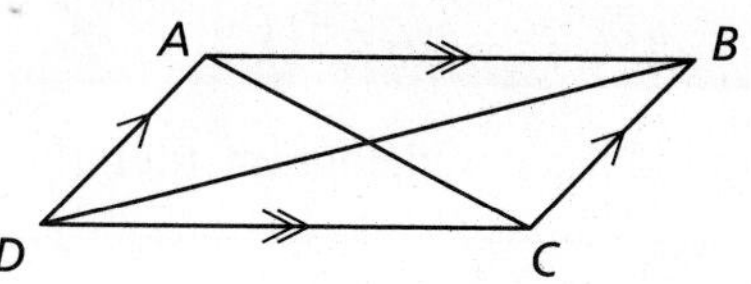

3 Investigate diagonals of parallelograms.

A Use geometry software to construct a parallelogram. (See Lesson 4-2 for detailed instructions.) Label the vertices of the parallelogram *A, B, C,* and *D.*

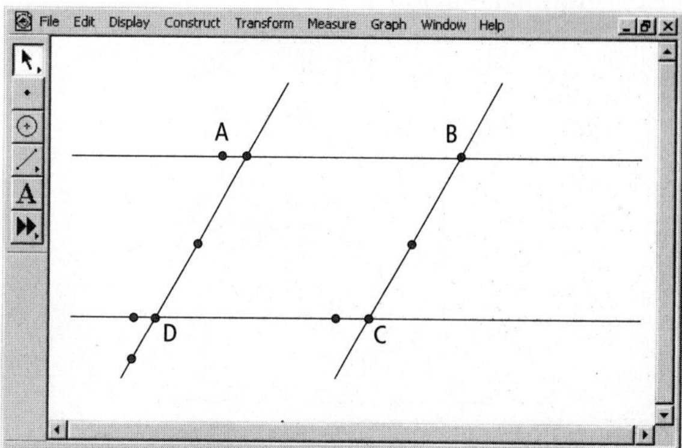

B Use the segment tool to construct the diagonals, $\overline{AC}$ and $\overline{BD}$.

C Plot a point at the intersection of the diagonals. Label this point *E.*

D Use the Measure menu to measure the length of $\overline{AE}$, $\overline{BE}$, $\overline{CE}$, and $\overline{DE}$. (You can do this by measuring the distance between the relevant endpoints.)

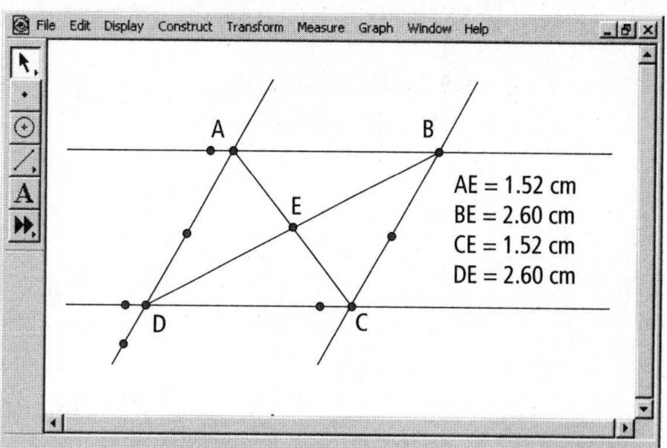

E Drag the points and lines in your construction to change the shape of the parallelogram. As you do so, look for relationships in the measurements.

REFLECT

3a. Make a conjecture about the diagonals of a parallelogram.

____

3b. A student claims that the perimeter of $\triangle AEB$ is always equal to the perimeter of $\triangle CED$. Without doing any further measurements in your construction, explain whether or not you agree with the student's statement.

____

____

You may have discovered the following theorem about parallelograms.

Theorem

If a quadrilateral is a parallelogram, then the diagonals bisect each other.

4 Prove diagonals of a parallelogram bisect each other.

Complete the proof.

Given: ABCD is a parallelogram.

Prove: $\overline{AE} \cong \overline{CE}$ and $\overline{BE} \cong \overline{DE}$.

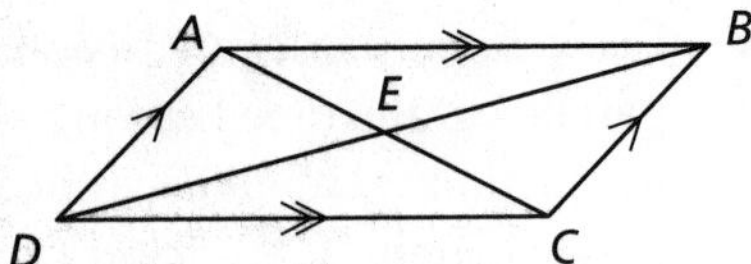

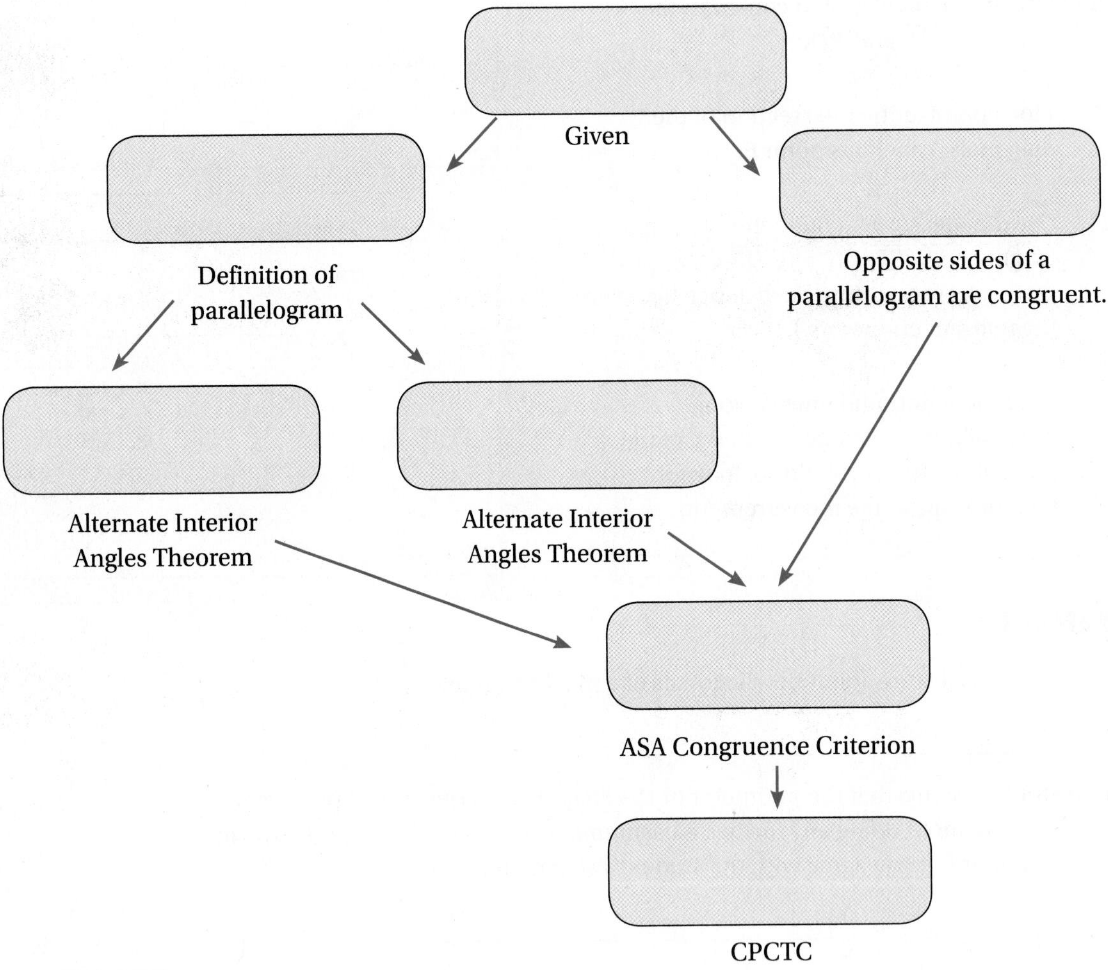

Given

Definition of parallelogram

Opposite sides of a parallelogram are congruent.

Alternate Interior Angles Theorem

Alternate Interior Angles Theorem

ASA Congruence Criterion

CPCTC

REFLECT

4a. Explain how you can prove the theorem using a different congruence criterion.

The angles of a parallelogram also have an important property. It is stated in the following theorem, which you will prove as an exercise.

Theorem

If a quadrilateral is a parallelogram, then opposite angles are congruent.

PRACTICE

1. Prove the above theorem about opposite angles of a parallelogram.

Given: *ABCD* is a parallelogram.
Prove: $\angle A \cong \angle C$ and $\angle B \cong \angle D$

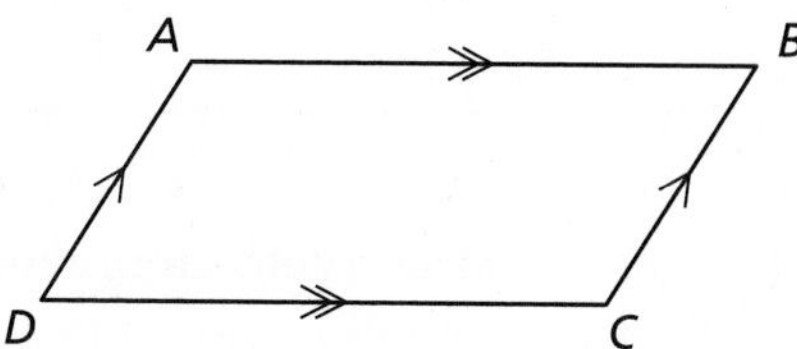

(*Hint:* You only need to prove that $\angle A \cong \angle C$. A similar argument can be used to prove that $\angle B \cong \angle D$. Also, you may or may not need to use all the rows of the table in your proof.)

Statements	Reasons
1.	1.
2.	2.
3.	3.
4.	4.
5.	5.
6.	6.
7.	7.

2. Explain why consecutive angles of a parallelogram are supplementary.

3. In the figure, *JKLM* is a parallelogram. Find the measure of each of the numbered angles.

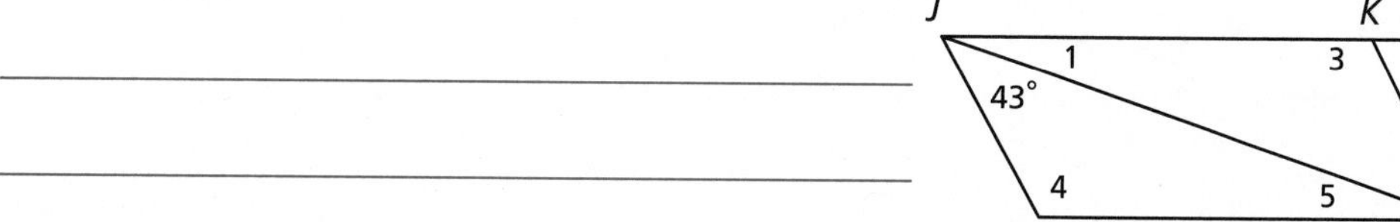

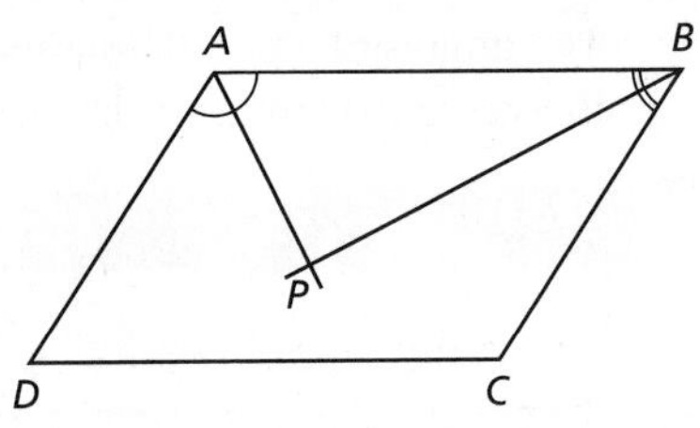

4. A city planner is designing a park in the shape of a parallelogram. As shown in the figure, there will be two straight paths through which visitors may enter the park. The paths are bisectors of consecutive angles of the parallelogram, and the paths intersect at point P.

a. Work directly on the parallelograms below and use a compass and straightedge to construct the bisectors of $\angle A$ and $\angle B$. Then use a protractor to measure $\angle APB$ in each case.

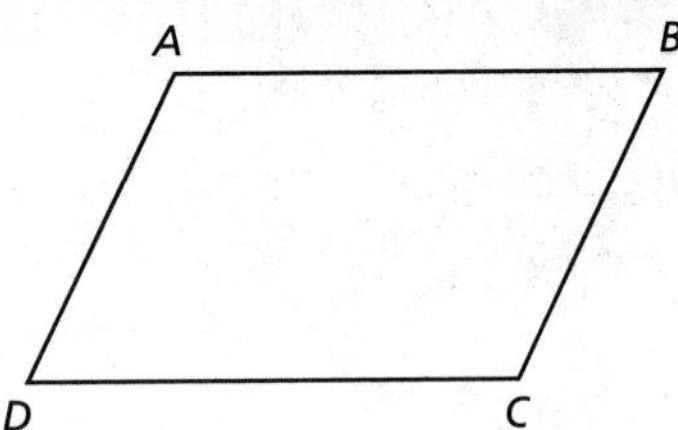

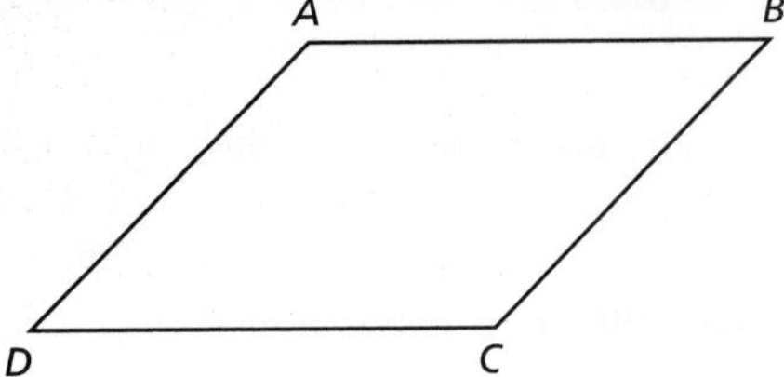

Make a conjecture about $\angle APB$.

____

b. Write a paragraph proof to show that your conjecture is always true. (*Hint:* Suppose $m\angle BAP = x°$, $m\angle ABP = y°$, and $m\angle APB = z°$. What do you know about $x + y + z$? What do you know about $2x + 2y$?)

____

____

____

____

c. When the city planner takes into account the dimensions of the park, she finds that point P lies on $\overline{DC}$, as shown. Explain why it must be the case that $DC = 2AD$. (*Hint:* Use congruent base angles to show that $\triangle DAP$ and $\triangle CPB$ are isosceles.)

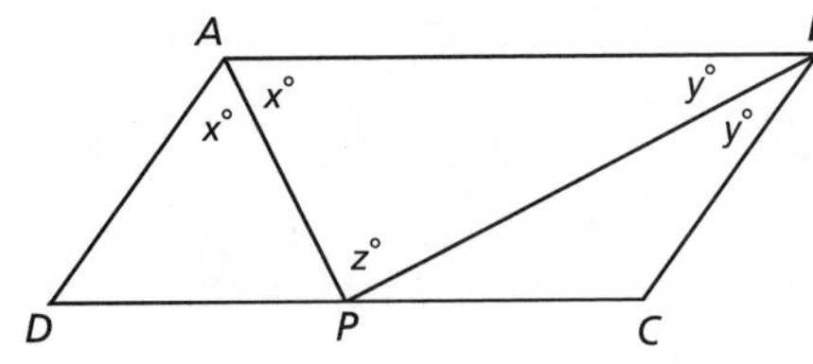

____

____

____

____

____

Name______________________ Class______________ Date__________

Additional Practice

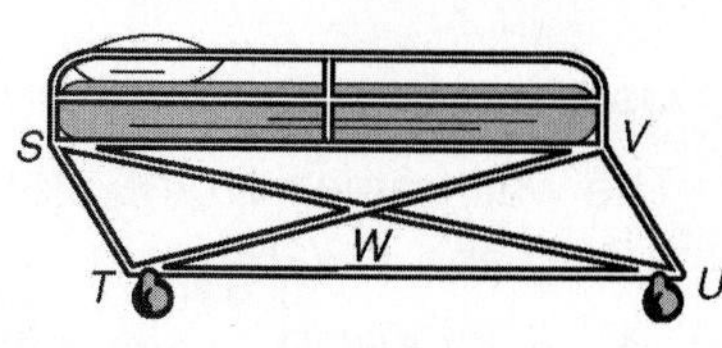

A gurney is a wheeled cot or stretcher used in hospitals. Many gurneys are made so that the base will fold up for easy storage in an ambulance. When partially folded, the base forms a parallelogram. In ▱ *STUV*, *VU* = 91 centimeters, *UW* = 108.8 centimeters, and m∠*TSV* = 57°. Find each measure.

1. *SW* ______________
2. *TS* ______________
3. *US* ______________
4. m∠*SVU* ______________
5. m∠*STU* ______________
6. m∠*TUV* ______________

***JKLM* is a parallelogram. Find each measure.**

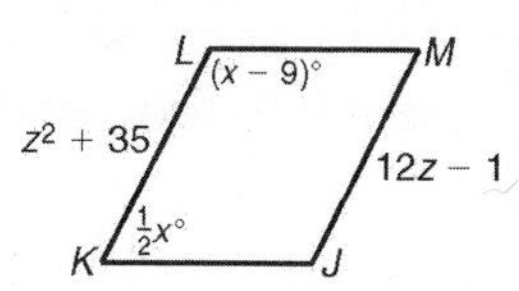

7. m∠*L* ______________
8. m∠*K* ______________
9. *MJ* ______________

***VWXY* is a parallelogram. Find each measure.**

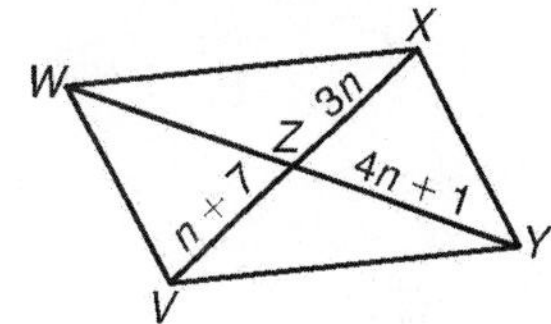

10. *VX* ______________
11. *XZ* ______________
12. *ZW* ______________
13. *WY* ______________

14. Three vertices of ▱ *ABCD* are *B*(−3, 3), *C*(2, 7), and *D*(5, 1). Find the coordinates of vertex *A*. ______________

Write a two-column proof.

15. **Given:** *DEFG* is a parallelogram.

    Prove: m∠*DHG* = m∠*EDH* + m∠*FGH*

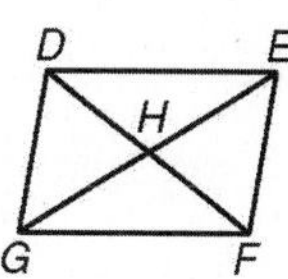

Problem Solving

Use the diagram for Exercises 1 and 2.

The wall frames on the staircase wall form parallelograms *ABCD* and *EFGH*.

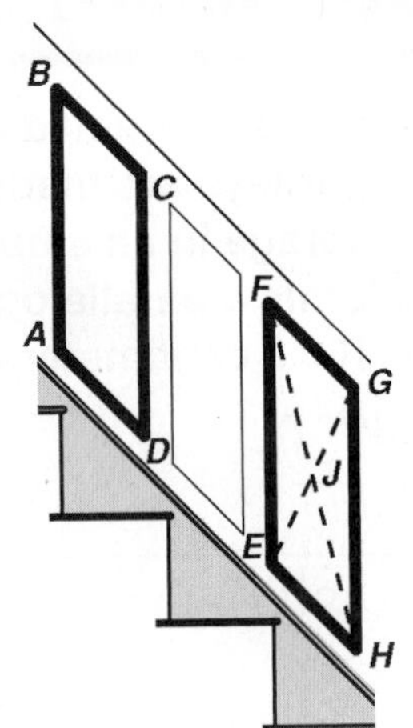

1. In ▱*ABCD*, the measure of $\angle A$ is three times the measure of $\angle B$. What are the measures of $\angle C$ and $\angle D$?

____

2. In ▱*EFGH*, $FH = 5x$ inches, $EG = (2x + 4)$ inches, and $JG = 8$ inches. What is the length of *JH*?

____

3. The diagram shows a section of the support structure of a roller coaster. In ▱*JKLM*, $JK = (3z - 0.9)$ feet, and $LM = (z + 2.7)$ feet. Find *JK*.

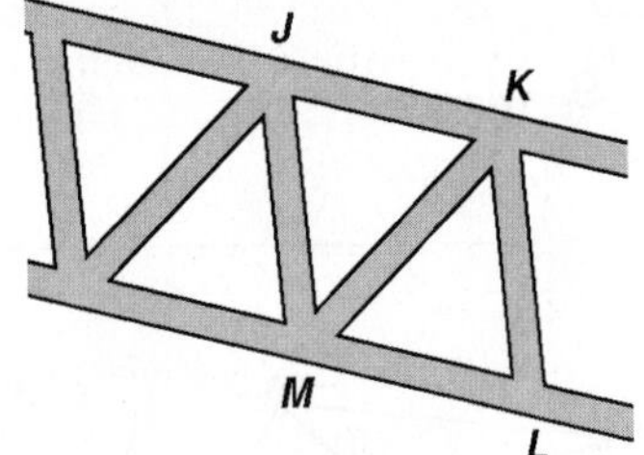

____

4. In ▱*TUVW*, part of a ceramic tile pattern, $m\angle TUV = (8x + 1)°$ and $m\angle UVW = (12x + 19)°$. Find $m\angle TUV$.

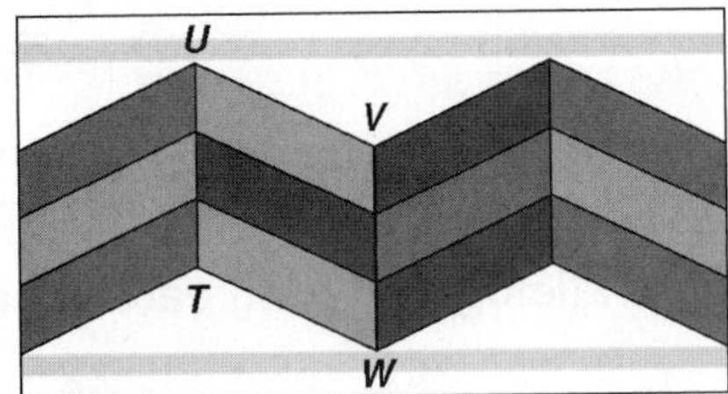

____

Choose the best answer.

5. What is the measure of $\angle Z$ in parallelogram *WXYZ*?

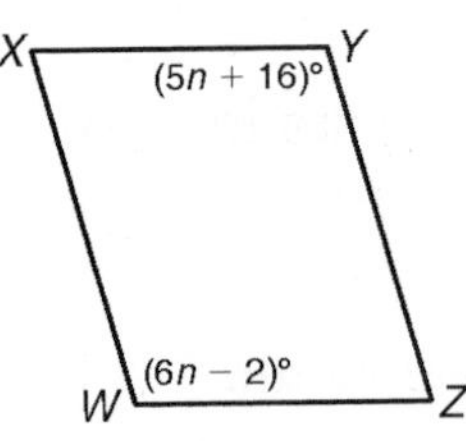

A 18°

B 74°

C 106°

D 108°

6. The perimeter of ▱*CDEF* is 54 centimeters. Find the length of $\overline{FC}$ if $\overline{DE}$ is 5 centimeters longer than $\overline{EF}$.

F 11 cm

G 14 cm

H 16 cm

J 44 cm

7. In ▱*PQRS*, $QT = 7x$, $TS = 2x + 2.5$, $RT = 2y$, and $TP = y + 3$. Find the perimeter of $\triangle PTS$.

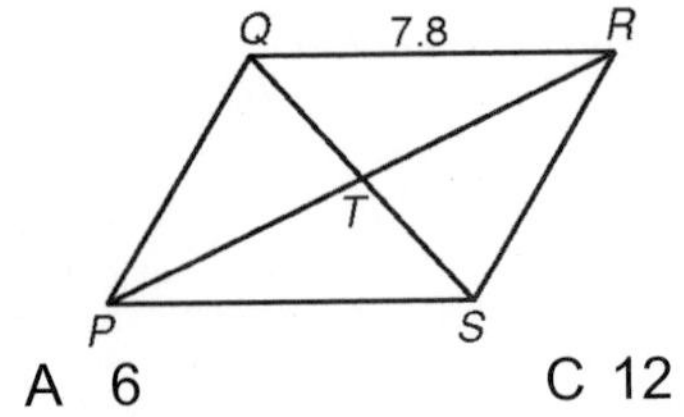

A 6

B 9.5

C 12

D 17.3

Name________________________ Class________________ Date__________

7-2

Conditions for Parallelograms

Going Deeper

Essential question: *What criteria can you use to prove that a quadrilateral is a parallelogram?*

The converses of the theorems you developed in the last two lessons are all true. These provide several criteria that can be used to prove that a quadrilateral is a parallelogram.

Opposite Sides Criterion for a Parallelogram

If both pairs of opposite sides of a quadrilateral are congruent, then the quadrilateral is a parallelogram.

MCC9–12.G.SRT.5

1 PROOF Opposite Sides Criterion for a Parallelogram

Complete the proof.

Given: $\overline{AB} \cong \overline{DC}$ and $\overline{AD} \cong \overline{BC}$

Prove: *ABCD* is a parallelogram.

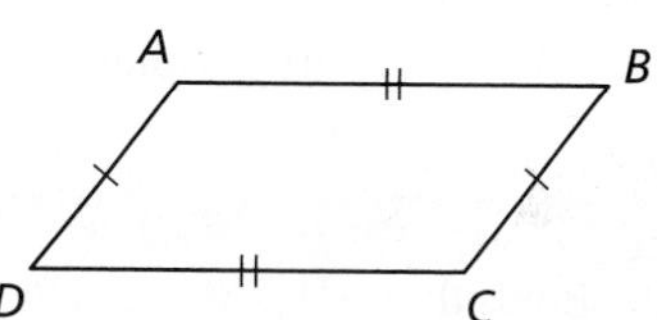

Statements	Reasons
1. Draw $\overline{DB}$.	1. Through any two points there exists exactly one line.
2. $\overline{DB} \cong \overline{DB}$	2.
3. $\overline{AB} \cong \overline{DC}$; $\overline{AD} \cong \overline{BC}$	3.
4.	4. SSS Congruence Criterion
5. $\angle ABD \cong \angle CDB$; $\angle ADB \cong \angle CBD$	5.
6. $\overline{AB} \parallel \overline{DC}$; $\overline{AD} \parallel \overline{BC}$	6.
7. *ABCD* is a parallelogram.	7.

REFLECT

1a. A quadrilateral has two sides that are 3 cm long and two sides that are 5 cm long. A student states that the quadrilateral must be a parallelogram. Do you agree? Why or why not?

____

____

Opposite Angles Criterion for a Parallelogram

If both pairs of opposite angles of a quadrilateral are congruent, then the quadrilateral is a parallelogram.

MCC9-12.G.CO.11

2 PROOF Opposite Angles Criterion for a Parallelogram

Complete the paragraph proof.

Given: $\angle A \cong \angle C$ and $\angle B \cong \angle D$.

Prove: $ABCD$ is a parallelogram.

$m\angle A + m\angle B + m\angle C + m\angle D = 360°$ by  .

From the given information, $m\angle A = m\angle C$ and $m\angle B = m\angle D$. By substitution,

$m\angle A + m\angle D + m\angle A + m\angle D = 360°$ or $2m\angle A + 2m\angle D = 360°$. Dividing both

sides by 2 gives ______________________.

Therefore, $\angle A$ and $\angle D$ are supplementary and so $\overline{AB} \parallel \overline{DC}$ by

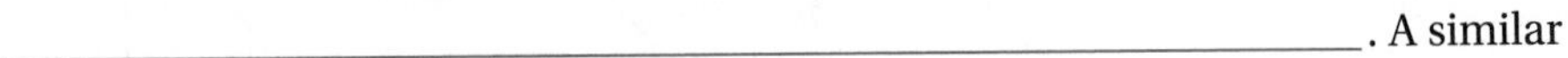. A similar

argument shows that $\overline{AD} \parallel \overline{BC}$, so $ABCD$ is a parallelogram by definition.

REFLECT

2a. What property or theorem justifies dividing both sides of the equation by 2 in the above proof?

____

PRACTICE

1. Write a paragraph proof for the following.

Bisecting Diagonals Criterion for a Parallelogram

If the diagonals of a quadrilateral bisect each other, then the quadrilateral is a parallelogram.

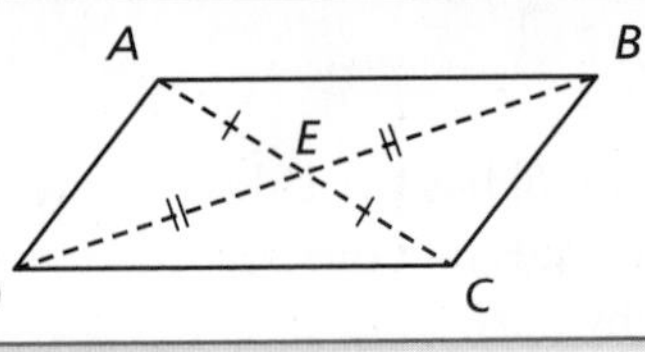

____

____

____

____

Name________________ Class__________ Date__________

7-2

Additional Practice

For Exercises 1 and 2, determine whether the figure is a parallelogram for the given values of the variables. Explain your answers.

1. $x = 9$ and $y = 11$

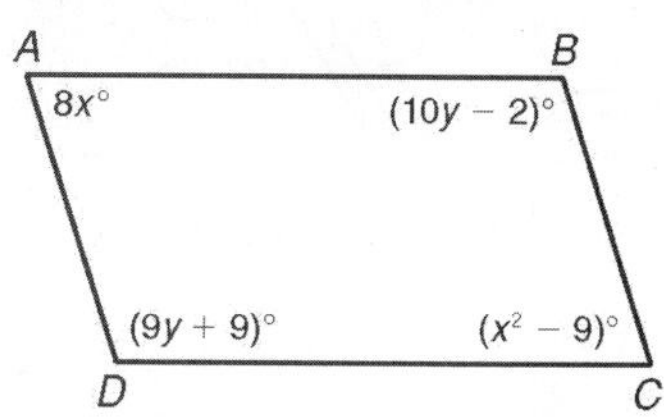

____

____

____

2. $a = 4.3$ and $b = 13$

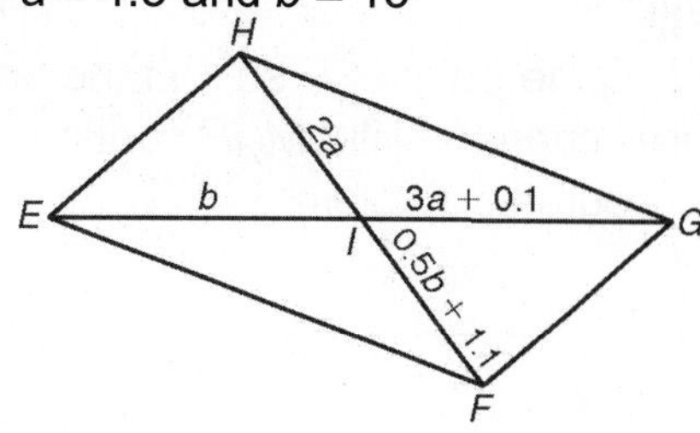

____

____

____

Determine whether each quadrilateral must be a parallelogram. Justify your answers.

3.

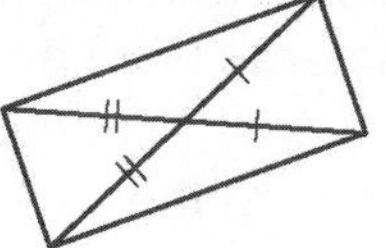

____

____

____

____

____

4.

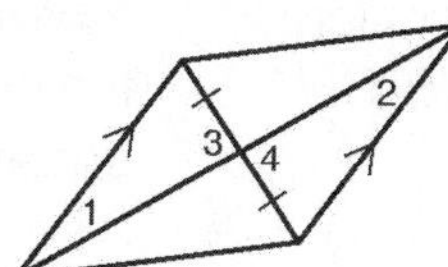

____

____

____

____

____

5.

$x°$ $(180 - x)°$

$x°$

____

____

____

____

____

Use the given method to determine whether the quadrilateral with the given vertices is a parallelogram.

6. Find the slopes of all four sides: $J(-4, -1)$, $K(-7, -4)$, $L(2, -10)$, $M(5, -7)$

____

____

7. Find the lengths of all four sides: $P(2, 2)$, $Q(1, -3)$, $R(-4, 2)$, $S(-3, 7)$

____

8. Find the slopes and lengths of one pair of opposite sides:

$T\left(\frac{3}{2}, -2\right), U\left(\frac{3}{2}, 4\right), V\left(-\frac{1}{2}, 0\right), W\left(-\frac{1}{2}, -6\right)$

____

Problem Solving

Use the diagram for Exercises 1 and 2.

A *pantograph* is a drawing instrument used to magnify figures.

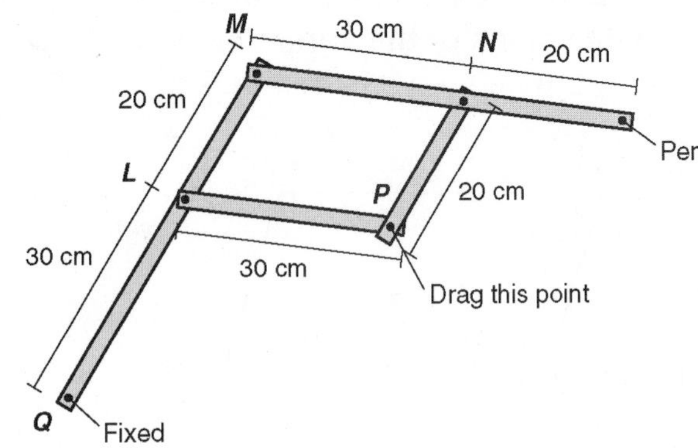

1. If you drag the point at P so that the angle measures change, will $LMNP$ continue to be a parallelogram? Explain.

____

____

____

2. If you drag the point at P so that $m\angle LMN = 56°$, what will be the measure of $\angle QLP$?

____

3. In the state flag of Maryland, $m\angle G = 60°$ and $m\angle H = 120°$. Name one more condition that would allow you to conclude that $EFGH$ is a parallelogram.

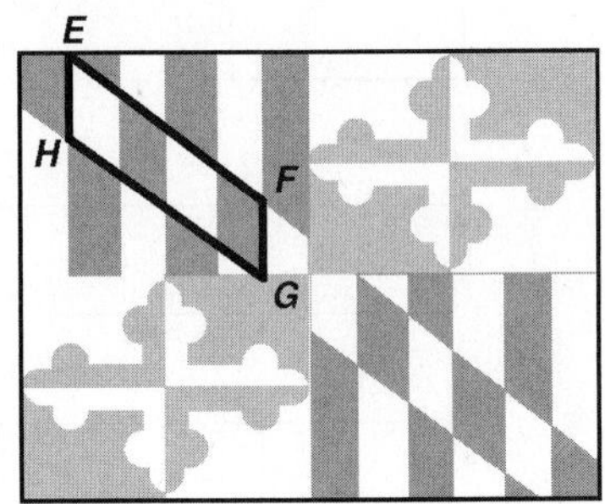

____

4. The graphs of $y = 2x$, $y = 2x - 5$, and $y = -x$ in the coordinate plane contain three sides of a quadrilateral. Give an equation of a line whose graph contains a segment that can complete the quadrilateral to form a parallelogram. Explain.

____

____

____

Choose the best answer.

5. For which value of n is $QRST$ a parallelogram?

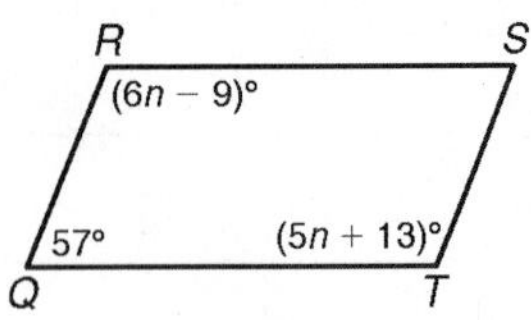

A 15.5

B 20.6

C 22

D 25

6. Under what conditions must $ABCD$ be a parallelogram?

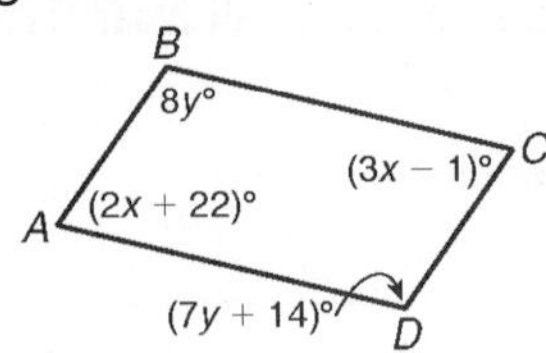

F $x = 23$

G $y = 14$

H $x = 23$ and $y = 14$

J $x = 14$ and $y = 23$

Name ______________________ Class ______________ Date ________

7-3

Properties of Special Parallelograms

Focus on Reasoning

Video Tutor

Essential question: *What are the properties of rectangles and rhombuses?*

A **rectangle** is a quadrilateral with four right angles. The figure shows rectangle *ABCD*.

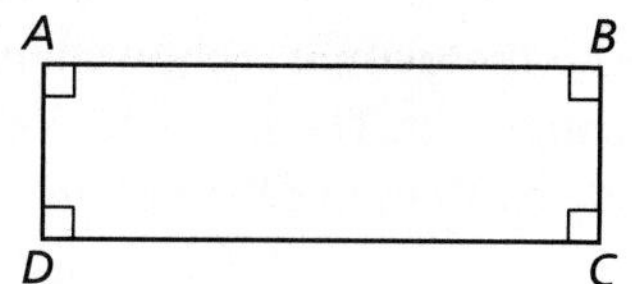

1 Investigate properties of rectangles.

A Use a tile or pattern block and the following method to draw three different rectangles on a separate sheet of paper.

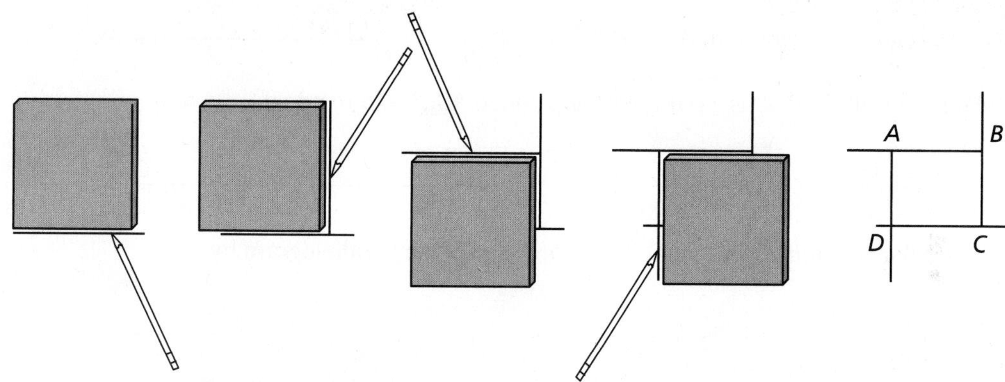

B Use a ruler to measure the sides and the diagonals of each rectangle. Keep track of the measurements and compare your results to those of other students.

REFLECT

1a. Why does the above method produce a rectangle? What must you assume about the tile?

____

____

____

1b. Do you think every rectangle is a parallelogram? Make a conjecture based upon your measurements and explain your thinking.

____

____

1c. Make a conjecture about the diagonals of a rectangle.

____

You may have discovered the following theorem about rectangles.

Rectangle Theorem

A rectangle is a parallelogram with congruent diagonals.

In order to prove the above theorem, it is convenient to use a theorem that states that all right angles are congruent. The proof of this theorem is straightforward: If $\angle X$ and $\angle Y$ are right angles, then $m\angle X = 90°$ and $m\angle Y = 90°$ so $m\angle X = m\angle Y$ and $\angle X \cong \angle Y$.

2 Prove the Rectangle Theorem.

Complete the proof.

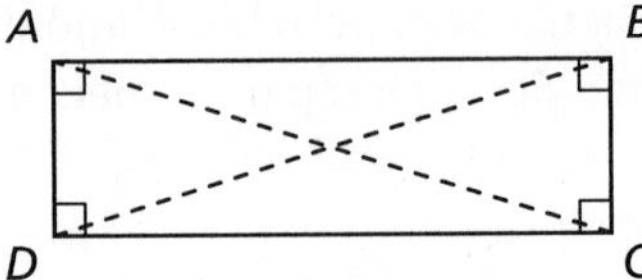

Given: *ABCD* is a rectangle.
Prove: *ABCD* is a parallelogram; $\overline{AC} \cong \overline{BD}$.

A First prove that *ABCD* is a parallelogram. Since *ABCD* is a rectangle, $\angle A$ and $\angle C$ are right angles. So, $\angle A \cong \angle C$ because ________________________.

By similar reasoning, $\angle B \cong \angle D$. Therefore, *ABCD* is a parallelogram by

____.

B Now prove that the diagonals are congruent. Since *ABCD* is a parallelogram, $\overline{AD} \cong \overline{BC}$ because ________________________.

Also, $\overline{DC} \cong \overline{DC}$ by the reflexive property of congruence. By the definition of a rectangle, $\angle D$ and $\angle C$ are right angles, and so $\angle D \cong \angle C$ because all right angles are congruent.

Therefore, $\triangle ADC \cong \triangle BCD$ by ________________________

and $\overline{AC} \cong \overline{BD}$ by ________________________.

REFLECT

2a. Error Analysis A student says you can also prove the diagonals are congruent by using the SSS Congruence Criterion to show that $\triangle ADC \cong \triangle BCD$. Do you agree? Explain.

____

____

A **rhombus** is a quadrilateral with four congruent sides. The figure shows rhombus *JKLM*.

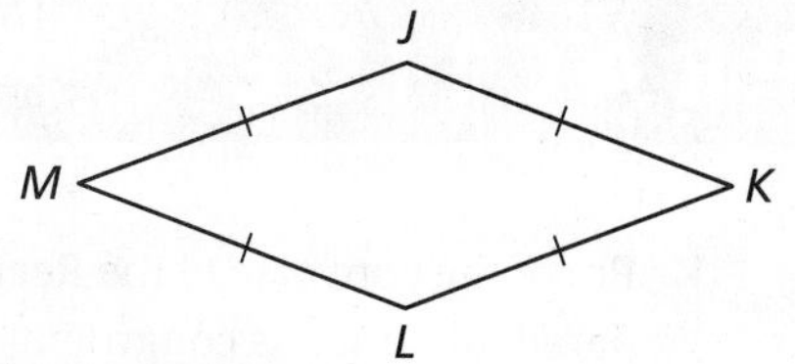

The following is a summary of some properties of rhombuses. You will prove these properties below and in the exercises.

Properties of Rhombuses

If a quadrilateral is a rhombus, then

- the quadrilateral is a parallelogram.
- the diagonals are perpendicular.
- each diagonal bisects a pair of opposite angles.

The proof of the first property is straightforward. If a quadrilateral is a rhombus, then opposite sides are congruent. Therefore, the quadrilateral is also a parallelogram by the Opposite Sides Criterion for a Parallelogram.

3 Prove diagonals of a rhombus are perpendicular.

Complete the proof.

Given: *JKLM* is a rhombus.
Prove: $\overline{JL} \perp \overline{MK}$

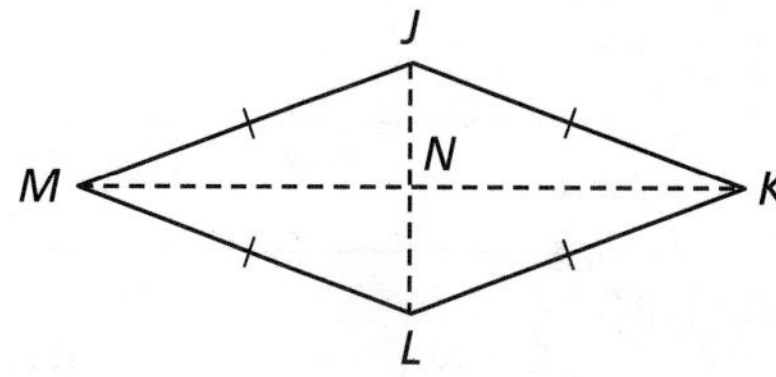

Since *JKLM* is a rhombus, $\overline{JM} \cong \overline{JK}$. Because *JKLM* is also a parallelogram,

$\overline{MN} \cong \overline{KN}$ because ________________________________.

By the Reflexive Property of Congruence, $\overline{JN} \cong \overline{JN}$, so ____________________

by the SSS Congruence Criterion. So, $\angle JNM \cong \angle JNK$ by ____________________.

By the Linear Pair Theorem, $\angle JNM$ and $\angle JNK$ are ____________________.

This means $m\angle JNM + m\angle JNK = 180°$.

Since the angles are congruent, $m\angle JNM =$ ____________________

so $m\angle JNK + m\angle JNK = 180°$ or $2m\angle JNK = 180°$. Therefore, $m\angle JNK = 90°$

and $\overline{JL} \perp \overline{MK}$.

REFLECT

3a. What can you say about the image of *J* after a reflection across $\overline{MK}$? Why?

____

PRACTICE

1. Prove the converse of the Rectangle Theorem. That is, if a parallelogram has congruent diagonals, then the parallelogram is a rectangle.

   Given: *ABCD* is a parallelogram; $\overline{AC} \cong \overline{BD}$.
   Prove: *ABCD* is a rectangle.

2. Prove that if a quadrilateral is a rhombus, then each diagonal bisects a pair of opposite angles.

   Given: *JKLM* is a rhombus.
   Prove: $\overline{MK}$ bisects $\angle JML$ and $\angle JKL$; $\overline{JL}$ bisects $\angle MJK$ and $\angle MLK$.

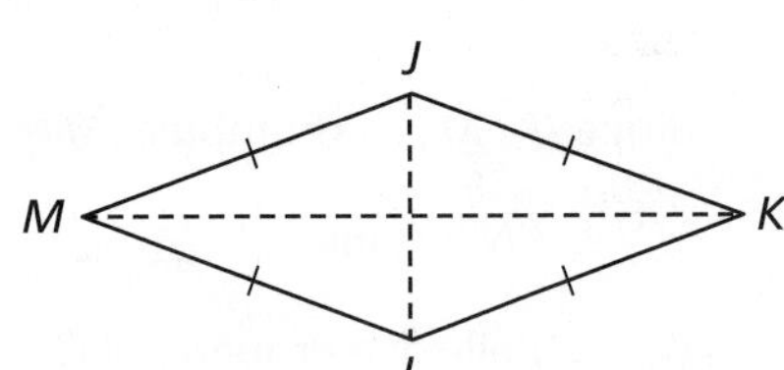

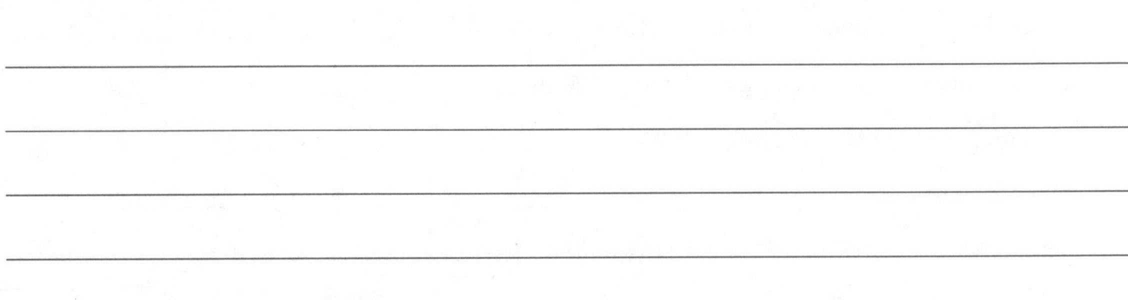

3. A *square* is a quadrilateral with four right angles and four congruent sides. In the space at right, draw a Venn diagram to show how squares, rectangles, rhombuses, and parallelograms are related to each other.

Name________________________ Class______________ Date__________ 7-3

Additional Practice

Tell whether each figure must be a rectangle, rhombus, or square based on the information given. Use the most specific name possible.

1. 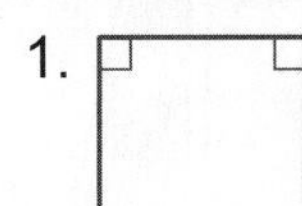

2. 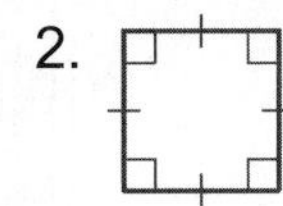

3. 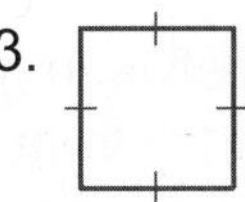

______________ ______________ ______________

A modern artist's sculpture has rectangular faces. The face shown here is 9 feet long and 4 feet wide. Find each measure in simplest radical form. (*Hint:* Use the Pythagorean Theorem.)

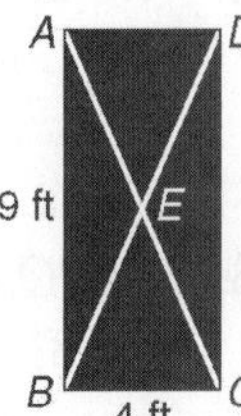

4. $DC =$ ______________
5. $AD =$ ______________
6. $DB =$ ______________
7. $AE =$ ______________

***VWXY* is a rhombus. Find each measure.**

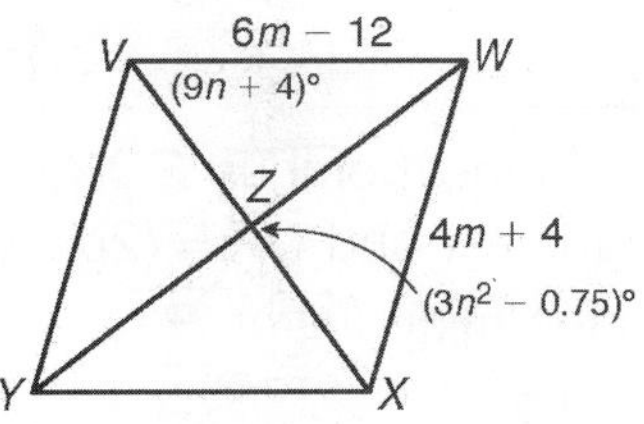

8. $XY =$ ______________
9. $m\angle YVW =$ ______________
10. $m\angle VYX =$ ______________
11. $m\angle XYZ =$ ______________
12. The vertices of square *JKLM* are $J(-2, 4)$, $K(-3, -1)$, $L(2, -2)$, and $M(3, 3)$. Find each of the following to show that the diagonals of square *JKLM* are congruent perpendicular bisectors of each other.

$JL =$ ________ $KM =$ ________

slope of $\overline{JL} =$ ________ slope of $\overline{KM} =$ ________

midpoint of $\overline{JL} = ($________, ________$)$ midpoint of $\overline{KM} = ($________, ________$)$

Write a paragraph proof.

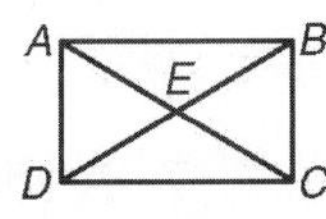

13. **Given:** *ABCD* is a rectangle.
Prove: $\angle EDC \cong \angle ECD$

Problem Solving

Use the diagram for Exercises 1 and 2.

The soccer goalposts determine rectangle *ABCD*.

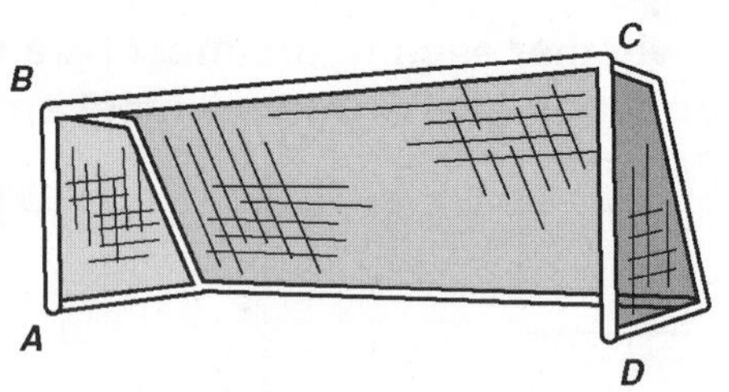

1. The distance between goalposts, *BC*, is three times the distance from the top of the goalpost to the ground. If the perimeter of *ABCD* is $21\frac{1}{3}$ yards, what is the length of $\overline{BC}$?

____

2. The distance from *B* to *D* is approximately $(x + 10)$ feet, and the distance from *A* to *C* is approximately $(2x - 5.3)$ feet. What is the approximate distance from *A* to *C*?

____

3. *MNPQ* is a rhombus. The measure of $\angle MRQ$ is $(13t - 1)°$, and the measure of $\angle PQR$ is $(7t + 4)°$. What is the measure of $\angle PQM$?

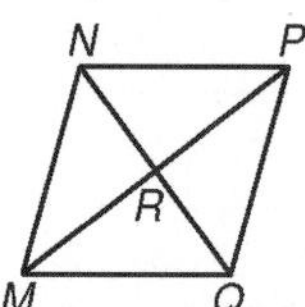

____

4. The *scissor lift* forms rhombus *PQRS* with $PQ = (7b - 5)$ meters and $QR = (2b - 0.5)$ meters. If *S* is the midpoint of $\overline{RT}$, what is the length of $\overline{RT}$?

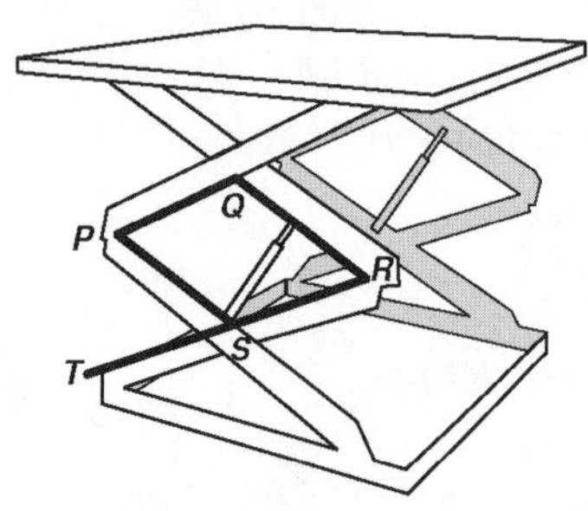

____

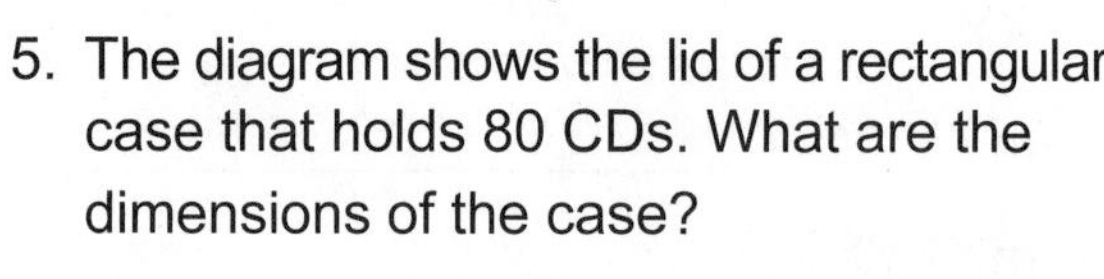

5. The diagram shows the lid of a rectangular case that holds 80 CDs. What are the dimensions of the case?

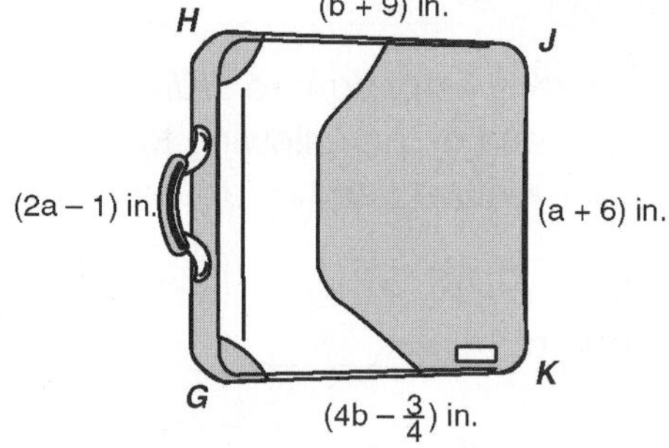

____

Choose the best answer.

6. What is the measure of $\angle 1$ in the rectangle?

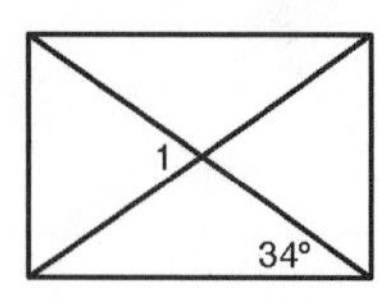

A 34°
B 68°
C 90°
D 146°

7. A square graphed on the coordinate plane has a diagonal with endpoints *E*(2, 3) and *F*(0, –3). What are the coordinates of the endpoints of the other diagonal?

F (4, –1) and (–2, 1)
G (4, 0) and (–2, 1)
H (4, –1) and (–3, 1)
J (3, –1) and (–2, 1)

Name ______________________ Class ______________ Date __________

7-4

Video Tutor

Conditions for Special Parallelograms

Connection: Using Coordinate Methods

Essential question: *How can you use slope in coordinate proofs?*

You have already used the distance formula and the midpoint formula in coordinate proofs. As you will see, slope is useful in coordinate proofs whenever you need to show that lines are parallel or perpendicular.

MCC9–12.G.GPE.4

1 EXAMPLE Proving a Quadrilateral Is a Parallelogram

Prove or disprove that the quadrilateral determined by the points $A(4, 4)$, $B(3, 1)$, $C(-2, -1)$, and $D(-1, 2)$ is a parallelogram.

A Plot the points on the coordinate plane at right.

Then draw quadrilateral $ABCD$.

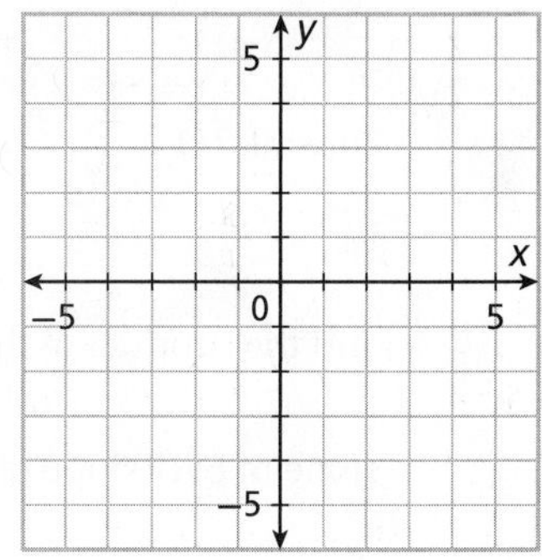

B To determine whether $ABCD$ is a parallelogram, find the slope of each side of the quadrilateral.

Slope of $\overline{AB} = \frac{y_2 - y_1}{x_2 - x_1} = \frac{1 - 4}{3 - 4} = \frac{-3}{-1} = 3$

Slope of $\overline{BC} = \frac{y_2 - y_1}{x_2 - x_1} = \frac{\square - \square}{\square - \square} = \frac{\square}{\square} = \square$

Slope of $\overline{CD} = \frac{y_2 - y_1}{x_2 - x_1} = \frac{\square - \square}{\square - \square} = \frac{\square}{\square} = \square$

Slope of $\overline{DA} = \frac{y_2 - y_1}{x_2 - x_1} = \frac{\square - \square}{\square - \square} = \frac{\square}{\square} = \square$

C Compare slopes. The slopes of opposite sides are ______________________.

This means opposite sides are ______________________.

So, ______________________.

REFLECT

1a. Is there a way to write a proof that does not use slope? Explain.

____

____

MCC9–12.G.GPE.4

2 EXAMPLE Proving a Quadrilateral Is a Rectangle

Prove or disprove that the quadrilateral determined by the points $Q(2, -3)$, $R(-4, 0)$, $S(-2, 4)$, and $T(4, 1)$ is a rectangle.

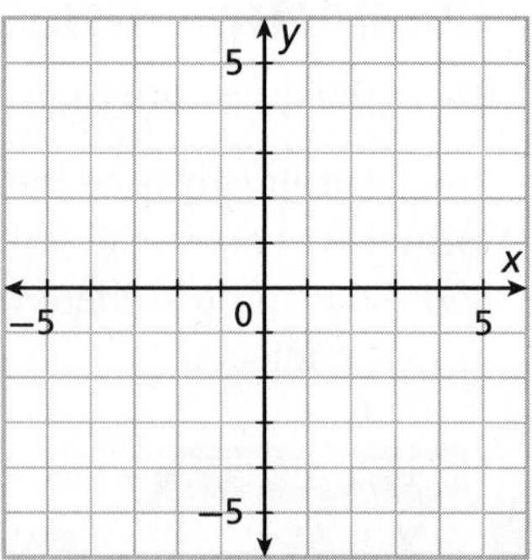

A Plot the points on the coordinate plane at right.

Then draw quadrilateral *QRST*.

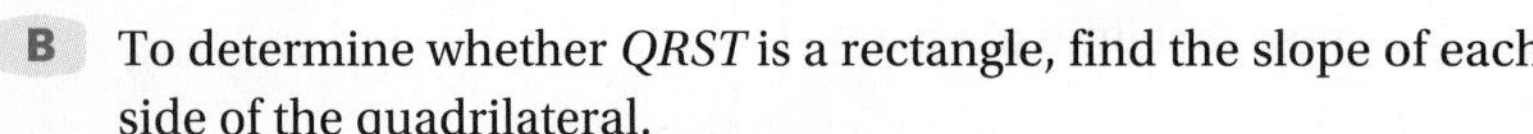

B To determine whether *QRST* is a rectangle, find the slope of each side of the quadrilateral.

Slope of $\overline{QR} = \frac{y_2 - y_1}{x_2 - x_1} = \frac{0 - (-3)}{-4 - 2} = \frac{3}{-6} = -\frac{1}{2}$

Slope of $\overline{RS} = \frac{y_2 - y_1}{x_2 - x_1} = \frac{\square - \square}{\square - \square} = \frac{\square}{\square} = \square$

Slope of $\overline{ST} = \frac{y_2 - y_1}{x_2 - x_1} = \frac{\square - \square}{\square - \square} = \frac{\square}{\square} = \square$

Slope of $\overline{TQ} = \frac{y_2 - y_1}{x_2 - x_1} = \frac{\square - \square}{\square - \square} = \frac{\square}{\square} = \square$

C Find the product of the slopes of adjacent sides.

(slope of $\overline{QR}$)(slope of $\overline{RS}$) = __________ • __________ = __________

(slope of $\overline{RS}$)(slope of $\overline{ST}$) = __________ • __________ = __________

(slope of $\overline{ST}$)(slope of $\overline{TQ}$) = __________ • __________ = __________

(slope of $\overline{TQ}$)(slope of $\overline{QR}$) = __________ • __________ = __________

You can conclude that adjacent sides are ______________________________.

So, ____.

REFLECT

2a. What would you expect to find if you used the distance formula to calculate *SQ* and *RT*? Explain.

____

____

2b. Explain how to prove that *QRST* is not a square.

____

____

PRACTICE

1. Prove or disprove that the quadrilateral determined by the points $J(-3, 1)$, $K(3, 3)$, $L(2, -1)$, and $M(-4, -3)$ is a parallelogram.

2. Prove or disprove that the quadrilateral determined by the points $A(-2, 3)$, $B(5, 3)$, $C(3, -1)$, and $D(-3, -1)$ is a parallelogram.

3. Prove or disprove that the quadrilateral determined by the points $Q(-3, 4)$, $R(5, 2)$, $S(4, -1)$, and $T(-4, 1)$ is a rectangle.

4. Prove or disprove that the quadrilateral determined by the points $W(1, 5)$, $X(4, 4)$, $Y(2, -2)$, and $Z(-1, -1)$ is a rectangle.

5. Prove or disprove that the quadrilateral determined by the points $D(-2, 3)$, $E(3, 4)$, $F(0, -2)$, and $G(-4, -1)$ has exactly two parallel sides.

6. Consider points $L(3, -4)$, $M(1, -2)$, and $N(5, 2)$.

a. Find the coordinates of point P so that the quadrilateral determined by points L, M, N, and P is a parallelogram. Is there more than one possibility? Explain.

b. Are any of the parallelograms a rectangle? Why?

7. You are using a coordinate plane to create a quadrilateral. You start by drawing $\overline{MN}$, as shown.

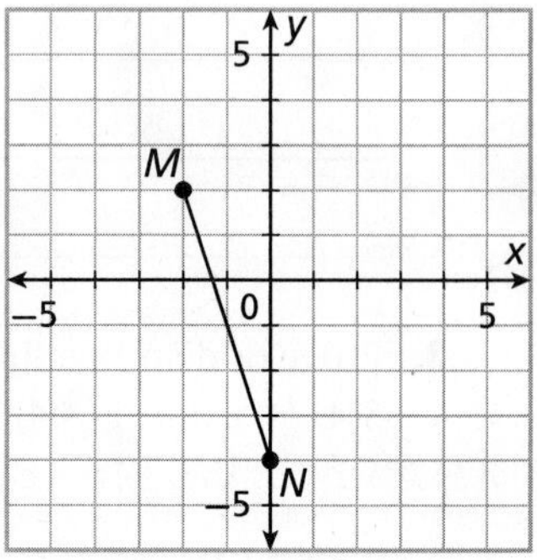

a. You decide to translate $\overline{MN}$ by the translation $(x, y) \rightarrow (x + 3, y + 2)$. What type of quadrilateral is $MM'N'N$? Why?

b. Do you get the same type of quadrilateral for any translation of $\overline{MN}$ that results in a quadrilateral $MM'N'N$? Explain. (*Hint:* Find the coordinates of M' and N' under a general translation, $(x, y) \rightarrow (x + a, y + b)$. Then consider the slopes of the sides of quadrilateral $MM'N'N$.)

c. You decide you want $MM'N'N$ to be a rectangle. What translations can you use? (*Hint:* What must be true about a and b?)

8. Rhombus $OPQR$ has vertices $O(0, 0)$, $P(a, b)$, $Q(a + b, a + b)$, and $R(b, a)$.

Prove the diagonals of the rhombus are perpendicular.

Name________________________ Class______________ Date__________

Additional Practice

1. On the National Mall in Washington, D.C., a reflecting pool lies between the Lincoln Memorial and the World War II Memorial. The pool has two 2300-foot-long sides and two 150-foot-long sides. Tell what additional information you need to know in order to determine whether the reflecting pool is a rectangle. (*Hint:* Remember that you have to show it is a parallelogram first.)

____

____

____

____

Use the figure for Exercises 2–5. Determine whether each conclusion is valid. If not, tell what additional information is needed to make it valid.

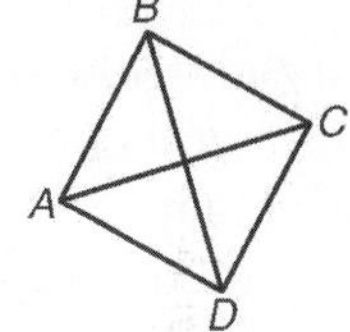

2. **Given:** $\overline{AC}$ and $\overline{BD}$ bisect each other. $\overline{AC} \cong \overline{BD}$

   Conclusion: *ABCD* is a square.

   ____

3. **Given:** $\overline{AC} \perp \overline{BD}$, $\overline{AB} \cong \overline{BC}$

   Conclusion: *ABCD* is a rhombus.

   ____

4. **Given:** $\overline{AB} \cong \overline{DC}$, $\overline{AD} \cong \overline{BC}$, $m\angle ADB = m\angle ABD = 45°$

   Conclusion: *ABCD* is a square.

   ____

5. **Given:** $\overline{AB} \parallel \overline{DC}$, $\overline{AD} \cong \overline{BC}$, $\overline{AC} \cong \overline{BD}$

   Conclusion: *ABCD* is a rectangle.

   ____

Find the lengths and slopes of the diagonals to determine whether a parallelogram with the given vertices is a rectangle, rhombus, or square. Give all names that apply.

6. $E(-2, -4)$, $F(0, -1)$, $G(-3, 1)$, $H(-5, -2)$ ____________________

   $EG =$ ________ $FH =$ ________

   slope of $\overline{EG}$ = ________ slope of $\overline{FH}$ = ________

7. $P(-1, 3)$, $Q(-2, 5)$, $R(0, 4)$, $S(1, 2)$ ____________________

   $PR =$ ________ $QS =$ ________

   slope of $\overline{PR}$ = ________ slope of $\overline{QS}$ = ________

Problem Solving

1. An amusement park has a rectangular observation deck with walkways above the bungee jumping and sky jumping. The distance from the center of the deck to points E, F, G, and H is 15 meters. Explain why $EFGH$ must be a rectangle.

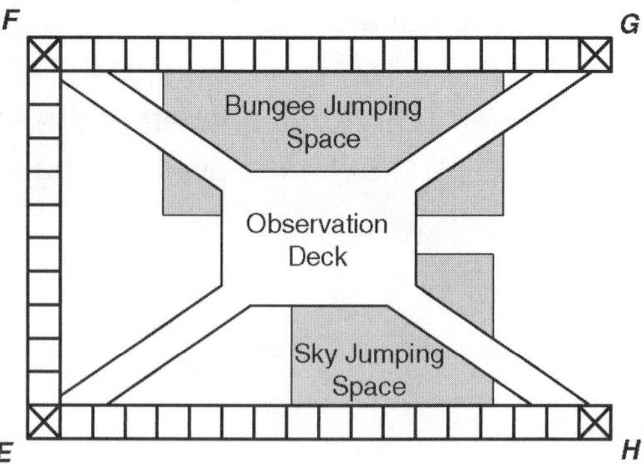

____

____

____

____

2. In the mosaic, $\overline{AB} \parallel \overline{CD}$ and $\overline{BC} \parallel \overline{DA}$. If $AB = 4$ inches and $BC = 4$ inches, can you conclude that $ABCD$ is a square? Explain.

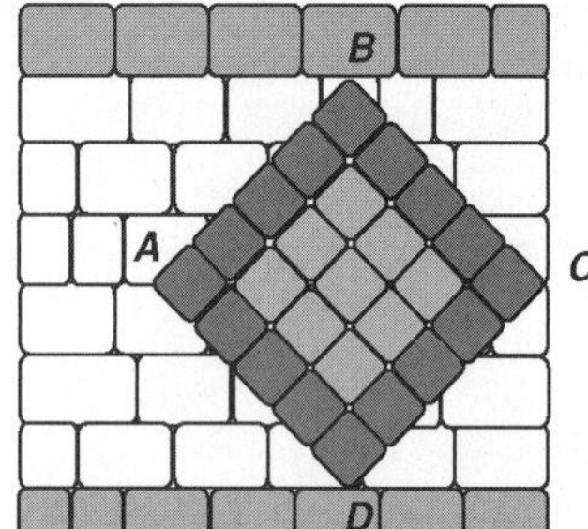

____

____

3. If $\overline{TV} \cong \overline{US}$, explain why the basketball backboard must be a rectangle.

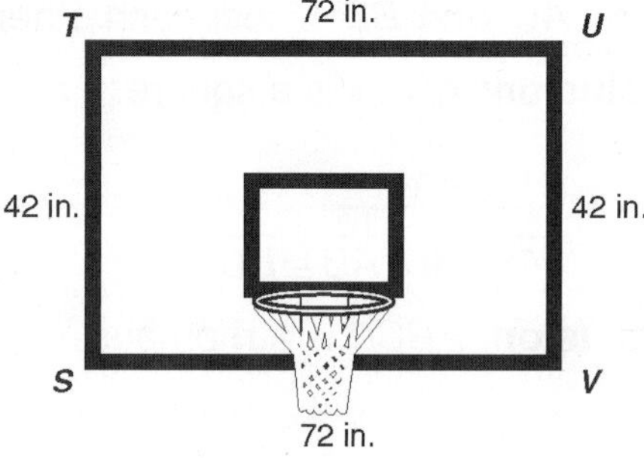

____

____

____

Choose the best answer.

4. The vertices of a parallelogram are $N(0, -4)$, $P(6, -1)$, $Q(4, 3)$, and $R(-2, 0)$. Classify the parallelogram as specifically as possible.

   A rectangle only
   B square
   C rhombus only
   D quadrilateral

5. Choose the best description for the quadrilateral.

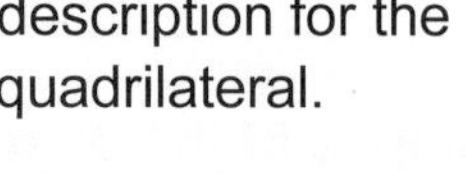

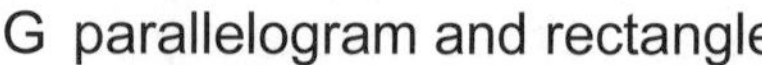

   F parallelogram
   G parallelogram and rectangle
   H parallelogram and rhombus
   J parallelogram and square

6. In parallelogram $KLMN$, $m\angle L = (4w + 5)°$. Choose the value of w that makes $KLMN$ a rectangle.

   A 90　　C 43.75
   B 85　　D 21.25

7. The coordinates of three vertices of quadrilateral $ABCD$ are $A(3, -1)$, $B(10, 0)$, and $C(5, 5)$. For which coordinates of D will the quadrilateral be a rhombus?

   F (–1, 4)　　H (–1, 3)
   G (–2, 4)　　J (–2, 3)

Name ______________________ Class ______________ Date __________

8-1

Ratios in Similar Polygons

Going Deeper

Essential question: *How can you use ratios of corresponding side lengths to solve problems involving similar polygons?*

Two polygons are **similar polygons** if and only if their corresponding angles are congruent and their corresponding side lengths are proportional. The *similarity ratio* of two similar figures is the ratio of any side length in the first figure to the corresponding side length in the second figure. To prove that two figures with corresponding angles congruent are similar, show that corresponding side lengths are proportional.

PREP FOR MCC9–12.G.SRT.2

1 EXAMPLE Determining Polygon Similarity

Corresponding angles in each pair are congruent. Use ratios of corresponding side lengths to tell whether the figures are similar. If so, name the similarity ratio.

A rectangle *ABCD* to rectangle *WXYZ*

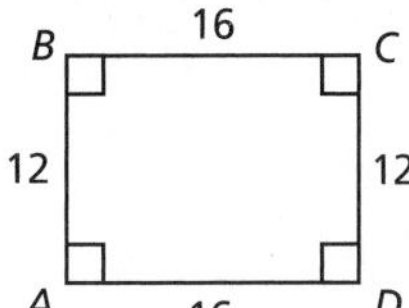

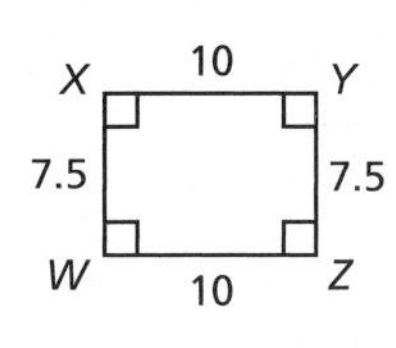

Determine the ratios of corresponding lengths and corresponding widths.

$\frac{BC}{XY} = \frac{\square}{\square} = \frac{\square}{\square} = \square$

$\frac{AB}{WX} = \frac{\square}{\square} = \square$

The polygons __________ similar. The similarity ratio is $\frac{8}{5}$, or 8 to 5.

B parallelogram *KLMN* to parallelogram *PQRS*

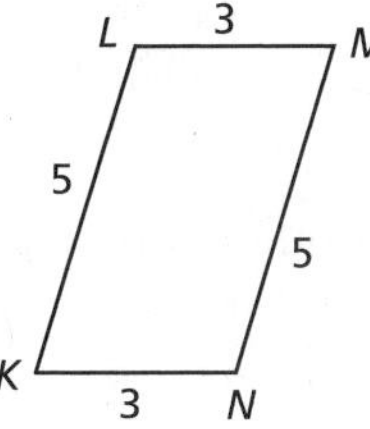

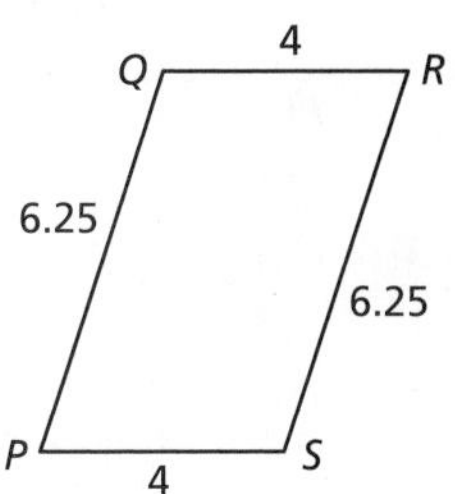

Determine the ratios of the lengths of corresponding opposite sides.

$\frac{KL}{PQ} = \frac{\square}{\square} = \square$

$\frac{KN}{PS} = \frac{\square}{\square} = \square$

The polygons __________ similar, because $0.8 \neq 0.75$. There is no similarity ratio.

REFLECT

1a. If you measure the angles in two figures and find that corresponding angles are not congruent, what conclusion can you draw about the figures? How is this a shortcut in determining if figures are similar?

____

____

1b. Describe how to find the *similarity ratio* of two similar figures when you are given lengths of corresponding sides.

____

____

PREP FOR MCC9–12.G.SRT.1b

2 EXPLORE Finding Unknown Lengths in Similar Polygons

The trapezoids below are similar.

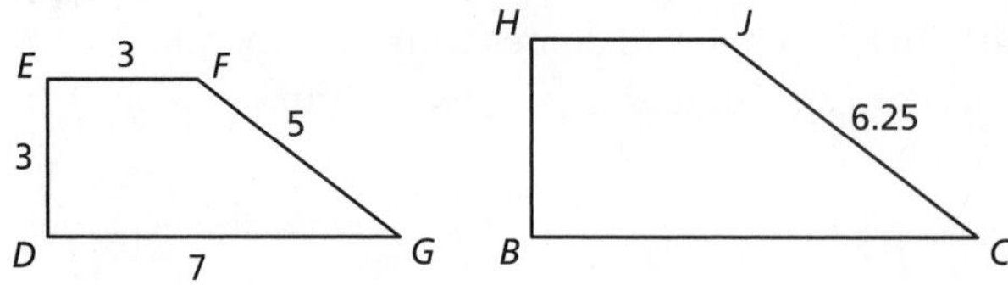

A What ratio can you use to multiply the known length 5 in trapezoid *DEFG* to get the known length 6.25 in trapezoid *BHJC*?

The known length of a side of trapezoid *BHJC* will be the ____________ of a fraction and the corresponding side length of trapezoid *DEFG* will be the ____________ of that fraction.

$\frac{JC}{FG} = \frac{\square}{\square} = \square$ The required ratio is ________.

B Use this ratio as a multiplier to find the unknown side lengths in trapezoid *BHJC*.

$\frac{HJ}{EF} = \square \rightarrow HJ = \square \times EF \rightarrow HJ = \square$

$\frac{BH}{DE} = \square \rightarrow BH = \square \times DE \rightarrow BH = \square$

$\frac{BC}{DG} = \square \rightarrow BC = \square \times DG \rightarrow BC = \square$

REFLECT

2a. The ratio you used in the Explore can be called the *scale factor* of the first figure to the second figure. Complete the following: To find the scale factor of two similar figures, use the ratio of a side length in the ____________ figure to the corresponding side length in the ____________ figure.

2b. How is a scale factor used to find unknown side lengths in the second figure?

____

____

2c. Suppose figure A is similar to figure B. How is the similarity ratio of A to B related to the scale factor of A to B?

____

PRACTICE

Corresponding angles in each pair are congruent. Use ratios of corresponding sides to tell whether the figures are similar. If so, identify the similarity ratio.

1. triangle *XYZ* to triangle *ABC*

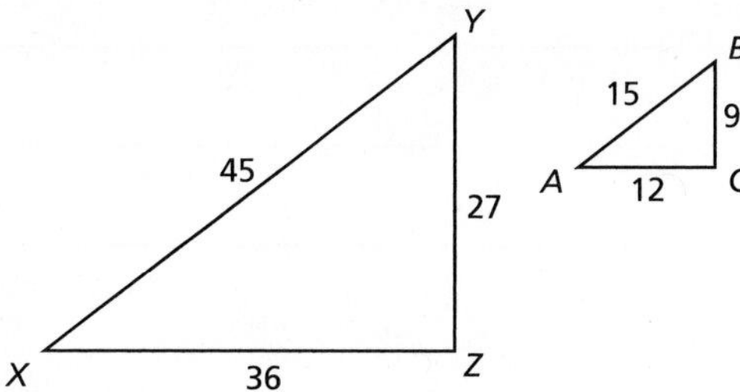

2. trapezoid *JHLK* to trapezoid *DGFE*

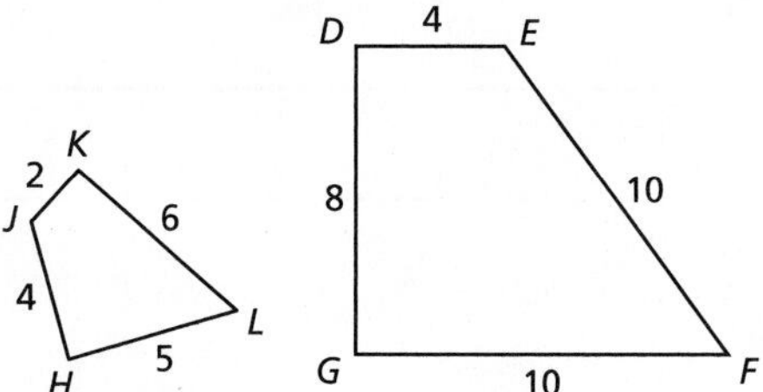

3. polygon *MNBCE* to polygon *RSTUV*

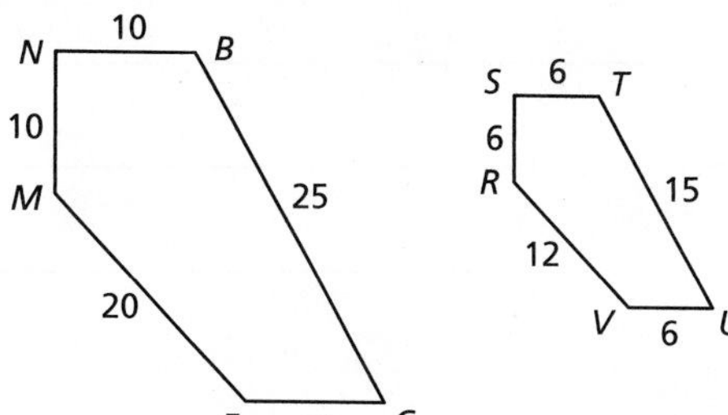

4. The angles in rhombus A are congruent to the corresponding angles in rhombus B. The sides of rhombus A are 7 units long. The sides of rhombus B are 9 units long. Explain why the rhombuses are similar.

The figures in each pair are similar. Find the lengths of the sides in the second figure. Show your work.

5. quadrilateral *ABCD* quadrilateral *PQRS*

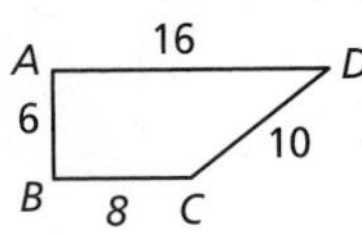

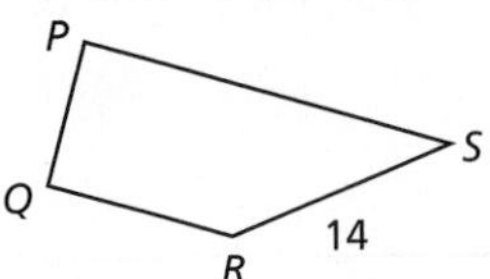

6. polygon *BCHZRT* polygon *ANGYPJ*

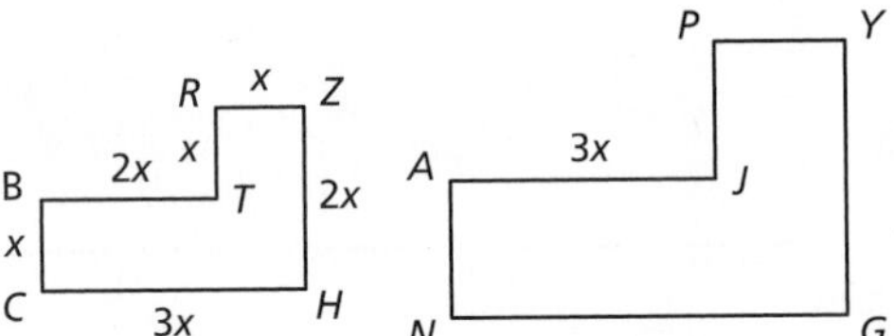

7. $\triangle AED \sim \triangle ABC$. In the diagram below, consider $\triangle AED$ to be the first triangle and $\triangle ABC$ to be the second triangle.

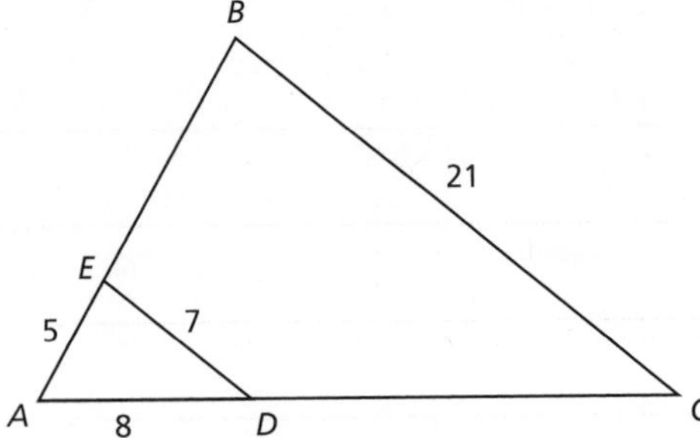

8. Polygons *WXYZ* and *DEFG* are similar and $k > 0$. Identify the similarity ratio of *WXYZ* to *DEFG* and the scale factor. Explain.

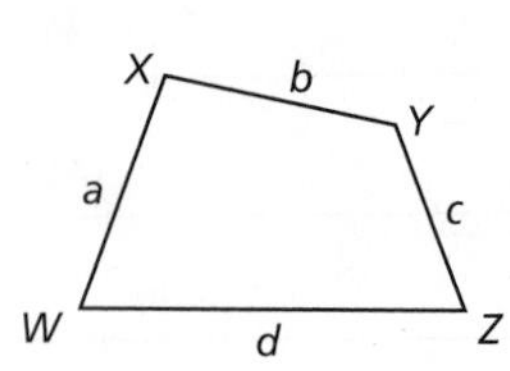

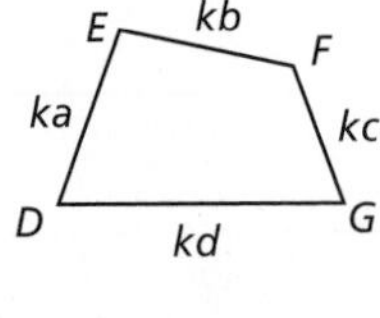

Name ______________________ Class ______________ Date __________ 8-1

Additional Practice

Identify the pairs of congruent corresponding angles and the corresponding sides.

1. 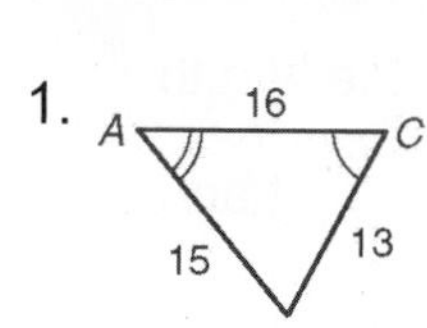

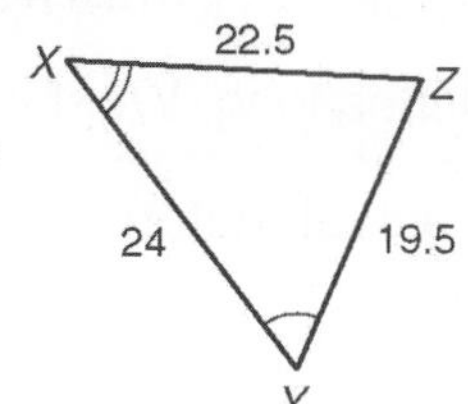

2. 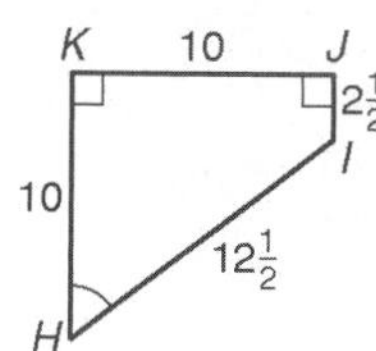

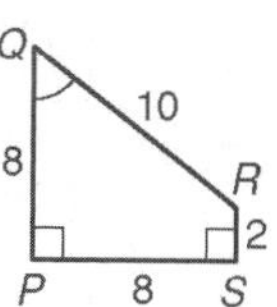

Determine whether the polygons are similar. If so, write the similarity ratio and a similarity statement. If not, explain why not.

3. parallelograms *EFGH* and *TUVW*

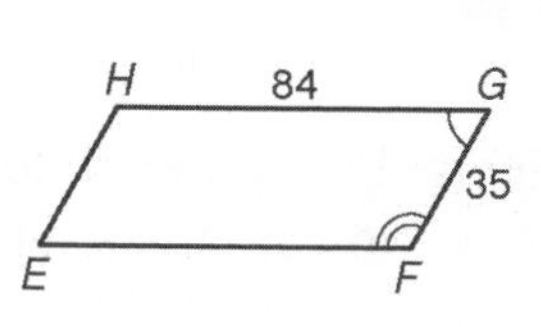

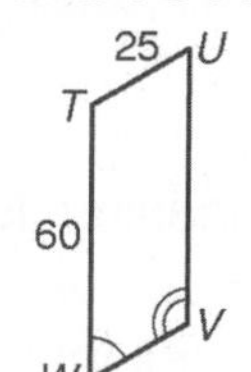

4. $\triangle CDE$ and $\triangle LMN$

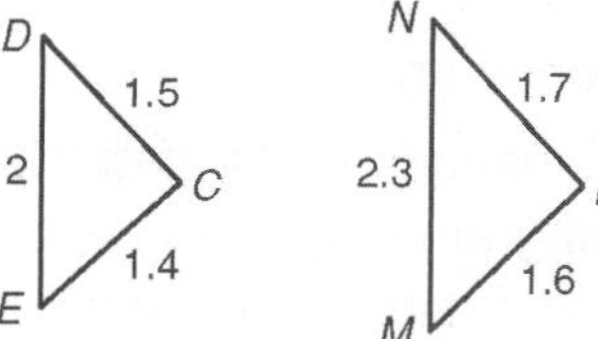

Tell whether the polygons must be similar based on the information given in the figures.

5. 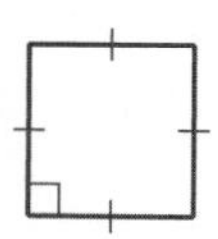 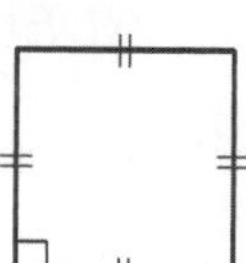

6. 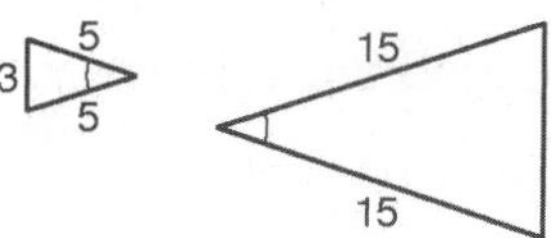

7. 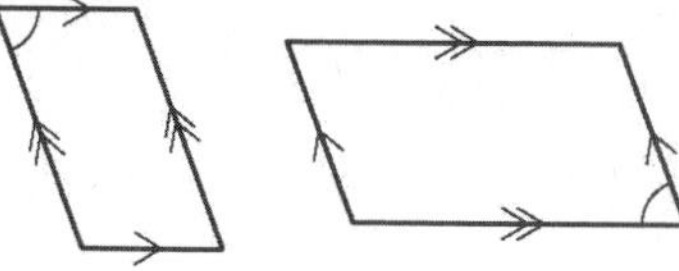

8. 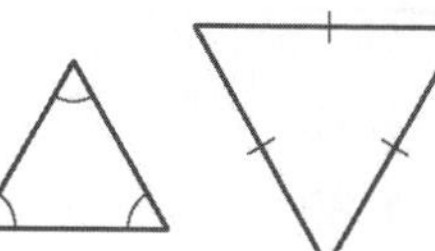

Problem Solving

1. $EFGH \sim JKLM$. What is the value of x?

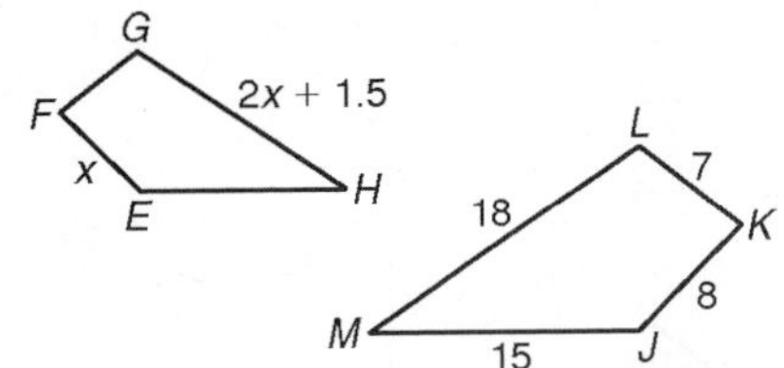

2. The ratio of a model scale die cast motorcycle is 1 : 18. The model is $5\frac{1}{4}$ inches long. What is the length of the actual motorcycle in feet and inches?

____

3. A diagram of a new competition swimming pool is shown. If the width of the pool is 25 meters, find the length of the actual pool.

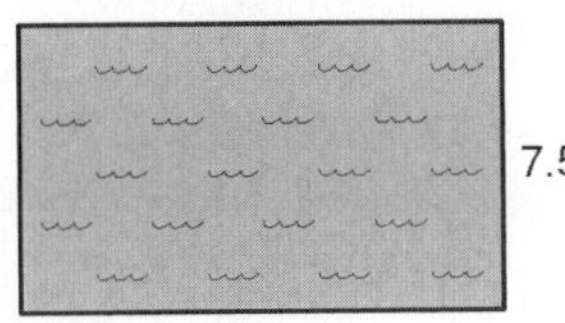

____

4. Rectangle A has side lengths 16.4 centimeters and 10.8 centimeters. Rectangle B has side lengths 10.25 centimeters and 6.75 centimeters. Determine whether the rectangles are similar. If so, write the similarity ratio.

____

Choose the best answer.

5. A pet store has various sizes of guinea pig cages. A diagram of the top view of one of the cages is shown. What are possible dimensions of this cage?

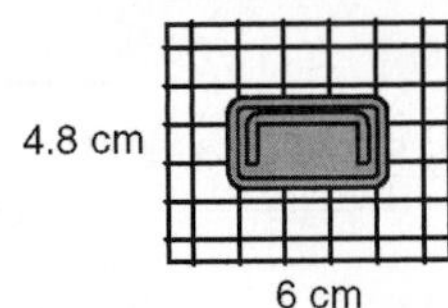

A 28 in. by 24 in. C 30 in. by 24 in.

B 28 in. by 18 in. D 30 in. by 18 in.

6. A gymnasium is 96 feet long and 75 feet wide. On a blueprint, the gymnasium is 5.5 inches long. To the nearest tenth of an inch, what is the width of the gymnasium on the blueprint?

F 3.7 in. H 7.0 in.

G 4.3 in. J 13.6 in.

7. $\triangle QRS \sim \triangle TUV$. Find the value of y.

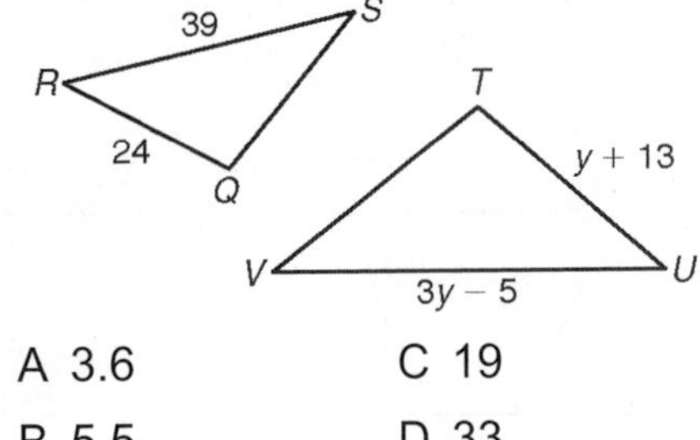

A 3.6 C 19

B 5.5 D 33

8. $\triangle ABC$ has side lengths 14, 8, and 10.4. What are possible side lengths of $\triangle DEF$ if $\triangle ABC \sim \triangle DEF$?

F 28, 20, 20.8

G 35, 16, 20.8

H 28, 20, 26

J 35, 20, 26

Name________________________ Class______________ Date__________

8-2

Similarity and Transformations

Going Deeper

Video Tutor

Essential question: *What are the key properties of dilations, and how can dilations be used to show figures are similar?*

You have already worked extensively with three transformations: reflections, translations, and rotations. Now you will focus on a fourth type of transformation: dilations. Dilations are defined as follows.

Let O be a point and let k be a positive real number. For any point P, let $D(P) = P'$, where P' is the point on $\overrightarrow{OP}$ such that $OP' = k \cdot OP$. Then D is the **dilation** with **center of dilation** O and **scale factor** k. If necessary, the center of dilation and scale factor can be included in the function notation by writing $D_{O,k}(P) = P'$.

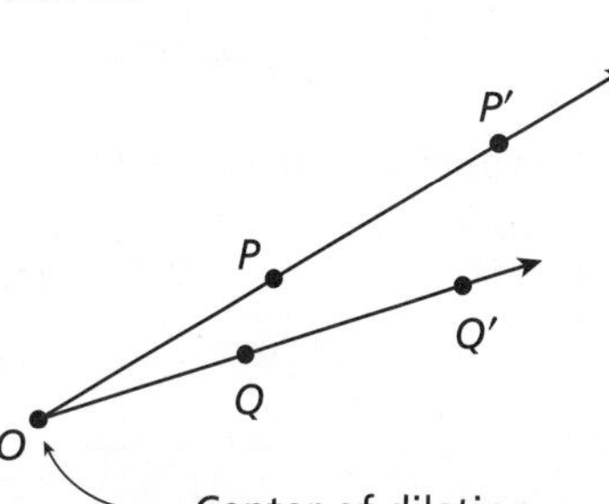
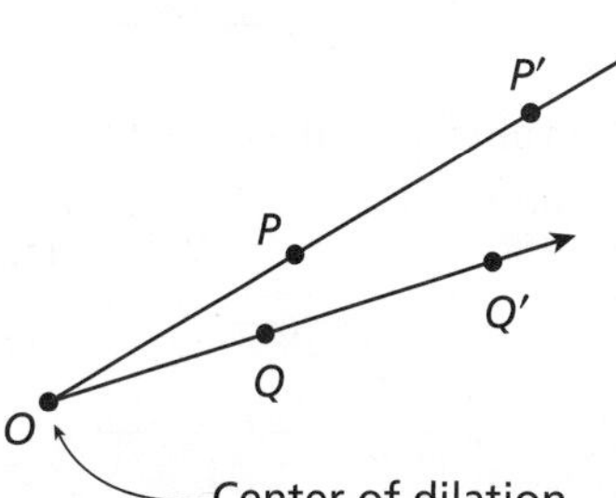

The figure shows a dilation with scale factor 2 because $OP' = 2OP$ and $OQ' = 2OQ$.

MCC9–12.G.CO.2

1 EXPLORE Investigating Dilations

A Use geometry software to plot a point. Label the point O. Then construct a triangle and label the vertices P, Q, and R.

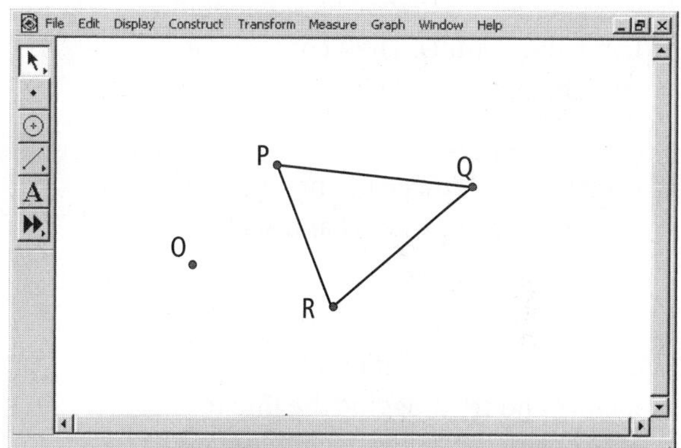

B Select point O. Go to the Transform menu and choose Mark Center. This makes point O the center of a dilation.

C Select $\triangle PQR$. Go to the Transform menu and choose Dilate. In the pop-up window, the "fixed ratio" is the scale factor k. Enter a scale factor of 2 and click the Dilate button.

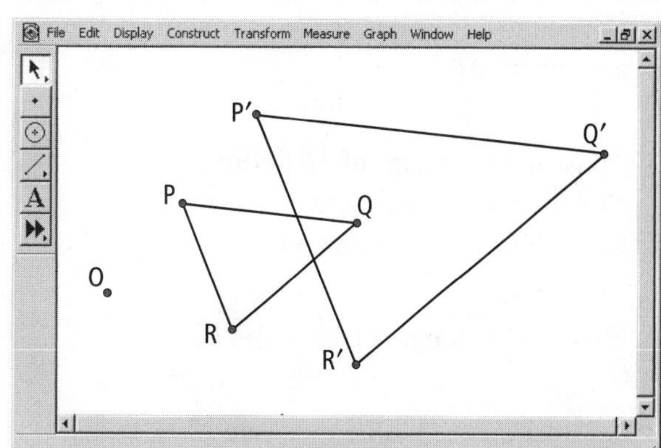

D Label the image of $\triangle PQR$ as $\triangle P'Q'R'$. Measure the angles and the side lengths of the pre-image and the image. Change the shape of $\triangle PQR$ and observe the results.

E Experiment with dilations that have different scale factors. Be sure to try scale factors less than 1, equal to 1, and greater than 1.

REFLECT

1a. In general, how does a dilation transform a figure?

____

____

1b. Do you think dilations are rigid motions? Why or why not?

____

____

1c. How does the value of k affect a dilation? What can you say about a dilation when $0 < k < 1$? when $k > 1$?

____

____

MCC9–12.G.SRT.1

2 EXPLORE Investigating Properties of Dilations

A Use geometry software to plot a point. Label the point O. Then construct a straight line and label it m.

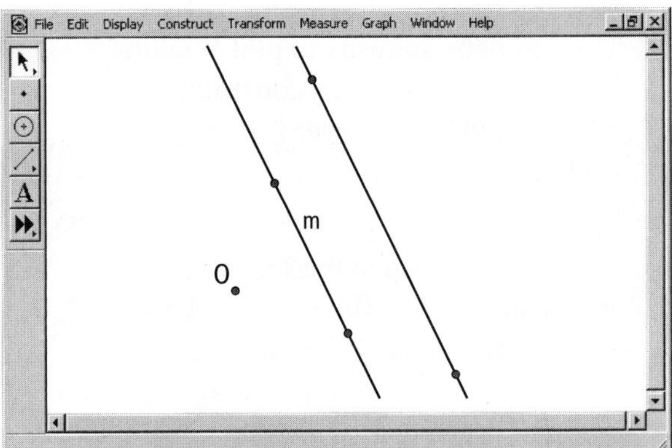

B Construct the image of line m under a dilation with center O and scale factor 2.

C Try dilations with different scale factors and try dragging the line to new positions. Notice what happens when the line passes through O.

D Delete the line and its image. Construct a segment, $\overline{AB}$.

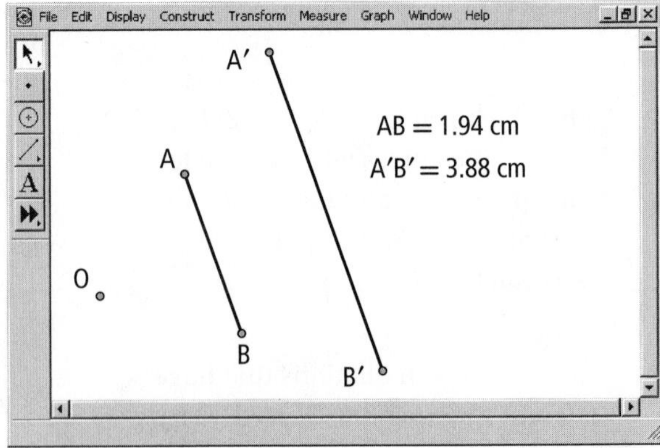

E Construct the image of $\overline{AB}$ under a dilation with center O and scale factor 2. Label the image $\overline{A'B'}$.

F Measure the length of $\overline{AB}$ and $\overline{A'B'}$.

G Try dilations with different scale factors. In each case, compare the lengths of $\overline{AB}$ and $\overline{A'B'}$.

REFLECT

2a. What can you say about the image of a straight line under a dilation? Does your answer depend upon the location of the line? Explain.

2b. How is the length of a line segment related to the length of its image under a dilation with scale factor k?

2c. Suppose the points $A(x_1, y_1)$ and $B(x_2, y_2)$ are transformed by a dilation with scale factor k and center O. Give the coordinates of the image points A' and B'. Then show that the slope of $\overline{AB}$ equals the slope of $\overline{A'B'}$. What can you conclude about the segments?

You may have discovered that dilations preserve the shape, but not the size, of figures. The following summary describes the key properties of dilations.

Properties of Dilations

- Dilations preserve angle measure.
- Dilations preserve betweenness.
- Dilations preserve collinearity.
- A dilation maps a line not passing through the center of dilation to a parallel line and leaves a line passing through the center unchanged.
- The dilation of a line segment is longer or shorter in the ratio given by the scale factor.

MCC9–12.G.SRT.2

3 ENGAGE Introducing Similarity

A **similarity transformation** is a transformation in which the image has the same shape as the pre-image. Specifically, the similarity transformations are the rigid motions (reflections, translations, and rotations) as well as dilations.

Two plane figures are **similar** if and only if one can be obtained from the other by similarity transformations (that is, by a sequence of reflections, translations, rotations, and/or dilations).

The symbol for similar is ~. As with congruence, it is customary to write a similarity statement so that corresponding vertices of the figures are listed in the same order. In the figure below, $\triangle A'B'C'$ is the image of $\triangle ABC$ after a dilation with center O and scale factor 2. Since a dilation is a similarity transformation, the two triangles are similar and you write $\triangle ABC \sim \triangle A'B'C'$.

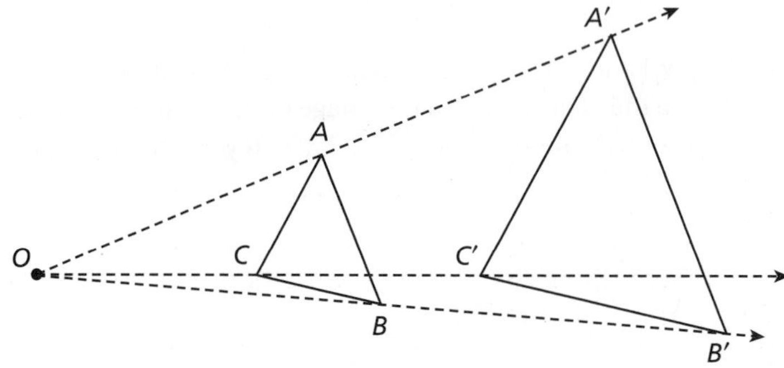

REFLECT

3a. Explain why congruence can be considered a special case of similarity.

____

____

3b. If you know that two figures are similar, can you conclude that corresponding angles are congruent? Why or why not?

____

____

3c. Given that $\triangle RST \sim \triangle R'S'T'$, can you conclude that $\overline{RS} \cong \overline{R'S'}$? Explain.

____

____

MCC9–12.G.SRT.2

4 EXAMPLE Determining If Figures Are Similar

Use the definition of similarity in terms of similarity transformations to determine whether the two figures are similar. Explain your answer.

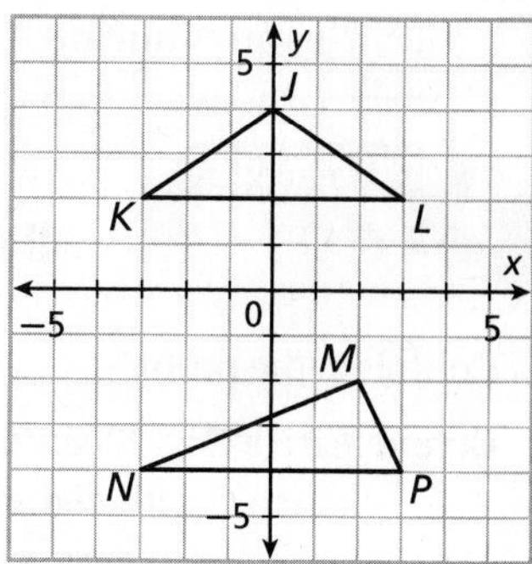

A △*JKL* and △*MNP* have different angle measures.

Since similarity transformations preserve angle measure, there is no sequence of similarity transformations that will map △*JKL* to △*MNP*.

Therefore, ________________________________.

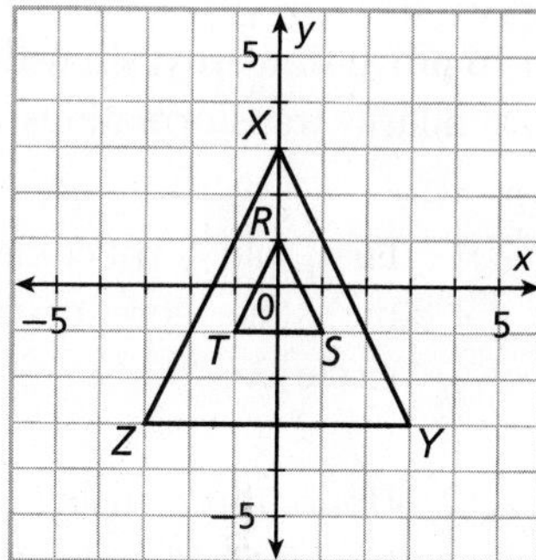

B You can map △*RST* to △*XYZ* by the dilation that has the coordinate notation

________________________________.

A dilation is a similarity transformation.

Therefore, ________________________________.

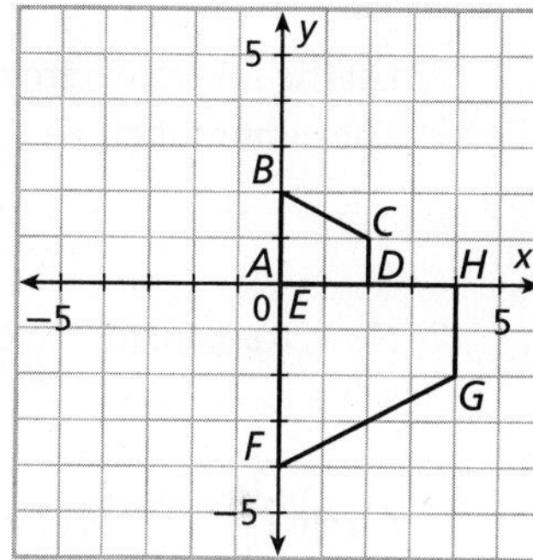

C You can map *ABCD* to *EFGH* by the dilation that has the coordinate notation

________________________________.

followed by the reflection that has the coordinate notation

________________________________.

Dilations and reflections are similarity transformations.

Therefore, ________________________________.

REFLECT

4a. In Part B above, how can you show that the triangles are similar using a different similarity transformation?

____

4b. In Part C above, does the order in which you perform the similarity transformations matter? Explain.

____

____

You can use the definition of similarity to prove theorems about figures.

Theorem

All circles are similar.

MCC9–12.G.C.1

5 PROOF All Circles Are Similar

Complete the proof.

Given: Circle C with center C and radius r;
circle D with center D and radius s.

Prove: Circle C is similar to circle D.

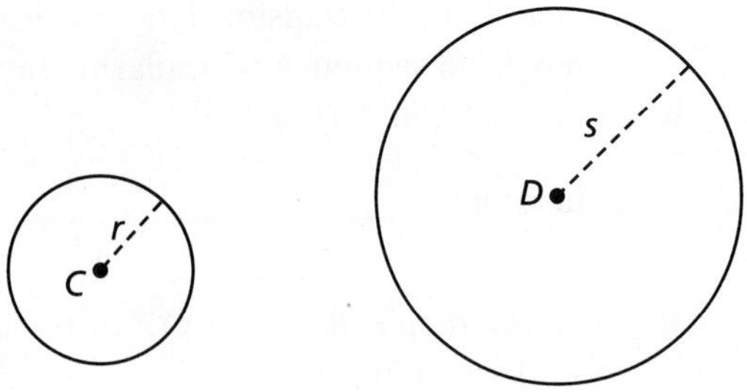

To prove similarity, show that there is a sequence of similarity transformations that maps circle C to circle D.

A First, transform circle C with the translation that maps the center of circle C to the center of circle D.

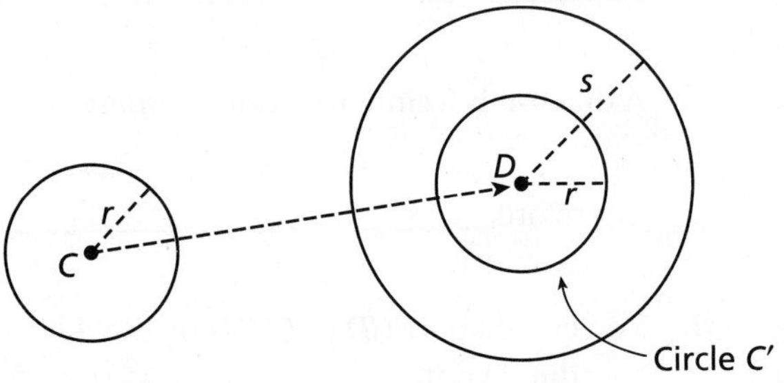

Under this translation, the image of point C is ______________.

Let the image of circle C be circle C'. The center of circle C' must lie at point ______________.

B Now, transform circle C' with the dilation that has center of dilation D and scale factor $\frac{s}{r}$.

Circle C' consists of all points at distance ______________ from point D.

After the dilation, the image of circle C' consists of all points at distance

______________ from point D. But these are exactly the points that form circle D.

Therefore, the translation followed by the dilation maps circle C to circle D.

Since translations and dilations are ______________________________,

you can conclude that ______________________________.

REFLECT

5a. Explain how to use a reflection and a dilation to prove that circle C is similar to circle D.

____

____

PRACTICE

1. The figure shows the image A' of point A under a dilation with center O. Explain how you can use a ruler to find the scale factor of the dilation. Then find the scale factor.

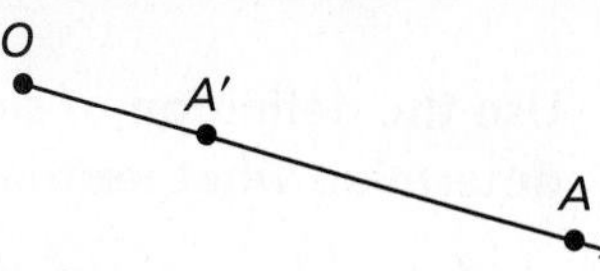

____

____

2. Compare dilations to rigid motions. How are they similar? How are they different?

____

____

3. Describe the effect of a dilation with scale factor 1.

____

For Exercises 4–6, refer to the diagram of the dilation below.

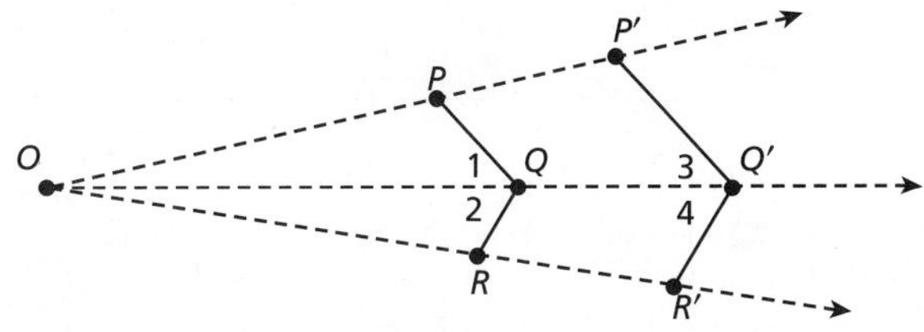

4. Suppose the points $P(x_1, y_1)$, $Q(x_2, y_2)$, and $R(x_3, y_3)$ are transformed by a dilation with scale factor k and center O. Show that the slope of $\overline{PQ}$ equals the slope of $\overline{P'Q'}$ and that the slope of $\overline{QR}$ equals the slope of $\overline{Q'R'}$.

____

____

____

5. Make a convincing argument for why $m\angle 1 = m\angle 3$ and $m\angle 2 = m\angle 4$. Use reasoning related to transversals and parallel lines.

____

____

____

6. Explain why $m\angle PQR = m\angle P'Q'R'$. What property of dilations does this reasoning support?

____

____

____

7. Given that $\triangle GMX \sim \triangle DPW$, write as many congruence statements as possible about the sides and/or angles of the triangles.

Use the definition of similarity in terms of similarity transformations to determine whether the two figures are similar. Explain your answer.

8.

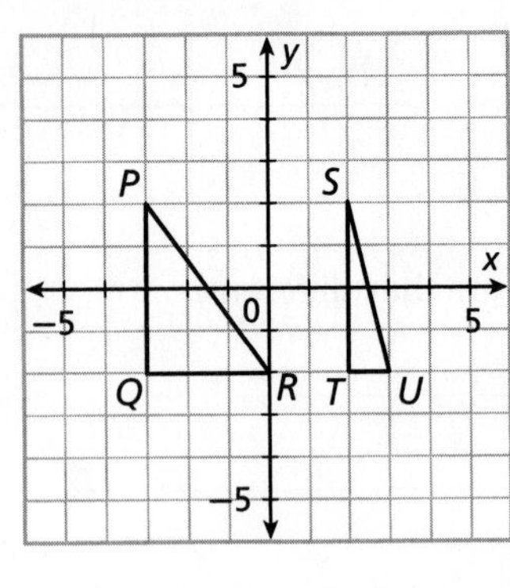

9.

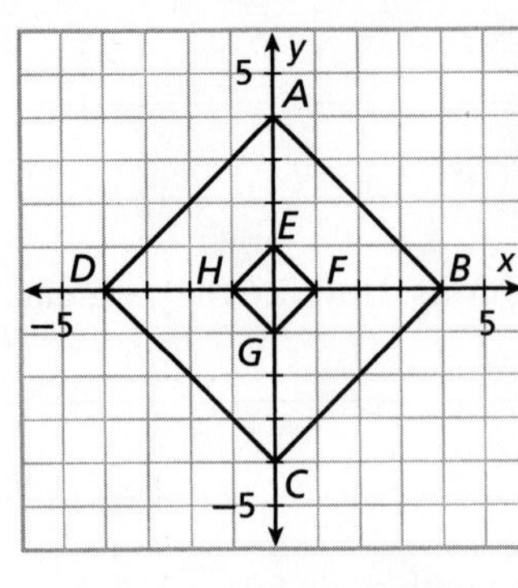

10.

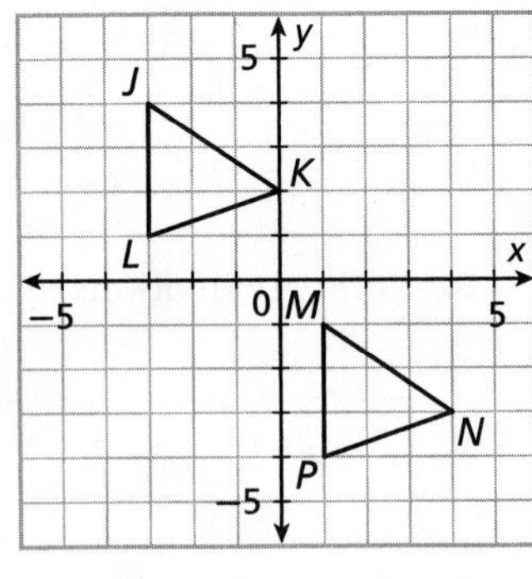

11.

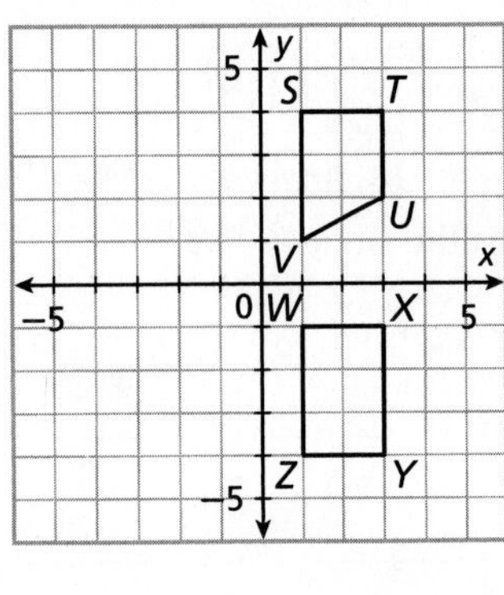

12.

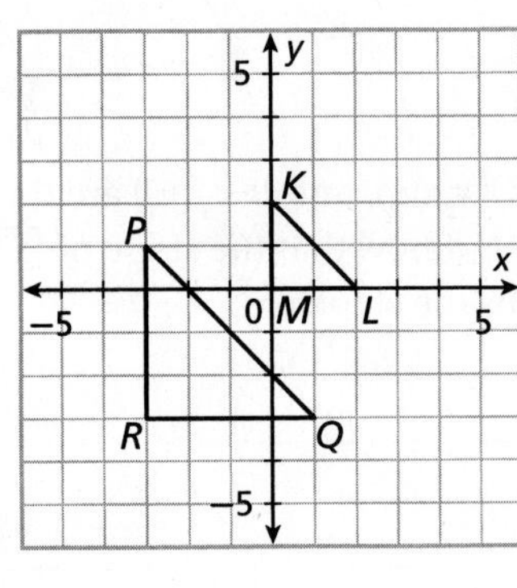

13.

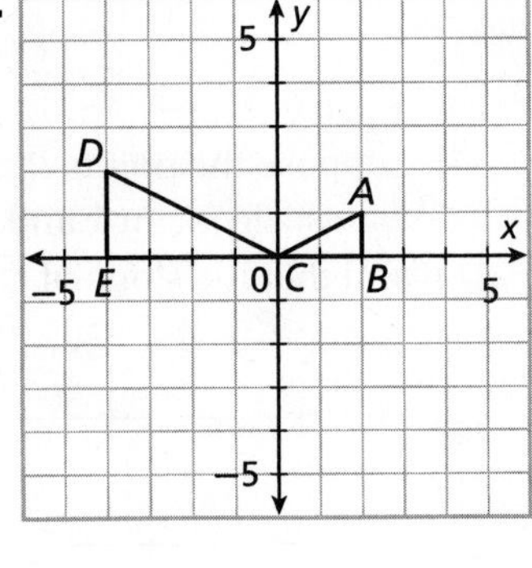

Name________________________ Class________________ Date____________ 8-2

Additional Practice

Apply the dilation D to the polygon with the given vertices. Describe the dilation.

1. $D: (x, y) \rightarrow (2x, 2y)$

   $A(1, 2)$, $B(3, 3)$, $C(4, 1)$

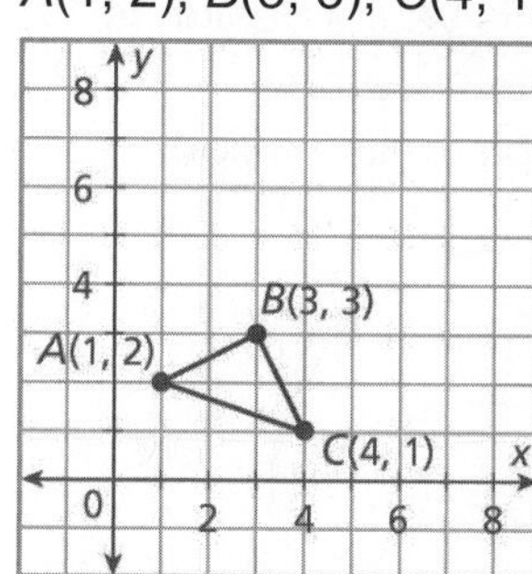

____

2. $D: (x, y) \rightarrow (\frac{1}{2}x, \frac{1}{2}y)$

   $P(-6, 8)$, $Q(0, 6)$, $R(-4, 2)$

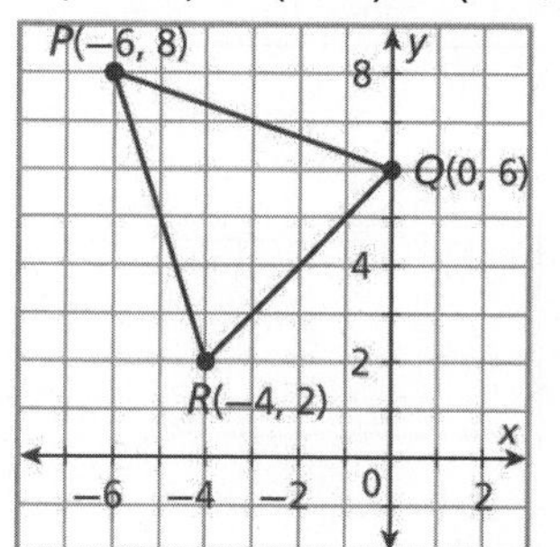

____

3. $D: (x, y) \rightarrow (1.5x, 1.5y)$

   $G(-4, 1)$, $H(-2, 1)$, $J(-2, 6)$, $K(-4, 6)$

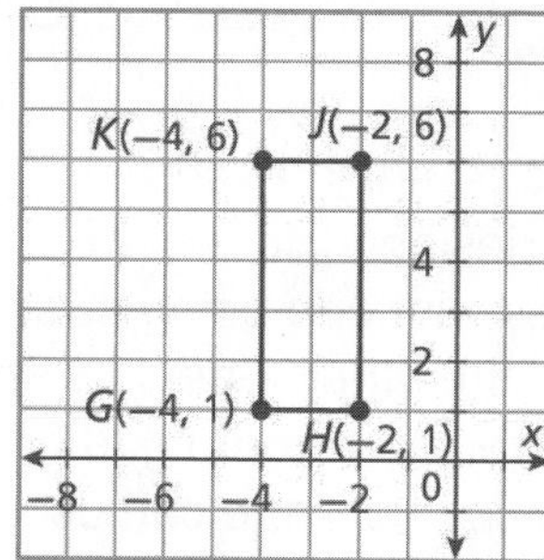

____

4. $D: (x, y) \rightarrow (0.75x, 0.75y)$

   $E(-4, 6)$, $F(-2, 2)$, $G(4, -2)$, $H(4, 4)$

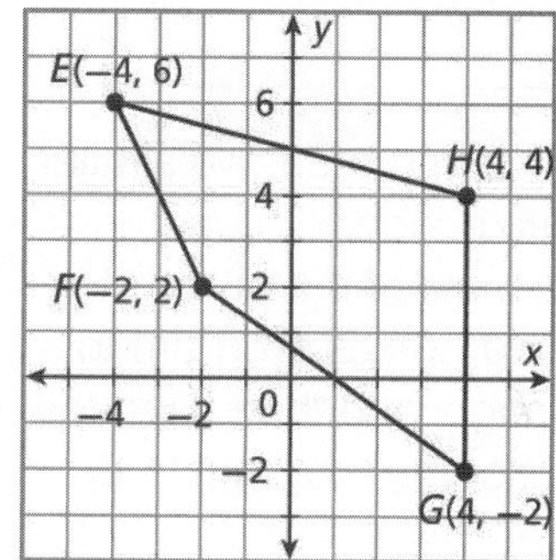

____

Determine whether the polygons with the given vertices are similar.

5. $A(-4, 4)$, $B(0, 4)$, $C(0, 0)$, $D(-2, -2)$, $E(-4, 0)$; $P(-3, 3)$, $Q(-1, 3)$, $R(-1, 1)$, $S(-2, 0)$, $T(-3, 1)$

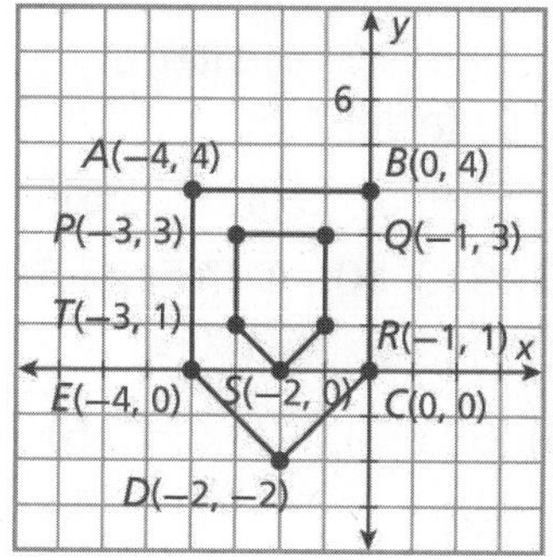

____

6. $J(-4, 6)$, $K(4, 6)$, $L(4, 4)$; $P(-2, 3)$, $Q(2, 3)$, $R(2, 2)$; $S(-4, 1)$, $T(0, 1)$, $O(0, 0)$

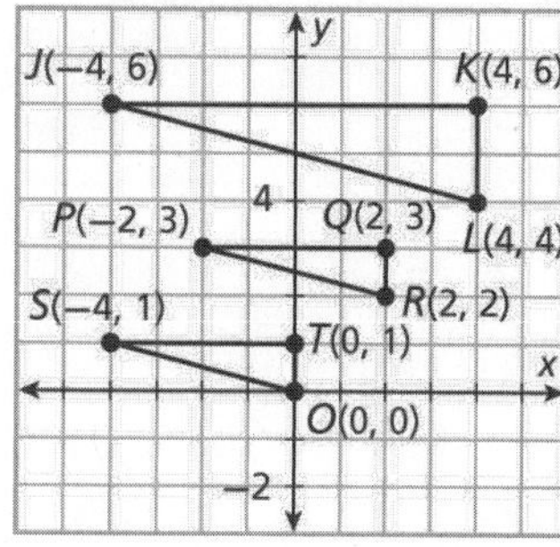

____

Problem Solving

1. Irena is designing a quilt. She started with a large square and then made this diagram to follow when making her quilt. Describe how she used dilations to make the pattern.

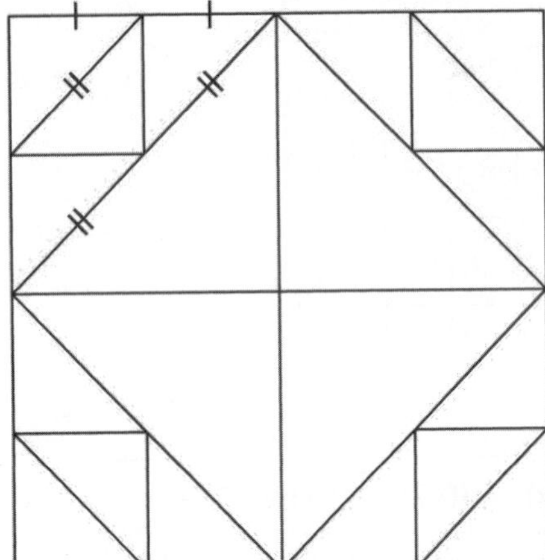

____

2. A crop circle is a large pattern formed by flattening or cutting crops so the design is apparent when viewed from above. Every year, Hector puts a crop circle into his corn field. This year's design is shown below. Describe how he used dilations to complete his design.

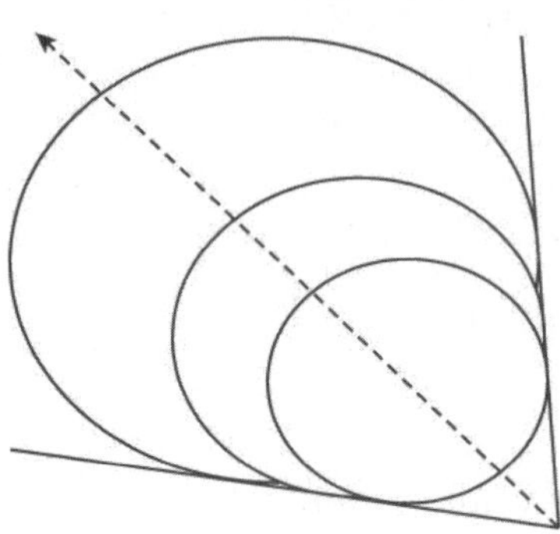

____

3. A graphic artist incorporated two similar right triangles into a logo with one triangle twice the size of the other. He used a computer graphics program to draw the first triangle and then used the enlargement tool of the program to draw the other triangle. How can he verify that the two triangles are similar?

____

4. A toy designer is planning to create a doll house. The design includes two similar rectangles with one being three times the size of the other. She cuts and traces the small rectangle onto grid paper first. Describe how she can use the tracing to make a pattern for the larger rectangle.

____

Choose the best answer.

5. Circle *A* with radius 4 and center (3, 0) is drawn in the coordinate plane. What is the scale factor that maps the circle with radius 3 and center (2, 3) onto circle *A*?

A $\frac{4}{3}$ C $\frac{7}{3}$

B $\frac{3}{4}$ D $\frac{3}{7}$

6. An art student uses dilations in all her art. She first plans the art piece on a coordinate grid. Determine the vertices of the image of the triangle with vertices *A*(1, 1), *B*(2, 4), and *C*(3, 9) after a dilation with scale factor 1.5.

F *A*′(1.5, 1.5), *B*′(3, 5), *C*′(4.5, 13.5)

G *A*′ (2.5, 2.5), *B*′(5, 10), *C*′(7.5, 22.5)

H *A*′ (1.5, 1.5), *B*′(4, 8), *C*′(6, 18)

J *A*′ (1.5, 1.5), *B*′(3, 6), *C*′(4.5, 13.5)

Name ______________________ Class ______________ Date ________

8-3

Triangle Similarity: AA, SSS, and SAS

Going Deeper

Essential question: *What can you conclude about similar triangles and how can you prove triangles are similar?*

Video Tutor

MCC9-12.G.SRT.2

1 ENGAGE Applying Similarity to Triangles

Recall that when two figures are similar, there is a sequence of similarity transformations that maps one figure to the other. In particular, given $\triangle ABC \sim \triangle DEF$, you can first apply a dilation to $\triangle ABC$ to make both triangles the same size. Then you can apply a sequence of rigid motions to the dilated image of $\triangle ABC$ to map it to $\triangle DEF$.

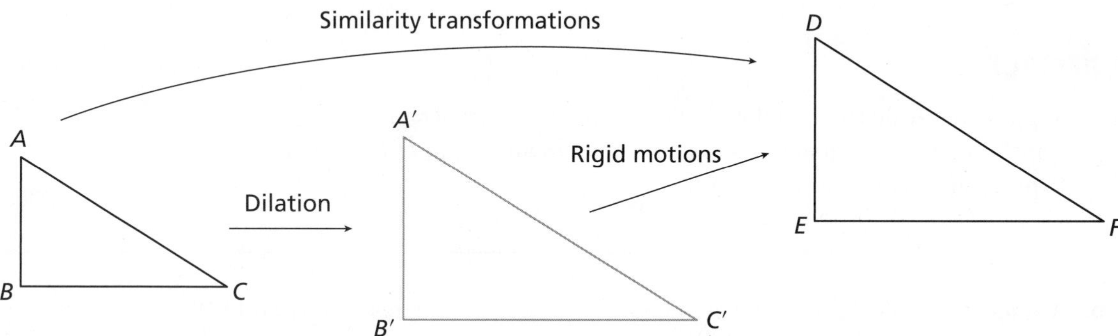

Because the similarity transformations that map $\triangle ABC$ to $\triangle DEF$ preserve angle measure, you can say that corresponding angles are congruent. Thus, $\triangle ABC \sim \triangle DEF$ implies $\angle A \cong \angle D$, $\angle B \cong \angle E$, and $\angle C \cong \angle F$.

Also, the initial dilation that makes the two triangles the same size shows that each side of $\triangle DEF$ is longer or shorter than the corresponding side of $\triangle ABC$ by the ratio given by the scale factor. Assuming the dilation has scale factor k, this means that $DE = k \cdot AB$, $EF = k \cdot BC$, and $DF = k \cdot AC$.

Solving for k in these equations gives $k = \frac{DE}{AB}$, $k = \frac{EF}{BC}$, and $k = \frac{DF}{AC}$.

This shows that corresponding sides are proportional. That is, $\frac{DE}{AB} = \frac{EF}{BC} = \frac{DF}{AC}$.

REFLECT

1a. Is triangle similarity transitive? That is, if $\triangle ABC \sim \triangle DEF$ and $\triangle DEF \sim \triangle GHK$, can you conclude that $\triangle ABC \sim \triangle GHK$? Explain.

____

____

____

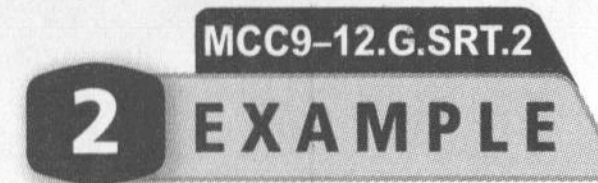

2 EXAMPLE Identifying Congruent Angles and Proportional Sides

Given that $\triangle RST \sim \triangle UVW$, write congruence statements for the corresponding angles and proportions for the corresponding sides.

A Corresponding angles are listed in the same position in each triangle name.

$\angle R \cong \angle U$, __________, __________

B Corresponding sides are named by pairs of letters in the same position in each triangle name.

$\frac{UV}{RS} =$ ____________________

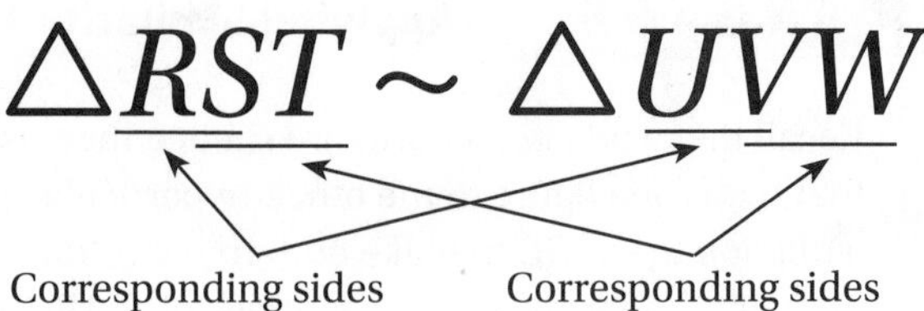

REFLECT

2a. Suppose the scale factor of the dilation in the sequence of similarity transformations that maps $\triangle RST$ to $\triangle UVW$ is 4 and suppose $RS = 8$ mm. Explain how to find the length of $\overline{UV}$.

____

2b. A student identified $\overline{RS}$ and $\overline{UV}$ as a pair of corresponding sides and $\overline{ST}$ and $\overline{VW}$ as a pair of corresponding sides. The student wrote $\frac{RS}{UV} = \frac{VW}{ST}$. Is this a correct proportion? Why or why not? If the proportion is not correct, explain how to write correctly.

____

____

You have seen that when two triangles are similar, corresponding angles are congruent and corresponding sides are proportional. The converse is also true. That is, if you are given two triangles and you know that the corresponding angles are congruent and corresponding sides are proportional, you can conclude that the triangles are similar.

As with congruence, there are some "shortcuts" that make it a bit easier to prove that two triangles are similar. The most important of these is known as the AA Similarity Criterion.

AA Similarity Criterion

If two angles of one triangle are congruent to two angles of another triangle, then the triangles are similar.

MCC9–12.G.SRT.3

3 PROOF AA Similarity Criterion

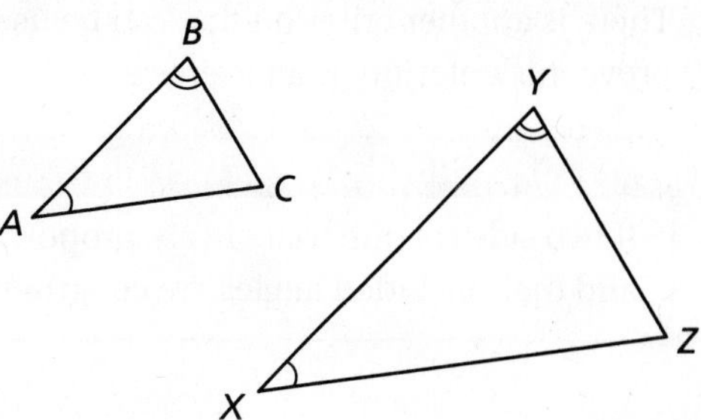

Given: $\angle A \cong \angle X$ and $\angle B \cong \angle Y$

Prove: $\triangle ABC \sim \triangle XYZ$

To prove the triangles are similar, you will find a sequence of similarity transformations that maps $\triangle ABC$ to $\triangle XYZ$. Complete the following steps of the proof.

A Apply a dilation to $\triangle ABC$ with scale factor $k = \frac{XY}{AB}$. Let the image of $\triangle ABC$ be $\triangle A'B'C'$.

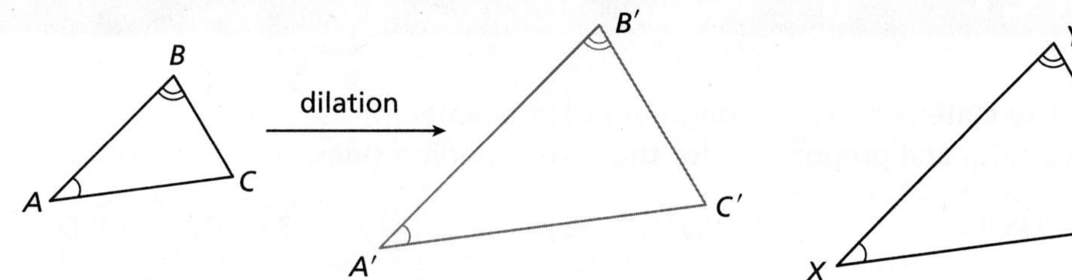

$\triangle A'B'C'$ is similar to $\triangle ABC$, and $\angle A' \cong$ ________ and $\angle B' \cong$ ________

because ____.

Also, $A'B' = k \cdot AB =$ ________________.

B It is given that $\angle A \cong \angle X$ and $\angle B \cong \angle Y$.

By the Transitive Property of Congruence, $\angle A' \cong$ ________ and $\angle B' \cong$ ________.

So, $\triangle A'B'C' \cong \triangle XYZ$ by ______________________________.

This means there is a sequence of rigid motions that maps $\triangle A'B'C'$ to $\triangle XYZ$.

The dilation followed by this sequence of rigid motions shows that there is a sequence of similarity transformations that maps $\triangle ABC$ to $\triangle XYZ$. Therefore, $\triangle ABC \sim \triangle XYZ$.

REFLECT

3a. In $\triangle JKL$, $m\angle J = 40°$ and $m\angle K = 60°$. In $\triangle MNP$, $m\angle M = 40°$ and $m\angle P = 80°$. A student concludes that the triangles are not similar. Do you agree or disagree? Why?

____

____

There is another criterion that can be used to show that two triangles are similar. You will prove this criterion as an exercise.

SAS Similarity Criterion

If two sides of one triangle are proportional to two sides of another triangle and their included angles are congruent, then the triangles are similar.

PRACTICE

For each similarity statement, write congruence statements for the corresponding angles and proportions for the corresponding sides.

1. $\triangle GHJ \sim \triangle PQR$

2. $\triangle TWR \sim \triangle YSP$

3. $\triangle PJL \sim \triangle WDM$

4. Prove the SAS Similarity Criterion.

Given: $\frac{XY}{AB} = \frac{XZ}{AC}$ and $\angle A \cong \angle X$

Prove: $\triangle ABC \sim \triangle XYZ$

(*Hint:* The main steps of the proof are similar to those of the proof of the AA Similarity Criterion.)

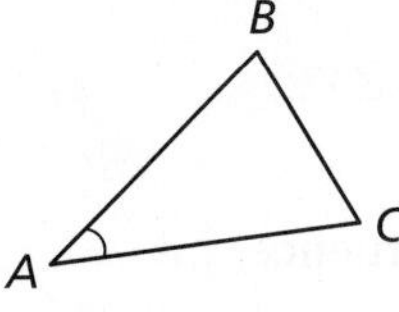

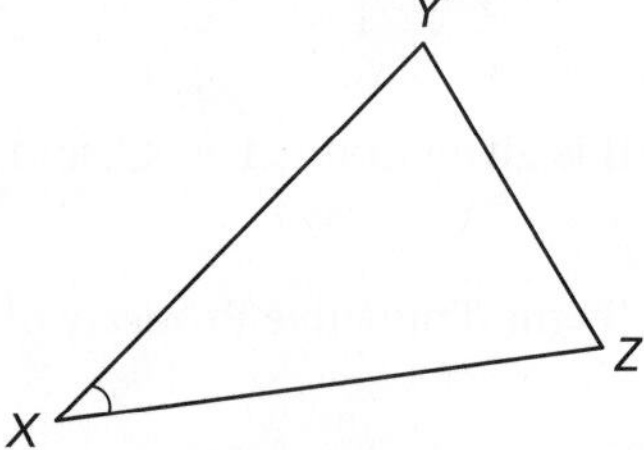

Name ______________________ Class ____________ Date ____________

8-3

Additional Practice

For Exercises 1 and 2, explain why the triangles are similar and write a similarity statement.

1. 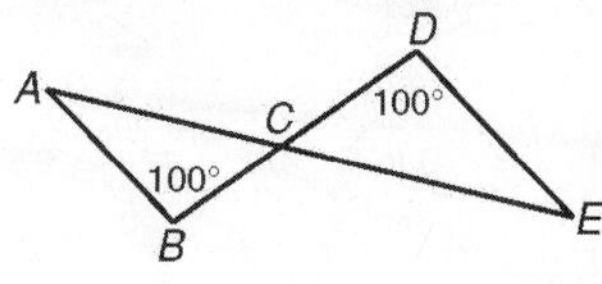

____

____

____

____

____

2. 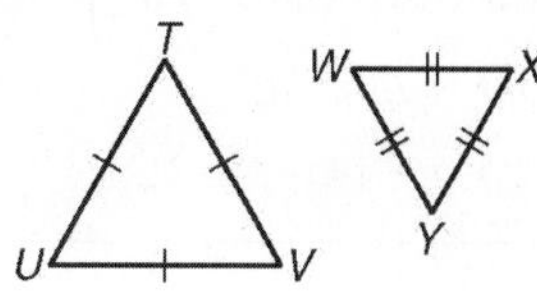

____

____

____

____

____

For Exercises 3 and 4, verify that the triangles are similar. Explain why.

3. $\triangle JLK$ and $\triangle JMN$

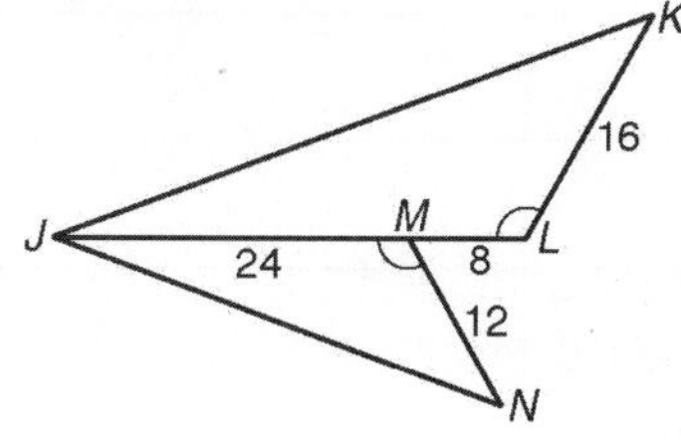

____

____

____

4. $\triangle PQR$ and $\triangle UTS$

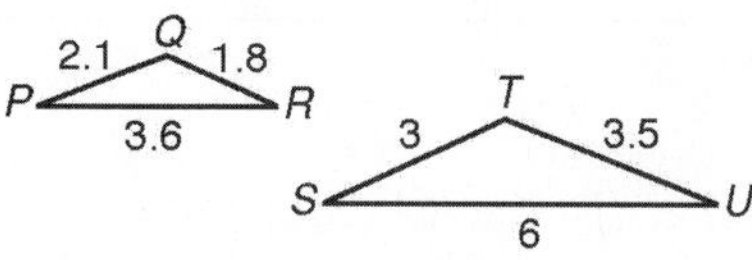

____

____

____

For Exercise 5, explain why the triangles are similar and find the stated length.

5. *DE*

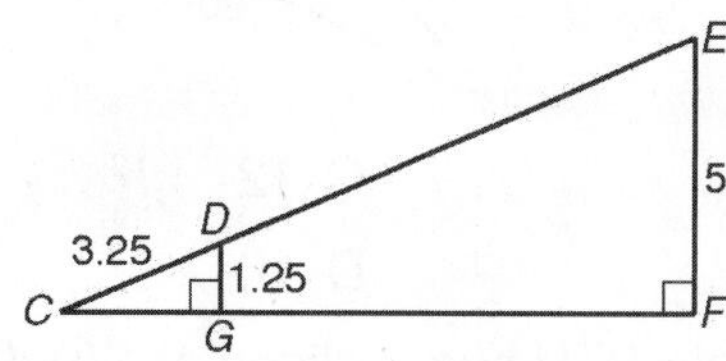

____

____

____

Problem Solving

Use the diagram for Exercises 1 and 2.

In the diagram of the tandem bike, $\overline{AE} \parallel \overline{BD}$.

1. Explain why $\triangle CBD \sim \triangle CAE$.

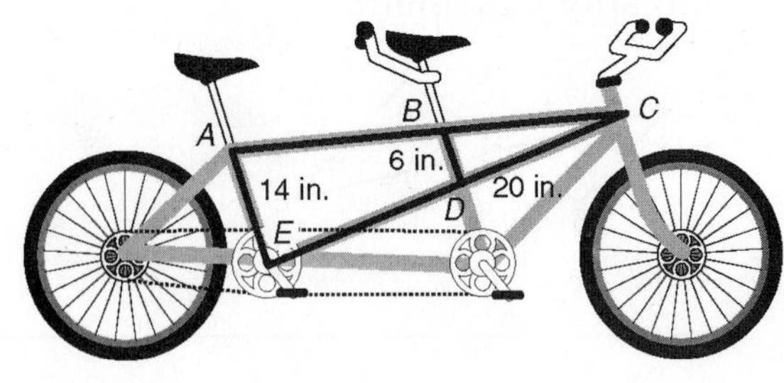

____

____

____

2. Find CE to the nearest tenth. ______________________________

3. Is $\triangle WXZ \sim \triangle XYZ$? Explain.

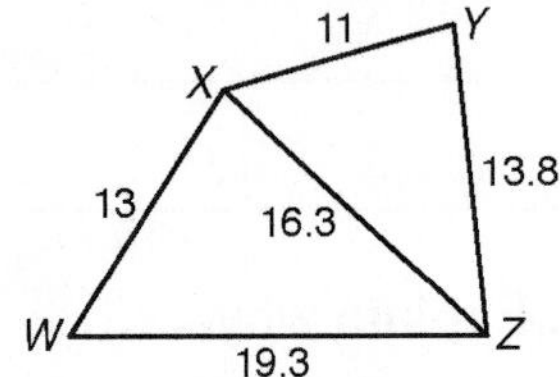

____

4. Find RQ. Explain how you found it.

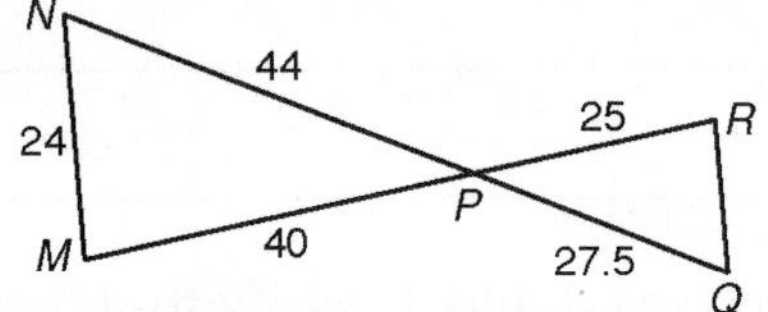

____

____

____

Choose the best answer.

5. Find the value of x that makes $\triangle FGH \sim \triangle JKL$.

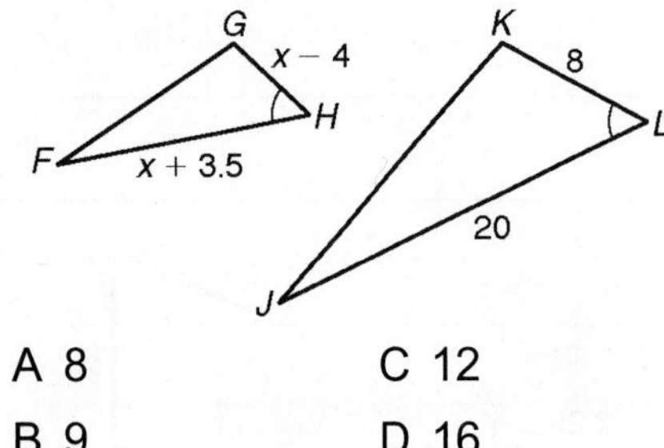

A 8   C 12

B 9   D 16

6. Triangle STU has vertices at $S(0, 0)$, $T(2, 6)$, and $U(8, 2)$. If $\triangle STU \sim \triangle WXY$ and the coordinates of W are $(0, 0)$, what are possible coordinates of X and Y?

F $X(1, 3)$ and $Y(4, 1)$

G $X(1, 3)$ and $Y(2, 0)$

H $X(3, 1)$ and $Y(2, 4)$

J $X(0, 3)$ and $Y(4, 0)$

7. To measure the distance EF across the lake, a surveyor at S locates points E, F, G, and H as shown. What is EF?

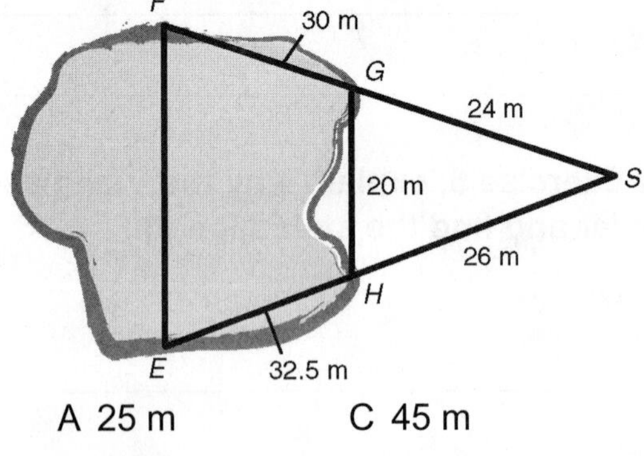

A 25 m   C 45 m

B 36 m   D 90 m

Name ________________________ Class ______________ Date ____________

8-4

Applying Properties of Similar Triangles

Going Deeper

Essential question: *How does a line that is parallel to one side of a triangle divide the two sides that it intersects?*

The following theorem is sometimes known as the Side-Splitting Theorem. It describes what happens when a line that is parallel to one side of a triangle "splits" the other two sides.

Triangle Proportionality Theorem

If a line parallel to one side of a triangle intersects the other two sides, then it divides those sides proportionally.

MCC9–12.G.SRT.4

1 PROOF Triangle Proportionality Theorem

Given: $\overleftrightarrow{EF} \parallel \overline{BC}$

Prove: $\frac{AE}{EB} = \frac{AF}{FC}$

Complete the proof.

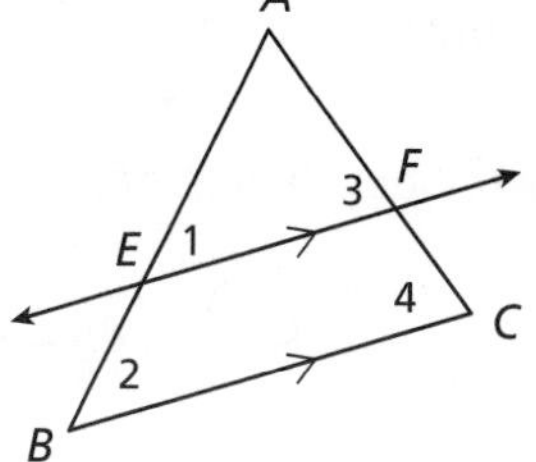

A Show that $\triangle AEF \sim \triangle ABC$.

Since $\overleftrightarrow{EF} \parallel \overline{BC}$, you can conclude that $\angle 1 \cong \angle 2$ and $\angle 3 \cong \angle 4$ by

____

So, $\triangle AEF \sim \triangle ABC$ by ______________________________

B Use the fact that corresponding sides of similar triangles are proportional.

$\frac{AB}{AE} =$ ______________	Corresponding sides are proportional.
$\frac{AE + EB}{AE} =$ ______________	Segment Addition Postulate
$1 + \frac{EB}{AE} =$ ______________	Use the property that $\frac{a+b}{c} = \frac{a}{c} + \frac{b}{c}$.
$\frac{EB}{AE} =$ ______________	Subtract 1 from both sides.
$\frac{AE}{EB} =$ ______________	Take the reciprocal of both sides.

REFLECT

1a. Explain how you can conclude $\triangle AEF \sim \triangle ABC$ without using $\angle 3$ and $\angle 4$.

____

____

Converse of the Triangle Proportionality Theorem

If a line divides two sides of a triangle proportionally, then it is parallel to the third side.

MCC9–12.G.SRT.5

2 PROOF Converse of the Triangle Proportionality Theorem

Given: $\frac{AE}{EB} = \frac{AF}{FC}$

Prove: $\overleftrightarrow{EF} \parallel \overline{BC}$

Complete the proof.

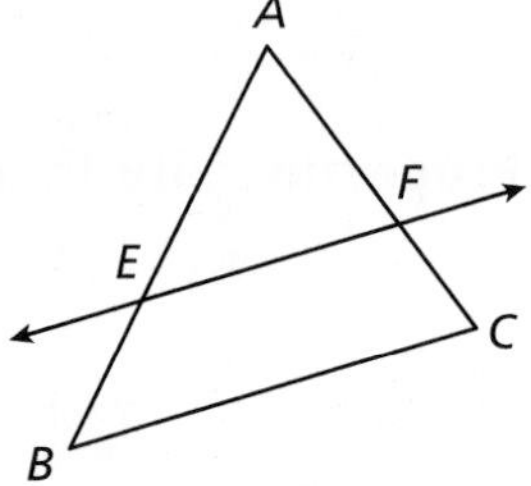

A Show that $\triangle AEF \sim \triangle ABC$.

It is given that $\frac{AE}{EB} = \frac{AF}{FC}$ and taking the reciprocal of both sides shows that ______________________. Now add 1 to both sides by adding $\frac{AE}{AE}$ to the left side and $\frac{AF}{AF}$ to the right side. This gives ______________________. Adding and using the Segment Addition Postulate gives ______________________.

Since $\angle A \cong \angle A$, $\triangle AEF \sim \triangle ABC$ by ______________________.

B As corresponding angles of similar triangles, $\angle AEF \cong$ ______________________.

So, $\overleftrightarrow{EF} \parallel \overline{BC}$ by ______________________.

REFLECT

2a. A student states that $\overline{UV}$ must be parallel to $\overline{ST}$. Do you agree? Why or why not?

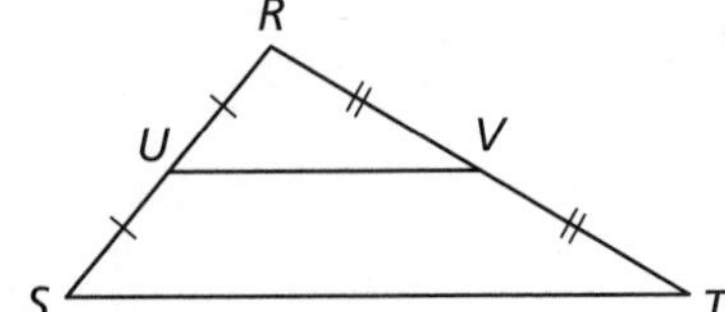

____

____

Name________________ Class________ Date________

Additional Practice

Find each length.

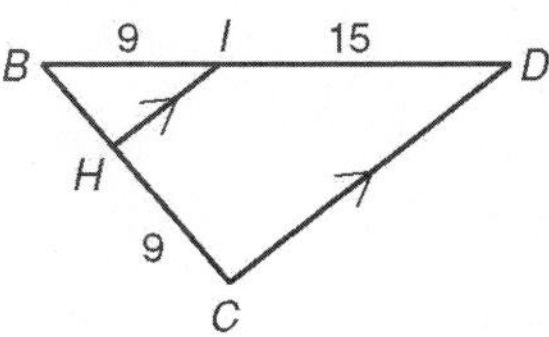

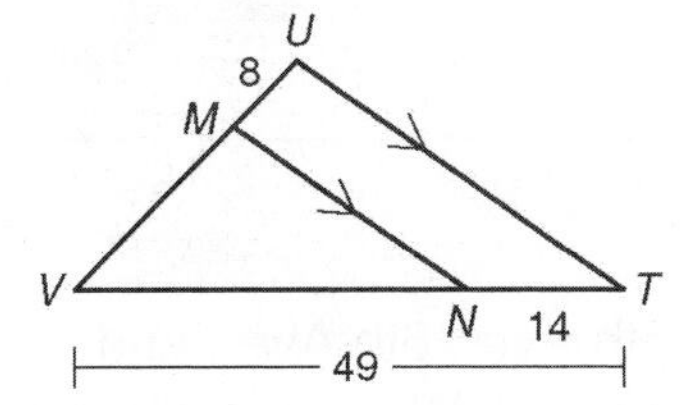

1. *BH* ________________

2. *MV* ________________

Verify that the given segments are parallel.

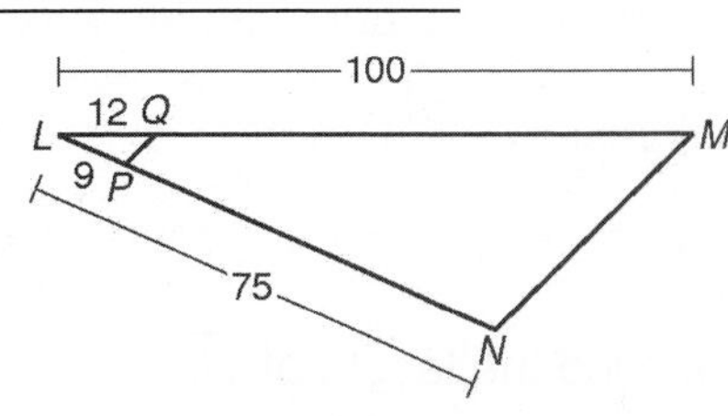

3. $\overline{PQ}$ and $\overline{NM}$

____

____

____

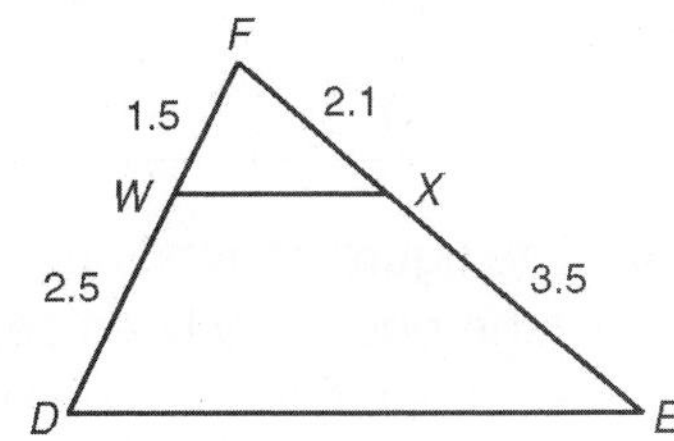

4. $\overline{WX}$ and $\overline{DE}$

____

____

____

Find each length.

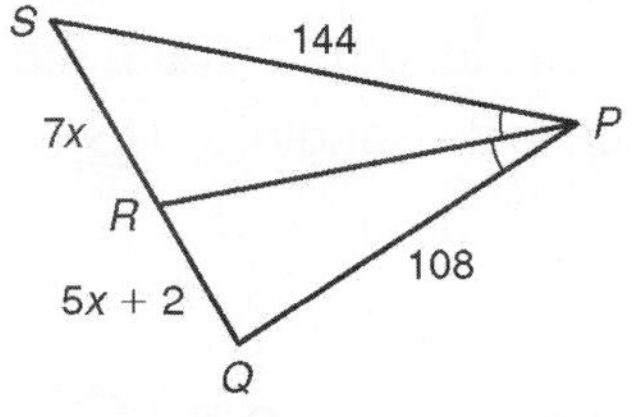

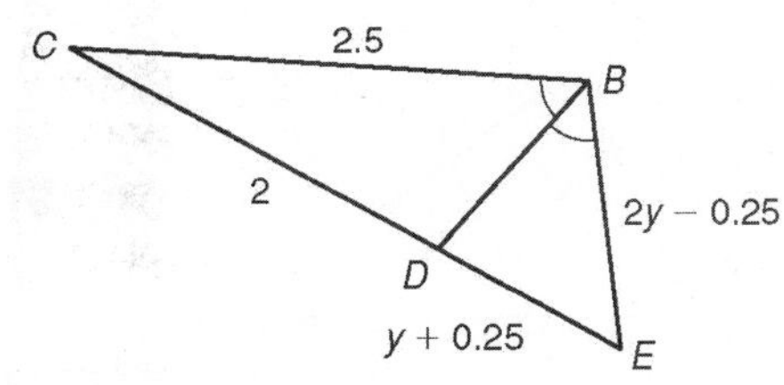

5. *SR* and *RQ* ________________

6. *BE* and *DE* ________________

7. In $\triangle ABC$, $\overline{BD}$ bisects $\angle ABC$ and $\overline{AD} \cong \overline{CD}$. Tell what kind of $\triangle ABC$ must be. ________________

Problem Solving

1. Is $\overline{GF} \parallel \overline{HJ}$ if $x = 5$? Explain.

____

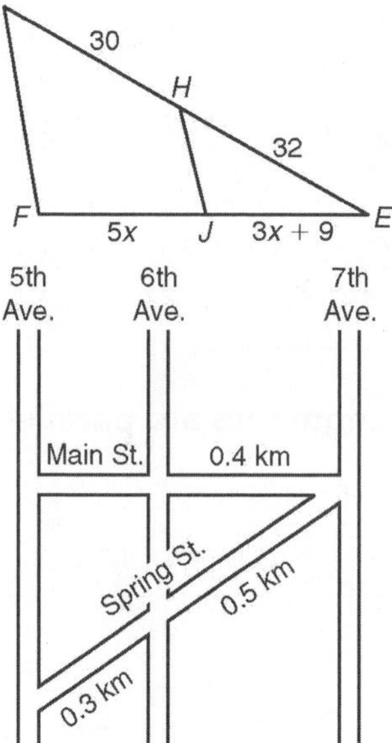

2. On the map, 5th Ave., 6th Ave., and 7th Ave. are parallel. What is the length of Main St. between 5th Ave. and 6th Ave.?

____

3. Find the length of $\overline{BC}$.

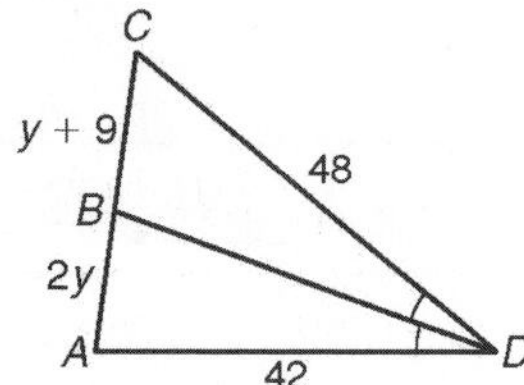

____

4. The figure shows three lots in a housing development. If the boundary lines separating the lots are parallel, what is GF to the nearest tenth?

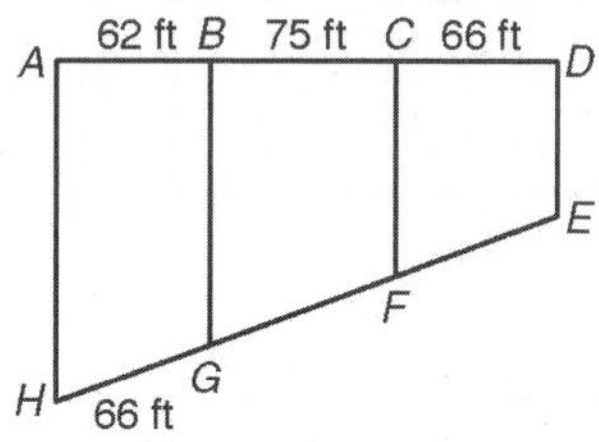

____

Choose the best answer.

5. If $LM = 22$, what is PM?

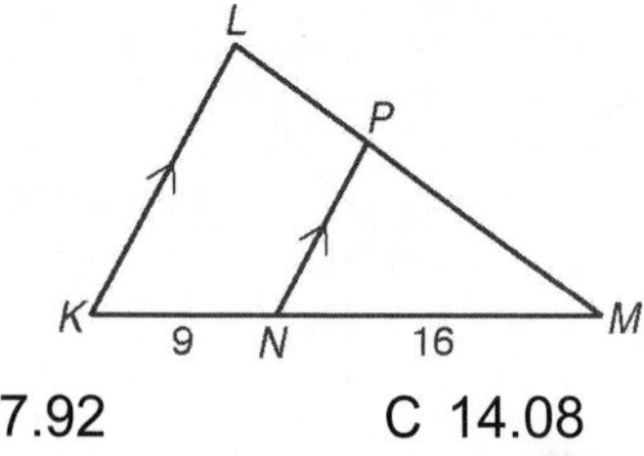

A 7.92 C 14.08

B 12.38 D 29.92

6. In $\triangle QRS$, the bisector of $\angle R$ divides $\overline{QS}$ into segments with lengths 2.1 and 2.8. If $RQ = 3$, which is the length of $\overline{RS}$?

F 2 H 4

G 2.25 J 4.5

7. In $\triangle CDE$, the bisector of $\angle C$ divides $\overline{DE}$ into segments with lengths $4x$ and $x + 13$. If $CD = 24$ and $CE = 32$, which is the length of $\overline{DE}$?

A 20 C 26

B 24 D 28

Name________________________ Class______________ Date________

8-5

Dilations and Similarity in the Coordinate Plane

Connection: Coordinate Methods

Essential question: *How can you represent dilations in the coordinate plane?*

Video Tutor

When you work with dilations in the coordinate plane, you can assume the center of dilation is the origin. To find the image of a point after a dilation with scale factor k, multiply each coordinate of the point by k. Using coordinate notation, a dilation with scale factor k is written as follows: $(x, y) \rightarrow (kx, ky)$.

MCC9–12.G.CO.2

1 EXAMPLE Drawing a Dilation in a Coordinate Plane

Draw the image of the pentagon after a dilation with scale factor $\frac{3}{2}$.

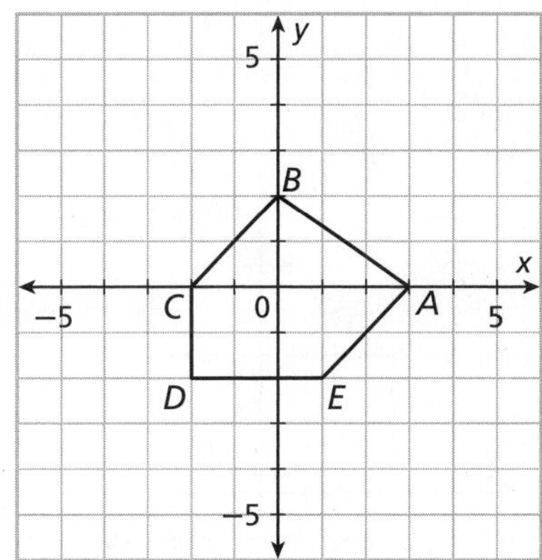

A In the table below, list the vertices of the pentagon. Then use the rule for the dilation to write the vertices of the image.

Pre-Image (x, y)	Image $\left(\frac{3}{2}x, \frac{3}{2}y\right)$
$A(3, 0)$	$A'(4\frac{1}{2}, 0)$
$B(0, 2)$	

B Plot the vertices of the image. Connect the vertices to complete the image.

REFLECT

1a. Explain how to use the distance formula to check that $\overline{B'C'}$ is the correct length.

____

____

1b. A student claims that under a dilation centered at the origin with scale factor k, a point and its image always lie in the same quadrant. Do you agree or disagree? Explain.

____

____

____

PRACTICE

Draw the image of the figure after a dilation with the given scale factor.

1. scale factor: 2

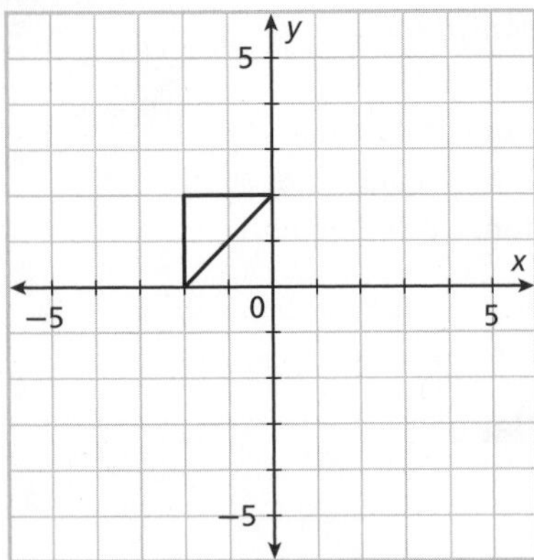

2. scale factor: $\frac{1}{4}$

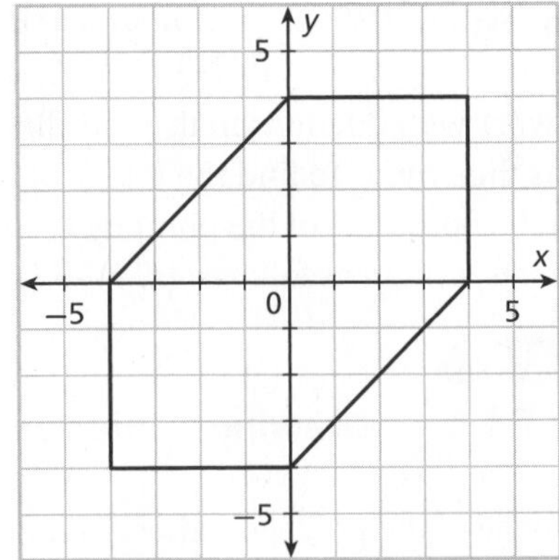

3. scale factor: $\frac{2}{3}$

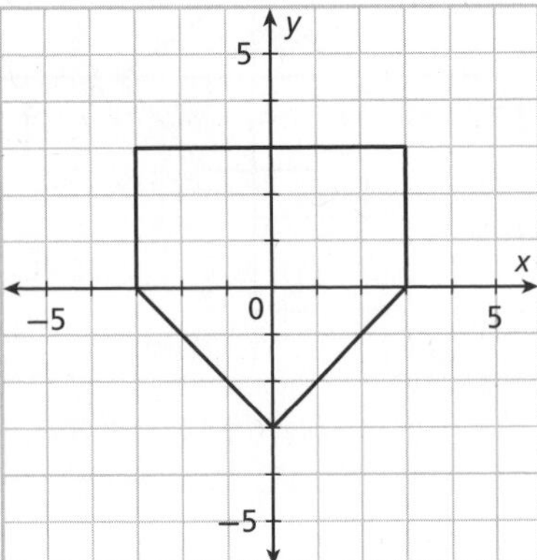

4. scale factor: 3

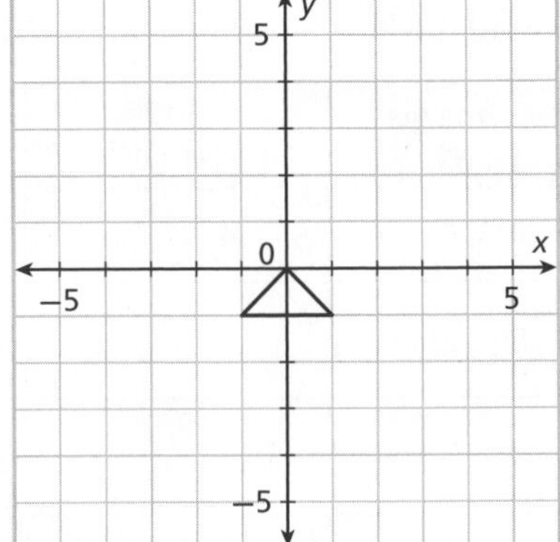

5. Each centimeter on a scale drawing of a park represents three meters of actual distance. What is the scale factor of the dilation that maps the park to the scale drawing?

____

6. Error Analysis A student claims that a dilation with scale factor m and center of dilation O that is followed by a dilation with scale factor n and center of dilation O is equivalent to a single dilation with scale factor $m + n$ and center of dilation O. Do you agree or disagree? Explain.

____

____

____

____

Additional Practice

A jeweler designs a setting that can hold a gem in the shape of a parallelogram. The figure shows the outline of the gem. The client, however, wants a gem and setting that is slightly larger.

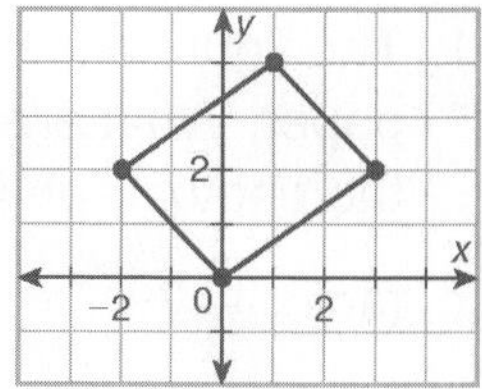

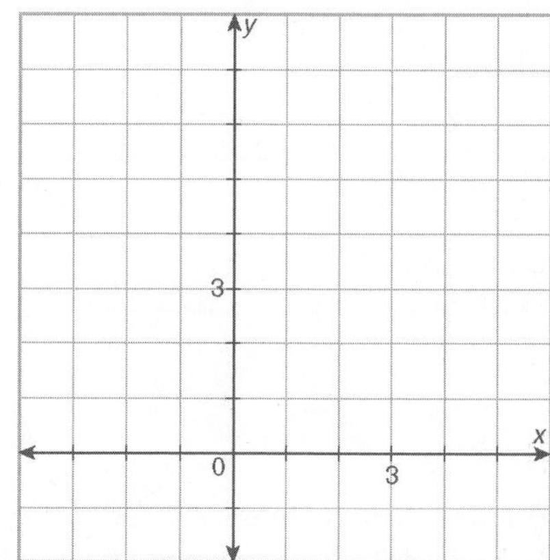

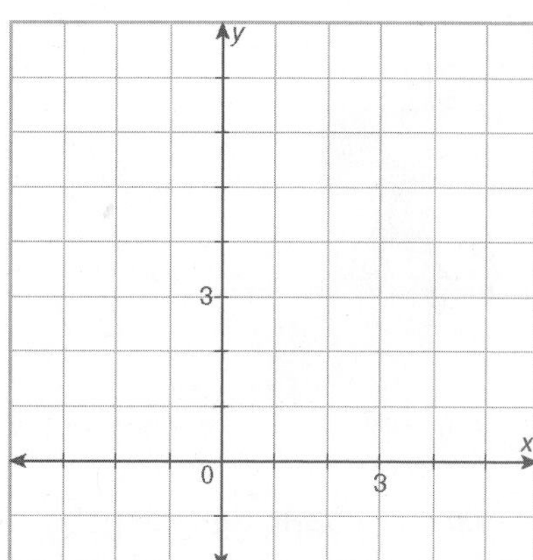

1. Draw the gem after a dilation with a scale factor of $\frac{3}{2}$.

2. The client is so pleased with her ring that she decides to have matching but smaller earrings made using the same pattern. Draw the gem after a dilation from the original pattern with a scale factor of $\frac{1}{2}$.

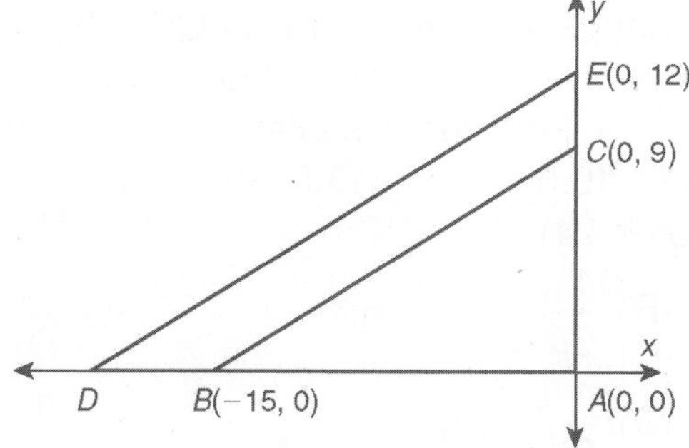

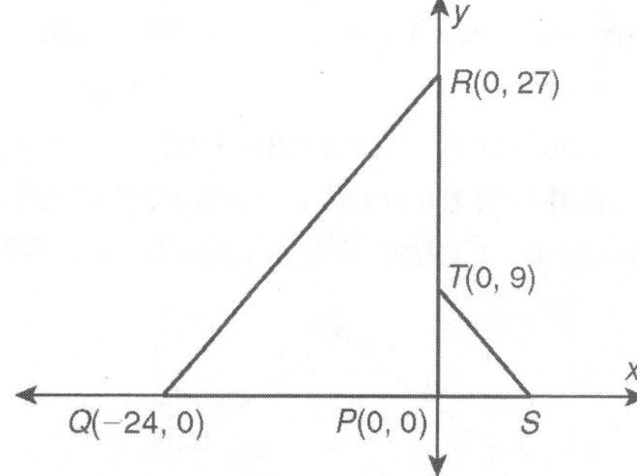

3. Given that $\triangle ABC \sim \triangle ADE$, find the scale factor and the coordinates of D.

____

4. Given that $\triangle PQR \sim \triangle PST$, find the scale factor and the coordinates of S.

____

Problem Solving

1. The figure shows a photograph on grid paper. What are the coordinates of C' if the photograph is enlarged with scale factor $\frac{4}{3}$?

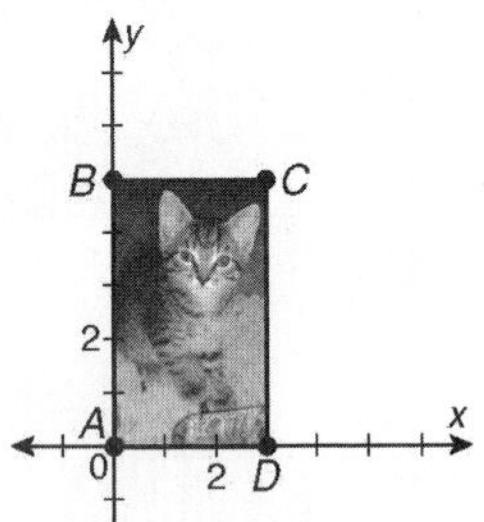

2. In the figure, $\triangle HFJ \sim \triangle EFG$. Find the coordinates of G and the scale factor.

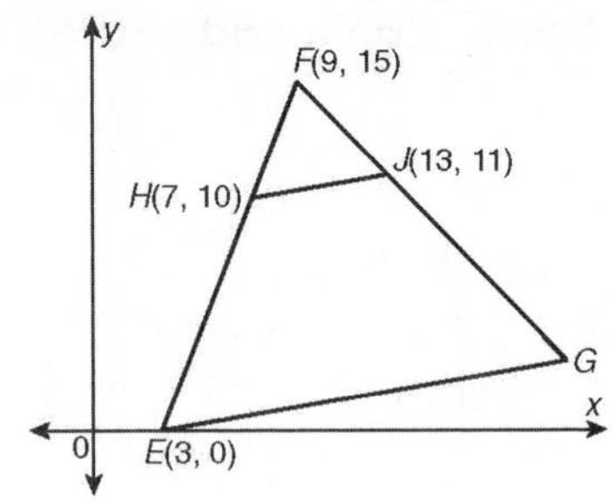

3. Triangle LMN has vertices $L(-10, 2)$, $M(-4, 11)$, and $N(6, -6)$. Find the vertices of the image of $\triangle LMN$ after a dilation with scale factor $\frac{5}{2}$.

4. Triangle HJM has vertices $H(-36, 0)$, $J(0, 20)$, and $M(0, 0)$. Triangle $H'J'M'$ has two vertices at $H'(-27, 0)$ and $M'(0, 0)$, and $\triangle H'J'M'$ is a dilation image of $\triangle HJM$. Find the coordinates of J' and the scale factor.

Choose the best answer.

5. The arrow is cut from a logo. The artist needs to make a copy five times as large for a sign. If the coordinates of T are $T(3, 4.5)$, what are the coordinates of T' after the arrow is dilated with scale factor 5?

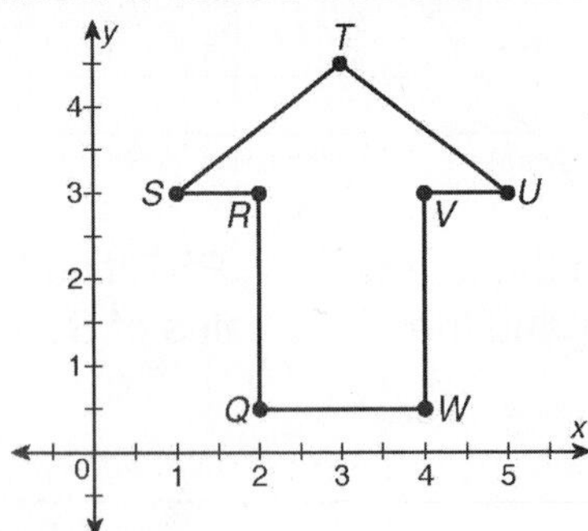

A $T'(15, 22.5)$
B $T'(7.5, 9)$
C $T'(4.5, 6.75)$
D $T'(2.5, 20)$

6. Triangle QRS has vertices $Q(-7, 3)$, $R(9, 8)$, and $S(2, 16)$. What is the scale factor if the vertices after a dilation are $Q'(-10.5, 4.5)$, $R'(13.5, 15)$, and $S'(3, 24)$?

F $\frac{1}{3}$

G $\frac{1}{2}$

H $\frac{2}{3}$

J $\frac{3}{2}$

7. A triangle has vertices $H(-4, 2)$, $J(-8, 6)$, and $K(0, 6)$. If $\triangle ABC \sim \triangle HJK$, what are possible vertices of $\triangle ABC$?

A $A(-4, 3)$, $B(-2, 1)$, $C(0, 3)$
B $A(-2, 1)$, $B(-4, 3)$, $C(0, 3)$
C $A(-2, 4)$, $B(0, 6)$, $C(-2, 8)$
D $A(-2, 4)$, $B(-8, 6)$, $C(-4, 2)$

Name________________ Class______________ Date________

UNIT 1

Performance Tasks

GPS COMMON CORE

MCC9-12.G.CO.9
MCC9-12.G.CO.11
MCC9-12.G.SRT.1
MCC9-12.G.SRT.2
MCC9-12.G.SRT.3
MCC9-12.G.SRT.5

 **1.** In the figure, $\overleftrightarrow{PQ}$ bisects $\angle RST$. Part of the proof that $\angle RSP \cong \angle TSP$ is provided below. Write the correct statement for each reason.

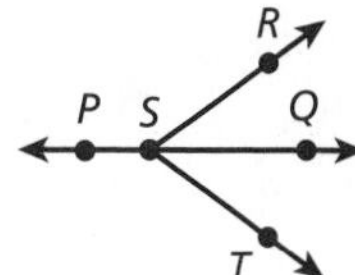

1. Given

2. Definition of angle bisector

3. Linear pairs are supplementary.

4. Linear pairs are supplementary.

5. Supplements of congruent angles are congruent.

 **2.** Sonia made the sketch shown of a logo for a new local nonprofit organization. She would like to enlarge the sketch by using a dilation whose center is the center of the circle.

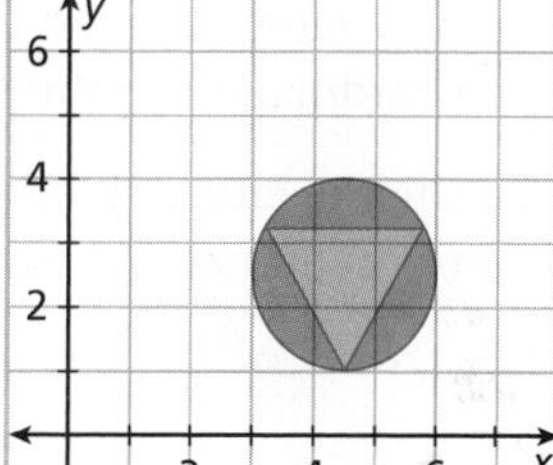

a. What is the largest scale factor of the dilation that will keep the logo in the first quadrant?

b. Sketch the logo after this dilation.

 **3.** The endpoints of one diagonal of quadrilateral *WXYZ* are *W*(7, 12) and *Y*(12, 2). The endpoints of the other diagonal are *X*(12, 12) and *Z*(4, 8).

a. Are the diagonals congruent? How do you know?

b. Are the diagonals perpendicular? Explain.

c. Do the diagonals bisect each other? Explain.

d. What is the most descriptive name for quadrilateral *WXYZ*?

continued

4. The vertices of a triangle are $X(2, 2)$, $Y(5, 6)$, and $Z(8, 2)$.

a. Prove that point Y lies on the perpendicular bisector of $\overline{XZ}$.

b. After a transformation, the images of points X and Z are $X'(-2, -2)$ and. $Z'(-2, -8)$. The transformation preserves distance and angle. Name two possibilities for the coordinates of point Y'.

c. Choose either of the possibilities for the location of point Y' you named in part **b**. Use it to prove that $\triangle XYZ \cong \triangle X'Y'Z'$.

UNIT 1  PARCC Assessment Readiness

Name ______________________ Class ______________ Date ________

SELECTED RESPONSE

1. Kendrick is using a compass and straightedge to copy $\angle Q$. The figure shows the portion of the construction that he has already completed. Where should Kendrick place the point of the compass to do the next step of the construction?

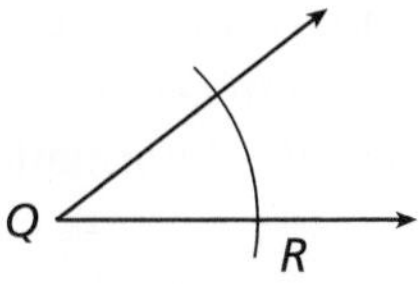

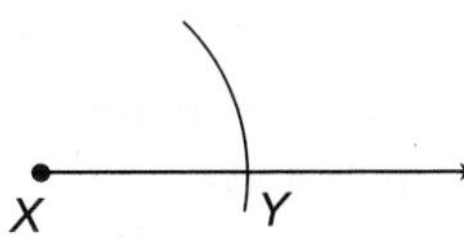

   A. point Q

   B. point R

   C. point X

   D. point Y

2. Which lines can be proven parallel given the following diagram?

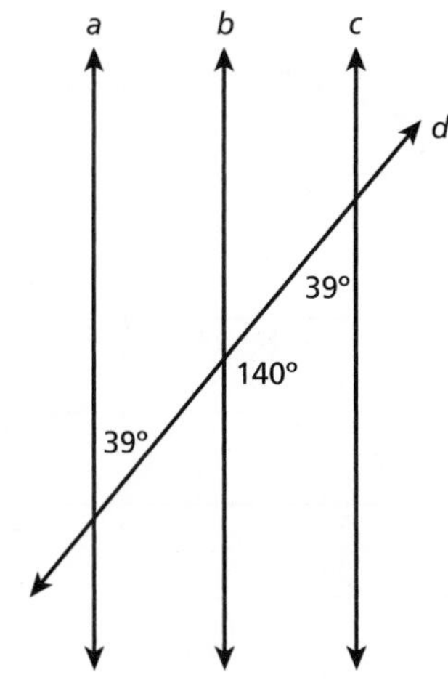

   F. $a \parallel b$ **H.** $b \parallel c$

   G. $a \parallel c$ **J.** $b \parallel d$

3. *DEFG* is a rhombus. You want to prove the property that a diagonal of a rhombus bisects a pair of opposite angles. To prove that $\overrightarrow{DF}$ bisects $\angle GDE$, you first show that $\triangle GDF \cong \triangle EDF$ using the definition of rhombus, the Reflexive Property of Congruence, and the SSS Congruence Criterion. What other reasons are needed to complete the proof?

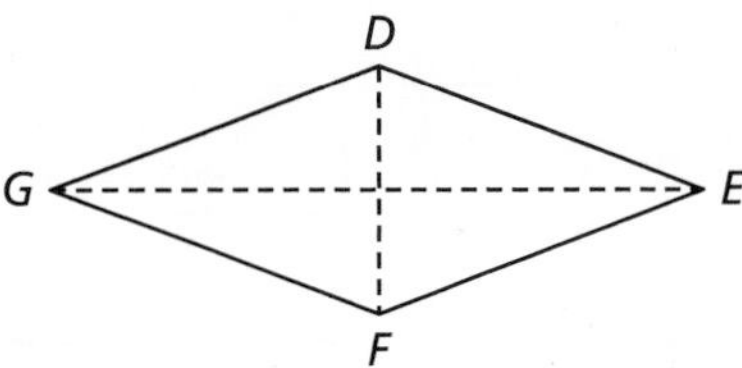

   A. Isosceles Triangle Theorem; SAS Congruence Criterion

   B. Definition of perpendicular; Triangle Sum Theorem

   C. If a quadrilateral is a parallelogram, then opposite angles are congruent; definition of angle bisector

   D. Congruent Parts of Congruent Triangles are Congruent; definition of angle bisector

4. Which of the following is *not* preserved under a dilation?

   F. angle measure

   G. betweenness

   H. collinearity

   J. distance

CONSTRUCTED RESPONSE

5. Use the definition of similarity in terms of similarity transformations to determine whether the two figures are similar. Explain your answer.

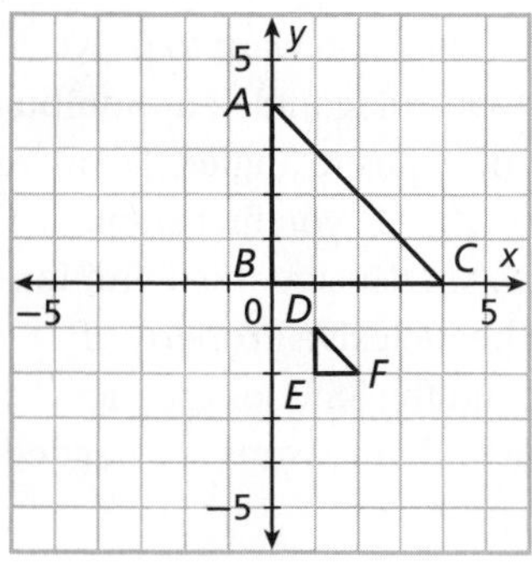

____

____

____

6. You are proving that the AA Similarity Criterion follows from the definition of similarity in terms of similarity transformations.

Given: $\angle R \cong \angle U$ and $\angle S \cong \angle V$
Prove: $\triangle RST \sim \triangle UVW$

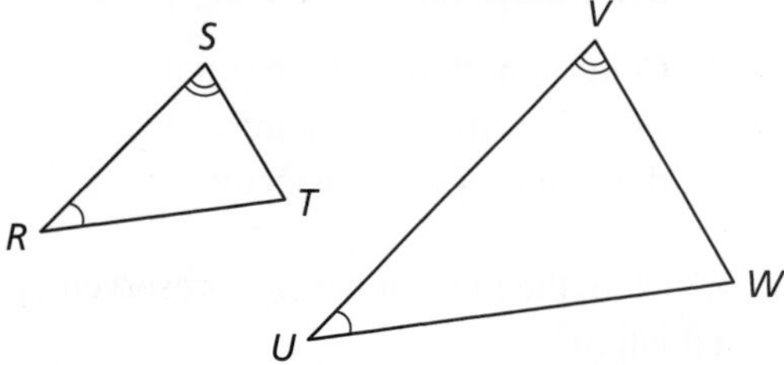

You begin by applying a dilation to $\triangle RST$. What is the scale factor k of the dilation? Why do you choose this scale factor?

____

____

____

7. To find the distance AB across a pond, you locate points as follows.

Starting at A and walking along a straight path, you walk 28 feet and put a marker at C. Then you walk 28 feet farther and put a marker at D.

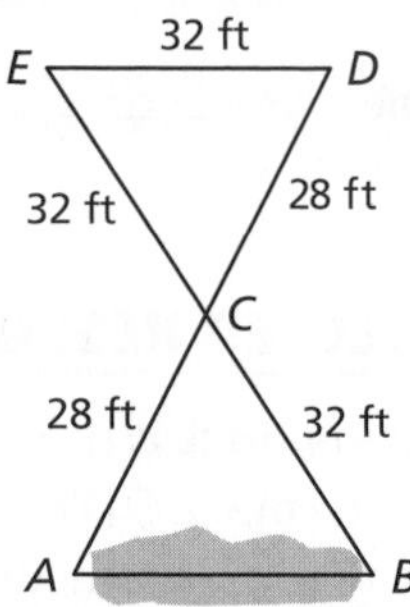

Starting at B, you walk to C, measuring the distance you walked (32 feet). Then you walk 32 feet farther and put a marker at E. Finally, you measure the distance from D to E, as shown. Explain how to use this information to find AB.

____

____

8 Find the value of x and justify each step, given that $m\angle JKL = 100°$.

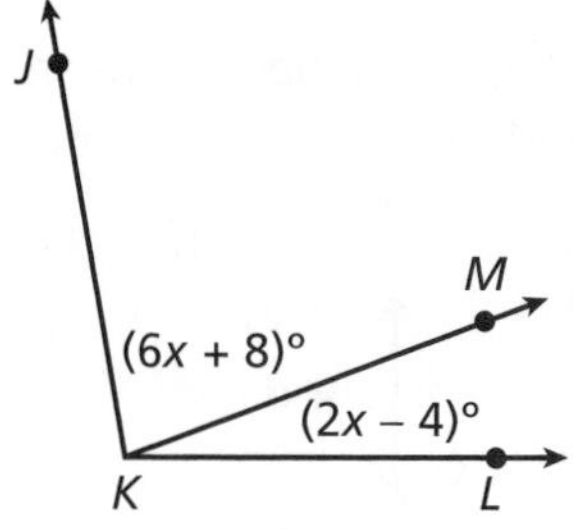

____

____

____

____

____

____

____

____

UNIT 2

Right Triangle Trigonometry

GPS COMMON CORE

Module 9 Right Triangles

9-1	The Pythagorean Theorem	**MCC9-12.G.SRT.8**
9-2	Applying Special Right Triangles	**MCC9-12.G.SRT.6**

Module 10 Trigonometry

10-1	Trigonometric Ratios	**MCC9-12.G.SRT.6**
10-2	Solving Right Triangles	**MCC9-12.G.SRT.8**
10-3	Angles of Elevation and Depression	**MCC9-12.G.SRT.8**
	Performance Tasks	
	PARCC Assessment Readiness	

Unpacking the Standards

Understanding the standards and the vocabulary terms in the standards will help you know exactly what you are expected to learn in this unit.

MCC9-12.G.SRT.8

Use … the Pythagorean Theorem to solve right triangles in applied problems.

Key Vocabulary

Pythagorean Theorem *(Teorema de Pitágoras)* If a right triangle has legs of lengths a and b and a hypotenuse of length c, then $a^2 + b^2 = c^2$.

right triangle *(triángulo rectángulo)* A triangle with one right angle.

What It Means For You

You can use the relationship between the side lengths of a right triangle to solve real-world problems.

EXAMPLE

The diagram shows the recommended position for placing a ladder. Given the length L of the ladder, you can use the Pythagorean Theorem to find x, the distance from the base of the wall to place the foot of the ladder.

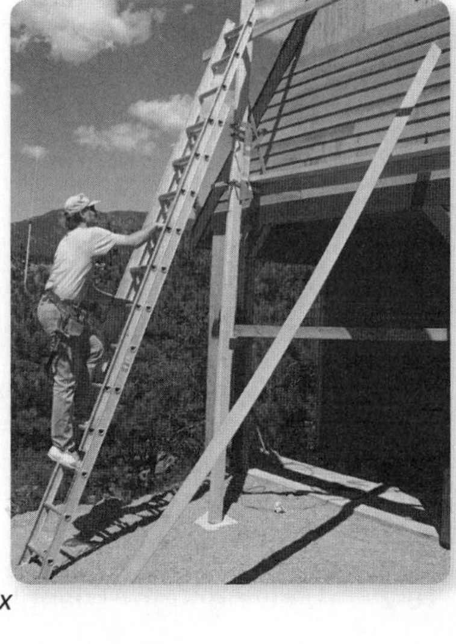

$$L^2 = x^2 + (4x)^2$$

$$L^2 = 17x^2$$

$$\frac{L^2}{17} = x^2$$

$$\frac{L}{\sqrt{17}} = x$$

L $4x$ x

MCC9-12.G.SRT.6

Understand that by similarity, side ratios in right triangles are properties of the angles in the triangle, leading to definitions of trigonometric ratios for acute angles.

Key Vocabulary

similar *(semejantes)* Two figures are similar if they have the same shape but not necessarily the same size.

ratio *(razón)* A comparison of two quantities by division.

right triangle *(triángulo rectángulo)* A triangle with one right (90°) angle.

angle *(ángulo)* A figure formed by two rays with a common endpoint.

trigonometric ratio *(razón trigonométrica)* A ratio of two sides of a right triangle.

acute angle *(ángulo agudo)* An angle that measures greater than 0° and less than 90°.

All right triangles with the same angle measures are similar, and similar triangles have proportional side lengths. So the measures of the acute angles in a given right triangle determine the ratios of the side lengths of that triangle and of all similar triangles. These ratios, called *trigonometric ratios*, can be used to solve problems.

EXAMPLE

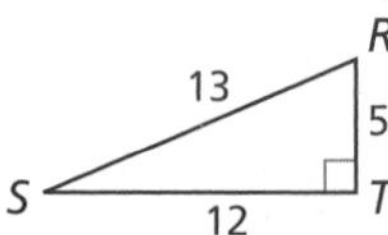

The sine of $\angle R$ is $\frac{\text{opposite leg}}{\text{hypotenuse}} = \frac{12}{13}$.

The cosine of $\angle R$ is $\frac{\text{adjacent leg}}{\text{hypotenuse}} = \frac{5}{13}$.

The tangent of $\angle R$ is $\frac{\text{opposite leg}}{\text{adjacent leg}} = \frac{12}{5}$.

MCC9-12.G.SRT.8

Use trigonometric ratios and the Pythagorean Theorem to solve right triangles in applied problems.

Key Vocabulary

Pythagorean Theorem *(Teorema de Pitágoras)* If a right triangle has legs of lengths *a* and *b* and a hypotenuse of length *c*, then $a^2 + b^2 = c^2$.

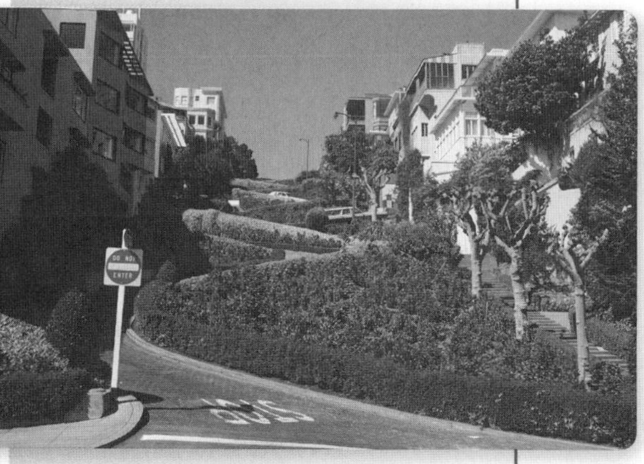

What It Means For You

You can use trigonometric ratios and the Pythagorean theorem to find unknown angle measures and side lengths in right triangles.

EXAMPLE **Using Trigonometric Ratios**

Lombard Street is on a hill in San Francisco, California, that rises 45 feet for every 100 feet of horizontal distance. What angle does the hill make with a horizontal line? Round to the nearest degree.

The right triangle below represents the hill. $\angle A$ is the angle the hill makes with a horizontal line.

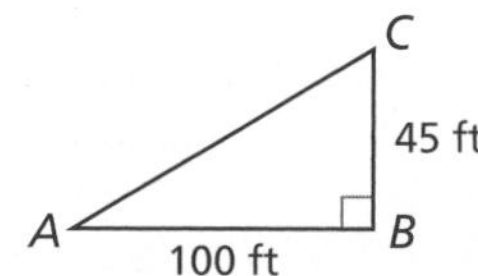

$$m\angle A = \tan^{-1}\left(\frac{45}{100}\right) \approx 27°$$

UNIT 2

Key Vocabulary

acute angle *(ángulo agudo)* An angle that measures greater than 0° and less than 90°.

angle of depression *(ángulo de depresión)* The angle formed by a horizontal line and a line of sight to a point below.

angle of elevation *(ángulo de elevación)* The angle formed by a horizontal line and a line of sight to a point above.

complementary angles *(ángulos complementarios)* Two angles whose measures have a sum of 90°.

cosine *(coseno)* In a right triangle, the cosine of angle A is the ratio of the length of the leg adjacent to angle A to the length of the hypotenuse. It is the reciprocal of the secant function.

leg of a right triangle *(cateto de un triángulo rectángulo)* One of the two sides of the right triangle that form the right angle.

Pythagorean Theorem *(Teorema de Pitágoras)* If a right triangle has legs of lengths a and b and a hypotenuse of length c, then $a^2 + b^2 = c^2$.

ratio *(razón)* A comparison of two quantities by division.

right triangle *(triángulo rectángulo)* A triangle with one right (90°) angle.

similar *(semejantes)* Two figures are similar if they have the same shape but not necessarily the same size.

sine *(seno)* In a right triangle, the ratio of the length of the leg opposite angle A to the length of the hypotenuse.

tangent of an angle *(tangente de un ángulo)* In a right triangle, the ratio of the length of the leg opposite angle A to the length of the leg adjacent to angle A.

triangle *(triángulo)* A three-sided polygon.

trigonometric ratio *(razón trigonométrica)* A ratio of two sides of a right triangle.

Name ________________________ Class ______________ Date ________

9-1

The Pythagorean Theorem

Going Deeper

Essential question: *How can you apply the Pythagorean Theorem?*

MCC9–12.G.SRT.8

1 EXAMPLE Using the Pythagorean Theorem with Lengths

A shelf extends perpendicularly 24 cm from a wall. You want to place a 28-cm brace under the shelf, as shown. To the nearest tenth of a centimeter, how far below the shelf will the brace be attached to the wall?

Shelf
C 24 cm A
Wall
28 cm
Brace
B

Use the Pythagorean Theorem to find the distance *BC*.

$BC^2 + AC^2 = AB^2$	Pythagorean Theorem
$BC^2 + \_\_\_^2 = \_\_\_^2$	Substitute.
$BC^2 + \_\_\_\_ = \_\_\_\_$	Find the squares.
$BC^2 = \_\_\_\_$	Subtract the same quantity from both sides.
$BC \approx \_\_\_\_\_$	Find the square root and round.

So, the brace should be attached to the wall about ________ below the shelf.

REFLECT

1a. Suppose you know that $m\angle CAB \approx 31°$. What is $m\angle CBA$? Explain.

____

____

MCC9–12.G.SRT.8

2 EXAMPLE Using the Pythagorean Theorem with Velocities

You paddle a canoe due north across a river at a rate of 3 mi/h. The river has a 1 mi/h current that flows due east. What is your canoe's actual speed?

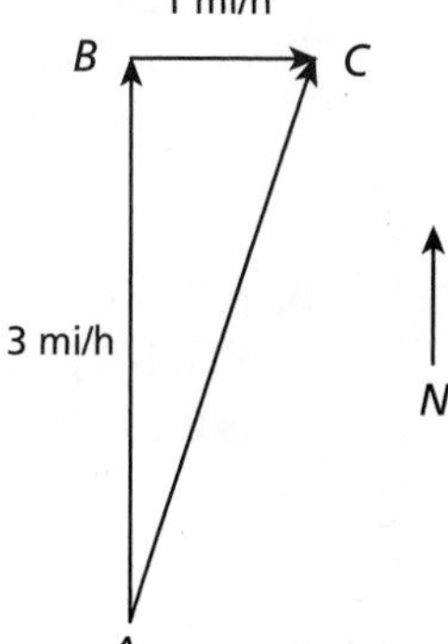

A Model the situation with arrows whose lengths represent speeds. The arrow that represents the paddling speed is three times the length of the arrow that represents the river speed.

B Use the Pythagorean Theorem to find *AC*.

$AC^2 = \_\_\_^2 + \_\_\_^2$	Pythagorean Theorem
$AC^2 = \_\_\_\_$	Square the terms and add.
$AC \approx \_\_\_\_\_$	Take the square root of both sides. Round to the nearest tenth.

So, the actual speed of the canoe is about ________________.

REFLECT

2a. Why does it make sense that the canoe's actual speed is greater than both the speed at which you paddle and the speed of the current?

____

____

PRACTICE

Use the Pythagorean Theorem to find the missing side length. Round to the nearest tenth.

1.

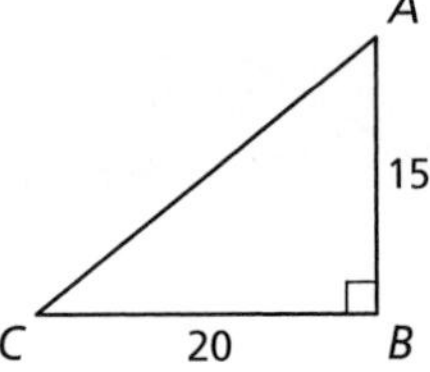

____

2.

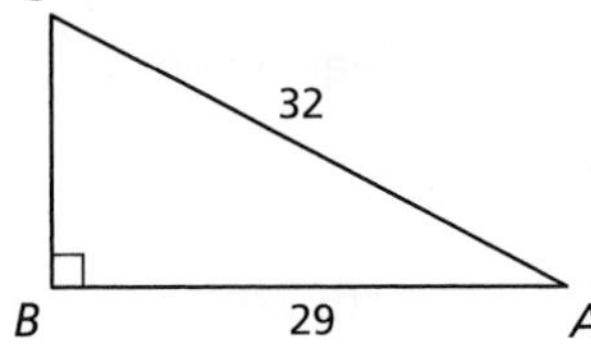

____

3.

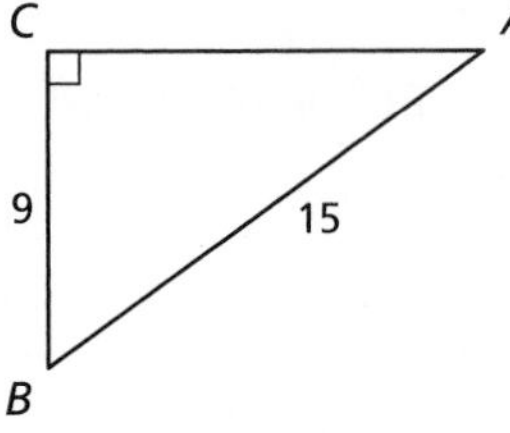

____

4.

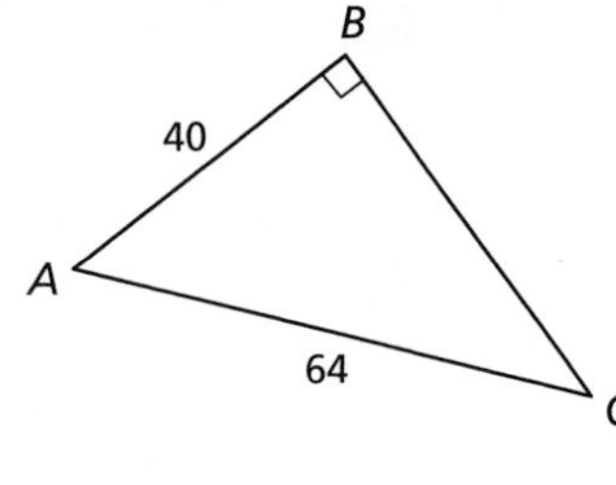

____

5.

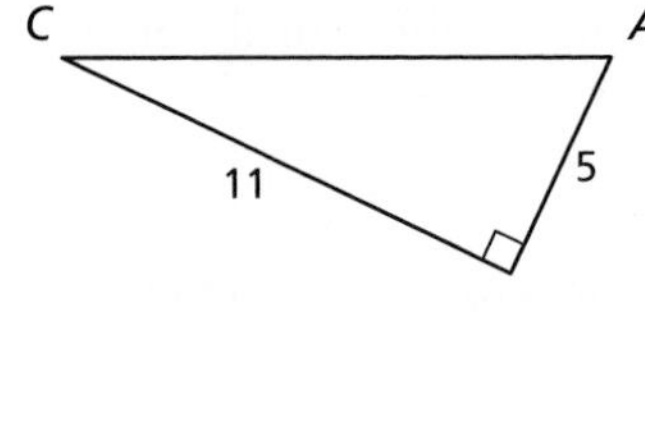

____

6.

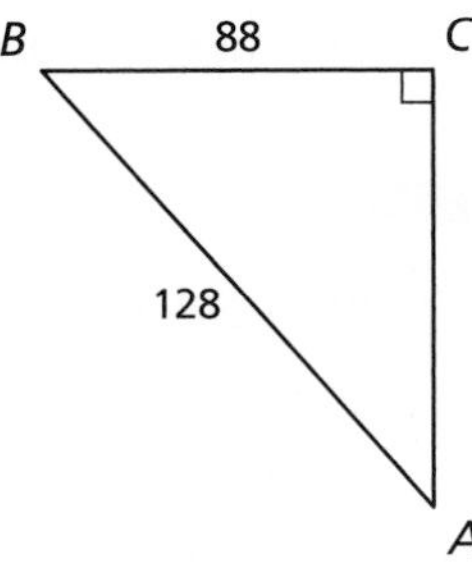

____

7. A ladder leans against a wall and reaches a point 15 feet up the wall. The base of the ladder is 3.9 feet from the wall. To the nearest tenth of a foot, what is the length of the ladder?

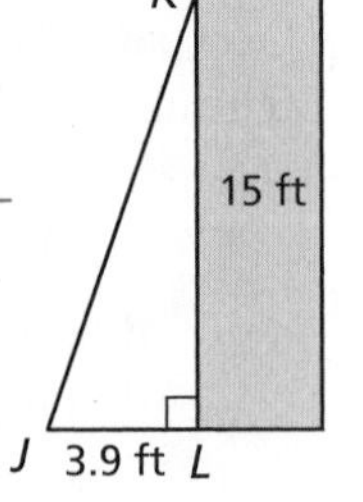

____

8. A 7.2-meter guy wire goes from the top of a utility pole to a point on the ground that is 3 meters from the base of the pole. To the nearest tenth of a meter, how tall is the utility pole?

____

9. A plane flies due north at 500 mi/h. There is a crosswind blowing due east at 60 mi/h. What is the plane's actual speed to the nearest tenth?

____

Name _______________ Class _______________ Date _______________

9-1

Additional Practice

Find the value of *x*. Give your answer in simplest radical form.

1.

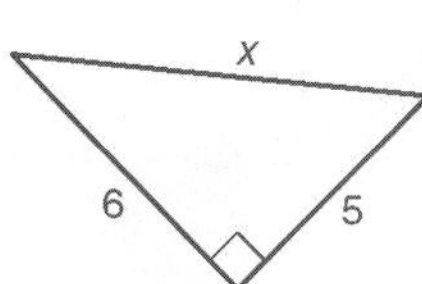

2.

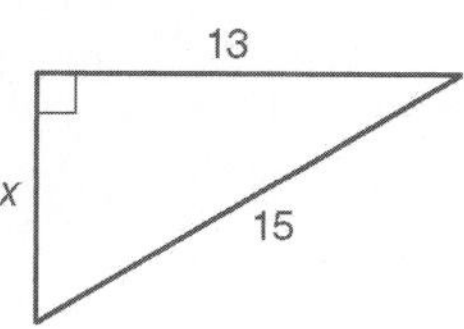

3.

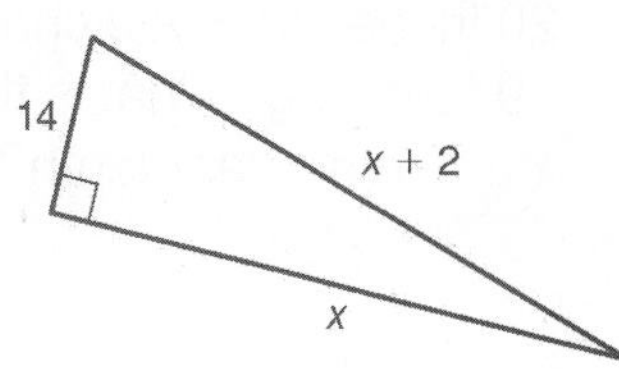

_______________ _______________ _______________

4. The aspect ratio of a TV screen is the ratio of the width to the height of the image. A regular TV has an aspect ratio of 4 : 3. Find the height and width of a 42-inch TV screen to the nearest tenth of an inch. (The measure given is the length of the diagonal across the screen.)

____

5. A "wide-screen" TV has an aspect ratio of 16 : 9. Find the length of a diagonal on a wide-screen TV screen that has the same height as the screen in Exercise 4. _______________

Find the missing side lengths. Give your answer in simplest radical form. Tell whether the side lengths form a Pythagorean Triple.

6.

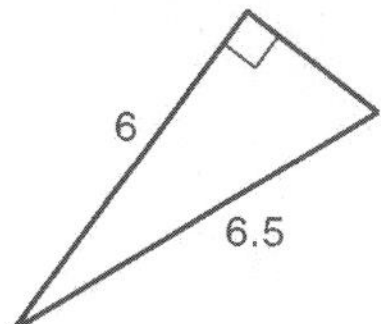

7.

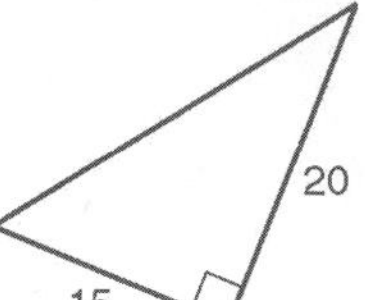

8.

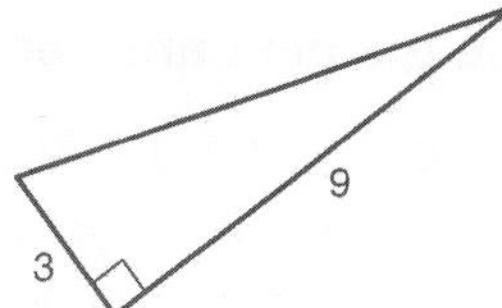

_______________ _______________ _______________

Tell whether the measures can be the side lengths of a triangle. If so, classify the triangle as acute, obtuse, or right.

9. 15, 18, 20

10. 7, 8, 11

11. 6, 7, $3\sqrt{13}$

_______________ _______________ _______________

12. Kitty has a triangle with sides that measure 16, 8, and 13. She does some calculations and finds that $256 + 64 > 169$. Kitty concludes that the triangle is obtuse. Evaluate Kitty's conclusion and Kitty's reasoning.

____
____
____
____

Problem Solving

1. It is recommended that for a height of 20 inches, a wheelchair ramp be 19 feet long. What is the value of x to the nearest tenth?

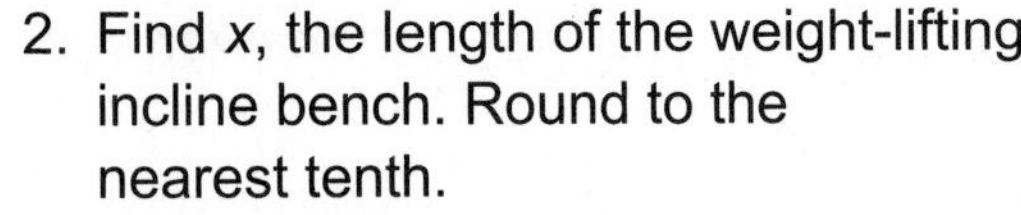

2. Find x, the length of the weight-lifting incline bench. Round to the nearest tenth.

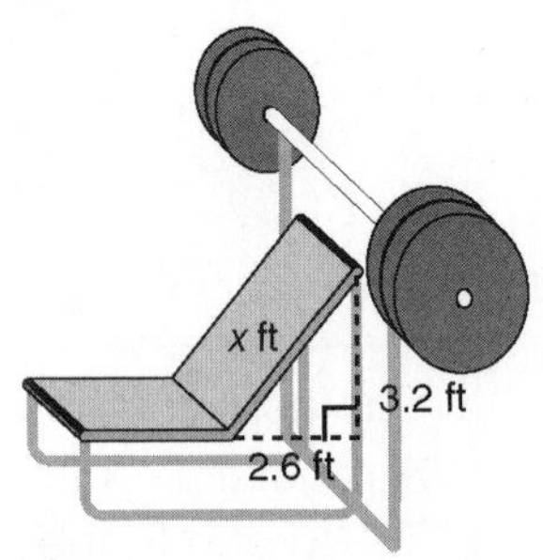

3. A ladder 15 feet from the base of a building reaches a window that is 35 feet high. What is the length of the ladder to the nearest foot?

4. In a wide-screen television, the ratio of width to height is 16 : 9. What are the width and height of a television that has a diagonal measure of 42 inches? Round to the nearest tenth.

Choose the best answer.

5. The distance from Austin to San Antonio is about 74 miles, and the distance from San Antonio to Victoria is about 102 miles. Find the approximate distance from Austin to Victoria.

   A 28 mi　　C 126 mi

   B 70 mi　　D 176 mi

6. What is the approximate perimeter of $\triangle DEC$ if rectangle $ABCD$ has a length of 4.6 centimeters?

   F 5.1 cm

   G 6.5 cm

   H 9.8 cm

   J 11.1 cm

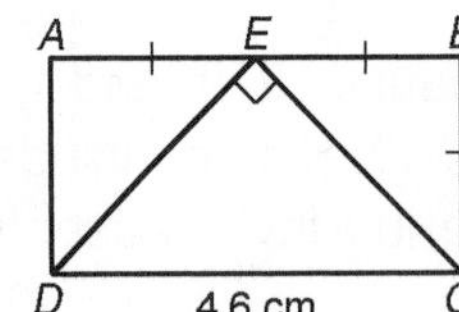

7. The legs of a right triangle measure $3x$ and 15. If the hypotenuse measures $3x + 3$, what is the value of x?

   A 12　　C 36

   B 16　　D 221

8. A cube has edge lengths of 6 inches. What is the approximate length of a diagonal d of the cube?

   F 6 in.　　H 10.4 in.

   G 8.4 in.　　J 12 in.

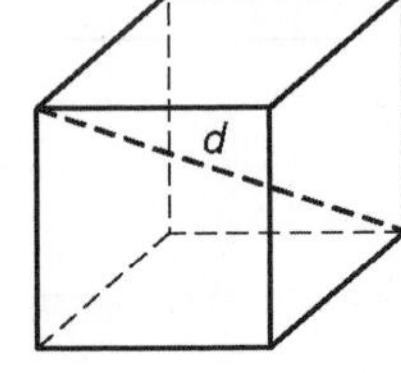

Name________________________ Class______________ Date__________

9-2

Applying Special Right Triangles

Going Deeper

Essential question: *What can you say about the side lengths associated with special right triangles?*

Video Tutor

There are two special right triangles that arise frequently in problem-solving situations. It is useful to know the relationships among the side lengths of these triangles.

MCC9–12.G.SRT.6

1 EXPLORE Investigating an Isosceles Right Triangle

A The figure shows an isosceles right triangle. What is the measure of each base angle of the triangle? Why?

____

____

B Let the legs of the right triangle have length x. You can use the Pythagorean Theorem to find the length of the hypotenuse in terms of x.

$AB^2 = x^2 + x^2$ Pythagorean Theorem

$AB^2 =$ __________ Combine like terms.

$AB =$ __________ Find the square root of both sides and simplify.

REFLECT

1a. A student claims that if you know one side length of an isosceles right triangle, then you know all the side lengths. Do you agree or disagree? Explain.

____

____

____

1b. Explain how to find y in the right triangle at right.

____

____

____

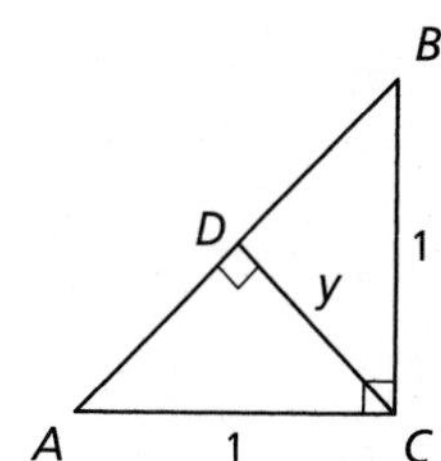

MCC9–12.G.SRT.6

2 EXPLORE Investigating Another Special Right Triangle

A In the figure, $\triangle ABD$ is an equilateral triangle and $\overline{BC}$ is a perpendicular from B to $\overline{AD}$. Explain how to find the angle measures in $\triangle ABC$.

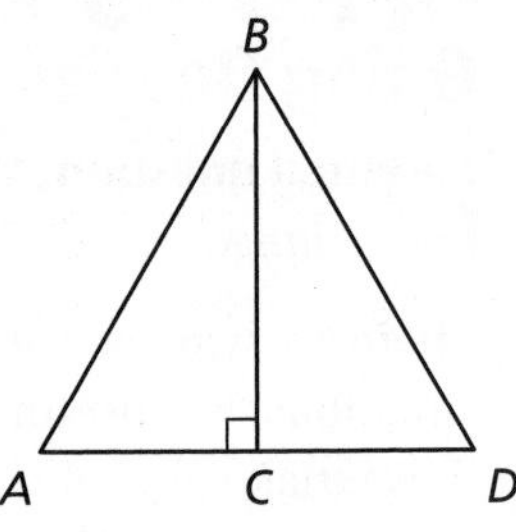

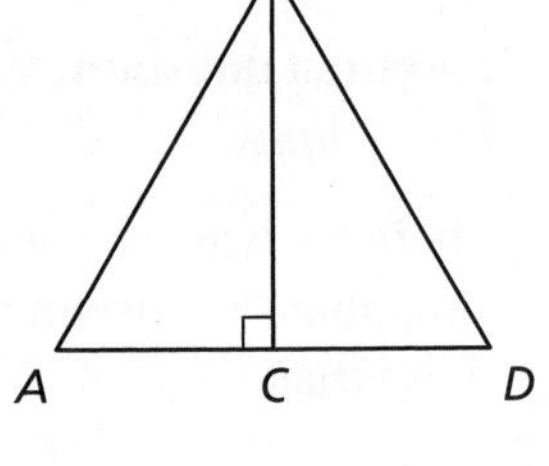

____

____

B Explain why $\triangle ACB \cong \triangle DCB$.

____

____

____

____

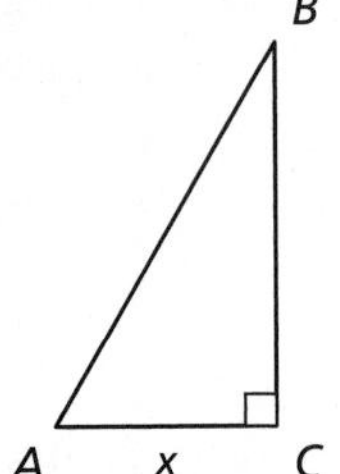

C Let the length of $\overline{AC}$ be x. What is the length of $\overline{AB}$? Why?

____

D In the space below, show how to use the Pythagorean Theorem to find the length of $\overline{BC}$.

____

____

____

____

REFLECT

2a. What is the ratio of the side lengths in a right triangle with acute angles that measure 30° and 60°?

____

2b. Error Analysis A student drew a right triangle with a 60° angle and a hypotenuse of length 10. Then he labeled the other side lengths as shown. Explain how you can tell just by glancing at the side lengths that the student made an error. Then explain the error.

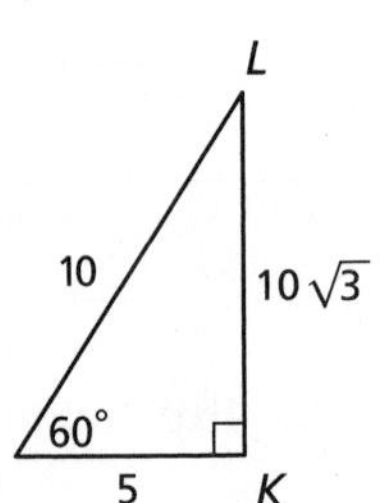

____

____

The right triangles you investigated are sometimes called 45°-45°-90° and 30°-60°-90° right triangles. The side-length relationships that you discovered can be used to find lengths in any such triangles.

MCC9–12.G.SRT.8

3 EXAMPLE Solving Special Right Triangles

A Refer to the diagram of the 45°-45°-90° triangle. Fill in the calculations that help you find the missing side lengths. Give answers in simplest radical form.

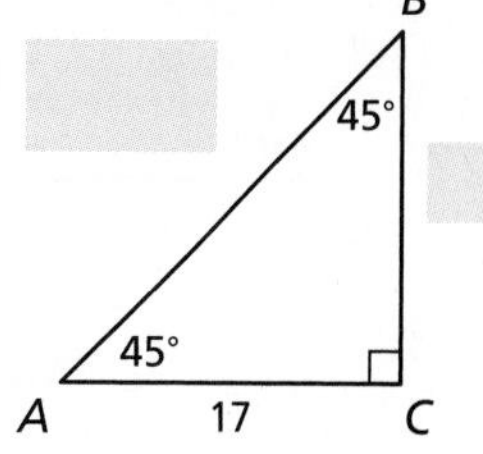

$AC =$ ______

$BC = AC \cdot$ ______ $=$ ______

$AB = AC \cdot$ ______ $=$ ______

B Refer to the diagram of the 30°-60°-90° triangle. Fill in the calculations that help you find the missing side lengths. Give answers in simplest radical form.

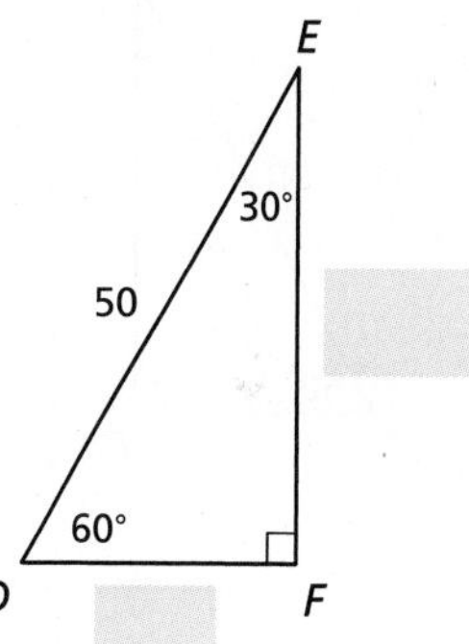

$DE =$ ______

$DF = DE \div$ ______ $=$ ______

$EF = DF \cdot$ ______ $=$ ______

C Add the side lengths you calculated to the diagrams.

REFLECT

3a. Suppose you are given the length of the hypotenuse of a 45°-45°-90° triangle. How can you calculate the length of a leg?

____

3b. Suppose you are given the length of the longer leg of a 30°-60°-90° triangle. How can you calculate the length of the shorter leg?

____

3c. When finding a leg length in a 45°-45°-90° triangle, one student gave the answer $\frac{30}{\sqrt{2}}$ and another gave the answer $15\sqrt{2}$. Show the answers are equivalent.

____

____

PRACTICE

Find the value of *x*. Give your answer in simplest radical form.

1.

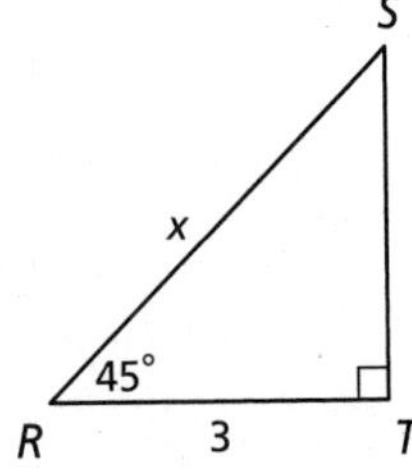

2.

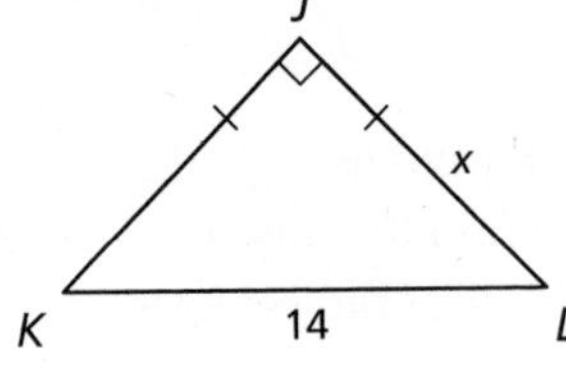

3.

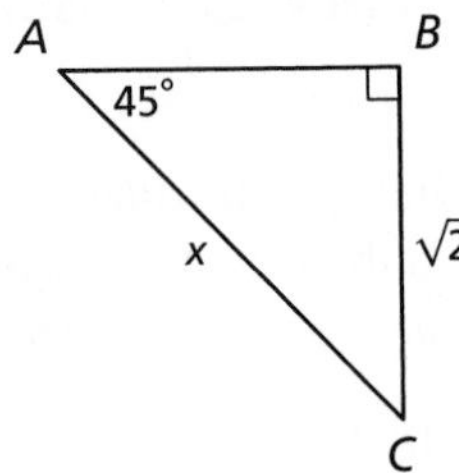

4.

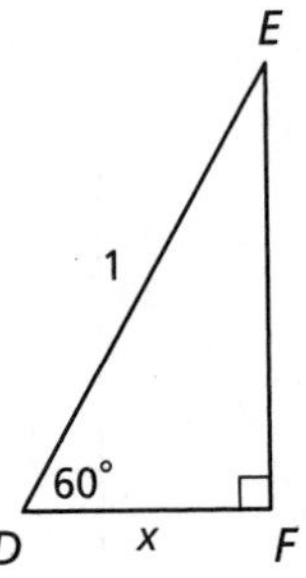

5.

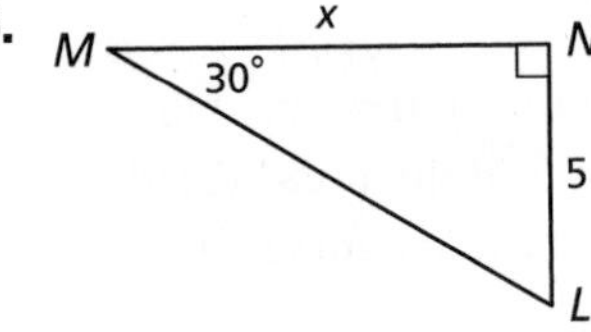

6.

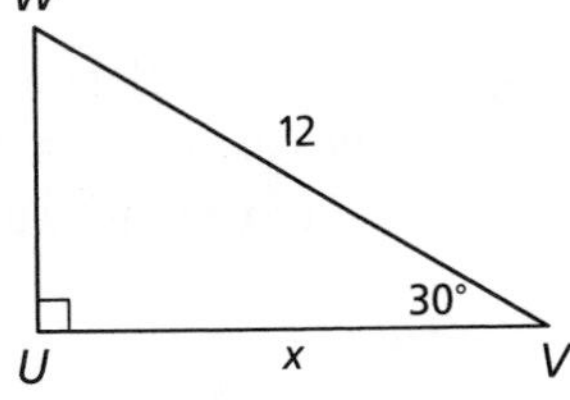

7.

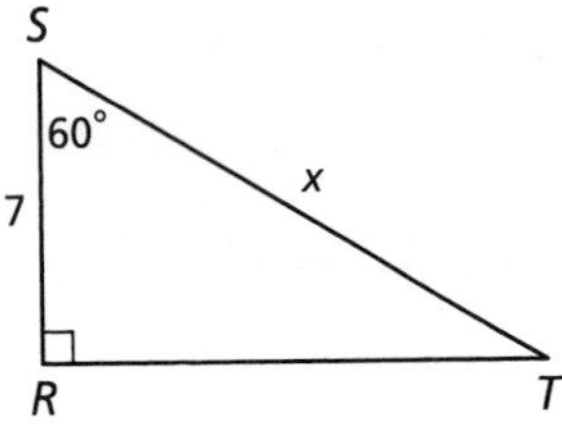

8.

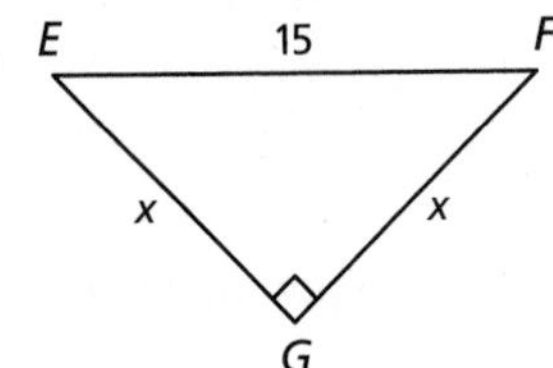

9.

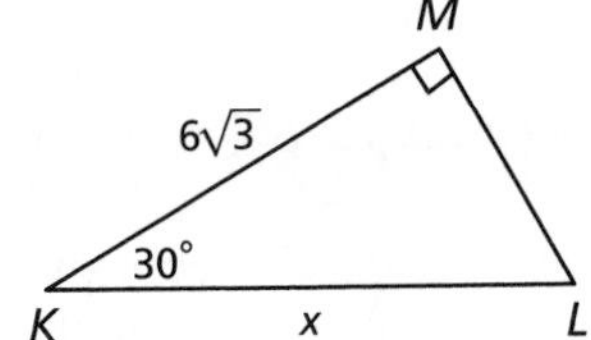

10. Error Analysis Two students were asked to find the value of x in the figure at right. Which student's work is correct? Explain the other student's error.

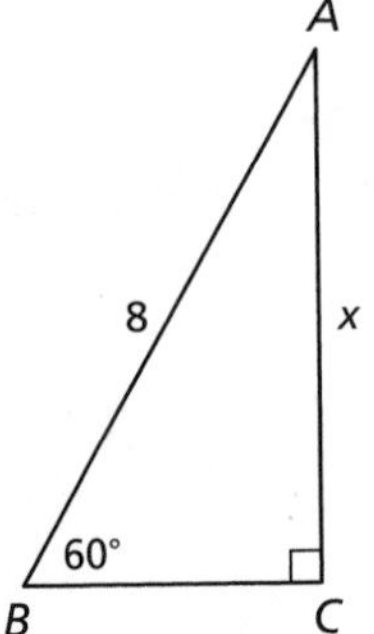

Roberto's Work	**Aaron's Work**
In a 30°-60°-90° triangle, the hypotenuse is twice as long as the shorter leg, so $BC = 4$. The ratio of the lengths of the legs is $1:\sqrt{3}$, so $x = 4\sqrt{3}$.	In a 30°-60°-90° triangle, the side lengths are in a ratio of $1:\sqrt{3}:2$, so x must be $\sqrt{3}$ times the length of $\overline{AB}$. Therefore, $x = 8\sqrt{3}$.

Name____________________________________ Class_________________ Date_______________

Additional Practice

Find the value of *x* in each figure. Give your answer in simplest radical form.

1. 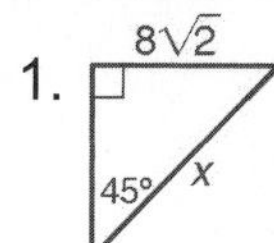

2. x
7
x

3. 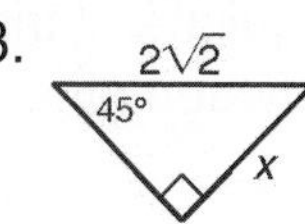

__________________ __________________ __________________

Find the values of *x* and *y*. Give your answers in simplest radical form.

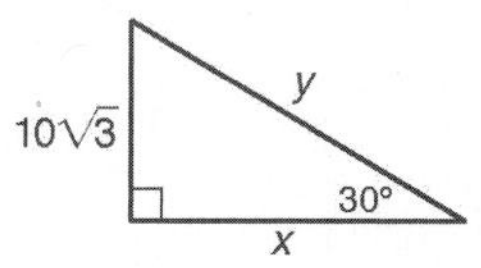

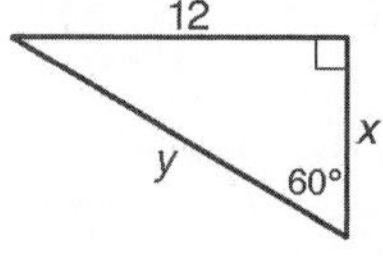

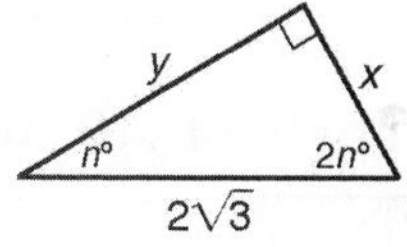

4. $x =$ ________ $y =$ ________ 5. $x =$ ________ $y =$ ________ 6. $x =$ ________ $y =$ ________

Lucia is an archaeologist trekking through the jungle of the Yucatan Peninsula. She stumbles upon a stone structure covered with creeper vines and ferns. She immediately begins taking measurements of her discovery. (*Hint:* Drawing some figures may help.)

7. Around the perimeter of the building, Lucia finds small alcoves at regular intervals carved into the stone. The alcoves are triangular in shape with a horizontal base and two sloped equal-length sides that meet at a right angle. Each of the sloped sides measures $14\frac{1}{4}$ inches. Lucia has also found several stone tablets inscribed with characters. The stone tablets measure $22\frac{1}{8}$ inches long. Lucia hypothesizes that the alcoves once held the stone tablets. Tell whether Lucia's hypothesis may be correct. Explain your answer.

____

____

8. Lucia also finds several statues around the building. The statues measure $9\frac{7}{16}$ inches tall. She wonders whether the statues might have been placed in the alcoves. Tell whether this is possible. Explain your answer.

____

____

____

____

____

Problem Solving

For Exercises 1–6, give your answers in simplest radical form.

1. In bowling, the pins are arranged in a pattern based on equilateral triangles. What is the distance between pins 1 and 5?

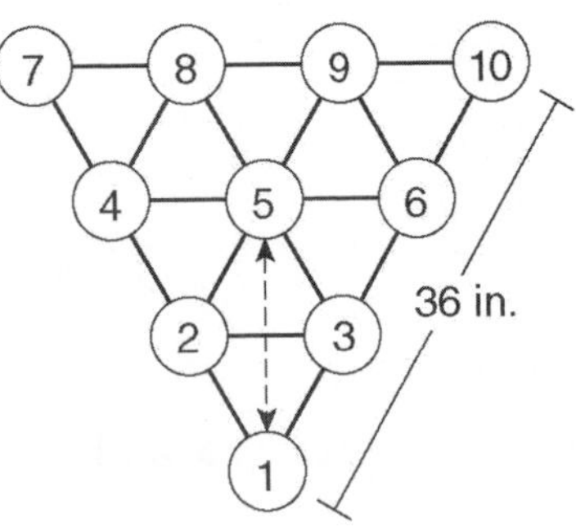

____

2. To secure an outdoor canopy, a 64-inch cord is extended from the top of a vertical pole to the ground. If the cord makes a 60° angle with the ground, how tall is the pole?

____

Find the length of $\overline{AB}$ in each quilt pattern.

3. 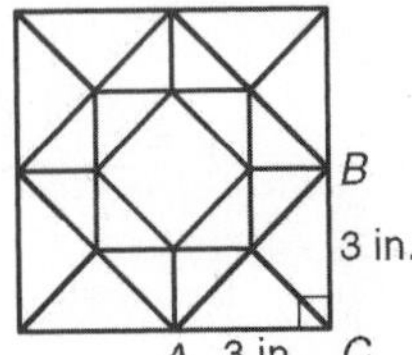

____

4. 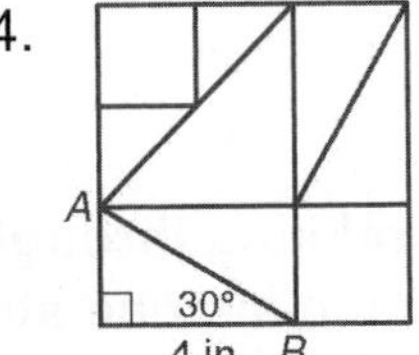

____

Choose the best answer.

5. An equilateral triangle has an altitude of 21 inches. What is the side length of the triangle?

____

6. A shelf is an isosceles right triangle, and the longest side is 38 centimeters. What is the length of each of the other two sides?

____

Use the figure for Exercises 7 and 8.

Assume $\triangle JKL$ is in the first quadrant, with $m\angle K = 90°$.

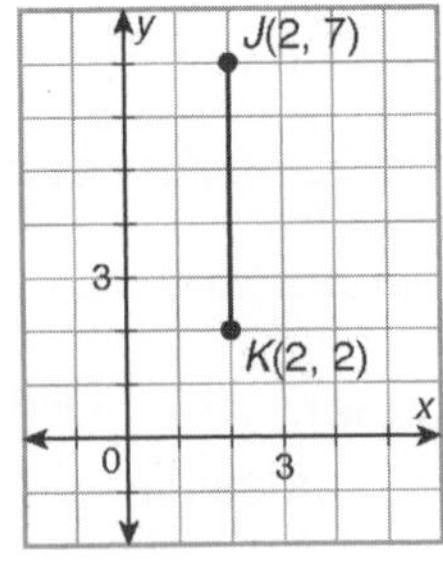

7. Suppose that $\overline{JK}$ is a leg of $\triangle JKL$, a 45°-45°-90° triangle. What are possible coordinates of point L?

   A (6, 4.5) C (6, 2)
   B (7, 2) D (8, 7)

8. Suppose $\triangle JKL$ is a 30°-60°-90° triangle and $\overline{JK}$ is the side opposite the 60° angle. What are the approximate coordinates of point L?

   F (4.9, 2) H (8.7, 2)
   G (4.5, 2) J (7.1, 2)

Name ______________________ Class ______________ Date ________

10-1

Trigonometric Ratios

Going Deeper

Essential question: *How do you find the tangent, sine, and cosine ratios for acute angles in a right triangle?*

In this chapter, you will be working extensively with right triangles, so some new vocabulary will be helpful. Given a right triangle, $\triangle ABC$, with a right angle at vertex C, the leg **adjacent** to $\angle A$ is the leg that forms one side of $\angle A$. The leg **opposite** $\angle A$ is the leg that does not form a side of $\angle A$.

MCC9–12.G.SRT.6

1 EXPLORE Investigating a Ratio in a Right Triangle

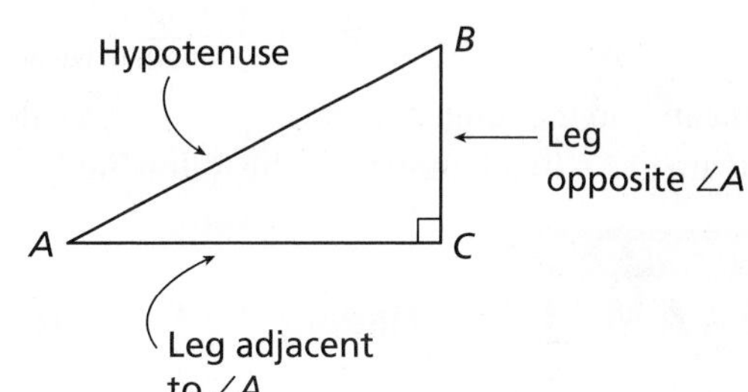

A Use geometry software to draw a horizontal segment. Label one endpoint of the segment A.

B Select point A, go to the Transform menu, and choose Mark Center.

C Select the segment, go to the Transform menu, and choose Rotate. Enter 30° for the angle of rotation. Label the endpoint of the rotation image B.

D Select point B and the original line segment. Use the Construct menu to construct a perpendicular from B to the segment. Plot a point at the point of intersection and label the point C.

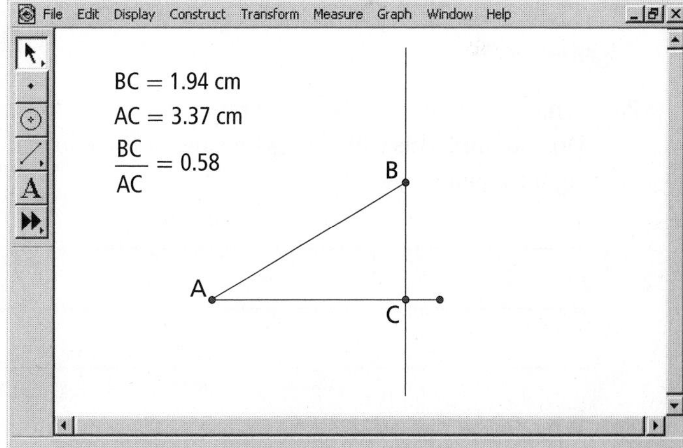

E Use the Measure menu to measure $\overline{BC}$ and $\overline{AC}$. Then use the Calculate tool to calculate the ratio $\frac{BC}{AC}$.

F Drag the points and lines to change the size and location of the triangle. Notice what happens to the measurements.

G Repeat the above steps using a different angle of rotation.

REFLECT

1a. Compare your findings with those of other students. For an acute angle in a right triangle, what can you say about the ratio of the length of the opposite leg to the length of the adjacent leg?

____

____

You may have discovered that in a right triangle the ratio of the length of the leg opposite an acute angle to the length of the leg adjacent to the angle is constant. You can use what you know about similarity to see why this is true.

Consider the right triangles $\triangle ABC$ and $\triangle DEF$, in which $\angle A \cong \angle D$, as shown. By the AA Similarity Criterion, $\triangle ABC \sim \triangle DEF$. This means the lengths of the sides of $\triangle DEF$ are each k times the lengths of the corresponding sides of $\triangle ABC$.

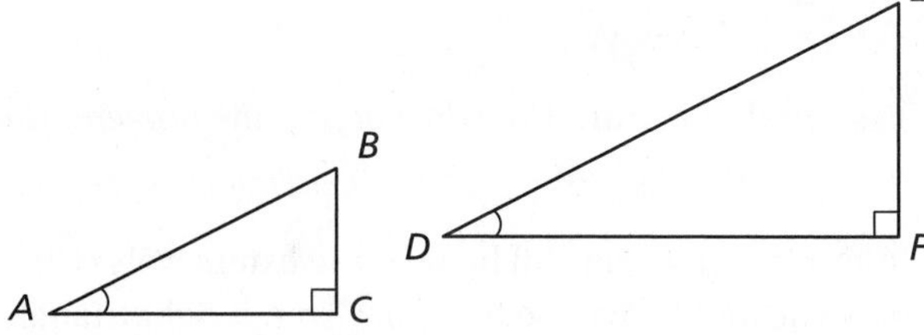

$$\frac{EF}{DF} = \frac{k \bullet BC}{k \bullet AC} = \frac{BC}{AC}$$

This shows that the ratio of the length of the leg opposite an acute angle to the length of the leg adjacent to the angle is constant. This ratio is called the *tangent* of the angle. Thus, the **tangent** of $\angle A$, written tan A, is defined as follows:

$$\tan A = \frac{\text{length of leg opposite } \angle A}{\text{length of leg adjacent to } \angle A} = \frac{BC}{AC}$$

You can find the tangent of an angle using a calculator or by using lengths that are given in a figure, as in the following example.

MCC9–12.G.SRT.6

2 EXAMPLE Finding the Tangent of an Angle

Find the tangent of $\angle J$ and $\angle K$. Write each ratio as a fraction and as a decimal rounded to the nearest hundredth.

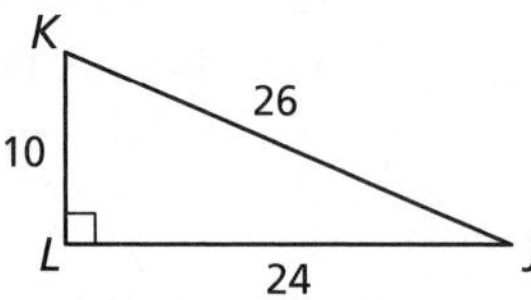

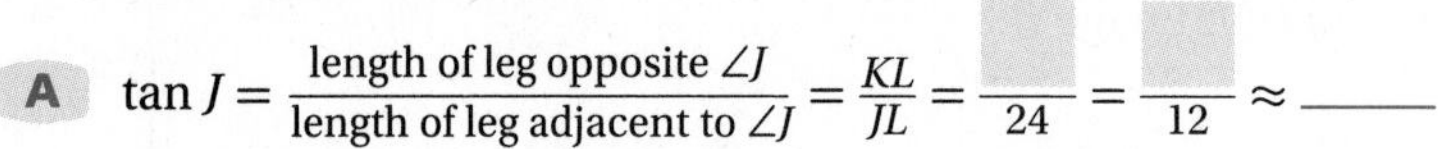

A $\tan J = \frac{\text{length of leg opposite } \angle J}{\text{length of leg adjacent to } \angle J} = \frac{KL}{JL} = \frac{\square}{24} = \frac{\square}{12} \approx$ ______

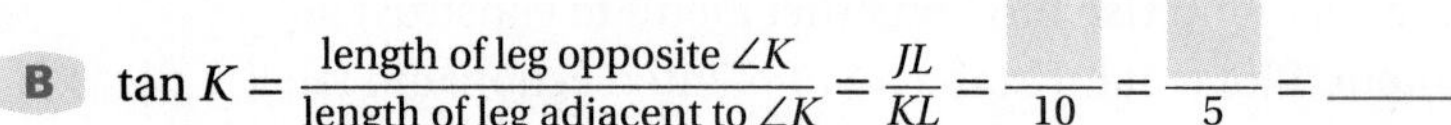

B $\tan K = \frac{\text{length of leg opposite } \angle K}{\text{length of leg adjacent to } \angle K} = \frac{JL}{KL} = \frac{\square}{10} = \frac{\square}{5} =$ ______

REFLECT

2a. What do you notice about the ratios you wrote for tan J and tan K? Do you think this will always be true for the two acute angles in a right triangle?

______

______

______

2b. Why does it not make sense to ask for the value of tan L?

______

______

When you know the length of a leg of a right triangle and the measure of one of the acute angles, you can use the tangent to find the length of the other leg. This is especially useful in real-world problems.

MCC9–12.G.SRT.8

3 EXAMPLE Solving a Real-World Problem

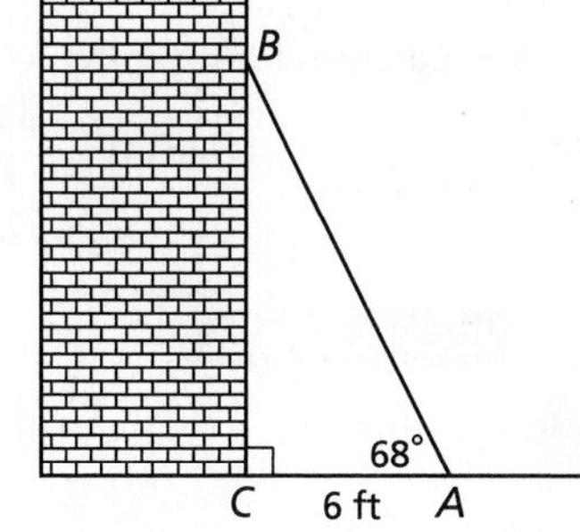

A long ladder leans against a building and makes an angle of 68° with the ground. The base of the ladder is 6 feet from the building. To the nearest tenth of a foot, how far up the side of the building does the ladder reach?

A Write a tangent ratio that involves the unknown length, *BC*.

$\tan A = \frac{\text{length of leg opposite } \angle A}{\text{length of leg adjacent to } \angle A} = \frac{BC}{6}$

Use the fact that $m\angle A = 68°$ to write the equation as $\tan 68° = \frac{BC}{6}$.

B Solve for *BC*.

$6 \cdot \tan 68° = BC$ Multiply both sides by 6.

$6 \cdot$ ______________ $= BC$ Use a calculator to find tan 68°. Do not round until the final step of the solution.

______________ $\approx BC$ Multiply. Round to the nearest tenth.

So, the ladder reaches about __________ up the side of the building.

REFLECT

3a. Why is it best to wait until the final step before rounding? What happens if you round the value of tan 68° to the nearest tenth before multiplying?

____

____

3b. A student claims that it is possible to solve the problem using the tangent of $\angle B$. Do you agree or disagree? If it is possible, show the solution. If it is not possible, explain why not.

____

____

A **trigonometric ratio** is a ratio of two sides of a right triangle. You have already seen one trigonometric ratio, the tangent. It is also possible to define two additional trigonometric ratios, the sine and the cosine, that involve the hypotenuse of a right triangle.

The **sine** of $\angle A$, written sin A, is defined as follows:

$$\sin A = \frac{\text{length of leg opposite } \angle A}{\text{length of hypotenuse}} = \frac{BC}{AB}$$

The **cosine** of $\angle A$, written cos A, is defined as follows:

$$\cos A = \frac{\text{length of leg adjacent to } \angle A}{\text{length of hypotenuse}} = \frac{AC}{AB}$$

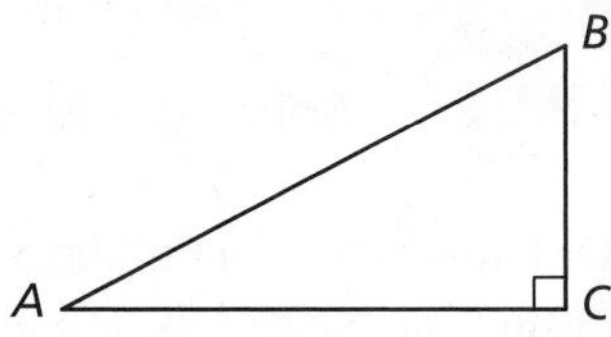

MCC9–12.G.SRT.6

4 EXAMPLE Finding the Sine and Cosine of an Angle

Write each trigonometric ratio as a fraction and as a decimal rounded to the nearest hundredth.

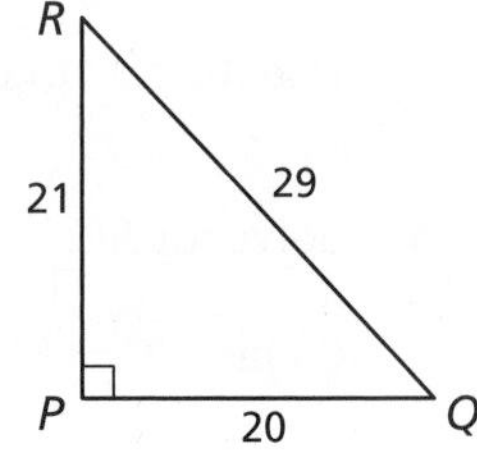

A 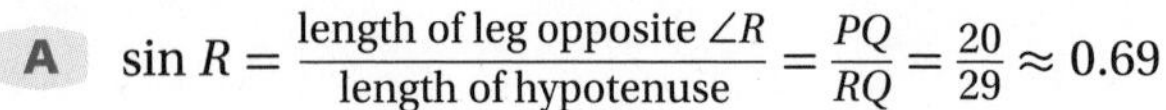

$$\sin R = \frac{\text{length of leg opposite } \angle R}{\text{length of hypotenuse}} = \frac{PQ}{RQ} = \frac{20}{29} \approx 0.69$$

B $$\sin Q = \frac{\text{length of leg opposite } \angle Q}{\text{length of hypotenuse}} = \frac{RP}{RQ} = \frac{\square}{29} \approx \_\_\_\_\_\_$$

C 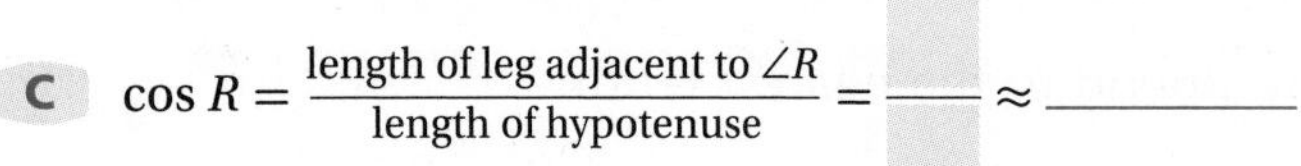

$$\cos R = \frac{\text{length of leg adjacent to } \angle R}{\text{length of hypotenuse}} = \frac{\square}{\square} \approx \_\_\_\_\_\_$$

D $$\cos Q = \frac{\text{length of leg adjacent to } \angle Q}{\text{length of hypotenuse}} = \frac{\square}{\square} \approx \_\_\_\_\_\_$$

REFLECT

4a. What do you notice about the sines and cosines you found? Do you think this relationship will be true for any pair of acute angles in a right triangle? Explain.

____

____

____

You may have discovered a relationship between the sines and cosines of the acute angles in a right triangle. In particular, if $\angle A$ and $\angle B$ are the acute angles in a right triangle, then $\sin A = \cos B$ and $\sin B = \cos A$.

Note that the acute angles in a right triangle are complementary. The above observation leads to a more general fact: the sine of an angle is equal to the cosine of its complement, and the cosine of an angle is equal to the sine of its complement.

MCC9–12.G.SRT.7

5 EXAMPLE Using Complementary Angles

Given that $\sin 57° \approx 0.839$, write the cosine of a complementary angle.

A Find the measure x of an angle that is complementary to a 57° angle.

$x + 57° = 90°$, so $x =$ ___________

B Use the fact that the cosine of an angle is equal to the sine of its complement.

cos ___________ ≈ 0.839

Given that $\cos 60° = 0.5$, write the sine of a complementary angle.

C Find the measure y of an angle that is complementary to a 60° angle.

$y + 60° = 90°$, so $y =$ ___________

D Use the fact that the sine of an angle is equal to the cosine of its complement.

sin ___________ $= 0.5$

REFLECT

5a. Is it possible to find $m\angle J$ in the figure? Explain.

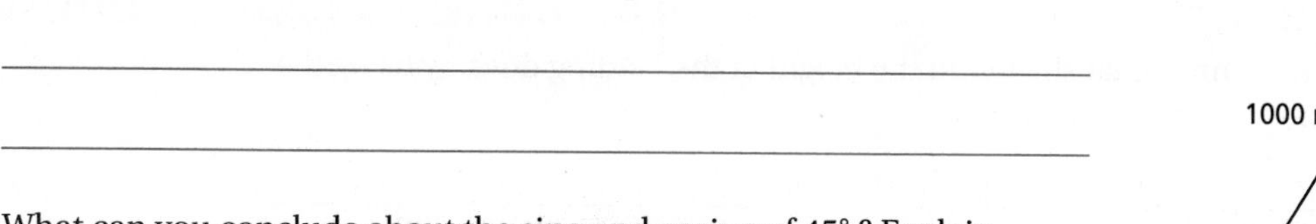

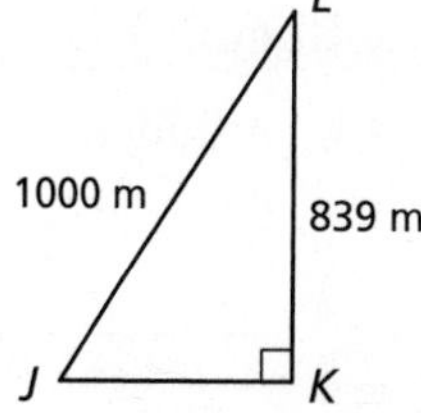

5b. What can you conclude about the sine and cosine of 45° ? Explain.

____

5c. Is it possible for the sine of an angle to equal 1? Why or why not?

____

____

MCC9–12.G.SRT.8

6 EXAMPLE Solving a Real-World Problem

A loading dock at a factory has a 16-foot ramp in front of it, as shown in the figure. The ramp makes an angle of 8° with the ground. To the nearest tenth of a foot, what is the height of the loading dock? How far does the ramp extend in front of the loading dock? (The figure is not drawn to scale, so you cannot measure it to solve the problem.)

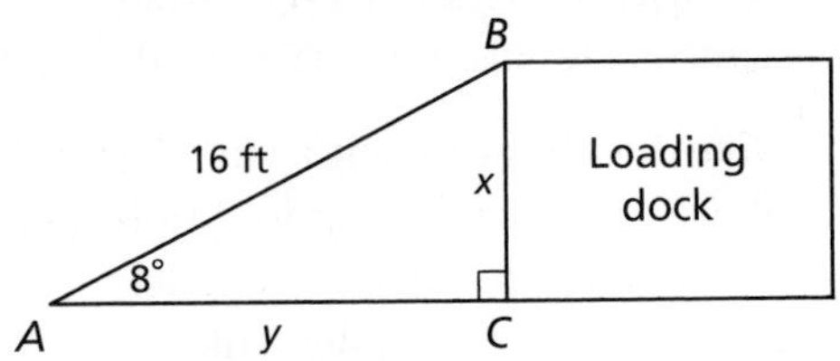

A Find the height x of the loading dock.

$\sin A = \frac{\text{length of leg opposite } \angle A}{\text{length of hypotenuse}} = \frac{x}{16}$, so $\sin 8° = \frac{x}{16}$.

Solve the equation for x.

____

Use a calculator to evaluate the expression, then round.

$x \approx$ ______________

So, the height of the loading dock is about ______________.

B Find the distance y that the ramp extends in front of the loading dock.

$\cos A = \frac{\text{length of leg adjacent to } \angle A}{\text{length of hypotenuse}} = \frac{\quad}{\quad}$, so cos ________ $= \frac{\quad}{\quad}$.

Solve the equation for y.

____

Use a calculator to evaluate the expression, then round.

$y \approx$ ______________

So, the distance the ramp extends in front of the loading dock is about ______________.

REFLECT

6a. A student claimed that she found the height of the loading dock by using the cosine. Explain her thinking.

____

____

6b. Suppose the owner of the factory decides to build a new ramp for the loading dock so that the new ramp makes an angle of 5° with the ground. How far will this ramp extend from the loading dock? Explain.

____

____

PRACTICE

Find the tangent of $\angle A$ and $\angle B$. Write each ratio as a fraction and as a decimal rounded to the nearest hundredth.

1.

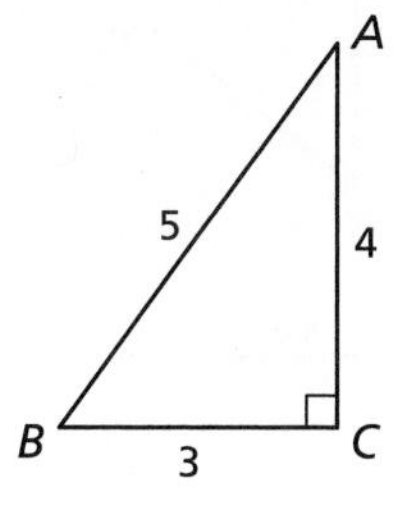

____

____

2.

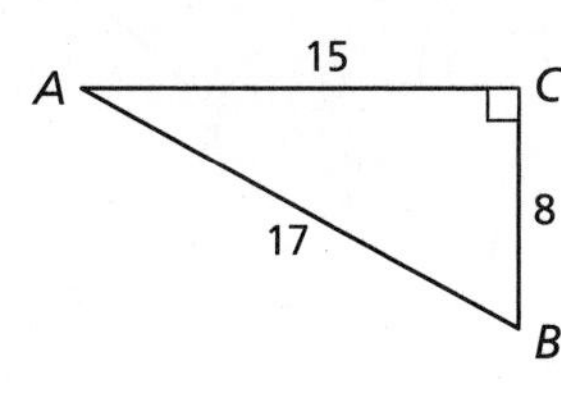

____

____

3.

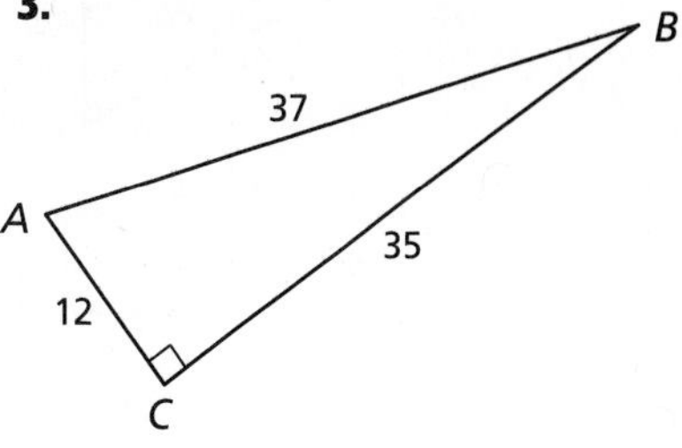

____

____

Find the value of x to the nearest tenth.

4.

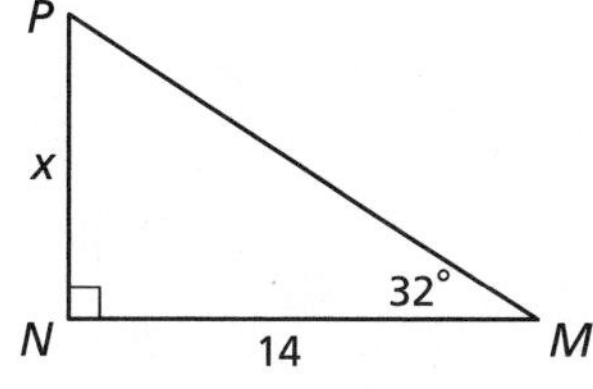

____

5.

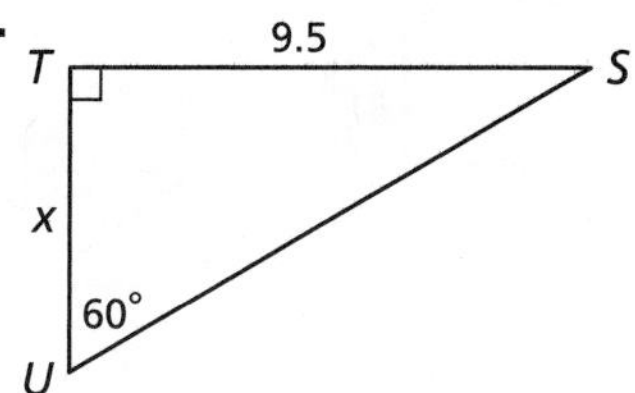

____

6.

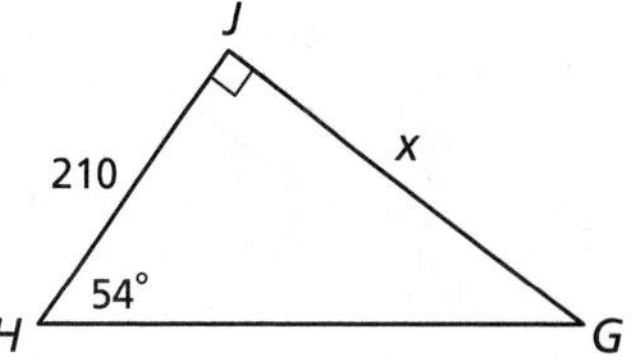

____

7. A hiker whose eyes are 5.5 feet above ground stands 25 feet from the base of a redwood tree. She looks up at an angle of 71° to see the top of the tree. To the nearest tenth of a foot, what is the height of the tree?

____

8. Error Analysis To find the distance XY across a large rock formation, a student stands facing one endpoint of the formation, backs away from it at a right angle for 20 meters, and then turns 55° to look at the other endpoint of the formation. The student's calculations are shown. Critique the student's work.

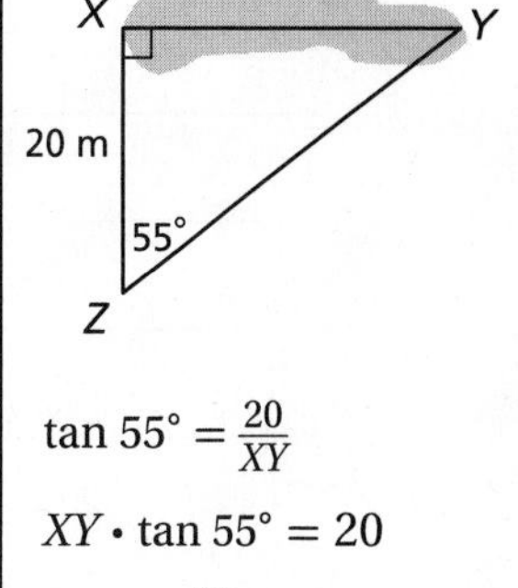

$\tan 55° = \frac{20}{XY}$

$XY \cdot \tan 55° = 20$

$XY = \frac{20}{\tan 55°} \approx 14.0 \text{ m}$

____

____

Find the given trigonometric ratios. Write each ratio as a fraction and as a decimal rounded to the nearest hundredth.

9. sin R, cos R

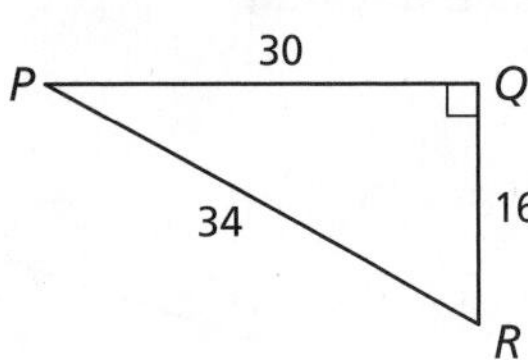

10. cos D, cos E

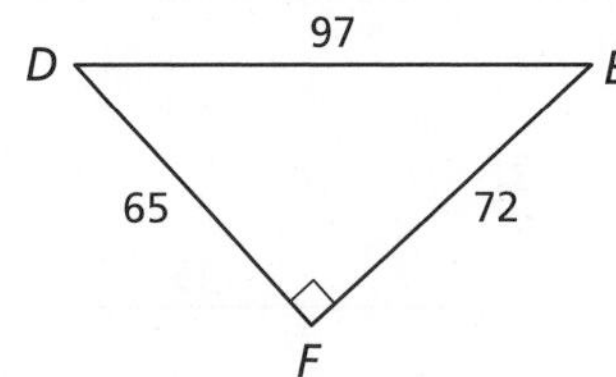

11. sin M, sin N

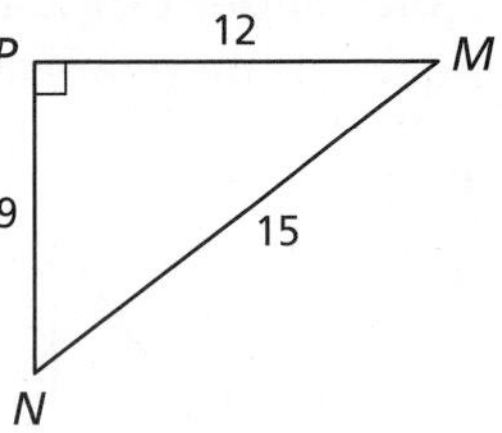

______________ ______________ ______________

______________ ______________ ______________

12. Given that $\sin 15° \approx 0.259$, write the cosine of a complementary angle. ______________

13. Given that $\cos 62° \approx 0.469$, write the sine of a complementary angle. ______________

Find the value of *x* to the nearest tenth.

14.

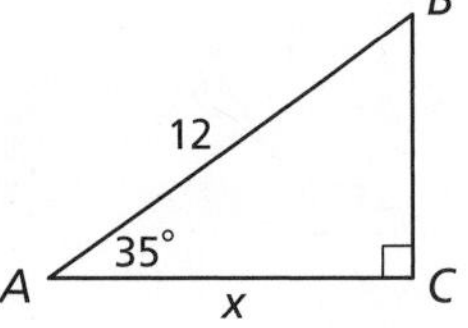

15.

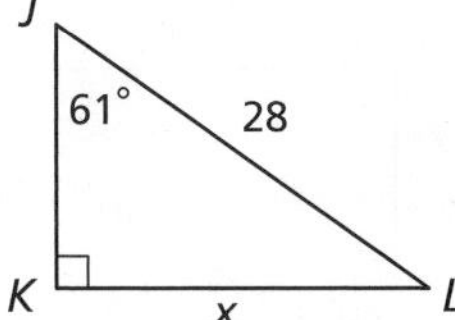

16.

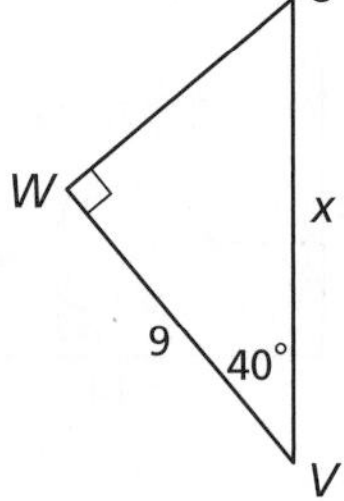

______________ ______________ ______________

17. You are building a skateboard ramp from a piece of wood that is 3.1 meters long. You want the ramp to make an angle of 25° with the ground. To the nearest tenth of a meter, what is the length of the ramp's base? What is its height?

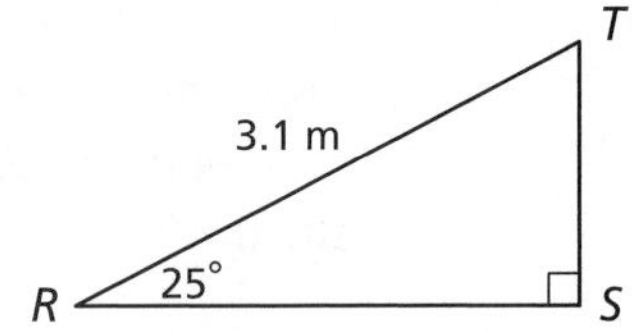

____

18. Error Analysis Three students were asked to find the value of x in the figure. The equations they used are shown at right. Which students, if any, used a correct equation? Explain the other students' errors and then find the value of x.

____

____

____

____

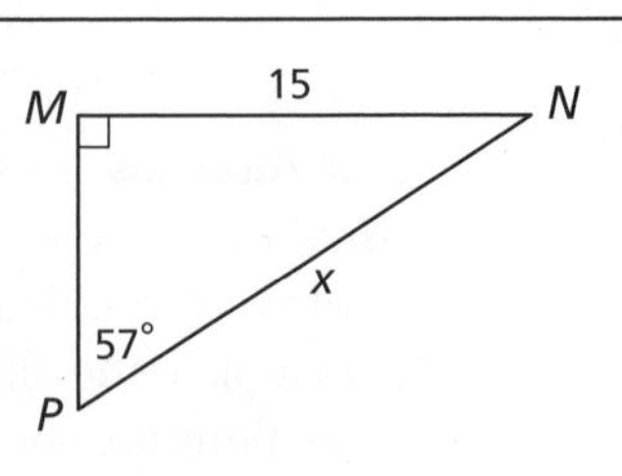

Lee's equation: $\sin 57° = \frac{x}{15}$

Jamila's equation: $\cos 33° = \frac{15}{x}$

Tyler's equation: $\sin 33° = \frac{x}{15}$

Name________________________ Class_______________ Date_____________ **10-1**

Additional Practice

Use the figure for Exercises 1–6. Write each trigonometric ratio as a simplified fraction and as a decimal rounded to the nearest hundredth.

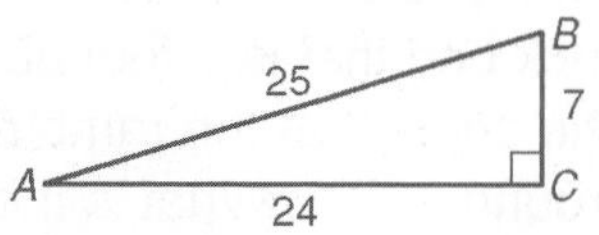

1. sin A ____________ 2. cos B ____________ 3. tan B ____________

4. sin B ____________ 5. cos A ____________ 6. tan A ____________

Use special right triangles to write each trigonometric ratio as a simplified fraction.

7. sin 30° ________ 8. cos 30° ________ 9. tan 45° ________

10. tan 30° ________ 11. cos 45° ________ 12. tan 60° ________

Use a calculator to find each trigonometric ratio. Round to the nearest hundredth.

13. sin 64° ________ 14. cos 58° ________ 15. tan 15° ________

Find each length. Round to the nearest hundredth.

16.

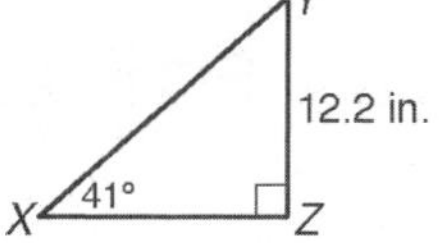

XZ ____________

17.

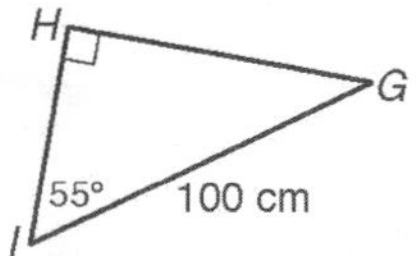

HI ____________

18.

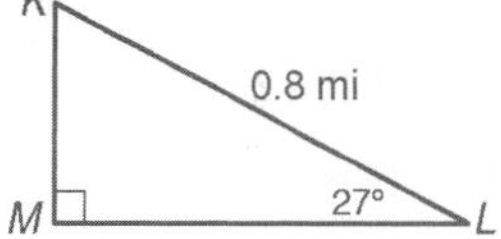

KM ____________

19.

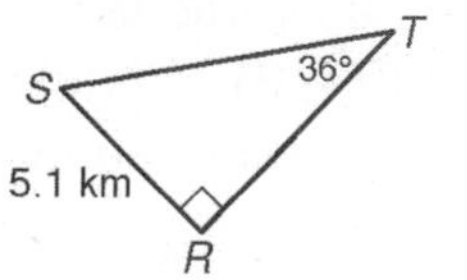

ST ____________

20.

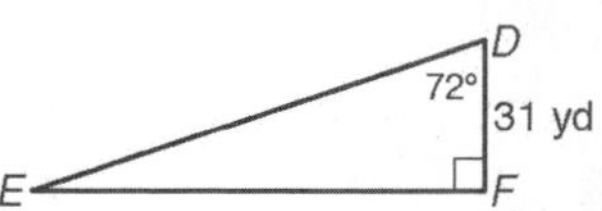

EF ____________

21.

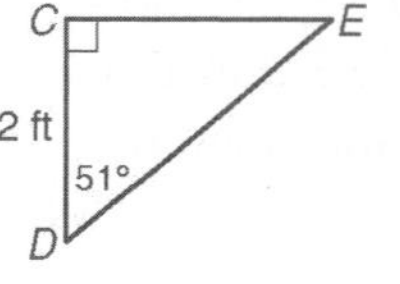

DE ____________

Problem Solving

1. A ramp is used to load a 4-wheeler onto a truck bed that is 3 feet above the ground. The angle that the ramp makes with the ground is 32°. What is the horizontal distance covered by the ramp? Round to the nearest hundredth.

____

2. Find the perimeter of the triangle. Round to the nearest hundredth.

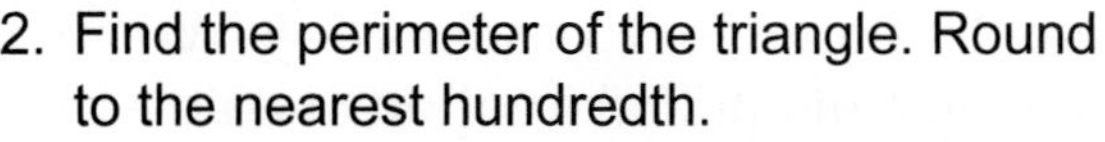

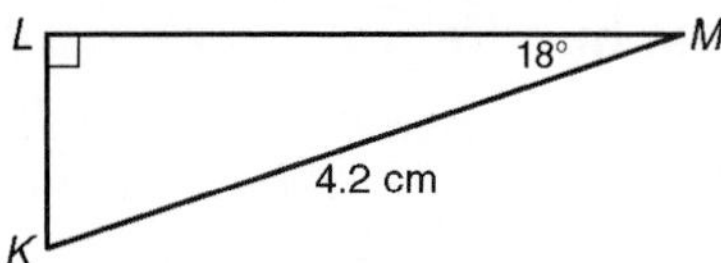

____

3. A right triangle has an angle that measures 55°. The leg adjacent to this angle has a length of 43 cm. What is the length of the other leg of the triangle? Round to the nearest tenth.

____

4. The hypotenuse of a right triangle measures 9 inches, and one of the acute angles measures 36°. What is the area of the triangle? Round to the nearest square inch.

____

Choose the best answer.

5. A 14-foot ladder makes a 62° angle with the ground. To the nearest foot, how far up the house does the ladder reach?

   A 6 ft

   B 7 ft

   C 12 ft

   D 16 ft

6. To the nearest inch, what is the length of the springboard shown below?

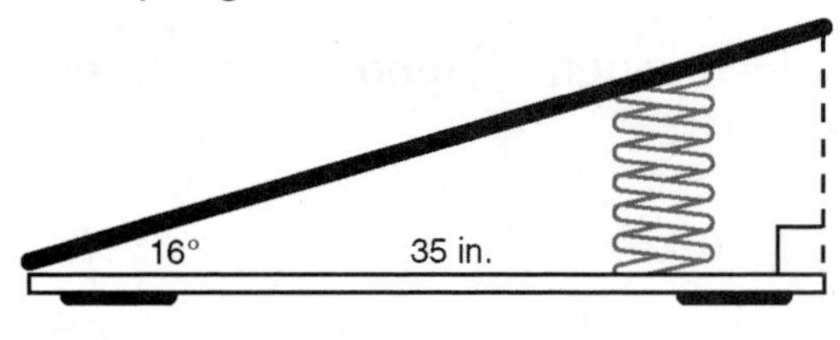

   F 24 in.

   G 36 in.

   H 38 in.

   J 127 in.

7. What is EF, the measure of the longest side of the sail on the model? Round to the nearest inch.

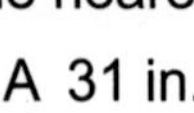

   A 31 in.

   B 35 in.

   C 40 in.

   D 60 in.

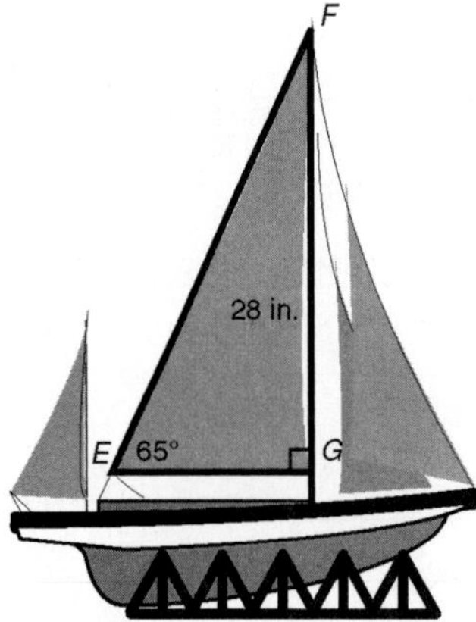

8. Right triangle ABC is graphed on the coordinate plane and has vertices at $A(-1, 3)$, $B(0, 5)$, and $C(4, 3)$. What is the measure of $\angle C$ to the nearest degree?

   F 27°

   G 29°

   H 32°

   J 43°

Name_________________________ Class_______________ Date__________

10-2

Solving Right Triangles

Going Deeper

Video Tutor

Essential question: *How do you find an unknown angle measure in a right triangle?*

In some cases, you may know the value of a trigonometric ratio and want to know the measure of the associated angle. For example, in the figure at right, $\sin A = \frac{7}{14} = \frac{1}{2}$. Because you know that $\sin 30° = \frac{1}{2}$, you can conclude that $m\angle A = 30°$ and you can write $\sin^{-1}\left(\frac{1}{2}\right) = 30°$.

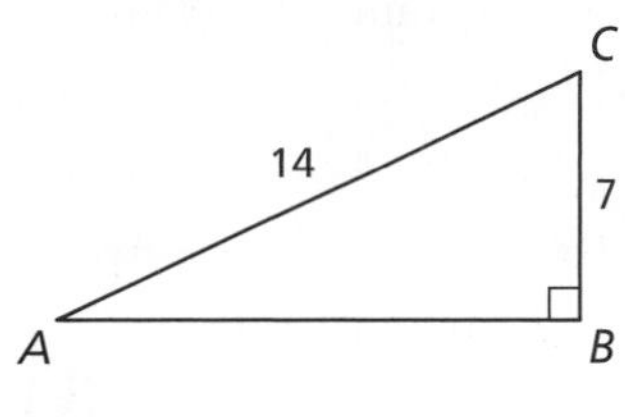

More generally, the **inverse trigonometric ratios** are defined as follows.

Given an acute angle, $\angle A$,

- if $\sin A = x$, then $\sin^{-1} x = m\angle A$.
- if $\cos A = x$, then $\cos^{-1} x = m\angle A$.
- if $\tan A = x$, then $\tan^{-1} x = m\angle A$.

You can use a calculator to evaluate inverse trigonometric ratios.

MCC9–12.G.SRT.8

1 EXAMPLE Using an Inverse Trigonometric Ratio

Find $m\angle J$. Round to the nearest degree.

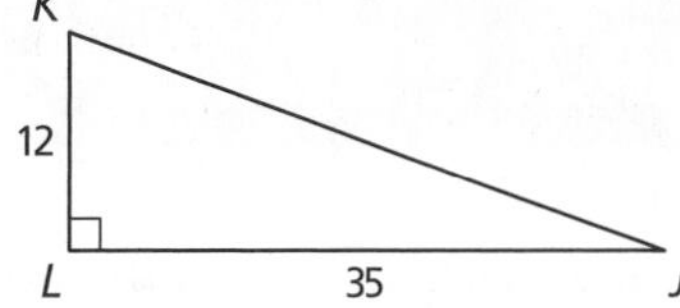

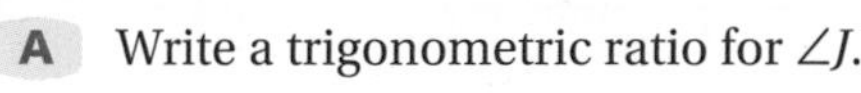

A Write a trigonometric ratio for $\angle J$.

Since you know the length of the side opposite $\angle J$ and the length of the side adjacent to $\angle J$, use the tangent ratio.

$\tan J = \frac{\square}{\square}$

B Write the inverse trigonometric ratio: $\tan^{-1}\left(\frac{\square}{\square}\right) = m\angle J$.

Use a calculator to evaluate the inverse trigonometric ratio. Round to the nearest degree.

So, $m\angle J \approx$ ___________.

REFLECT

1a. What other angle measures or side lengths of $\triangle JKL$ can you determine? How?

____

____

MCC9–12.G.SRT.8

2 EXAMPLE Using an Inverse Trigonometric Ratio

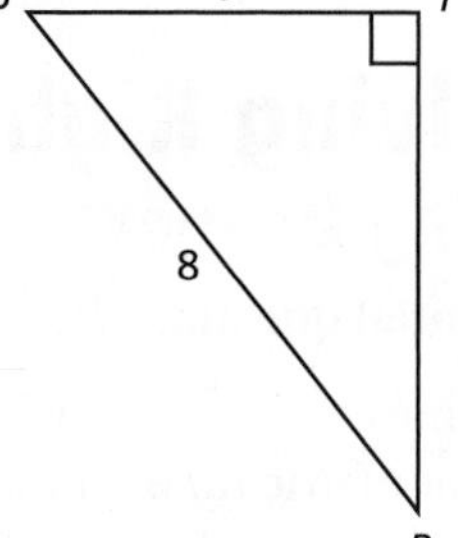

Find m∠R. Round to the nearest degree.

A Write a trigonometric ratio for ∠R.

Since you know the length of the side opposite ∠R and the length of the hypotenuse, use the sine ratio.

$\sin R = \frac{\quad}{\quad}$

B Write the inverse trigonometric ratio: $\sin^{-1}\left(\frac{\quad}{\quad}\right) = m\angle R$.

Use a calculator to evaluate the inverse trigonometric ratio. Round to the nearest degree.

So, m∠R ≈ ________.

REFLECT

2a. Find m∠S using inverse cosine. Is the result what you expect? Explain.

____

____

PRACTICE

Find m∠*A*. Round to the nearest degree.

1.

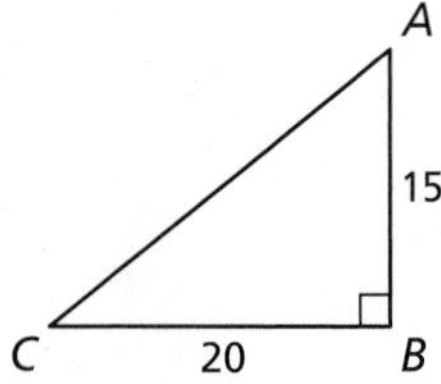

____

2.

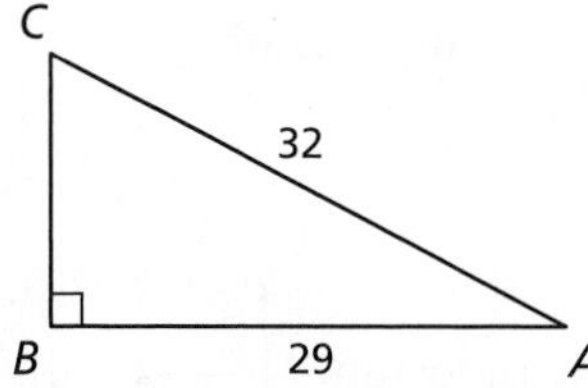

____

3.

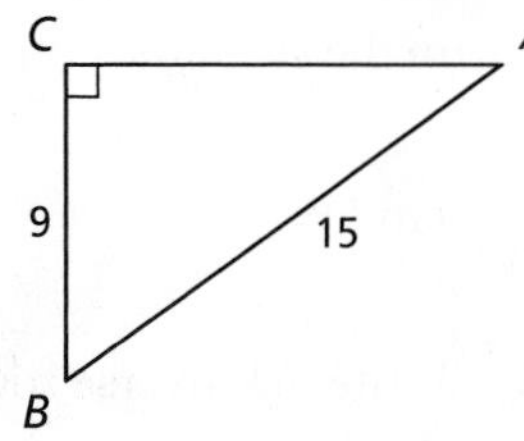

____

4.

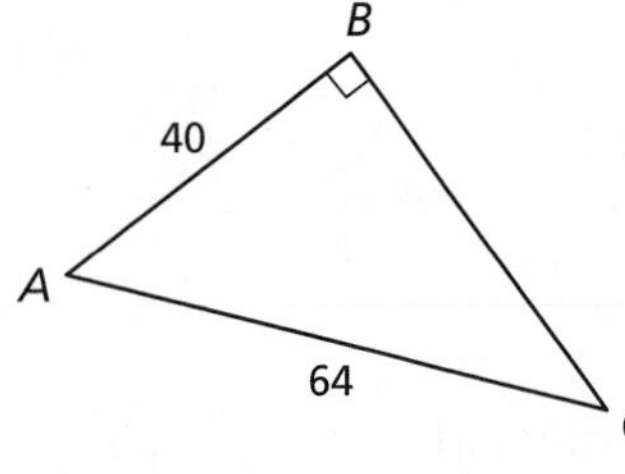

____

5.

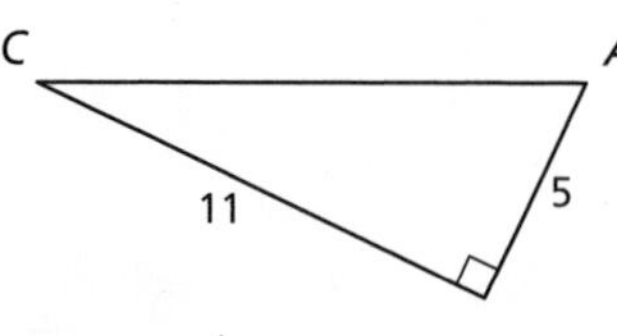

____

6.

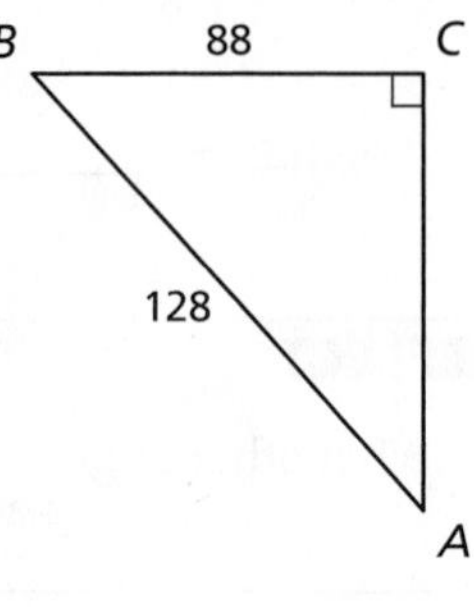

____

Name________________________ Class______________ Date___________

Additional Practice

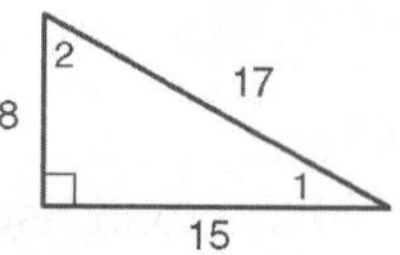

Use the given trigonometric ratio to determine which angle of the triangle is $\angle A$.

1. $\sin A = \frac{8}{17}$ ________
2. $\cos A = \frac{15}{17}$ ________
3. $\tan A = \frac{15}{8}$ ________
4. $\sin A = \frac{15}{17}$ ________
5. $\cos A = \frac{8}{17}$ ________
6. $\tan A = \frac{8}{15}$ ________

Use a calculator to find each angle measure to the nearest degree.

7. $\sin^{-1}(0.82)$ ________
8. $\cos^{-1}\left(\frac{11}{12}\right)$ ________
9. $\tan^{-1}(5.03)$ ________
10. $\sin^{-1}\left(\frac{3}{8}\right)$ ________
11. $\cos^{-1}(0.23)$ ________
12. $\tan^{-1}\left(\frac{1}{9}\right)$ ________

Find the unknown measures. Round lengths to the nearest hundredth and angle measures to the nearest degree.

13.

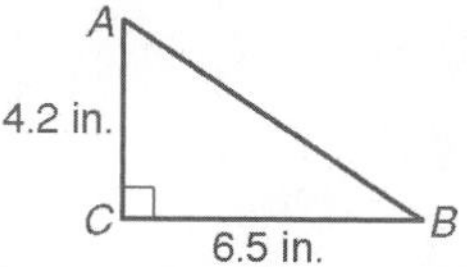

____

____

14.

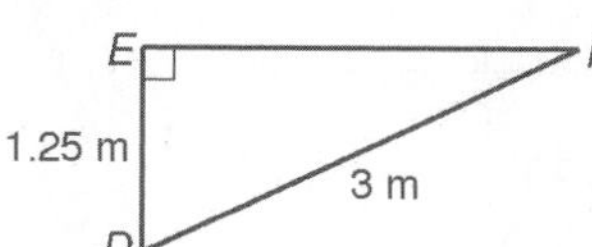

____

____

15.

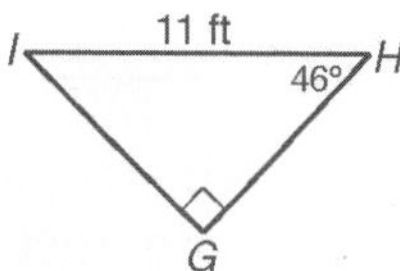

____

____

16.

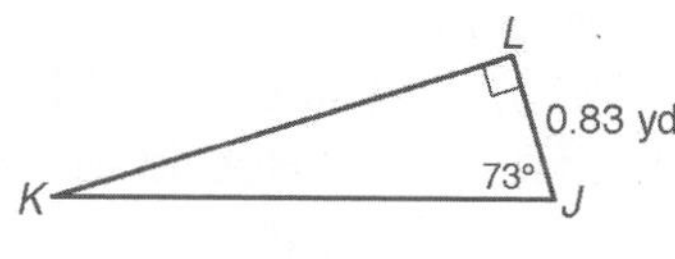

____

____

17.

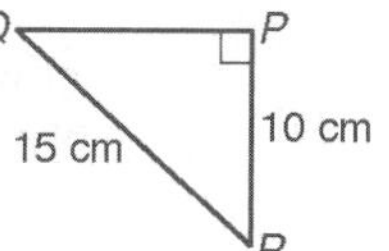

____

____

18.

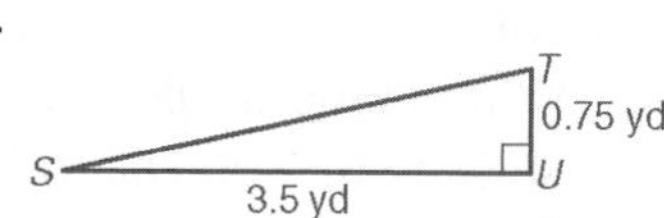

____

____

For each triangle, find all three side lengths to the nearest hundredth and all three angle measures to the nearest degree.

19. $B(-2, -4)$, $C(3, 3)$, $D(-2, 3)$

____

20. $L(-1, -6)$, $M(1, -6)$, $N(-1, 1)$

____

21. $X(-4, 5)$, $Y(-3, 5)$, $Z(-3, 4)$

____

Problem Solving

1. A road has a grade of 28.4%. This means that the road rises 28.4 ft over a horizontal distance of 100 ft. What angle does the hill make with a horizontal line? Round to the nearest degree.

____

2. Pet ramps for loading larger dogs into vehicles usually have slopes between $\frac{2}{5}$ and $\frac{1}{2}$. What is the range of angle measures that most pet ramps make with a horizontal line? Round to the nearest degree.

____

Use the side view of a water slide for Exercises 3 and 4.

The ladder, represented by $\overline{AB}$, is 17 feet long.

3. What is the measure of angle A, the angle that the ladder makes with a horizontal line?

____

4. What is BC, the length of the slide? Round to the nearest tenth of a foot.

____

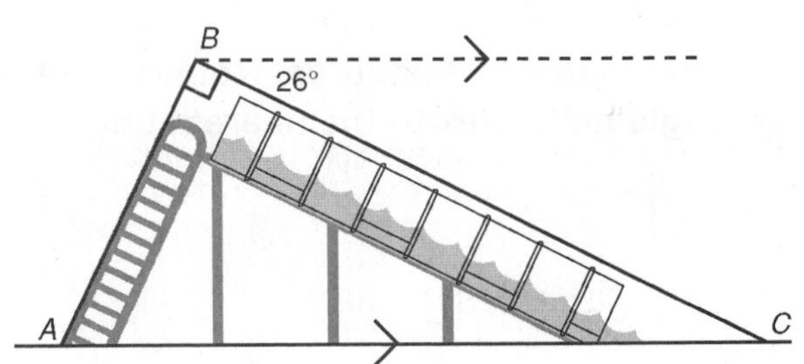

Choose the best answer.

5. Janelle sets her treadmill grade to 6%. What is the angle that the treadmill surface makes with a horizontal line? Round to the nearest degree.

   A 3° C 12°
   B 4° D 31°

6. The coordinates of the vertices of $\triangle RST$ are $R(3, 3)$, $S(8, 3)$, and $T(8, -6)$. What is the measures of angle T? Round to the nearest degree.

   F 18° H 61°
   G 29° J 65°

7. If $\cos A = 0.28$, which angle in the triangles below is $\angle A$?

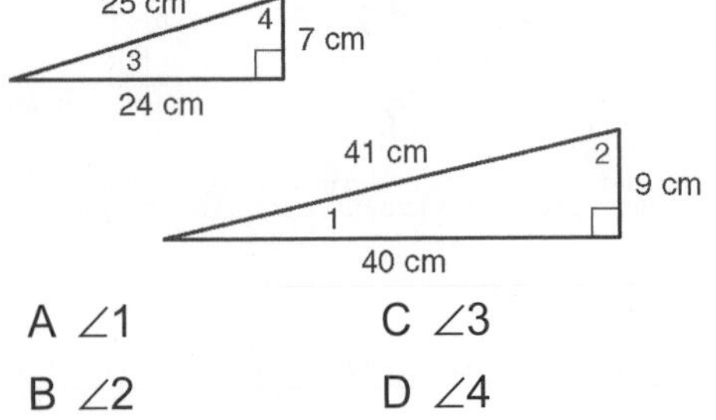

   A ∠1 C ∠3
   B ∠2 D ∠4

8. Find the measure of the acute angle formed by the graph of $y = \frac{3}{4}x$ and the x-axis. Round to the nearest degree.

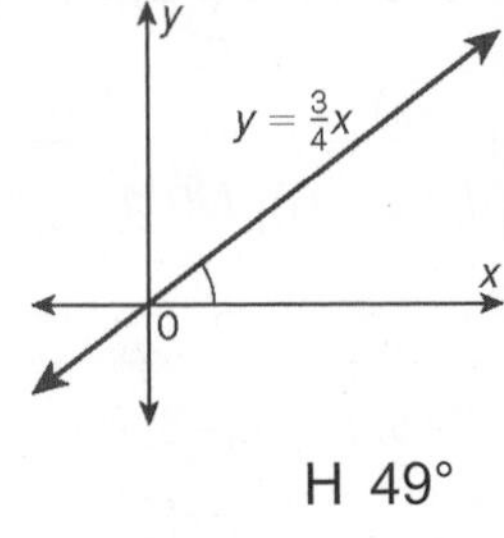

   F 37° H 49°
   G 41° J 53°

Name_________________________ Class_______________ Date___________

10-3

Angles of Elevation and Depression

Going Deeper

Essential question: *How can you use trigonometric ratios to solve problems involving angles of elevation and depression?*

The diagram shows what is meant by **angle of elevation** and **angle of depression**. These angles depend on your viewpoint, but because they are both measured relative to parallel horizontal lines, they are equal in measure.

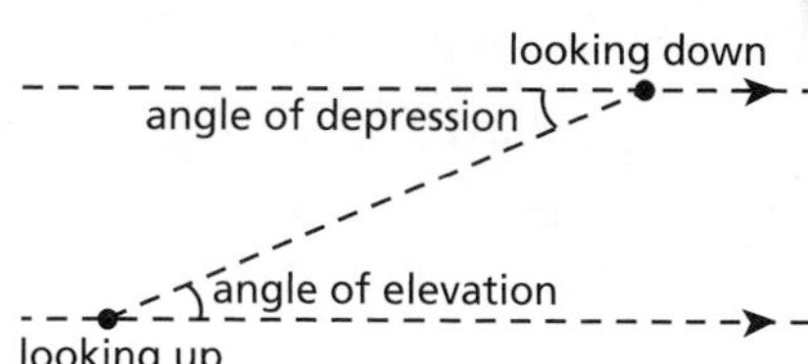

MCC9–12.G.SRT.8

1 EXAMPLE Solving a Problem with an Angle of Depression

A lighthouse keeper at the top of a 120-foot tall lighthouse with its base at sea level spots a small fishing boat. The angle of depression is 5°. What is the horizontal distance between the base of the lighthouse and the boat? Round to the nearest foot.

A In the space below, sketch sea level, the lighthouse, and the boat. Label the position of the boat along with the bottom and top of the lighthouse.

B Add lines that show the angle of depression. Use dashing to show the horizontal reference line and a solid line to show the line of sight.

C Add known and derived degree measures. Add known and unknown lengths to determine a right triangle you can use to answer the question.

D Solve an equation involving a trigonometric ratio to answer the question.

____

REFLECT

1a. What assumption is made about the lighthouse and sea level?

____

1b. Explain why the angle of elevation from the boat to the lighthouse is 5°.

____

1c. Explain how to find the horizontal distance using the other acute angle of the triangle.

____

MCC9–12.G.SRT.8

2 EXAMPLE Solving a Problem with an Angle of Elevation

A viewer watches a hot air balloon ascend. The viewer's line of sight forms a 20° angle with the ground when the balloon is 1200 feet above ground. How far is the viewer from where the balloon started its ascent?

A On the diagram at the right, add information that can be used to answer the question.

Show the right triangle and the angle of elevation. Label the diagram with known measures and use a variable for the unknown.

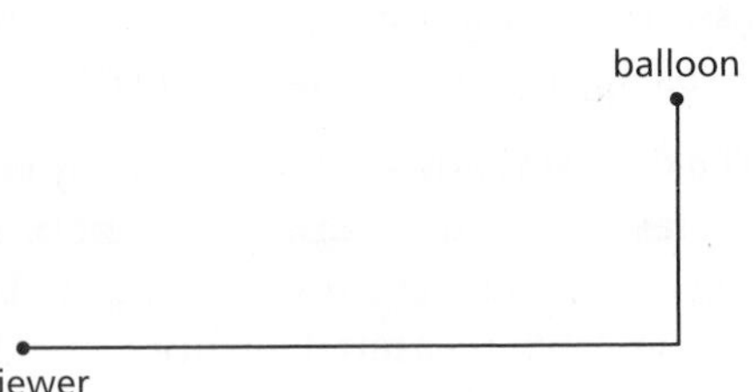

B Write an equation you can use in this situation.

____

C Solve the equation to answer the question. Show your work.

____

REFLECT

2a. Why is the sine ratio or cosine ratio not used in solving this Example?

____

PRACTICE

Use a trigonometric ratio to solve. Give answers to the nearest foot.

1. A spectator looks up at an angle of 25° to the top of a building 500 feet away. How tall is the building?

____

2. A worker looks down from the top of a bridge 240 feet above a river at a barge. The angle of depression is 60°. How far is the barge from the base of the bridge?

____

3. A helicopter pilot hovers 500 feet above a straight and flat road. The pilot looks down at two cars using 24° and 28° as angles of depression. How far apart are the cars? Explain your work.

____

____

4. The string of a flying kite is 360 feet long and makes a 40° angle with the ground. Find the altitude of the kite and the horizontal distance between the kite flyer and the point on the ground directly below the kite.

____

Additional Practice

Marco breeds and trains homing pigeons on the roof of his building. Classify each angle as an angle of elevation or an angle of depression.

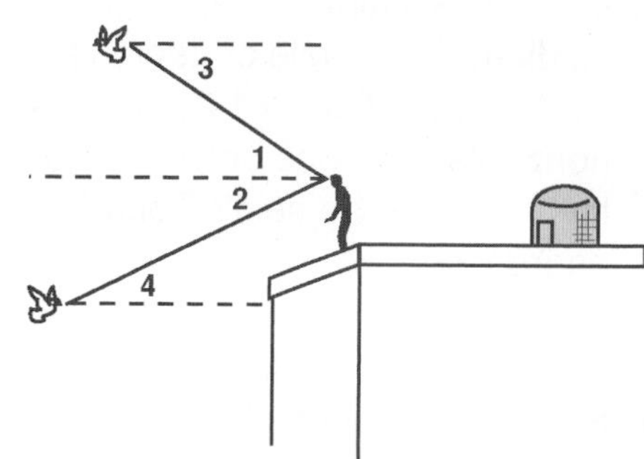

1. ∠1 ________________
2. ∠2 ________________
3. ∠3 ________________
4. ∠4 ________________

To attract customers to his car dealership, Frank tethers a large red balloon to the ground. In Exercises 5–7, give answers in feet and inches to the nearest inch. (*Note:* Assume the cord that attaches to the balloon makes a straight segment.)

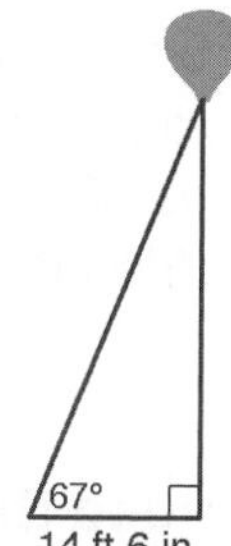

5. The sun is directly overhead. The shadow of the balloon falls 14 feet 6 inches from the tether. Frank sights an angle of elevation of 67°. Find the height of the balloon. ________________
6. Find the length of the cord that tethers the balloon. ________________
7. The wind picks up and the angle of elevation changes to 59°. Find the height of the balloon. ________________

Lindsey shouts down to Pete from her third-story window.

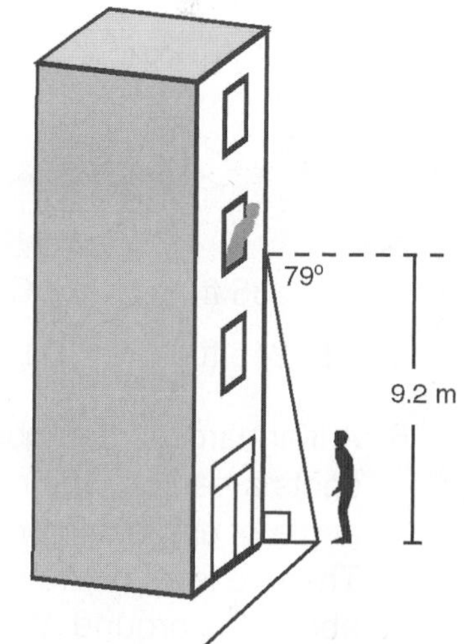

8. Lindsey is 9.2 meters up, and the angle of depression from Lindsey to Pete is 79°. Find the distance from Pete to the base of the building to the nearest tenth of a meter.

   ____

9. To see Lindsey better, Pete walks out into the street so he is 4.3 meters from the base of the building. Find the angle of depression from Lindsey to Pete to the nearest degree.

   ____

10. Mr. Shea lives in Lindsey's building. While Pete is still out in the street, Mr. Shea leans out his window to tell Lindsey and Pete to stop all the shouting. The angle of elevation from Pete to Mr. Shea is 72°. Tell whether Mr. Shea lives above or below Lindsey.

   ____

Problem Solving

1. Mayuko is sitting 30 feet high in a football stadium. The angle of depression to the center of the field is 14°. What is the horizontal distance between Mayuko and the center of the field? Round to the nearest foot.

____

2. A surveyor 50 meters from the base of a cliff measures the angle of elevation to the top of the cliff as 72°. What is the height of the cliff? Round to the nearest meter.

____

3. Shane is 61 feet high on a ride at an amusement park. The angle of depression to the park entrance is 42°, and the angle of depression to his friends standing below is 80°. How far from the entrance are his friends standing? Round to the nearest foot.

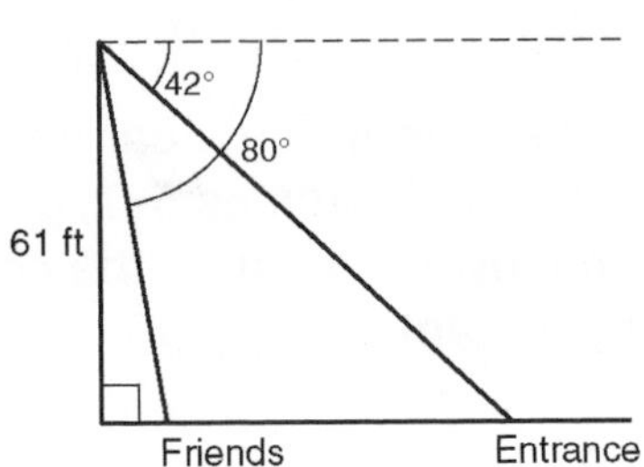

____

Choose the best answer.

4. The figure shows a person parasailing. What is x, the height of the parasailer, to the nearest foot?

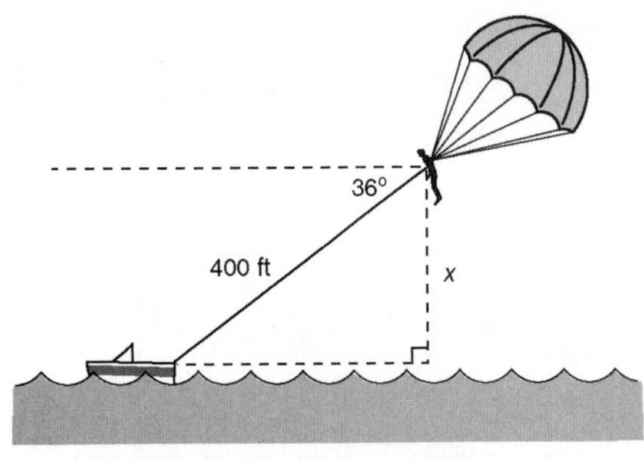

A 235 ft
B 245 ft
C 290 ft
D 323 ft

5. The elevation angle from the ground to the object to which the satellite dish is pointed is 32°. If $x = 2.5$ meters, which is the best estimate for y, the height of the satellite stand?

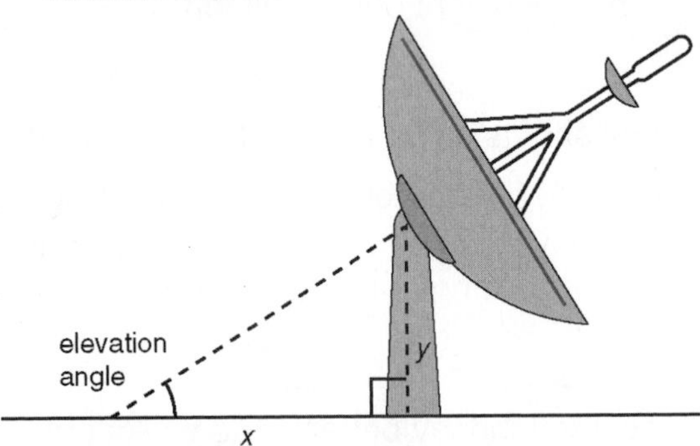

F 0.8 m
G 1.3 m
H 1.6 m
J 2.1 m

6. A lifeguard is in an observation chair and spots a person who needs help. The angle of depression to the person is 22°. The eye level of the lifeguard is 10 feet above the ground. What is the horizontal distance between the lifeguard and the person? Round to the nearest foot.

A 4 ft
B 11 ft
C 25 ft
D 27 ft

7. At a topiary garden, Emily is 8 feet from a shrub that is shaped like a dolphin. From where she is looking, the angle of elevation to the top of the shrub is 46°. If she is 5 feet tall, which is the best estimate for the height of the shrub?

F 6 ft
G 8 ft
H 10 ft
J 13 ft

Name_______________ Class_______________ Date_______________

UNIT 2

Performance Tasks

GPS COMMON CORE

MCC9-12.G.SRT.6
MCC9-12.G.SRT.8

★ **1.** A bookcase fits diagonally into the corner of a room. The front of the bookcase is 54 inches wide. Each side of the bookcase uses the same amount of wall space.

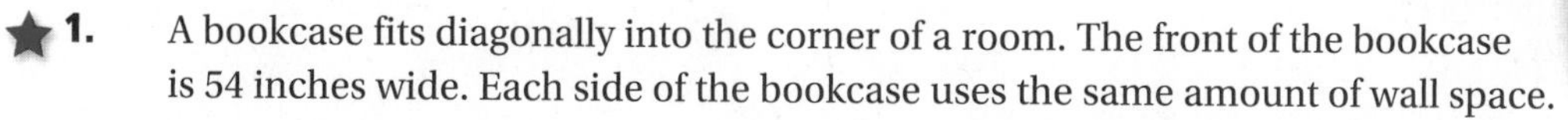

a. What angles are formed where the front of the bookcase touches the walls?

b. Calculate how much wall space each side of the bookcase uses.

★ **2.** The base of a hill is 545 feet above sea level. The top of the hill is 2108 feet above sea level. A straight road from the base of the hill to the top of the hill is 2.5 miles long. What is the angle of elevation from the base of the hill to the top of the hill? Round to the nearest tenth of a degree. Explain how you found your answer.

★★ **3.** A farmer is building a pen inside a barn. The pen will be in the shape of a right triangle. The farmer has 14 feet of barn wall to use for one side of the pen and wants another side of the pen to be 15 feet long.

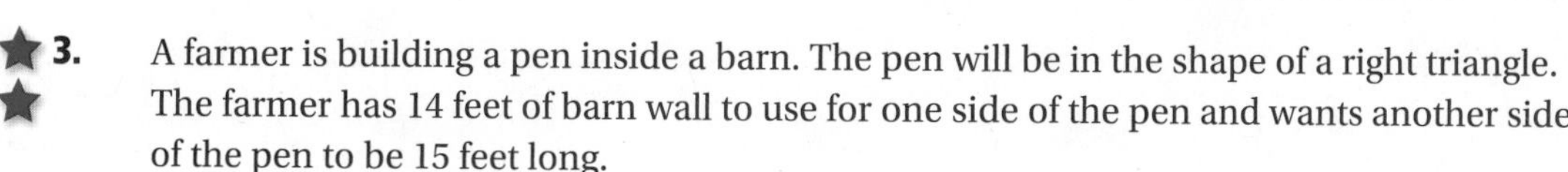

a. How many different lengths for the third side are possible? Explain.

b. To the nearest tenth of a foot, find all possible lengths for the third side of the triangle. Show your work.

c. The farmer wants the area of the pen to be as large as possible. What length should he choose for the third side? Justify your answer.

d. Find the measure of the acute angles for the triangle you described in part **c**. Round to the nearest degree. Show how you used trigonometric ratios to find the angles.

continued

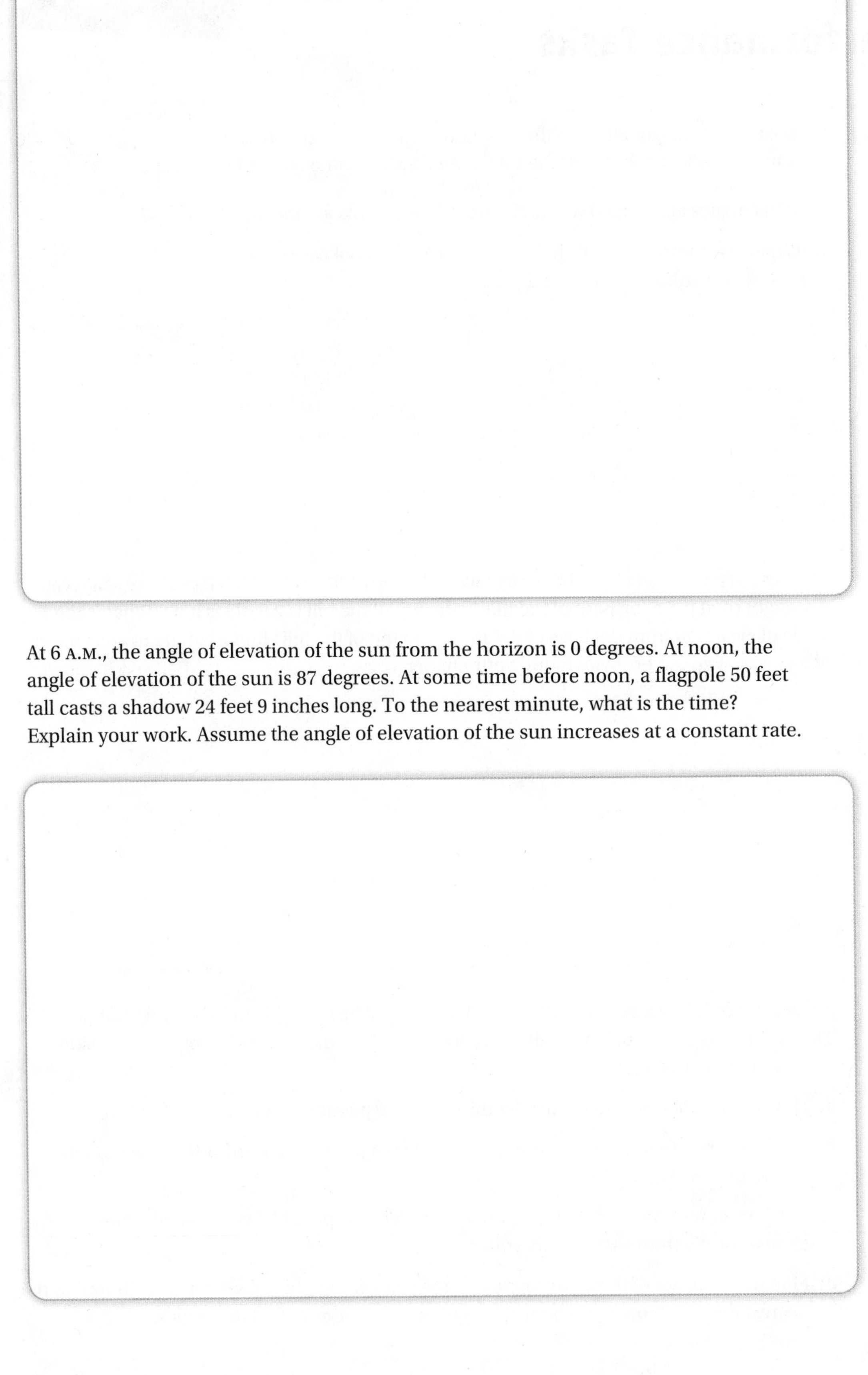

★★★ 4. At 6 A.M., the angle of elevation of the sun from the horizon is 0 degrees. At noon, the angle of elevation of the sun is 87 degrees. At some time before noon, a flagpole 50 feet tall casts a shadow 24 feet 9 inches long. To the nearest minute, what is the time? Explain your work. Assume the angle of elevation of the sun increases at a constant rate.

UNIT 2 GPS COMMON CORE PARCC Assessment Readiness

Name ______________________ Class ______________ Date ________

SELECTED RESPONSE

1. Given that $x°$ is the measure of an acute angle, which of the following is equal to $\sin x°$?

A. $\cos x°$

B. $\cos(90 - x)°$

C. $\sin(90 - x)°$

D. $\tan x°$

2. Connor is building a skateboard ramp with the dimensions shown. Which expression can he use to find the height b of the ramp?

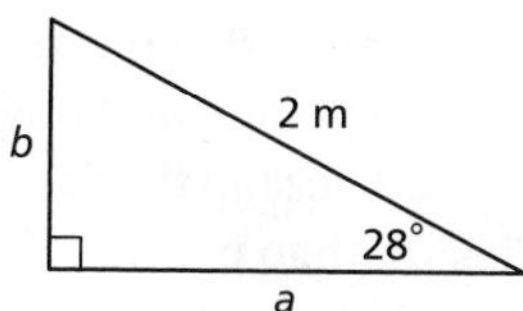

F. $2 \sin 28°$

G. $\frac{2}{\sin 28°}$

H. $2 \cos 28°$

J. $\frac{2}{\cos 28°}$

3. In the right triangles shown below, $\angle M \cong \angle Q$. This leads to the observation that $\triangle MNP \sim \triangle QRS$ by the AA Similarity Criterion. Therefore, corresponding sides are proportional, so $\frac{RS}{NP} = \frac{QR}{MN}$ and algebra shows that $\frac{RS}{QR} = \frac{NP}{MN}$. This last proportion is the basis for defining which of the following?

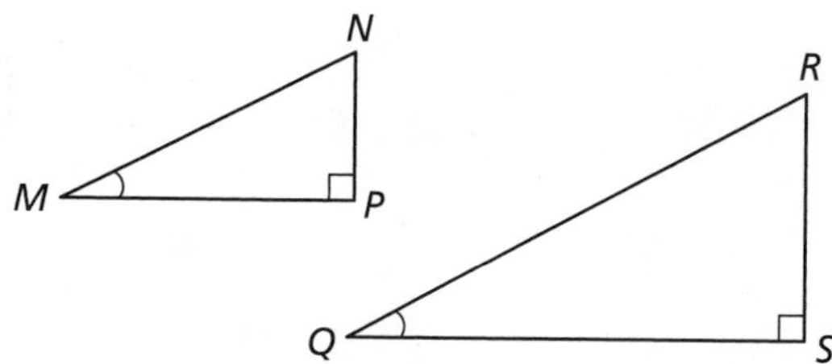

A. the cosine of $\angle M$

B. the cosine of $\angle P$

C. the sine of $\angle M$

D. the tangent of $\angle M$

4. The lengths of the two legs of a right triangle are 2 inches and 4 inches. What is the length of the hypotenuse in simplest radical form?

F. $\sqrt{6}$ inches

G. $2\sqrt{3}$ inches

H. $2\sqrt{5}$ inches

J. $\sqrt{20}$ inches

5. A square courtyard has a straight walkway from one corner to the opposite corner. If each wall of the courtyard is 20 feet long, what is the length of the walkway?

A. 10 feet

B. 20 feet

C. $20\sqrt{2}$ feet

D. $20\sqrt{3}$ feet

6. The sides of an equilateral triangle are 40 inches long. What is the height of the triangle?

F. 20 feet

G. 80 feet

H. $20\sqrt{3}$ feet

J. $40\sqrt{3}$ feet

7. $\triangle ABC$ and $\triangle PQR$ are similar right triangles, with right angles at B and Q. Which of the following represents the ratio of PQ to QR?

A. the sine of $\angle C$

B. the cosine of $\angle C$

C. the tangent of $\angle C$

D. the tangent of $\angle A$

CONSTRUCTED RESPONSE

8. You paddle a kayak due north at the rate of 2.5 mi/h. The river has a 2 mi/h current that flows due east. You want to find the kayak's actual speed and direction.

a. In the space below, sketch and label vectors that represent the situation.

b. Find the kayak's actual speed and direction.

____

____

____

9. From a point on the ground 12 feet in front of the building, the angle of elevation to the top of the building is 76°. How tall is the building? Round the answer to the nearest foot.

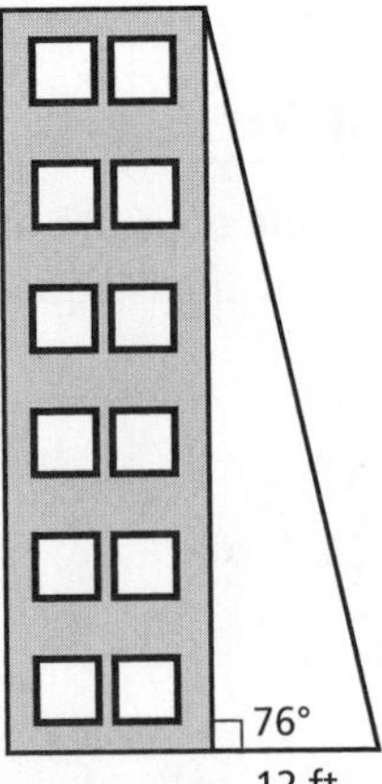

____

10. To avoid a large, shallow reef, a ship set a course from point A and traveled 11 miles east to point B. The ship then turned and traveled 22 miles south to point C. If the ship could have traveled in a straight line from point A to point C, how many less miles would the ship have traveled? Round your answer to the nearest tenth of a mile.

____

Circles and Volume

Module 11 Area and Volume

11-1	Developing Formulas for Circles and Regular Polygons	**MCC9-12.G.GMD.1**
11-2	Volume of Prisms and Cylinders	**MCC9-12.G.GMD.1, MCC9-12.G.GMD.3**
11-3	Volume of Pyramids and Cones	**MCC9-12.G.GMD.1, MCC9-12.G.GMD.3**
11-4	Spheres	**MCC9-12.G.GMD.2(+), MCC9-12.G.GMD.3**

Module 12 Circles

12-1	Lines That Intersect Circles	**MCC9-12.G.C.2**
12-2	Arcs and Chords	**MCC9-12.G.C.2**
12-3	Sector Area and Arc Length	**MCC9-12.G.C.5**
12-4	Inscribed Angles	**MCC9-12.G.C.2, MCC9-12.G.C.3, MCC9-12.G.C.4**
	Performance Tasks	
	PARCC Assessment Readiness	

Unpacking the Standards

Understanding the standards and the vocabulary terms in the standards will help you know exactly what you are expected to learn in this unit.

MCC9-12.G.GMD.3

Use volume formulas for cylinders, pyramids, cones, and spheres to solve problems.

Key Vocabulary

volume *(volumen)* The number of nonoverlapping unit cubes of a given size that will exactly fill the interior of a three-dimensional figure.

formula *(formula)* A literal equation that states a rule for a relationship among quantities.

cylinder *(cilindro)* A three-dimensional figure with two parallel congruent circular bases and a curved surface that connects the bases.

pyramid *(pirámide)* A polyhedron formed by a polygonal base and triangular lateral faces that meet at a common vertex.

cone *(cono)* A three-dimensional figure with a circular base and a curved surface that connects the base to a point called the vertex.

sphere *(esfera)* The set of points in space that are a fixed distance from a given point called the center of the sphere.

UNIT 3

What It Means For You

Volume problems appear frequently in real-world contexts. Learning the relationships among volume formulas helps you understand, remember, and apply them.

EXAMPLE **Volume of a cylinder**

A grain silo at a port has the dimensions shown. The volume is the base area B times the height h. Because the base is a circle, this gives:

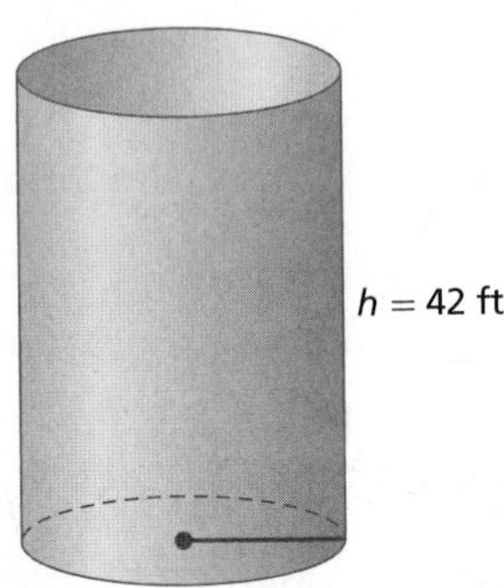

$$V = Bh = \pi r^2 h = \pi(15^2)(42) \approx 30{,}000 \text{ ft}^3$$

EXAMPLE **Volume of a cone**

The silo above contains just enough grain so that the grain reaches to the outer edge of the floor, forming a cone. The volume is one third the base area times the height. This gives:

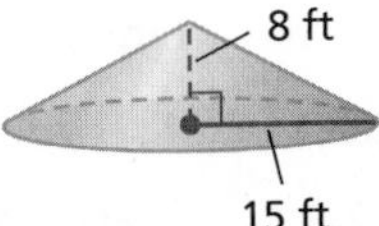

$$V = \frac{1}{3}Bh = \frac{1}{3}\pi r^2 h = \frac{1}{3}\pi(15^2)(8) \approx 1900 \text{ ft}^3$$

EXAMPLE **Volume of a sphere**

A liquefied natural gas tank at the port is in the shape of a sphere with the radius shown. The volume is:

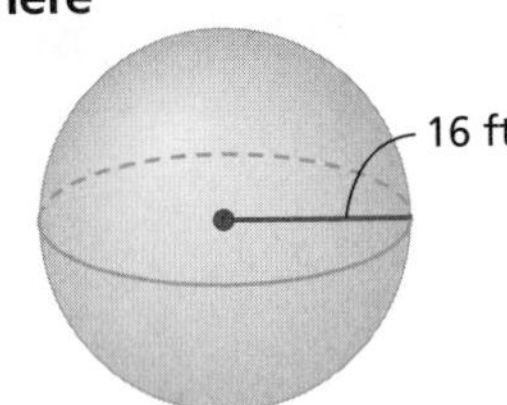

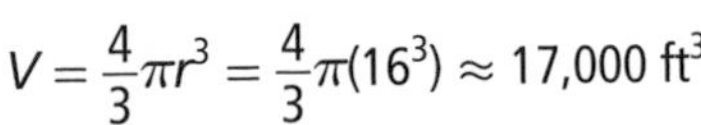

$$V = \frac{4}{3}\pi r^3 = \frac{4}{3}\pi(16^3) \approx 17{,}000 \text{ ft}^3$$

EXAMPLE **Volume of a pyramid**

A customs building at the port has a roof in the shape of a pyramid with the dimensions shown. As with a cone, the volume is one third the base area times the height. Because the base is a rectangle, this gives:

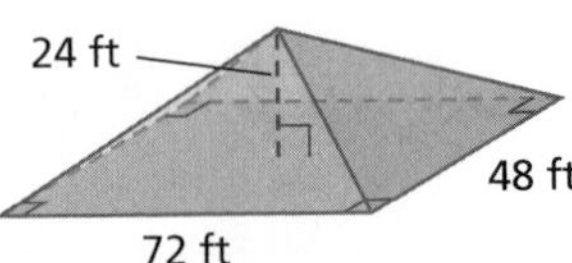

$$V = \frac{1}{3}Bh = \frac{1}{3}(72)(48)(24) \approx 28{,}000 \text{ ft}^3$$

MCC9-12.G.C.2

Identify and describe relationships among inscribed angles, radii, and chords.

Key Vocabulary

inscribed angle *(ángulo inscrito)* An angle whose vertex is on a circle and whose sides contain chords of the circle.

chord *(cuerda)* A segment whose endpoints lie on a circle.

What It Means For You

You will learn to recognize many relationships among angles, radii, and chords of circles, and use them to solve problems.

EXAMPLE

An artist's pattern for a stained glass window shows multiple inscribed angles, radii, and chords, and many relationships including the following:

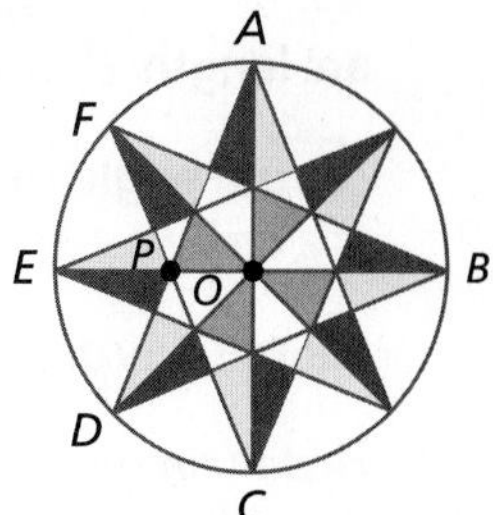

- Radius $\overline{OA}$ is perpendicular to chord $\overline{EB}$, so $\overline{OA}$ bisects $\overline{EB}$ and its arc.
- Chords $\overline{AD}$ and $\overline{FC}$ intersect at P, so $m\angle APF = \frac{1}{2}(m\widehat{AF} + m\widehat{CD})$ and $AP \cdot PD = FP \cdot PC$.

UNIT 3

Key Vocabulary

arc *(arco)* An unbroken part of a circle consisting of two points on the circle, called the endpoints, and all the points on the circle between them.

arc length *(longitud de arco)* The distance along an arc measured in linear units.

central angle of a circle *(ángulo central de un círculo)* An angle whose vertex is the center of a circle.

chord *(cuerda)* A segment whose endpoints lie on a circle.

circle *(círculo)* The set of points in a plane that are a fixed distance from a given point called the center of the circle.

cone *(cono)* A three-dimensional figure with a circular base and a curved surface that connects the base to a point called the vertex.

cylinder *(cilindro)* A three-dimensional figure with two parallel congruent circular bases and a curved surface that connects the bases.

inscribed angle *(ángulo inscrito)* An angle whose vertex is on a circle and whose sides contain chords of the circle.

radian *(radian)* A unit of angle measure based on arc length. In a circle of radius r, if a central angle has a measure of 1 radian, then the length of the intercepted arc is r units.

2π radians $= 360°$ 1 radian $\approx 57°$

radius of a circle *(radio de un círculo)* A segment whose endpoints are the center of a circle and a point on the circle; the distance from the center of a circle to any point on the circle.

secant of a circle *(secante de un círculo)* A line that intersects a circle at two points.

sector of a circle *(sector de un círculo)* A region inside a circle bounded by two radii of the circle and their intercepted arc.

prism *(prisma)* A polyhedron formed by two parallel congruent polygonal bases connected by lateral faces that are parallelograms.

pyramid *(pirámide)* A polyhedron formed by a polygonal base and triangular lateral faces that meet at a common vertex.

sphere *(esfera)* The set of points in space that are a fixed distance from a given point called the center of the sphere.

volume *(volumen)* The number of nonoverlapping unit cubes of a given size that will exactly fill the interior of a three-dimensional figure.

Name _______________ Class _______________ Date _______________

11-1

Developing Formulas for Circles and Regular Polygons

Connection: Using Trigonometry

Essential question: *How do you justify and use the formula for the circumference of a circle?*

Circumference of a Circle Formula

The circumference C of a circle with radius r is given by $C = 2\pi r$.

MCC9–12.G.GMD.1

1 EXPLORE Justifying the Circumference Formula

Plan: To find the circumference of a given circle, consider regular polygons that are inscribed in the circle. As the number of sides of the polygons increases, the perimeter of the polygons gets closer to the circumference of the circle. The first steps of the argument consist of writing an expression for the perimeter of an inscribed n-gon.

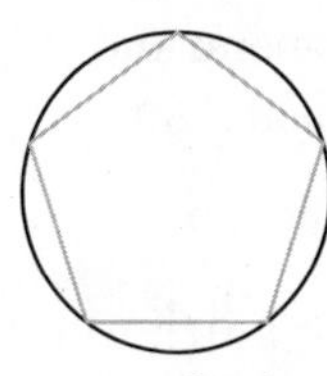
Inscribed pentagon

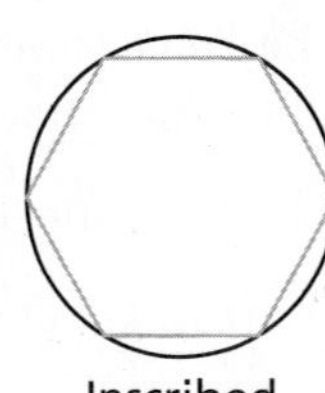
Inscribed hexagon

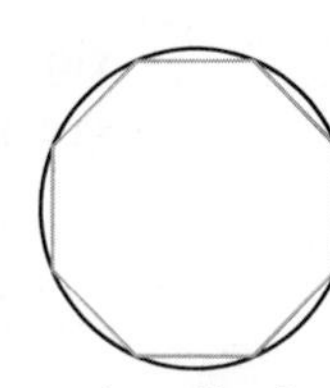
Inscribed octagon

A Let circle O be a circle with center O and radius r. Inscribe a regular n-gon in circle O and draw radii from O to the vertices of the n-gon.

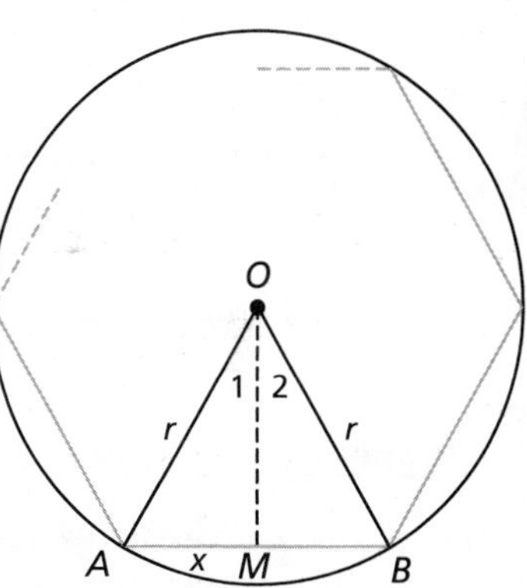

B Let $\overline{AB}$ be one side of the n-gon. Draw $\overline{OM}$, the segment from O to the midpoint of $\overline{AB}$.

Then $\triangle AOM \cong \triangle BOM$ by _______________.

So, $\angle 1 \cong \angle 2$ by _______________.

C There are _______ triangles, all congruent to $\triangle AOB$, that surround point O and fill the n-gon.

Therefore, $m\angle AOB =$ _______ and $m\angle 1 =$ _______.

D Since $\angle OMA \cong \angle OMB$ by CPCTC, and $\angle OMA$ and $\angle OMB$ form a linear pair, these angles are supplementary and must have measures of 90°. So, $\triangle AOM$ and $\triangle BOM$ are right triangles.

In $\triangle AOM$, $\sin \angle 1 = \dfrac{\text{length of opposite leg}}{\text{length of hypotenuse}} = \dfrac{x}{r}$.

So, $x = r\sin \angle 1$ and substituting the expression for $m\angle 1$ from above gives

$x = r\sin(\_\_\_\_\_)$

E Now express the perimeter of the n-gon in terms of x.

The length of $\overline{AB}$ is $2x$, since ______________________________.

This means the perimeter of the n-gon is ______________________________.

Substitute the expression for x from Step D.

Then the perimeter is given by the expression ______________________________.

F Your expression for the perimeter of the n-gon should include $n \sin\left(\frac{180°}{n}\right)$ as a factor. Use a calculator, as follows, to find out what happens to the value of this expression as n gets larger.

- Enter the expression $x \sin\left(\frac{180}{x}\right)$ as Y_1.
- Go to the Table Setup menu and enter the values shown at right.
- View a table for the function.
- Use the arrow keys to scroll down.

TABLE SETUP
TblStart=3
ΔTbl=1
Indpnt: Auto Ask
Depend: Auto Ask

X	Y1
3	2.5981
4	2.8284
5	2.9389
6	3
7	3.0372
8	3.0615
9	3.0782

X=3

What happens to the value of $n \sin\left(\frac{180°}{n}\right)$ as n gets larger?

____

G Consider the expression you wrote for the perimeter of the n-gon at the end of Step E. What happens to the value of this expression as n gets larger?

____

REFLECT

1a. When n is very large, does the perimeter of the n-gon ever equal the circumference of the circle? Why or why not?

____

____

1b. How does the above argument justify the formula $C = 2\pi r$?

____

____

____

PREP FOR MCC9–12.G.MG.1

2 EXAMPLE Finding the Circumference of a Circle

Find the circumference of circle O. Round to the nearest tenth.

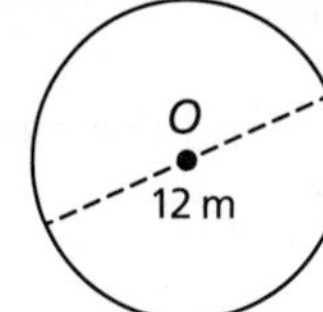

A Find the radius. The diameter is twice the radius, so $r =$ ________.

B Use the formula $C = 2\pi r$.

$C = 2\pi($________$)$ — Substitute the value for r.

$C \approx$ ________ — Use the π key to evaluate the expression on a calculator. Then round.

REFLECT

2a. Suppose you multiply the diameter of the circle by a factor k, for some $k > 0$. How does the circumference change? Explain.

____

____

MCC9–12.G.MG.1

3 EXAMPLE Solving a Circumference Problem

The General Sherman tree in Sequoia National Park, California, is considered the world's largest tree. The tree is approximately circular at its base, with a circumference of 102.6 feet. What is the approximate diameter of the tree? Round to the nearest foot.

A Substitute 102.6 for C in the formula for the circumference of a circle.

________ $= 2\pi r$ — Substitute 102.6 for C in the formula.

________ $= r$ — Solve for r.

$r \approx$ ________ — Use a calculator to evaluate the expression.

B The diameter of a circle is twice the radius.

So, the diameter of the tree is approximately ________.

REFLECT

3a. The maximum distance across the base of the General Sherman tree is 36.5 feet. What explains the difference between this distance and the diameter you calculated above?

____

____

PRACTICE

Find the circumference of each circle. Round to the nearest tenth.

1.

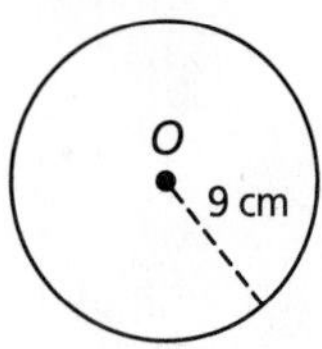

2.

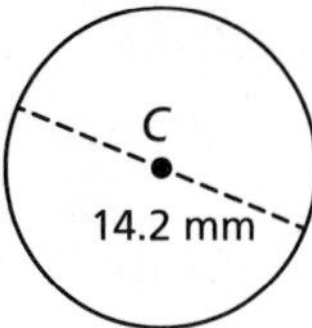

3.

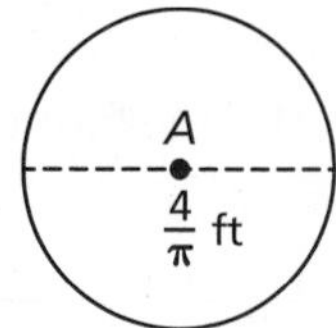

_______________ _______________ _______________

4. The Parthenon is a Greek temple dating to approximately 445 BCE. The temple features 46 Doric columns, which are approximately cylindrical. The circumference of each column at the base is approximately 5.65 meters. What is the approximate diameter of each column? Round to the nearest tenth.

____

5. A circular track for a model train has a diameter of 8.5 feet. The train moves around the track at a constant speed of 0.7 ft/s.

a. To the nearest foot, how far does the train travel when it goes completely around the track 10 times? _______________

b. To the nearest minute, how long does it take the train to go completely around the track 10 times? _______________

6. A standard bicycle wheel has a diameter of 26 inches. A student claims that during a one-mile bike ride the wheel makes more than 1000 complete revolutions. Do you agree or disagree? Explain. (*Hint:* 1 mile = 5280 feet)

____

____

____

7. In the figure, $\overline{AB}$ is a diameter of circle C, D is the midpoint of $\overline{AC}$, and E is the midpoint of $\overline{AD}$. How does the circumference of circle E compare to the circumference of circle C? Explain.

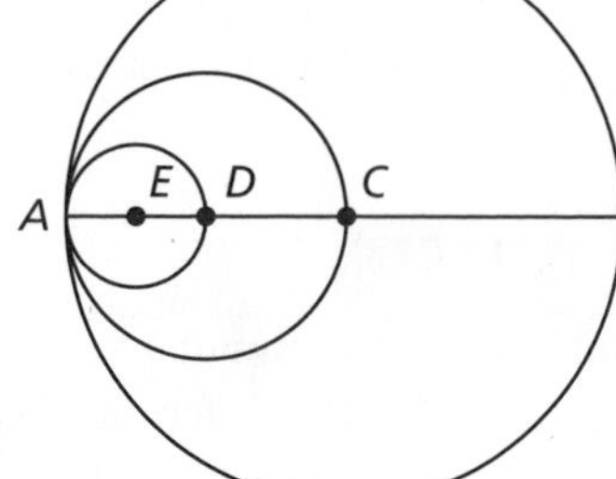

____

____

____

Name _______________ Class _______________ Date _______________

11-1

Additional Practice

Find each measurement. Give your answers in terms of π.

1. 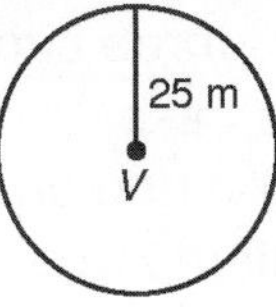

the circumference of $\odot V$

____

2. 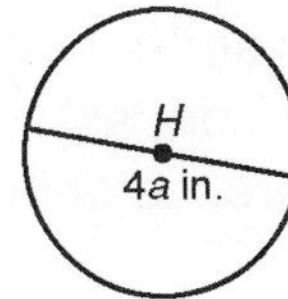

the circumference of $\odot H$

____

3. 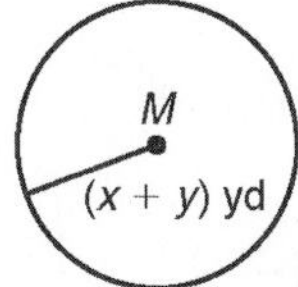

the circumference of $\odot M$

____

4. 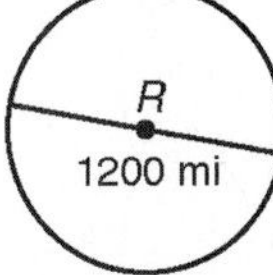

the circumference of $\odot R$

____

5. the radius of $\odot D$ in which $C = 2\pi^2$ cm _______________

6. the diameter of $\odot K$ in which $C = (4x + 4)\pi$ km _______________

7. Daniel is approximating the circumference of a circle by finding the perimeter of an inscribed polygon. The circle has a radius of 6 inches.

   a. Find the circumference of the circle using the expression $2\pi r$ with 3.1415 for π.

   ____

   b. Find the perimeter of an inscribed polygon with 14 sides. Round your answer to the nearest thousandth of an inch.

   ____

   c. Daniel claims that the perimeter of a 14-sided inscribed polygon is within 0.1 in. of the circumference of the circle as calculated in part a. Is he correct? Explain why or why not.

   ____

   ____

Problem Solving

Write the correct answer.

1. A circular swimming pool is surrounded by a walkway that is 3 feet wide, as shown below. The circumference of the outer edge of the walkway is 208 feet. What is the radius of the pool to the nearest foot? Use 3.14 for π.

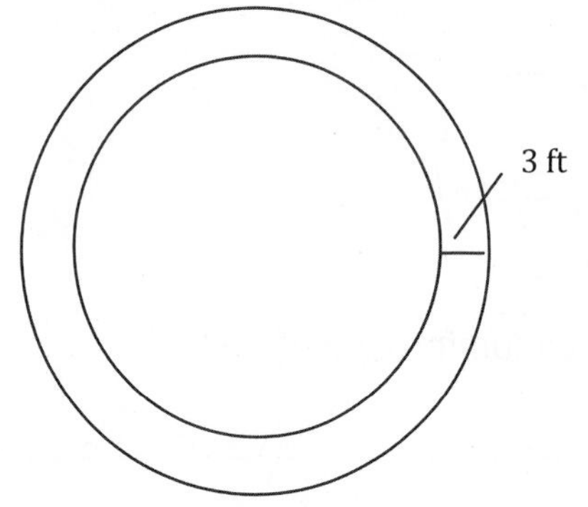

____

2. A wedding cake is made of three circular tiers, as shown below. The cake decorator is going to put one ring of frosting around the circumference of each tier. How many inches of frosting will the cake decorator need? Use 3.14 for π and round to the nearest whole inch.

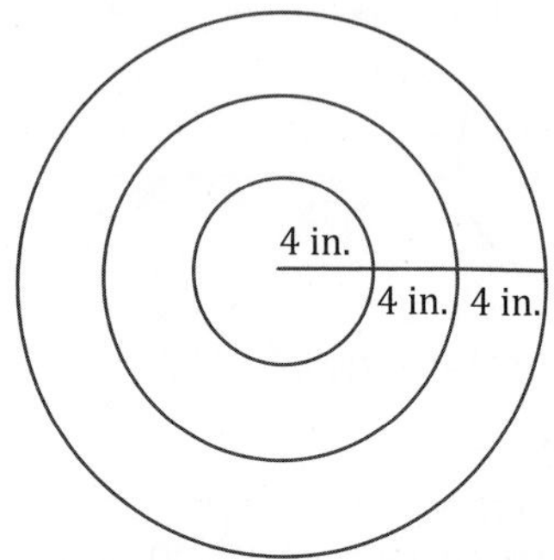

____

Choose the best answer.

3. The circumference of a circle with a radius of 2 meters is approximated by the perimeter of an inscribed polygon with 10 sides. Which expression gives the described approximation of the circumference?

   A $40\sin(18°)$

   B $2(2)\pi\sin(18°)$

   C $2(2)10\sin\left(\frac{180°}{2}\right)$

   D $2\pi(10)\sin\left(\frac{180°}{10}\right)$

4. An amusement park ride is made up of a large circular frame that holds 50 riders. The circumference of the frame is about 138 feet. What is the diameter of the ride to the nearest foot?

   F 22 ft
   H 69 ft
   G 44 ft
   J 138 ft

5. A cyclist travels 50 feet after 7.34 rotations of her bicycle wheels. What is the approximate diameter of the wheels?

   A 13 in.
   C 26 in.
   B 24 in.
   D 28 in.

6. A car has a wheel rim with a diameter of 19 inches. The tire itself has a diameter that is 5 inches wider than the rim. What is the approximate circumference of the tire to the nearest whole inch?

   F 37 inches

   G 42 inches

   H 75 inches

   J 151 inches

Name ______________________ Class ______________ Date __________

Volume of Prisms and Cylinders

Going Deeper

Essential question: *How do you calculate the volume of a prism or cylinder and use volume formulas to solve design problems?*

Recall that the *volume* of a three-dimensional figure is the number of nonoverlapping cubic units contained in the interior of the figure. For example, the prism at right has a volume of 8 cubic centimeters. You can use this idea to develop volume formulas.

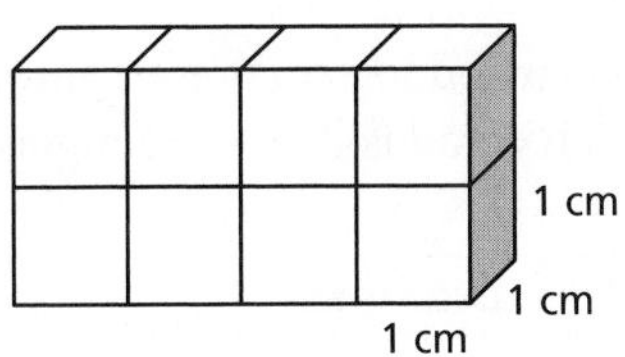

MCC9–12.G.GMD.1

1 EXPLORE Developing a Basic Volume Formula

A Consider a figure that is the base of a prism or cylinder. Assume the figure has an area of B square units.

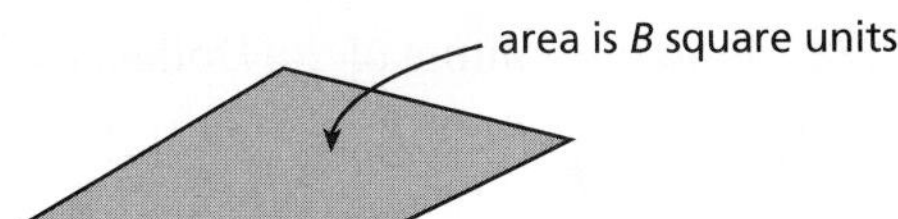

B Use the base to build a prism or cylinder with height 1 unit.

This means the prism or cylinder contains __________ cubic units.

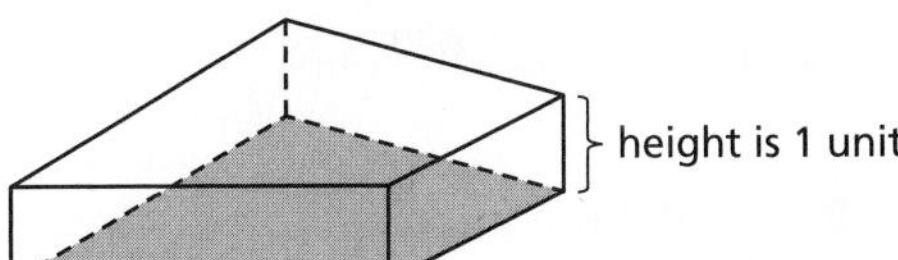

C Now use the base to build a prism or cylinder with a height of h units.

The volume of this prism or cylinder must be __________ times the volume of the prism or cylinder whose height is 1 unit.

So, the volume of the prism or cylinder is __________ cubic units.

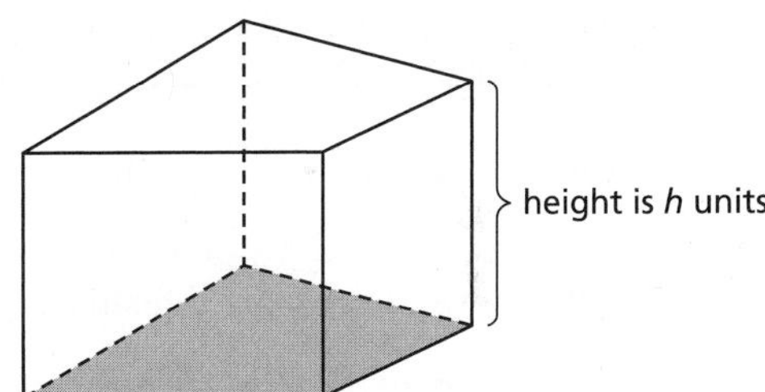

REFLECT

1a. Suppose the figure that is the base of the prism is a rectangle with length ℓ and width w. Explain how you can use your work in the Explore to write a formula for the volume of the prism.

____

____

1b. Explain how you can use your work in the Explore to write a formula for the volume of a cylinder whose base is a circle with radius r.

____

Volume of a Cylinder

The volume V of a cylinder with base area B and height h is given by $V = Bh$ (or $V = \pi r^2 h$, where r is the radius of the base).

MCC9–12.G.MG.2

2 EXAMPLE Comparing Densities

You gather data about two wood logs that are approximately cylindrical. Based on the data in the table, which wood is denser, Douglas fir or American redwood?

Type of Wood	Diameter (ft)	Height (ft)	Weight (lb)
Douglas fir	1	6	155.5
American redwood	3	4	791.7

A Find the volume of the Douglas fir log.

$V = \pi r^2 h$

$V = \pi(\_\_\_\_\_)^2 \cdot \_\_\_\_\_$ Substitute 0.5 for r and 6 for h.

$V \approx \_\_\_\_\_ \text{ ft}^3$ Use a calculator. Round to the nearest tenth.

B Find the volume of the American redwood log.

$V = \pi r^2 h$

$V = \pi(\_\_\_\_\_)^2 \cdot \_\_\_\_\_$ Substitute 1.5 for r and 4 for h.

$V \approx \_\_\_\_\_ \text{ ft}^3$ Use a calculator. Round to the nearest tenth.

C Calculate and compare densities.

The density of the wood is the ________________ per ________________.

Density of Douglas fir $= \frac{}{} \approx \_\_\_\_\_ \text{ lb/ft}^3$ Round to the nearest unit.

Density of American redwood $= \frac{}{} \approx \_\_\_\_\_ \text{ lb/ft}^3$ Round to the nearest unit.

So, ________________ is denser than ________________.

REFLECT

2a. Explain in your own words what your results tell you about the two types of wood.

____

____

The axis of a cylinder is the segment whose endpoints are the centers of the bases. A right cylinder is a cylinder whose axis is perpendicular to the bases. An **oblique cylinder** is a cylinder whose axis is not perpendicular to the bases. Cavalieri's principle makes it possible to extend the formula for the volume of a cylinder to oblique cylinders.

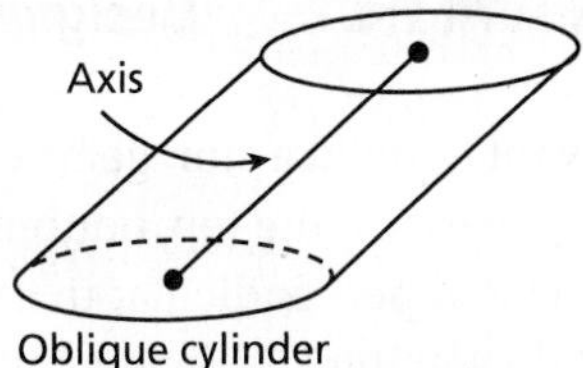

Cavalieri's Principle

If two solids have the same height and the same cross-sectional area at every level, then the two solids have the same volume.

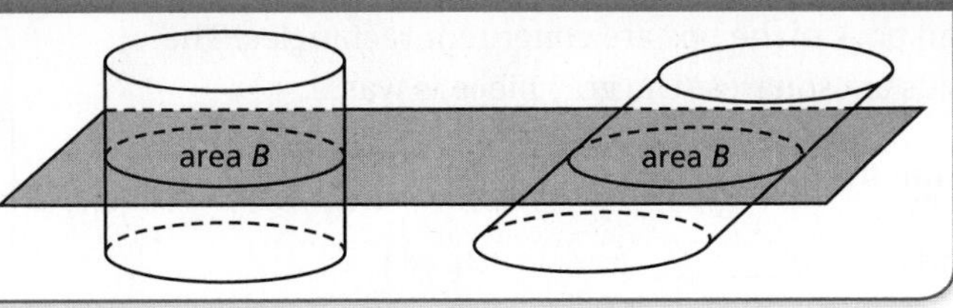

You can think of any oblique cylinder as a right cylinder that has been "pushed over" so that the cross sections at every level have equal areas. By Cavalieri's principle, the volume of an oblique cylinder is equal to the volume of the associated right cylinder. This means the formula $V = Bh = \pi r^2 h$ works for any cylinder.

MCC9–12.G.GMD.2(+)

3 EXAMPLE Finding the Volume of an Oblique Cylinder

The height of the cylinder shown here is twice the radius. What is the volume of the cylinder? Round to the nearest tenth.

$B = 64\pi$ cm²

A Find the height of the cylinder. To do so, first find the radius of the cylinder.

Use the fact that the area of the base B is 64π cm^2.

$\pi r^2 = 64\pi$	The base is a circle, so $B = \pi r^2$.
$r^2 =$ ______	Divide both sides by π.
$r =$ ______ cm	Take the square root of both sides.

Since the height is twice the radius, the height is ______ cm.

B Find the volume of the cylinder.

$V = Bh$	The volume V of any cylinder is $V = Bh$.
$V =$ ______ $\cdot$ ______	Substitute.
$V \approx$ ______ cm^3	Use a calulator. Round to the nearest tenth.

REFLECT

3a. A rectangular prism has the same height as the oblique cylinder in the example. The cross-sectional area at every level of the prism is 64π cm^2. Can you use Cavalieri's principle to make a conclusion about the volume of the prism? Why or why not?

____

____

MCC9–12.G.MG.3

4 EXAMPLE Designing a Box with Maximum Volume

You want to build a storage box from a piece of plywood that is 4 feet by 8 feet. You must use 6 pieces (for the top, bottom, and sides of the box) and you must make cuts that are parallel and perpendicular to the edges of the plywood. Describe three possible designs. What do you think is the maximum possible volume for the box?

Design 1

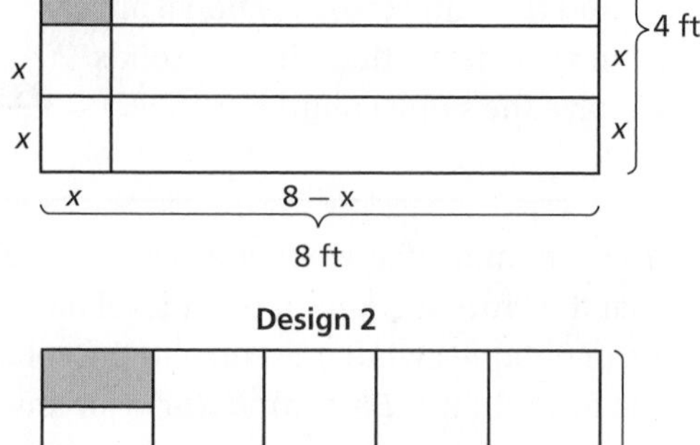

A Consider Design 1 at right. The top, bottom, front, and back of the box are congruent rectangles. The ends are squares. The gray piece is waste.

From the figure, $4x =$ ________, so $x =$ ________ ft

and $8 - x =$ ________ ft.

$V =$ ________ • ________ • ________ = ________ ft^3

Design 2

B Consider Design 2 at right. The top, bottom, front, and back of the box are congruent rectangles. The ends are squares. The gray piece is waste.

From the figure, $5x =$ ________, so $x =$ ________ ft.

$V =$ ________ • ________ • ________ = ________ ft^3

Design 3

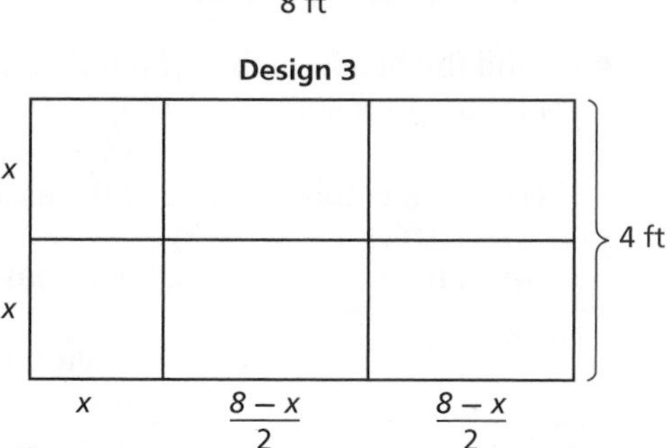

C Consider Design 3 at right. The top, bottom, front, and back of the box are congruent rectangles. The ends are squares. There is no waste.

From the figure, $2x =$ ________, so $x =$ ________ ft

and $\frac{8-x}{2} =$ ________ ft.

$V =$ ________ • ________ • ________ = ________ ft^3

D Based on these designs, the maximum possible volume appears to be ________.

REFLECT

4a. Is it possible to make a box all of whose sides are not squares? If so, give the dimensions of the box and find its volume.

____

____

4b. Is it possible to say what the maximum volume of the box is based on your work above? Why or why not?

____

____

PRACTICE

Find the volume of each prism or cylinder. Round to the nearest tenth.

1.

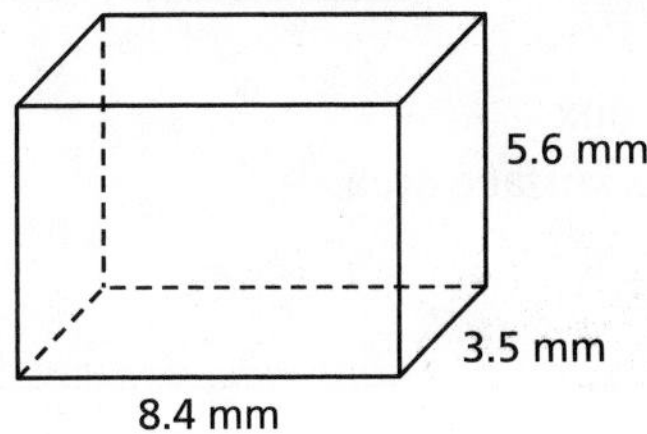

2.

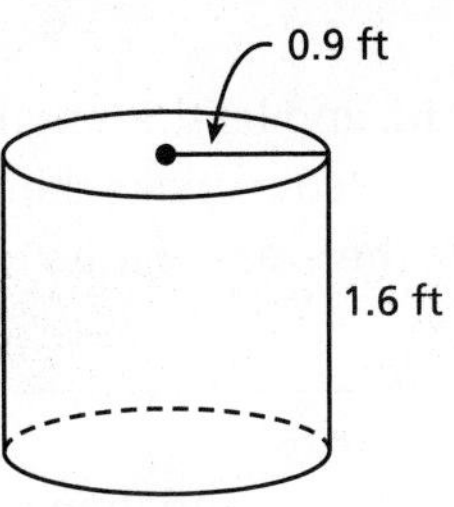

3.

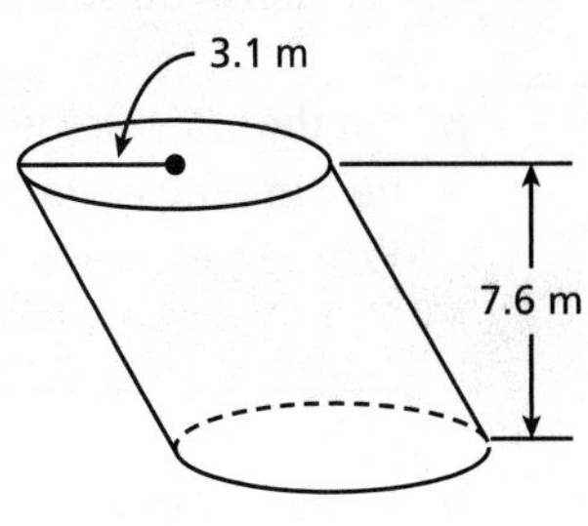

4. You gather data about two wood logs that are approximately cylindrical. The data are shown in the table. Based on your data, which wood is denser, aspen or juniper? Explain.

Type of Wood	Diameter (ft)	Height (ft)	Weight (lb)
Aspen	1.5	3	137.8
Juniper	2	5	549.8

5. A vase in the shape of an oblique cylinder has the dimensions shown at right. How many liters of water does the vase hold? Round to the nearest tenth. (*Hint:* 1 liter = 1000 cm^3)

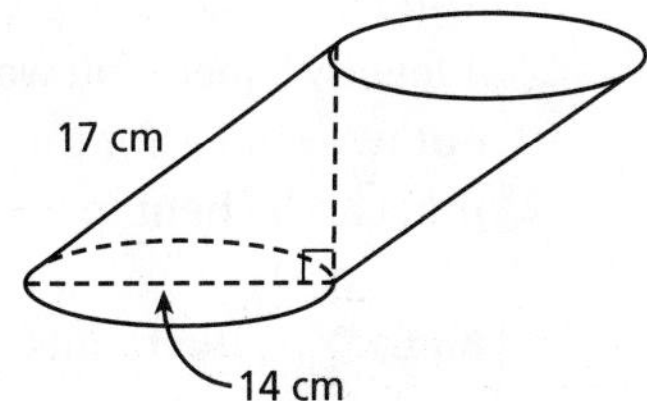

6. **Error Analysis** A student claims that the cylinder and cone at right have the same volume by Cavalieri's principle. Explain the student's error.

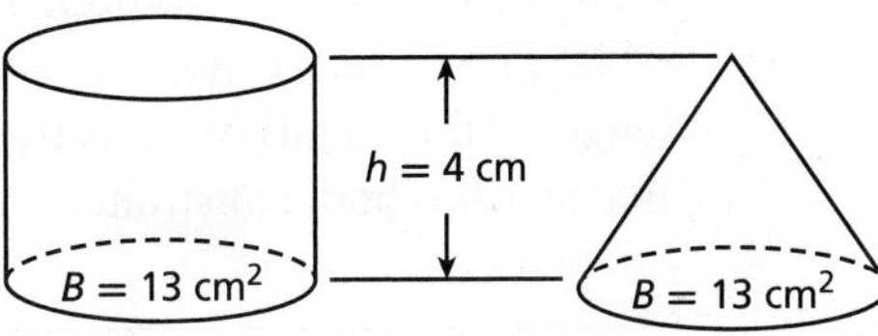

7. You have 500 cm^3 of clay and want to make a sculpture in the shape of a cylinder. You want the height of the cylinder to be 3 times the cylinder's radius and you want to use all the clay. What radius and height should the sculpture have?

8. You want to build a box in the shape of a rectangular prism. The box must have a volume of 420 in.^{3} As shown in the figure, the ends of the box must be squares. In order to minimize the cost, you want to use the least possible amount of material. Follow these steps to determine the dimensions you should use for the box.

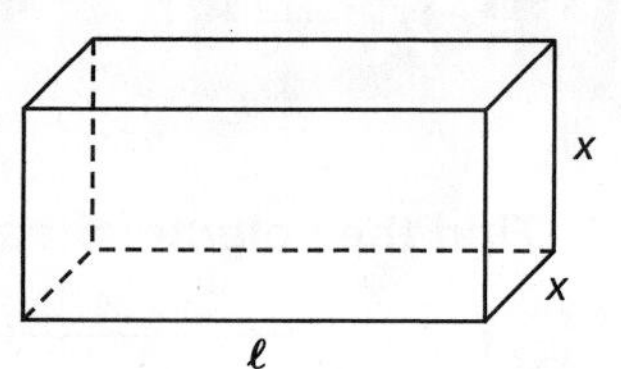

a. Let the ends of the box be x in. by x in. and let the length of the box be ℓ in. The amount of material M needed to make the box is its surface area. Write an expression for M by adding the areas of the six faces.

____

b. Write an equation for the volume of the box and then solve it for ℓ.

____

c. Substitute the expression for ℓ in the expression for M from part (a).

____

d. To find the value of x that minimizes M, enter the expression for M as Y_1 in your calculator. Graph the function in a suitable viewing window. Go to the Calc menu and choose **3: minimum** to find the value of x that minimizes M. Use your equation from part (b) to find the corresponding value of ℓ. What dimensions should you use for the box?

____

9. You have a flexible piece of sheet metal that measures 4 feet by 8 feet. You want to build a cylinder by cutting out two circles for the bases and a rectangular piece that can be bent to form the lateral surface.

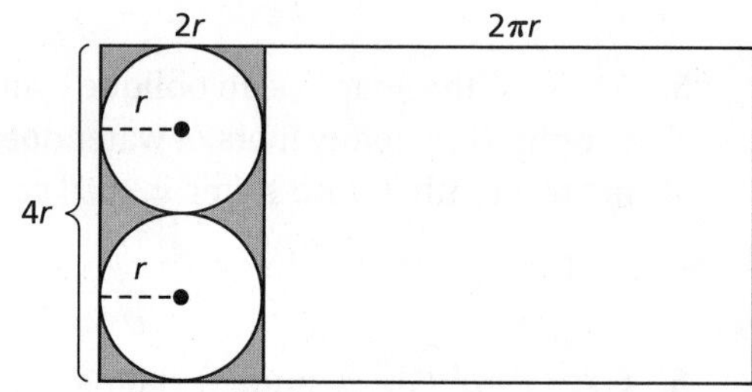

a. Let r be the radius of the cylinder. From the figure, there are two constraints on r: $4r \leq 4$ (based on the width of the metal) and $2r + 2\pi r \leq 8$ (based on the length of the metal). What is the greatest value of r that satisfies both constraints?

____

b. What is the approximate volume of the cylinder with this radius?

____

Name ____________________ Class ____________ Date ____________

11-2

Additional Practice

Find the volume of each prism. Round to the nearest tenth if necessary.

1. 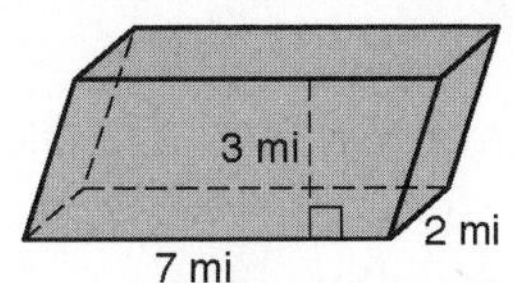

the oblique rectangular prism

____

2. 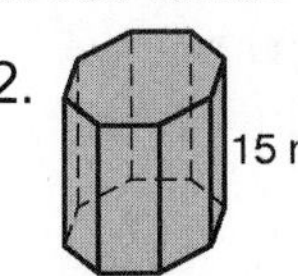

the regular octagonal prism

____

3. a cube with edge length 0.75 m _______________

Find the volume of each cylinder. Give your answers both in terms of π and rounded to the nearest tenth.

4. 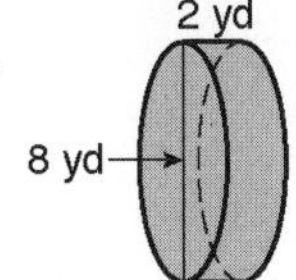

____

5. 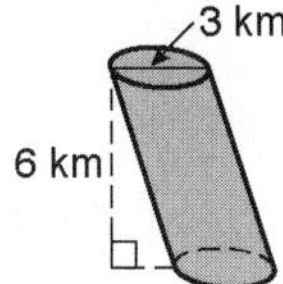

____

6. a cylinder with base circumference 18π ft and height 10 ft _______________

7. CDs have the dimensions shown in the figure. Each CD is 1 mm thick. Find the volume in cubic centimeters of a stack of 25 CDs. Round to the nearest tenth.

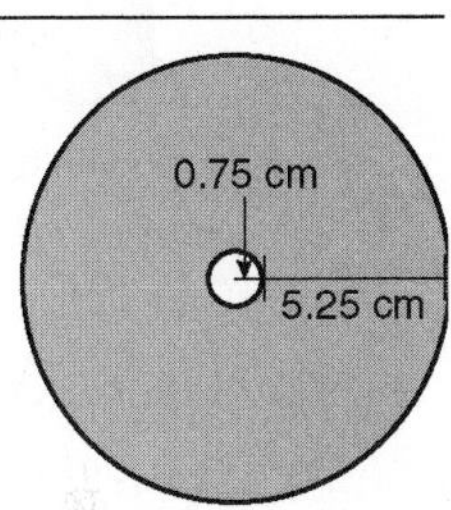

____

Describe the effect of each change on the volume of the given figure.

8. 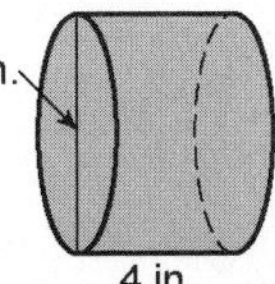

The dimensions are halved.

____

9. 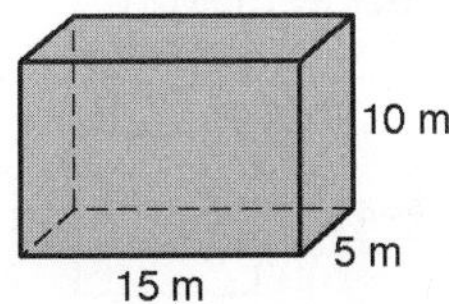

The dimensions are divided by 5.

____

Find the volume of each composite figure. Round to the nearest tenth.

10. 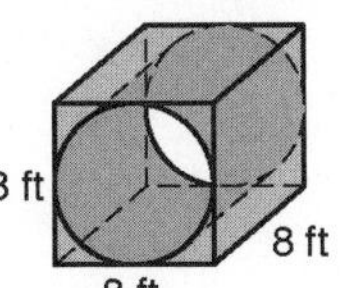

____

11. 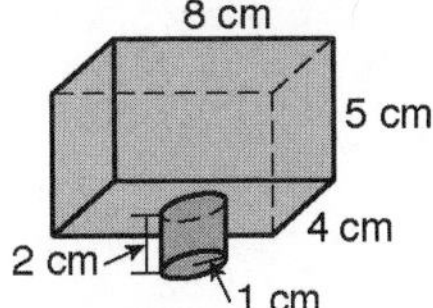

____

Problem Solving

1. A cylindrical juice container has the dimensions shown. About how many cups of juice does this container hold? (*Hint:* 1 cup $\approx$ 14.44 in^3)

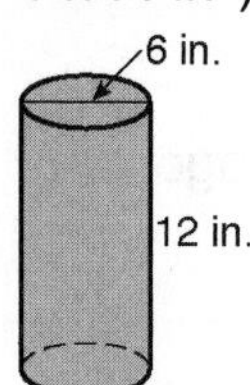

---

2. A large cylindrical cooler is $2\frac{1}{2}$ feet high and has a diameter of $1\frac{1}{2}$ feet. It is filled $\frac{3}{4}$ high with water for athletes to use during their soccer game. Estimate the volume of the water in the cooler in gallons. (*Hint:* 1 gallon $\approx$ 231 in^3)

Choose the best answer.

3. How many 3-inch cubes can be placed inside the box?

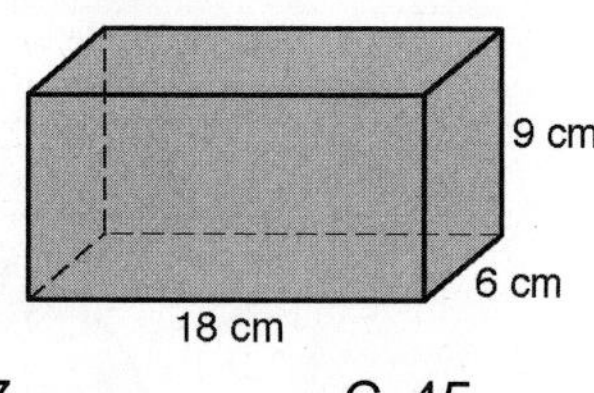

A 27 C 45

B 36 D 72

4. A cylinder has a volume of 4π cm^3. If the radius and height are each tripled, what will be the new volume of the cylinder?

F 12π cm^3 H 64π cm^3

G 36π cm^3 J 108π cm^3

5. What is the volume of the composite figure with the dimensions shown in the three views? Round to the nearest tenth.

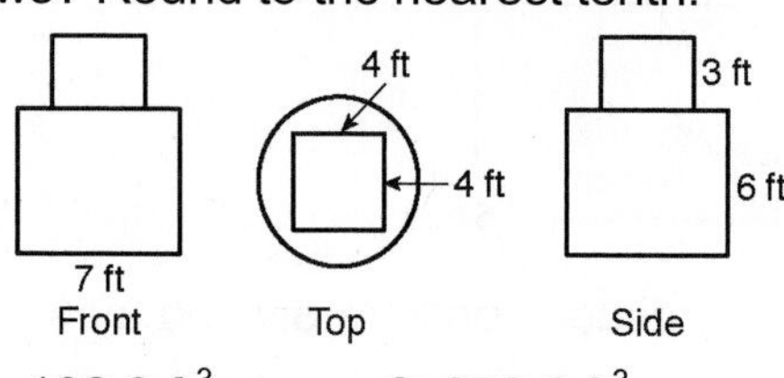

A 182.9 ft^3 C 278.9 ft^3

B 205.7 ft^3 D 971.6 ft^3

6. Find the expression that can be used to determine the volume of the composite figure shown.

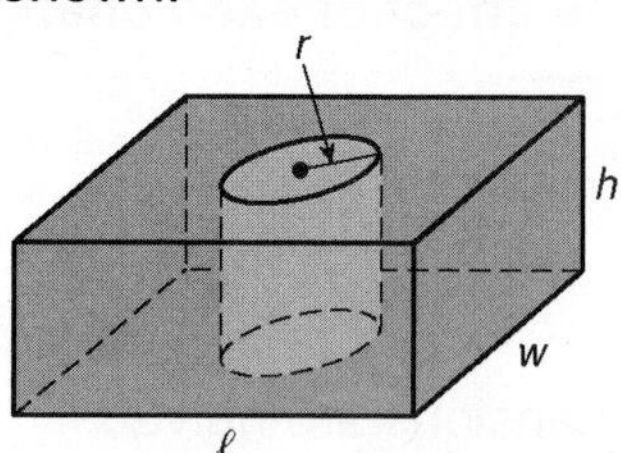

F $\ell wh - \pi r^2 h$ H $\pi r^2 h - \ell wh$

G $\pi r^2 h + \ell wh$ J $\ell wh + 2\pi r^2 h$

Name ______________________ Class ______________ Date ________

11-3

Volume of Pyramids and Cones

Going Deeper

Essential question: *How do you calculate the volume of a pyramid or cone and use volume formulas to solve problems?*

Recall that a *pyramid* is a polyhedron formed by a polygonal base and triangular lateral faces that meet at a common point, called the vertex of the pyramid. The goal of this lesson is to develop a formula for volume of a pyramid.

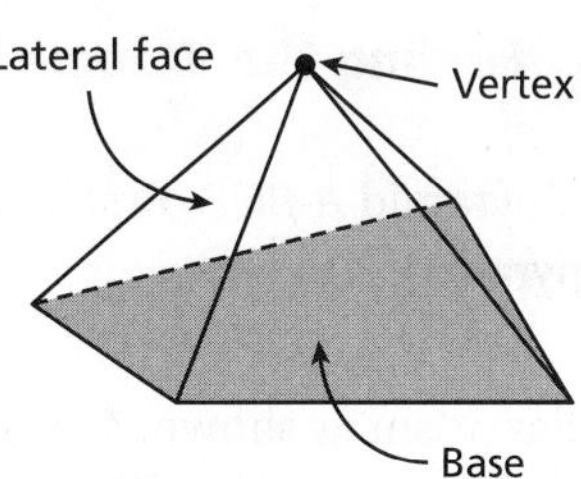

MCC9–12.G.GMD.1

1 EXPLORE Developing a Volume Postulate

A Consider a segment, $\overline{AB}$, with length b and a line ℓ that is parallel to $\overline{AB}$. Let h be the distance between $\overline{AB}$ and line ℓ.

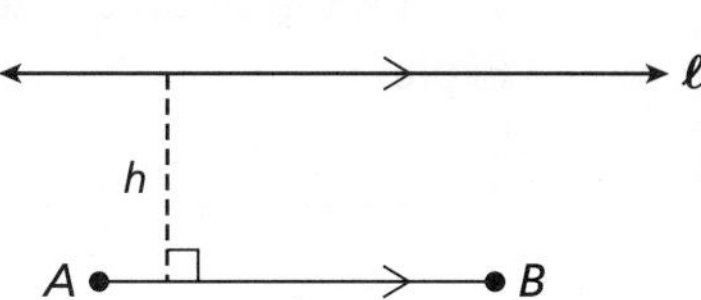

Choose a point C on line ℓ and draw $\triangle ABC$. What is the area of $\triangle ABC$ in terms of b and h?

____

B Choose a different point C on line ℓ and draw $\triangle ABC$. What is the area of $\triangle ABC$ in terms of b and h?

____

C What do you think is true about all triangles that share the same base and have the same height?

____

REFLECT

1a. Consider a three-dimensional figure that is analogous to the situation you explored above. Suppose you are given a polygon and a plane R that is parallel to the plane containing the polygon. You can form a pyramid by choosing a point in plane R and connecting it to each vertex of the polygon. What do you think is true of all pyramids formed in this way?

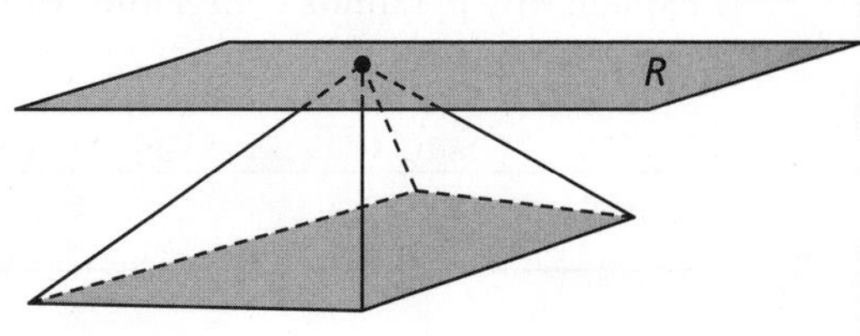

____

Based on your work in the Explore, the following postulate should seem reasonable.

Postulate

Pyramids that have equal base areas and equal heights have equal volumes.

In order to find a formula for the volume of any pyramid, you will first find a formula for the volume of a "wedge pyramid." A wedge pyramid is one in which the base is a triangle and a perpendicular segment from the pyramid's vertex to the base intersects the base at a vertex of the triangle. Pyramid *A-BCD* is a wedge pyramid.

MCC9–12.G.GMD.1

2 EXPLORE Finding the Volume of a Wedge Pyramid

To find the volume of pyramid *A-BCD*, first let the area of $\triangle BCD$ be *B* and let the height of the pyramid, *AD*, be *h*.

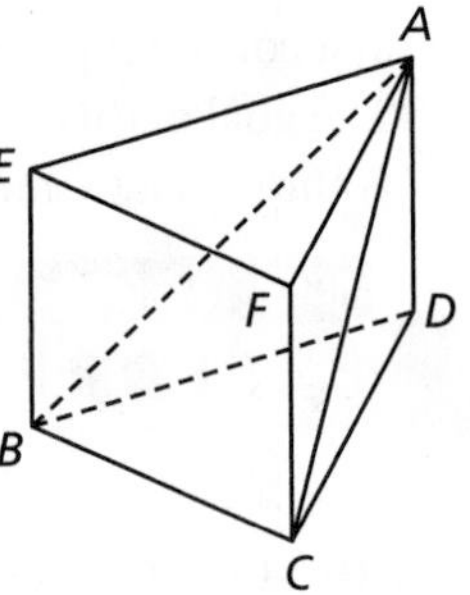

A Form a triangular prism as shown. The edges $\overline{EB}$ and $\overline{FC}$ are congruent to $\overline{AD}$ and parallel to $\overline{AD}$. The bases of the prism, $\triangle EFA$ and $\triangle BCD$ are congruent.

B What is the volume of the triangular prism in terms of *B* and *h*? Explain.

____

____

C You will now compare the volume of pyramid *A-BCD* and the volume of the triangular prism.

Draw $\overline{EC}$. This is the diagonal of a rectangle so, $\triangle$ __________ $\cong \triangle$ __________.

Explain why pyramids *A-EBC* and *A-CFE* have the same volume.

____

____

____

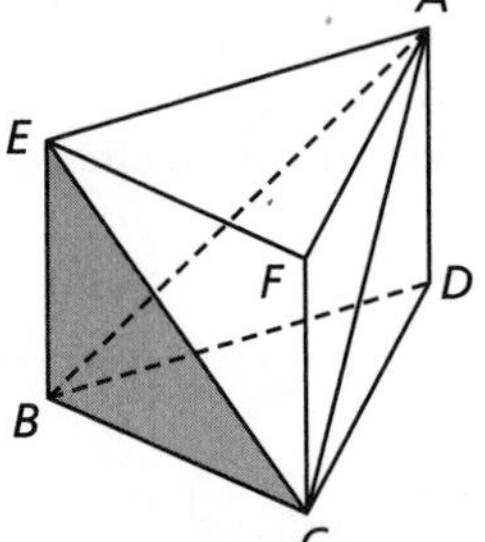

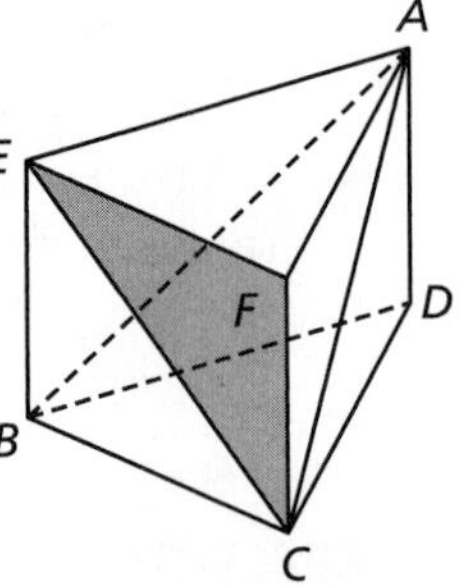

Explain why pyramids *C-EFA* and *A-BCD* have the same volume.

____

____

____

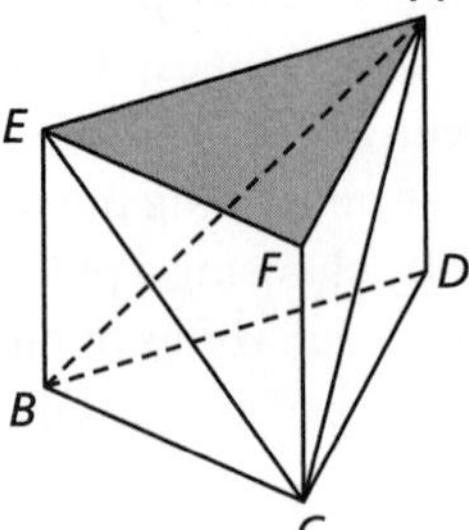

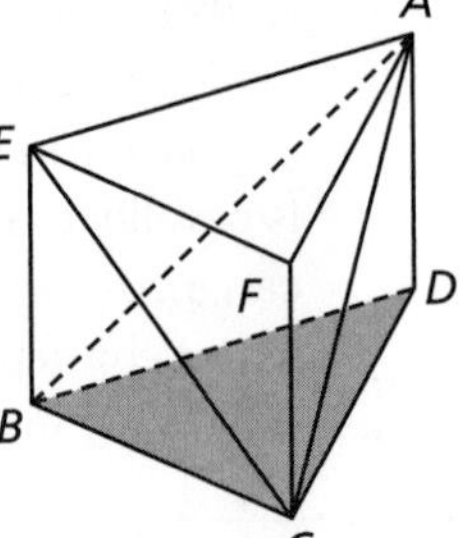

D You have shown that the three pyramids that form the triangular prism all have the same volume. Compare the volume of pyramid *A-BCD* and the volume of the triangular prism.

____

____

E Write the volume of pyramid *A-BCD* in terms of *B* and *h*.

____

REFLECT

2a. Explain how you know that the three pyramids that form that triangular prism all have the same volume.

____

____

____

____

In the Explore, you showed that the volume of any "wedge pyramid" is one-third the product of the base area and the height. Now consider a general pyramid. As shown in the figure, the pyramid can be partitioned into nonoverlapping wedge pyramids by drawing a perpendicular from the vertex to the base.

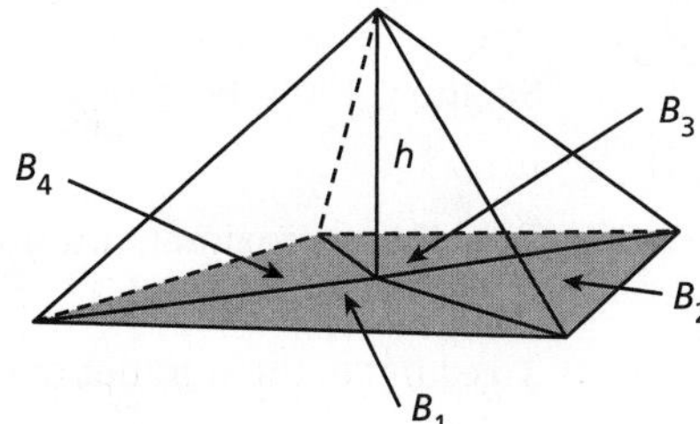

The volume *V* of the given pyramid is the sum of the volumes of the wedge pyramids.

That is, $V = \frac{1}{3}B_1h + \frac{1}{3}B_2h + \frac{1}{3}B_3h + \frac{1}{3}B_4h$.

Using the distributive property, this may be rewritten as $V = \frac{1}{3}h(B_1 + B_2 + B_3 + B_4)$.

Notice that $B_1 + B_2 + B_3 + B_4 = B$, where *B* is the base area of the given pyramid.

So, $V = \frac{1}{3}Bh$.

The above argument provides an informal justification for the following result.

Volume of a Pyramid

The volume *V* of a pyramid with base area *B* and height *h* is given by $V = \frac{1}{3}Bh$.

MCC9–12.G.GMD.3

3 EXAMPLE Solving a Volume Problem

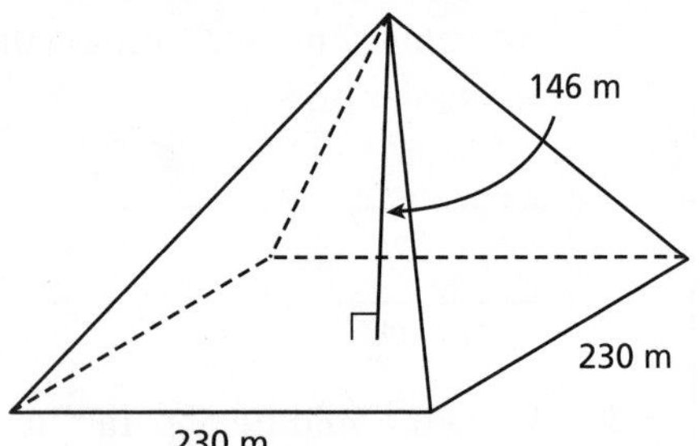

The Great Pyramid in Giza, Egypt, is approximately a square pyramid with the dimensions shown. The pyramid is composed of stone blocks that are rectangular prisms. An average block has dimensions 1.3 m by 1.3 m by 0.7 m. Approximately how many stone blocks were used to build the pyramid? Round to the nearest hundred thousand.

A Find the volume of the pyramid.

The area of the base B is the area of a square with sides of length 230 m.

So, $B =$ ______________

The volume V of the pyramid is $\frac{1}{3}Bh = \frac{1}{3} \cdot$ ______________ $\cdot$ ______________

So, $V =$ ____________________

B Find the volume of an average block.

The volume of a rectangular prism is given by the formula ______________.

So, the volume W of an average block is ________________________.

C Find the approximate number of stone blocks in the pyramid.

To estimate the number of blocks in the pyramid, divide _______ by _______.

So, the approximate number of blocks is ________________________.

REFLECT

3a. What aspects of the model in this problem may lead to inaccuracies in your estimate?

____

____

____

3b. Suppose you are told that the average height of a stone block is 0.69 m rather than 0.7 m. Would this increase or decrease your estimate of the total number of blocks in the pyramid? Explain.

____

Recall that a *cone* is a three-dimensional figure with a circular base and a curved lateral surface that connects the base to a point called the vertex. You can use the formula for the volume of a pyramid to develop a formula for the volume of a cone.

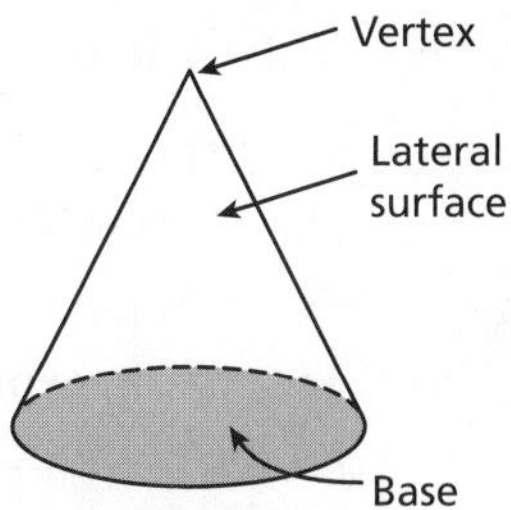

MCC9–12.G.GMD.1

4 EXPLORE Developing a Volume Formula

Plan: To find the volume of a given cone, consider pyramids with regular polygonal bases that are inscribed in the cone. As the number of sides of the polygonal bases increases, the volume of the pyramid gets closer to the volume of the cone. The first steps of the argument consist of writing an expression for the volume of an inscribed pyramid.

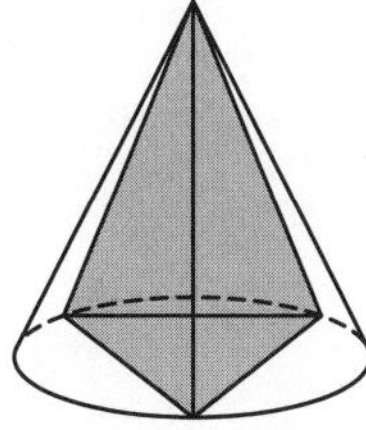
Base of inscribed pyramid has 3 sides.

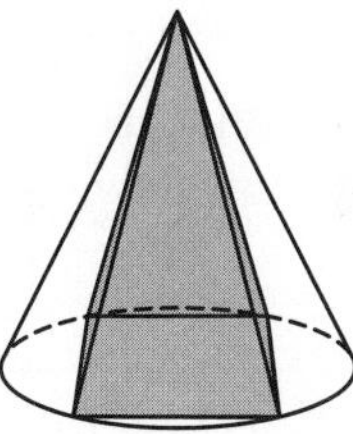
Base of inscribed pyramid has 4 sides.

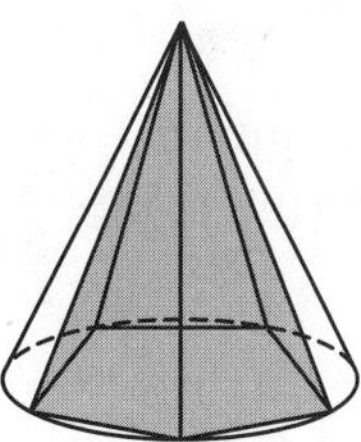
Base of inscribed pyramid has 5 sides.

A Let O be the center of the cone's base and let r be the radius of the cone. Let h be the height of the cone. Inscribe a pyramid whose base is a regular n-gon in the cone. Draw radii from O to the vertices of the n-gon.

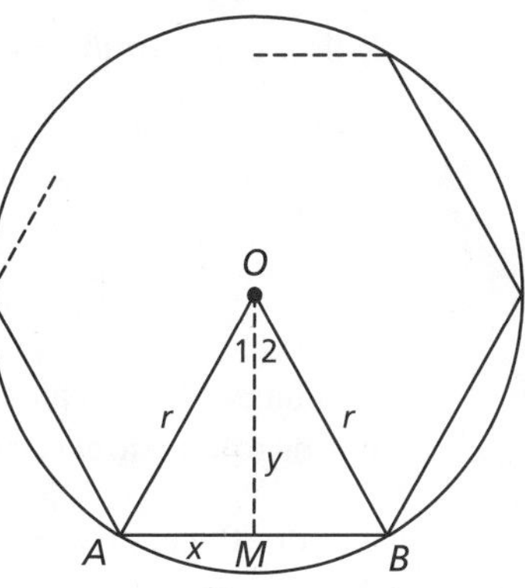

B Let $\overline{AB}$ be one side of the n-gon. Draw $\overline{OM}$, the segment from O to the midpoint of $\overline{AB}$.

Then $\triangle AOM \cong \triangle BOM$ by ______________________________.

So, $\angle 1 \cong \angle 2$ by ______________________.

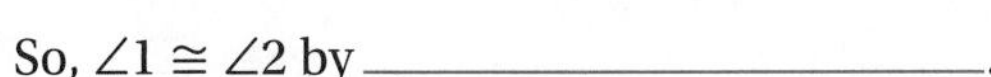

C There are ________ triangles, all congruent to $\triangle AOB$, that surround point O and fill the n-gon.

Therefore, $m\angle AOB =$ ________ and $m\angle 1 =$ ________.

D Since $\angle OMA \cong \angle OMB$ by CPCTC, and $\angle OMA$ and $\angle OMB$ form a linear pair, these angles are supplementary and must have measures of 90°. So, $\triangle AOM$ and $\triangle BOM$ are right triangles.

In $\triangle AOM$, $\sin \angle 1 = \frac{x}{r}$, so $x = r \sin \angle 1$.

Substituting the expression for $m\angle 1$ from above gives $x = r \sin$ (________).

E In $\triangle AOM$, $\cos \angle 1 = \frac{y}{r}$, so $y = r \cos \angle 1$.

Substituting the expression for $m\angle 1$ from above gives $y = r \cos$ (__________).

F To write an expression for the area of the base of the pyramid, first write an expression for the area of $\triangle AOB$.

$\text{Area}(\triangle AOB) = \frac{1}{2} \cdot \text{base} \cdot \text{height} = \frac{1}{2} \cdot 2x \cdot y = xy$

Substituting the expressions for x and y from above gives the following.

Area ($\triangle AOB$) = ____________________

The base of the pyramid is composed of n triangles that are congruent to $\triangle AOB$, so the area of the base of the pyramid is given by the following.

Area (base of pyramid) = ____________________

The volume of the pyramid is $\frac{1}{3} \cdot \text{base} \cdot \text{height}$, which may be written as

Volume (pyramid) = ____________________

G Your expression for the pyramid's volume should include the expression

$$n \sin\left(\frac{180°}{n}\right) \cos\left(\frac{180°}{n}\right)$$

as a factor. Use a calculator, as follows, to find out what happens to the value of this expression as n gets larger and larger.

- Enter the expression $x \sin\left(\frac{180}{x}\right) \cos\left(\frac{180}{x}\right)$ as Y_1.
- Go to the Table Setup menu and enter the values shown at right.
- View a table for the function.
- Use the arrow keys to scroll down.

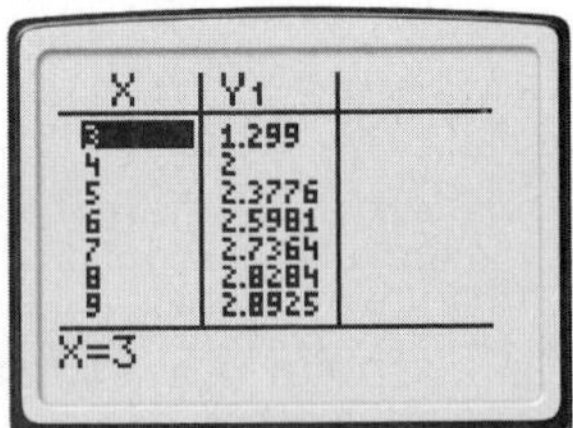

What happens to the value of $n \sin\left(\frac{180°}{n}\right) \cos\left(\frac{180°}{n}\right)$ as n gets larger?

____

H Consider the expression you wrote for the volume of the inscribed pyramid at the end of Step F. What happens to the value of this expression as n gets larger?

____

REFLECT

4a. How is the formula for the volume of a cone, which you derived above, similar to the formula for the volume of a pyramid?

____

____

The argument in the Explore provides a justification for the following result.

Volume of a Cone

The volume V of a cone with base area B and height h is given by $V = \frac{1}{3}Bh$ (or $V = \frac{1}{3}\pi r^2 h$, where r is the radius of the base).

MCC9–12.G.GMD.3

5 EXAMPLE Solving a Volume Problem

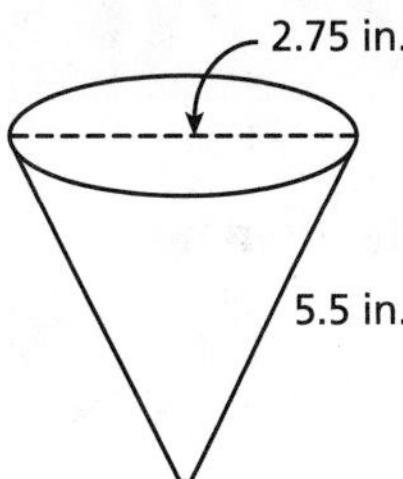

A conical paper cup has the dimensions shown. How many fluid ounces of liquid does the cup hold? Round to the nearest tenth. (*Hint:* 1 in.^{3} ≈ 0.554 fl oz.)

A Find the radius and height of the cone.

The radius r is half the diameter, so $r =$ __________.

To find the height h of the cone, use the Pythagorean Theorem.

$h^2 + r^2 = 5.5^2$	Pythagorean Theorem
$h^2 + (\_\_\_\_\_\_)^2 = 5.5^2$	Substitute the value of r.
$h^2 =$ __________	Solve for h^2.
$h \approx$ __________	Solve for h. Round to the nearest thousandth.

B Find the volume of the cone to the nearest hundredth.

$V = \frac{1}{3}\pi r^2 h = \frac{1}{3}\pi \cdot (\_\_\_\_\_\_)^2 \cdot (\_\_\_\_\_\_) \approx$ __________

C Convert the volume to fluid ounces.

__________ in.^{3} ≈ __________ • 0.554 fl oz ≈ __________ fl oz

So, the cup holds approximately __________ fluid ounces.

REFLECT

5a. A cylindrical cup has the same diameter and height as the conical cup. How can you find the number of fluid ounces that the cylindrical cup holds?

5b. Suppose the height of the conical paper cup is doubled, but the base radius is not changed. How would the volume of the cup change?

5c. Suppose the height of the conical paper cup is not changed, but the base radius is doubled. How would the volume of the cup change?

PRACTICE

Find the volume of each pyramid. Round to the nearest tenth.

1.

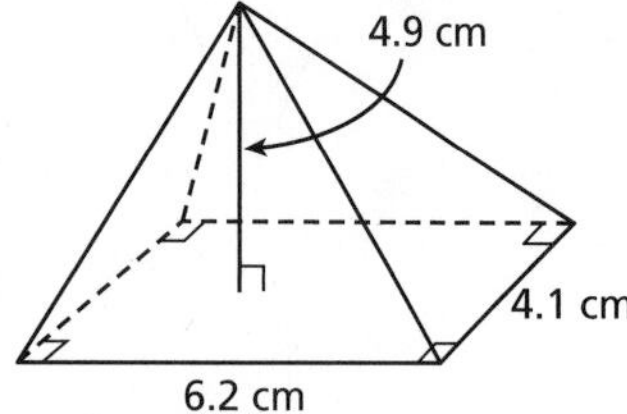

2.

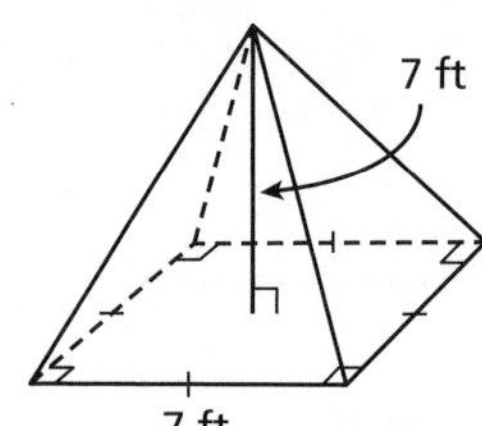

3.

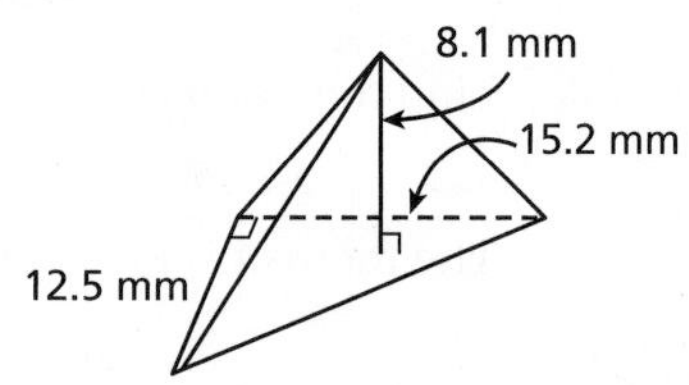

4. As shown in the figure, polyhedron *ABCDEFGH* is a cube and *P* is any point on face *EFGH*. Compare the volume of pyramid *P-ABCD* and the volume of the cube.

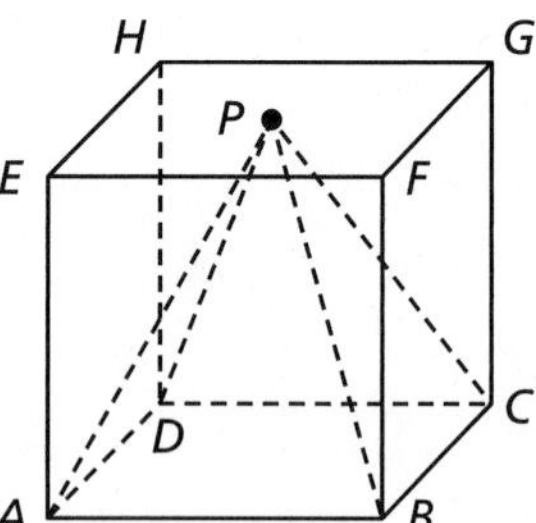

5. A storage container for grain is in the shape of a square pyramid with the dimensions shown.

a. What is the volume of the container in cubic centimeters?

b. Grain leaks from the container at a rate of 4 cm^3 per second. Assuming the container starts completely full, about how many hours does it take until the container is empty?

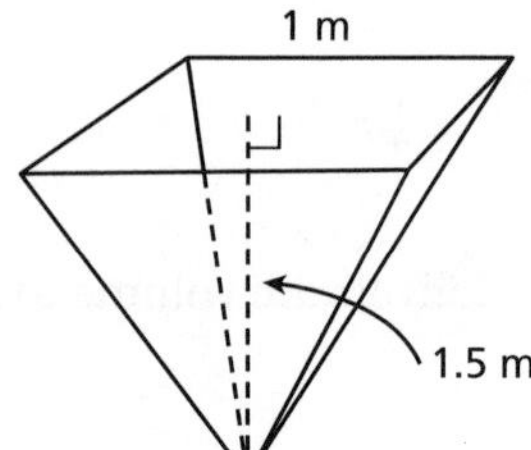

6. A piece of pure silver in the shape of a rectangular pyramid with the dimensions shown at right has a mass of 19.7 grams.

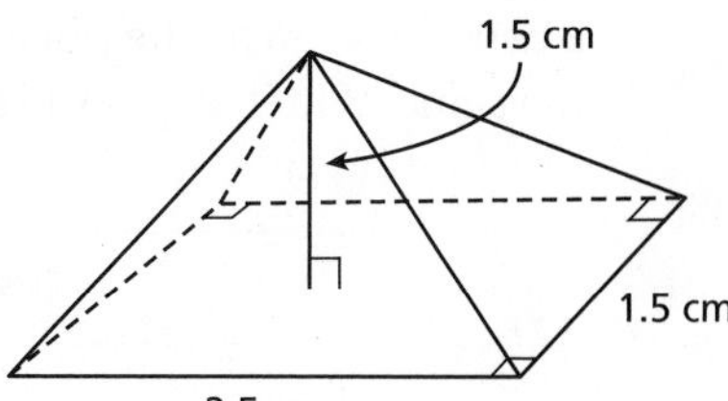

a. What is the area of the base?

____

b. What is the volume of the rectangular pyramid?

____

c. Use the mass of silver and the volume you calculated to estimate the density of silver.

____

7. A pyramid has a square base and a height of 5 ft. The volume of the pyramid is 60 ft^3. Explain how to find the length of a side of the pyramid's base.

____

____

____

Find the volume of each cone. Round to the nearest tenth.

8.

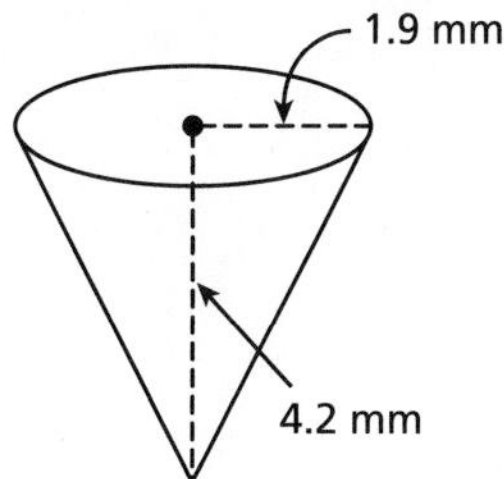

____

9.

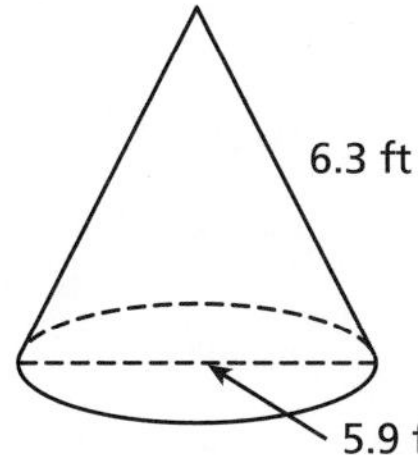

____

10.

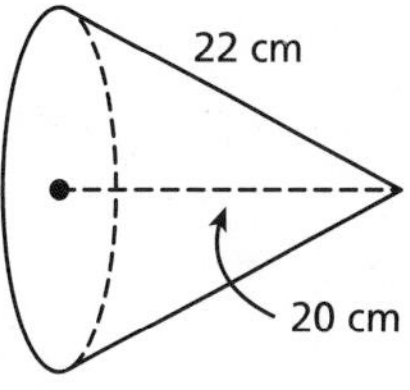

____

11. The figure shows a water tank that consists of a cylinder and cone. How many gallons of water does the tank hold? Round to the nearest gallon. (*Hint:* 1 $ft^3 \approx 7.48$ gal)

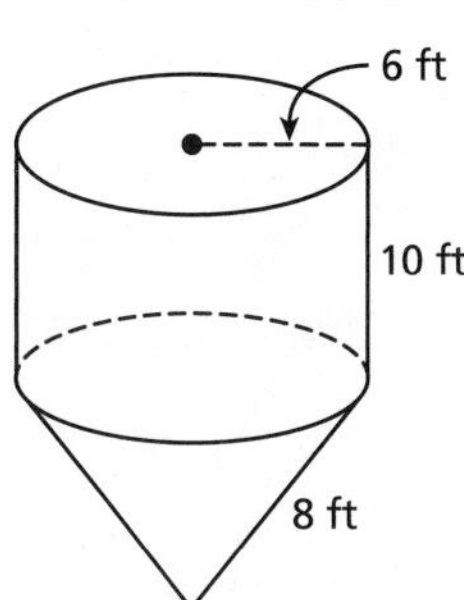

____

12. Popcorn is available in two cups: a square pyramid or a cone, as shown. The price of each cup of popcorn is the same. Which cup is the better deal? Explain.

12 cm
12 cm
20 cm

13. A sculptor removes a cone from a cylindrical block of wood so that the vertex of the cone is the center of the cylinder's base, as shown. Explain how the volume of the remaining solid compares with the volume of the original cylindrical block of wood.

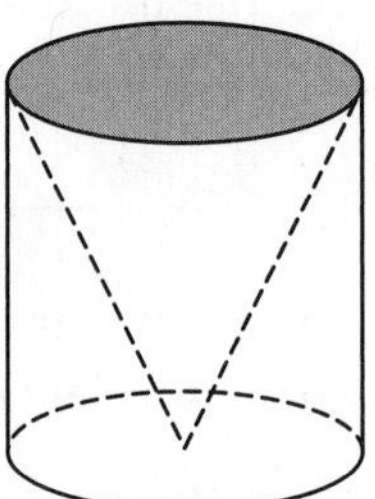

Name ________________ Class ________ Date ________

11-3

Additional Practice

Find the volume of each pyramid. Round to the nearest tenth if necessary.

1. 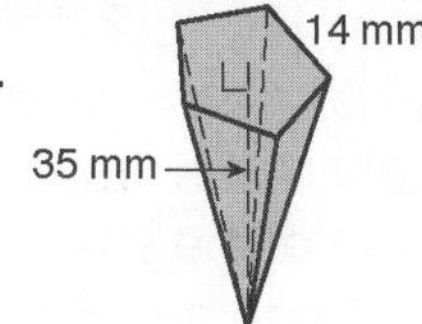

the regular pentagonal pyramid

____

2. 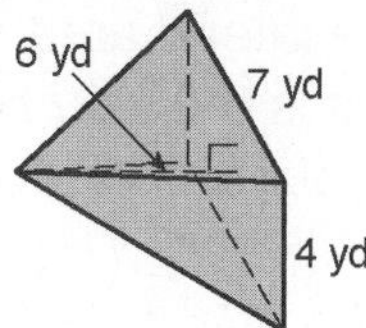

the rectangular right pyramid

____

3. Giza in Egypt is the site of the three great Egyptian pyramids. Each pyramid has a square base. The largest pyramid was built for Khufu. When first built, it had base edges of 754 feet and a height of 481 feet. Over the centuries, some of the stone eroded away and some was taken for newer buildings. Khufu's pyramid today has base edges of 745 feet and a height of 471 feet. To the nearest cubic foot, find the difference between the original and current volumes of the pyramid.

____

Find the volume of each cone. Give your answers both in terms of π and rounded to the nearest tenth.

4. 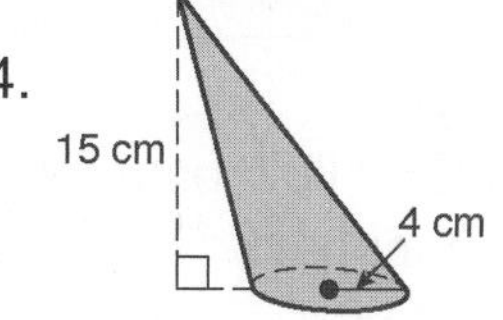

____

5. 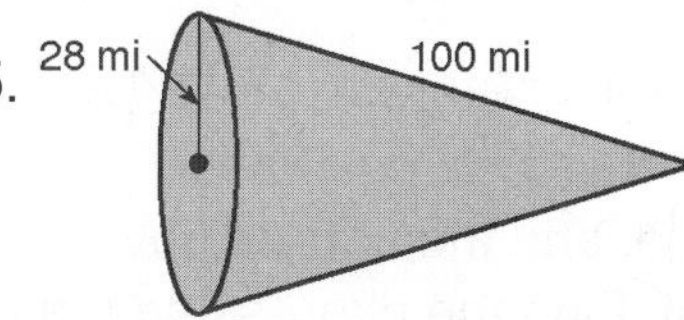

____

6. a cone with base circumference 6π m and a height equal to half the radius

____

7. Compare the volume of a cone and the volume of a cylinder with equal height and base area.

____

Describe the effect of each change on the volume of the given figure.

8. 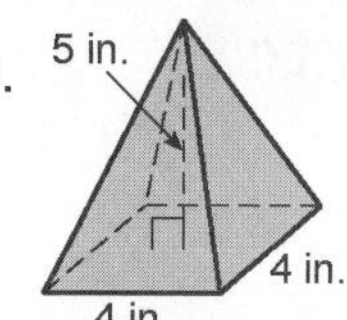

The dimensions are multiplied by $\frac{2}{3}$.

____

9. 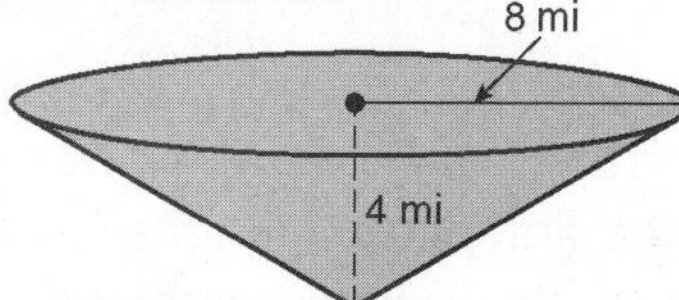

The dimensions are tripled.

____

Find the volume of each composite figure. Round to the nearest tenth.

10. 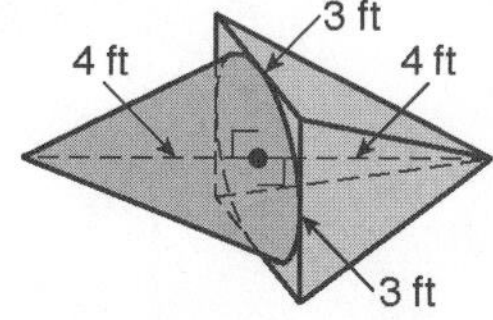

11. 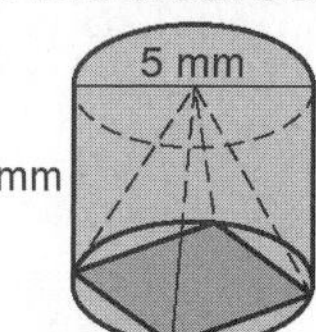

Problem Solving

1. A regular square pyramid has a base area of 196 meters and a lateral area of 448 square meters. What is the volume of the pyramid? Round your answer to the nearest tenth.

____

2. A paper cone for serving roasted almonds has a volume of 406π cubic centimeters. A smaller cone has half the radius and half the height of the first cone. What is the volume of the smaller cone? Give your answer in terms of π.

____

3. The hexagonal base in the pyramid is a regular polygon. What is the volume of the pyramid if its height is 9 centimeters? Round to the nearest tenth.

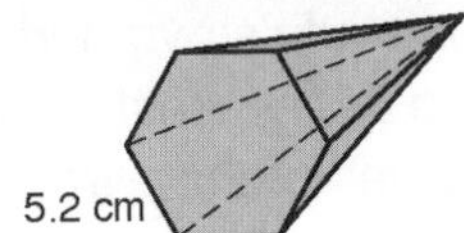

____

4. Find the volume of the shaded solid in the figure shown. Give your answer in terms of π.

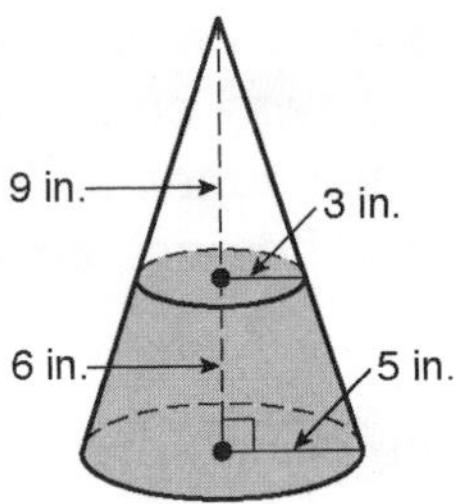

____

Choose the best answer.

5. The diameter of the cone equals the width of the cube, and the figures have the same height. Find the expression that can be used to determine the volume of the composite figure.

   A $4(4)(4) - \frac{1}{3}\pi(2^2)(4)$

   B $4(4)(4) + \frac{1}{3}\pi(2^2)(4)$

   C $4(4)(4) - \pi(2^2)(4)$

   D $4(4)(4) + \frac{1}{3}\pi(2^2)$

   4 ft
   4 ft
   4 ft

6. Approximately how many fluid ounces of water can the paper cup hold? (*Hint:* 1 fl oz $\approx$ 1.805 in^3)

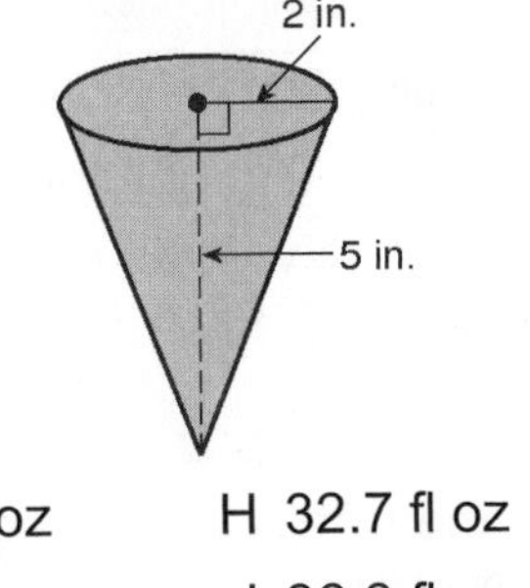

   F 10.9 fl oz   H 32.7 fl oz

   G 11.6 fl oz   J 36.3 fl oz

7. The Step Pyramid of Djoser in Lower Egypt was the first pyramid in the history of architecture. Its original height was 204 feet, and it had a rectangular base measuring 411 feet by 358 feet. Which is the best estimate for the volume of the pyramid in cubic yards?

   A 370,570 yd^3 C 3,335,128 yd^3

   B 1,111,709 yd^3 D 10,005,384 yd^3

Name ________________ Class ________ Date ______

Spheres

Going Deeper

Essential question: *How do you calculate the volume of a sphere and use the volume formula to solve problems?*

Recall that a *sphere* is the set of points in space that are a fixed distance from a point called the *center* of the sphere. The intersection of a sphere and a plane that contains the center of the sphere is a *great circle.* A great circle divides a sphere into two congruent halves that are called *hemispheres.*

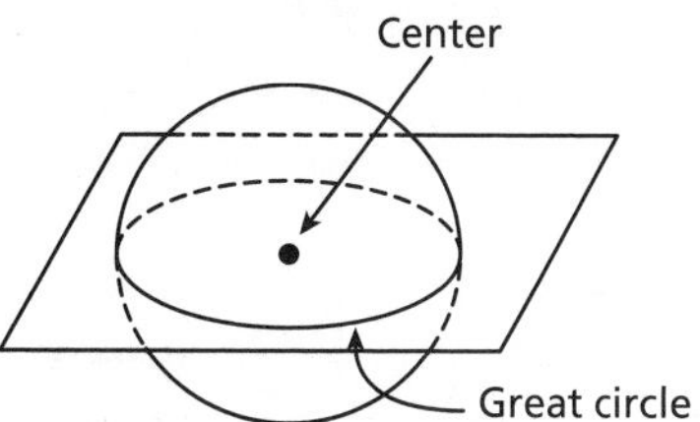

MCC9–12.G.GMD.2(+)

1 EXPLORE Developing a Volume Formula

Plan: To find the volume of a given sphere, consider a hemisphere of the sphere and a cylinder with the same radius and height as the hemisphere from which a cone has been removed. Show that the two solids have the same cross-sectional area at every level and apply Cavalieri's principle to conclude that the figures have the same volume.

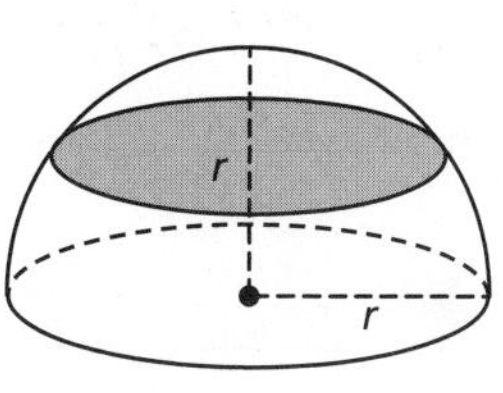

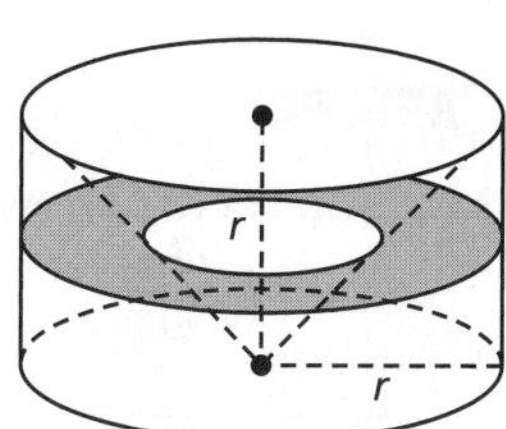

A To show that cross sections have the same area at every level, consider cross sections at a distance of x above the base, as shown.

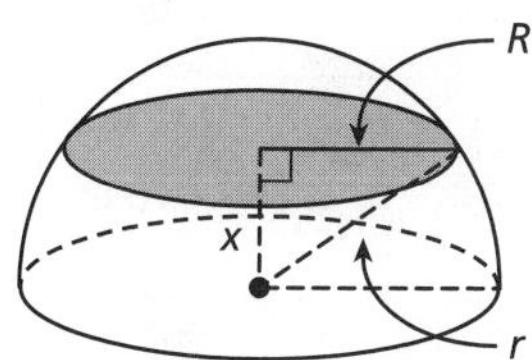

The cross section of the hemisphere is a disc. Use the Pythagorean Theorem to write a relationship among r, x, and R.

____

Solving for R gives $R =$ ________________.

So, the area of the cross-sectional disc is πR^2 or ____________.

The cross section of the cylinder with the cone removed is a ring. To find the area of the ring, find the area of the outer circle and subtract the area of the inner circle.

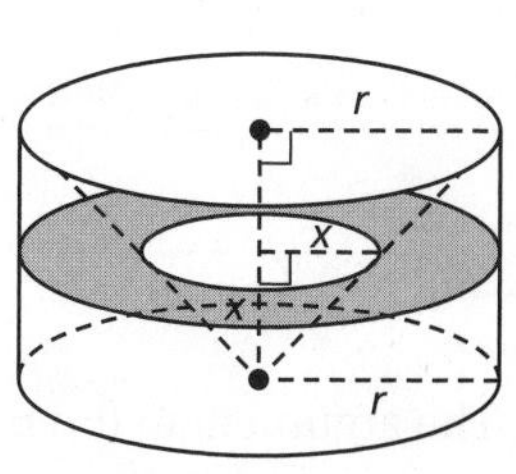

The outer circle has radius ________, so its area is ________.

The figure includes a pair of isosceles right triangles that are similar. This makes it possible to find the radius of the inner circle.

The inner circle has radius ________, so its area is ________.

So, the area of the cross-sectional ring is ____________.

By the distributive property, the areas of the cross sections are equal.

B By Cavalieri's principle, the hemisphere has the same volume as the cylinder with the cone removed.

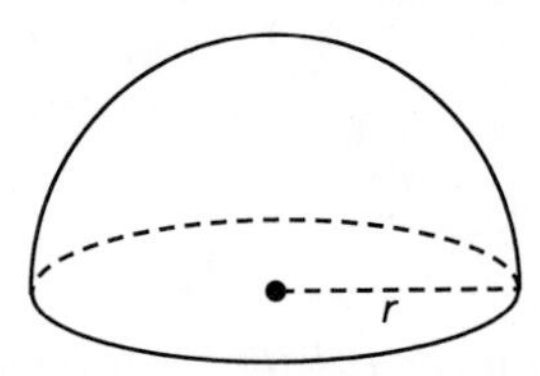

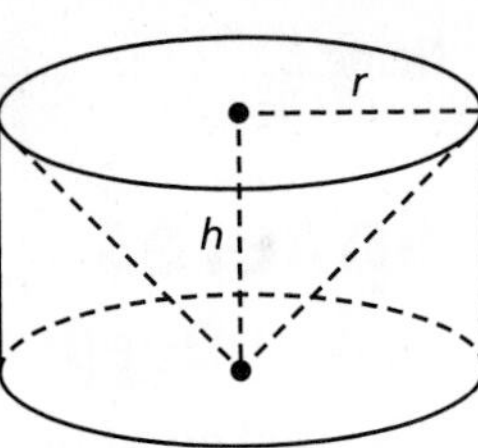

$V(\text{hemisphere}) = V(\text{cylinder}) - V(\text{cone})$

$= \pi r^2 h - \frac{1}{3}\pi r^2 h$ Use volume formulas.

$=$ __________ Subtract.

$=$ __________ The height h is equal to the radius r.

The volume of the sphere is twice the volume of the hemisphere.

So, the volume of the sphere is ________________.

REFLECT

1a. How do you know that the height h of the cylinder with the cone removed is equal to the radius r?

____

____

____

1b. In the above argument, what is the range of possible values for x?

____

1c. What happens to the cross-sectional areas when $x = 0$? when $x = r$?

____

____

____

____

The argument in the Explore provides a justification for the following formula.

Volume of a Sphere

The volume V of a sphere with radius r is given by $V = \frac{4}{3}\pi r^3$.

A British thermal unit (BTU) is a unit of energy. It is approximately the amount of energy needed to increase the temperature of one pound of water by one degree Fahrenheit. As you will see in the following example, the energy content of a fuel may be measured in BTUs per unit of volume.

MCC9–12.G.GMD.3

2 EXAMPLE Solving a Volume Problem

A spherical gas tank has the dimensions shown. When filled with natural gas, it provides 275,321 BTU. How many BTUs does one cubic foot of natural gas yield? Round to the nearest BTU.

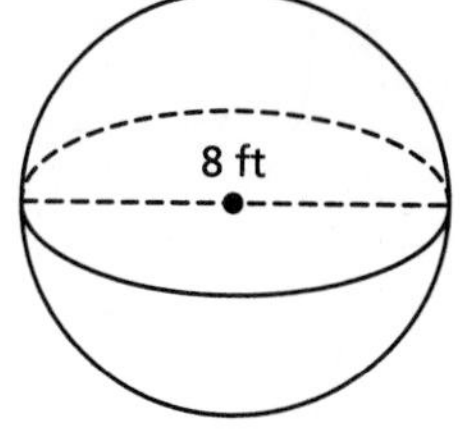

A Find the volume of the sphere.

The diameter is 8 feet, so the radius r is ________.

$V = \frac{4}{3}\pi r^3$ Use the volume formula for a sphere.

$V =$ ________ Substitute for r.

$V =$ ________ Simplify. Leave the answer in terms of π.

B Find the number of BTUs contained in one cubic foot of natural gas.

Since there are 275,321 BTU in ________ ft^3 of natural gas, divide

________ by ________ to find the number of BTUs in 1 ft^3.

Use a calculator to divide. Round to the nearest whole number.

So, one cubic foot of natural gas yields about ________ BTU.

REFLECT

2a. How many pounds of water can be heated from 59°F to 60°F by one cubic foot of natural gas? Explain.

____

____

2b. How many pounds of water can be heated from 70°F to 83°F by one cubic foot of natural gas? Explain.

____

____

PRACTICE

Find the volume of each sphere. Round to the nearest tenth.

1.

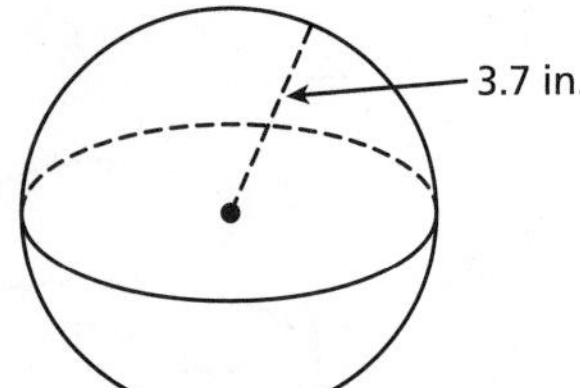

2.

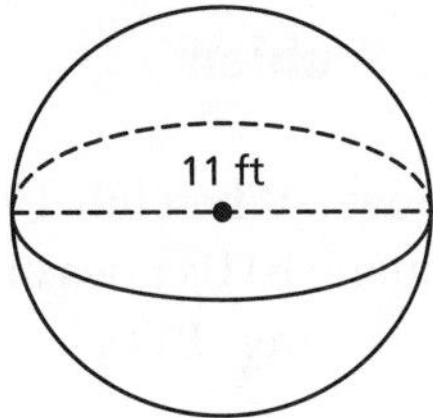

3.

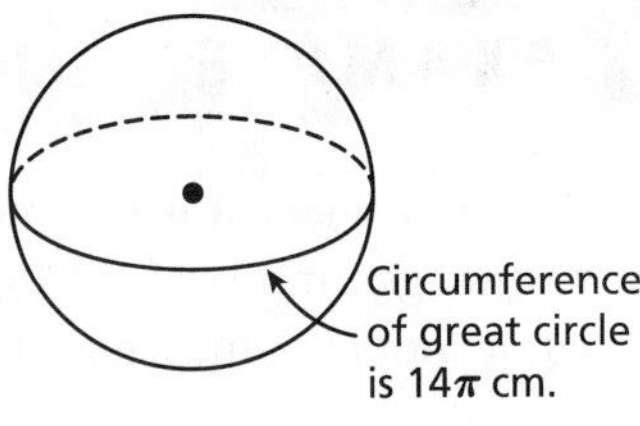

4. One gallon of propane yields approximately 91,500 BTU. About how many BTUs does the spherical storage tank at right provide? Round to the nearest million BTUs. (*Hint:* 1 ft^3 $\approx$ 7.48 gal)

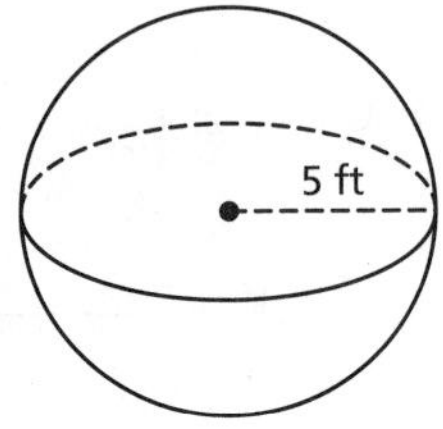

5. Error Analysis A student solved the following problem as shown below. Explain the student's error and give the correct answer to the problem.

A spherical gasoline tank has a radius of 0.5 ft. When filled, the tank provides 446,483 BTU. How many BTUs does one gallon of gasoline yield? Round to the nearest thousand BTUs and use the fact that 1 ft^3 $\approx$ 7.48 gal.

The volume of the tank is $\frac{4}{3}\pi r^3 = \frac{4}{3}\pi(0.5)^3$ ft^3. Multiplying by 7.48 shows that this is approximately 3.92 gal. So the number of BTUs in one gallon of gasoline is approximately $446{,}483 \times 3.92 \approx 1{,}750{,}000$ BTU.

6. The aquarium shown at right is a rectangular prism that is filled with water. You drop a spherical ball with a diameter of 6 inches into the aquarium. The ball sinks, causing water to spill from the tank. How much water is left in the tank? Express your answer to the nearest cubic inch and nearest gallon. (*Hint:* 1 in.^{3} $\approx$ 0.00433 gal)

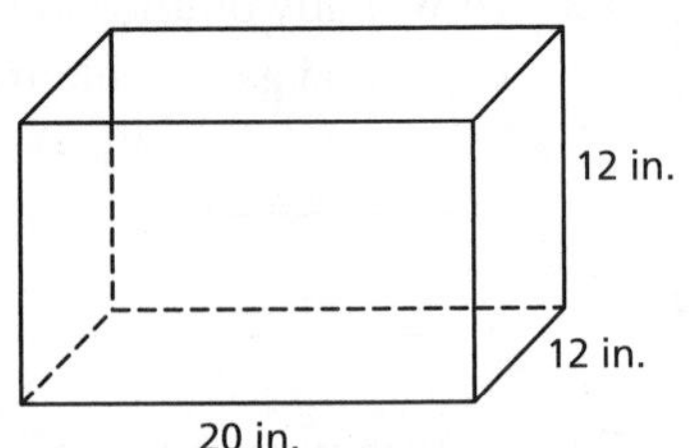

7. How does the volume of a sphere change when you multiply its radius by a factor k, where $k > 0$? Explain.

Name________________________ Class______________ Date____________

11-4

Additional Practice

Find each measurement. Give your answers in terms of π.

1. 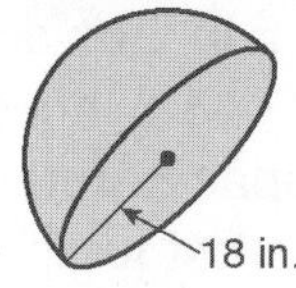

the volume of the hemisphere

____

2. 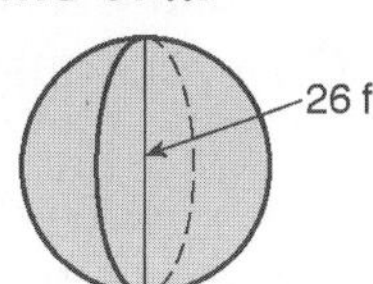

the volume of the sphere

____

3. the diameter of a sphere with volume $\frac{500\pi}{3}$ m^3 ________________________

4. The figure shows a grapefruit half. The radius to the outside of the rind is 5 cm. The radius to the inside of the rind is 4 cm. The edible part of the grapefruit is divided into 12 equal sections. Find the volume of the half grapefruit and the volume of one edible section. Give your answers in terms of π.

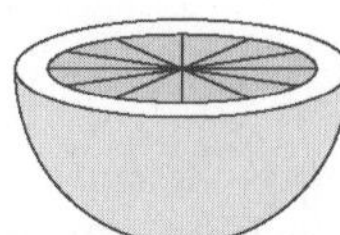

____

Find each measurement. Give your answers in terms of π.

5. 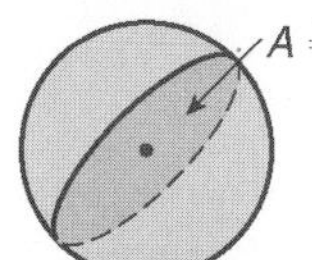

the volume of the sphere

____

6. 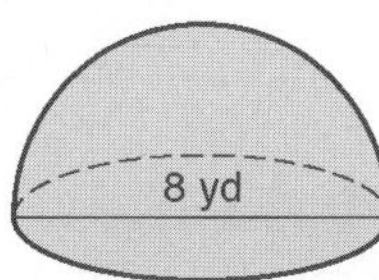

the volume of the closed hemisphere

____

Describe the effect of each change on the volume of the figure.

7. 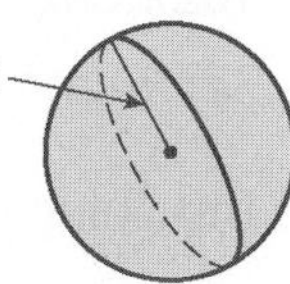

The dimensions are divided by 4.

____

8. 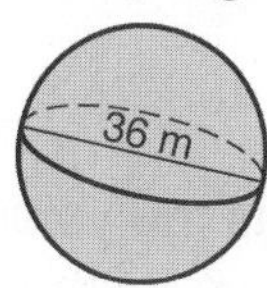

The dimensions are multiplied by $\frac{2}{5}$.

____

9. Find the volume of the hemisphere with the prism-shaped space removed. Round to the nearest tenth.

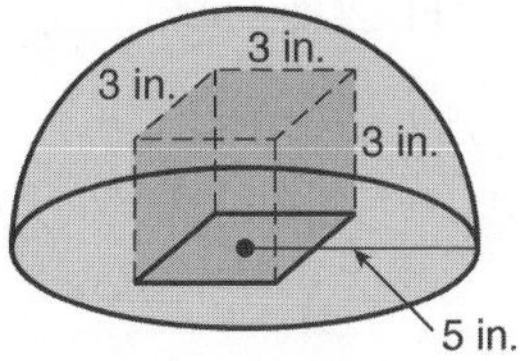

____

Problem Solving

1. A globe has a volume of 288π in^3. What is the radius of the globe? Give your answer in terms of π.

____

2. Eight bocce balls are in a box 18 inches long, 9 inches wide, and 4.5 inches deep. If each ball has a diameter of 4.5 inches, what is the volume of the space around the balls? Round to the nearest tenth.

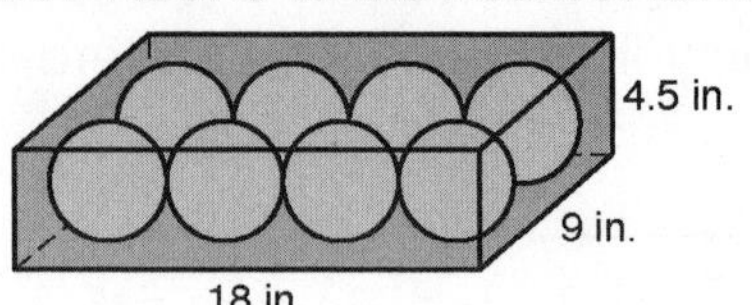

____

3. Ganymede, one of Jupiter's moons, is the largest moon in the solar system. Approximately how many times as great as the volume of Earth's moon is the volume of Ganymede?

Moon	Diameter
Earth's moon	2160 mi
Ganymede	3280 mi

____

Choose the best answer.

4. What is the volume of a sphere with a great circle that has an area of 225π cm^2?

A 300π cm^3 C 2500π cm^3
B 900π cm^3 D 4500π cm^3

5. A hemisphere has a volume of 972π cm^3. If the radius is multiplied by $\frac{1}{3}$, what will be the volume of the new hemisphere?

F 36π cm^3 H 162π cm^3
G 108π cm^3 J 324π cm^3

6. Which expression represents the volume of the composite figure formed by the hemisphere and cone?

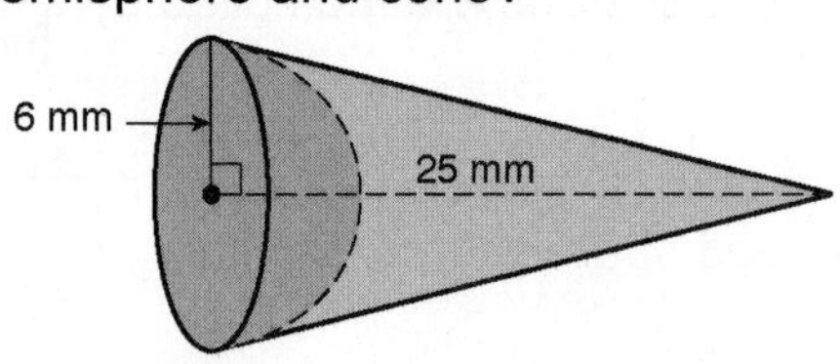

A 52π mm^3 C 276π mm^3
B 156π mm^3 D 288π mm^3

7. Which best represents the volume of the composite figure?

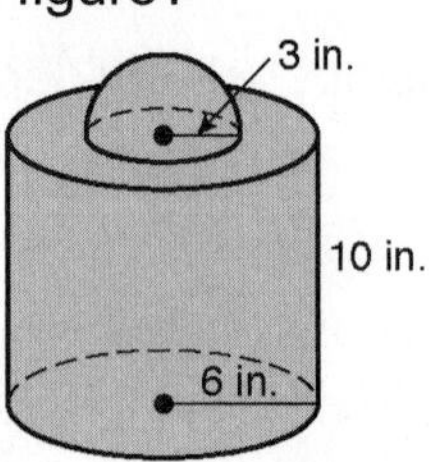

F 129π in^3 H 201π in^3
G 138π in^3 J 396π in^3

Name ______________________ Class ____________ Date ________

Lines That Intersect Circles

Focus on Reasoning

Essential question: *What is the relationship between a tangent line to a circle and the radius drawn from the center to the point of tangency?*

A **tangent** is a line in the same plane as a circle that intersects the circle in exactly one point. The point where a tangent and a circle intersect is the **point of tangency**. In the figure, line m is a tangent to circle C, and point P is the point of tangency.

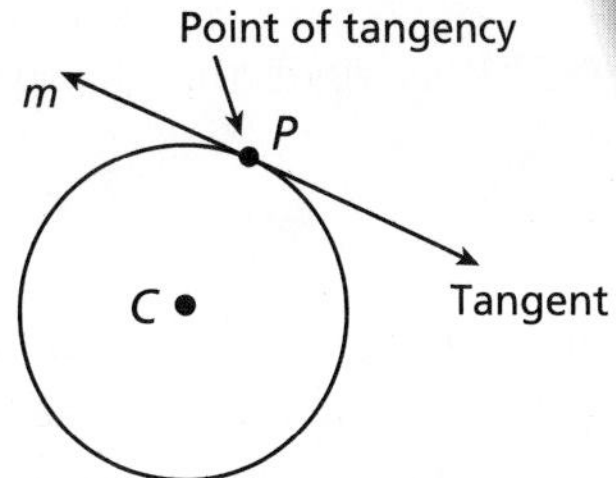

1 Investigate tangents and radii.

A Use a compass to draw a circle O.

B Plot a point P on the circle.

C Using a straightedge, carefully draw a tangent to circle O through point P. Plot another point Q on the tangent line.

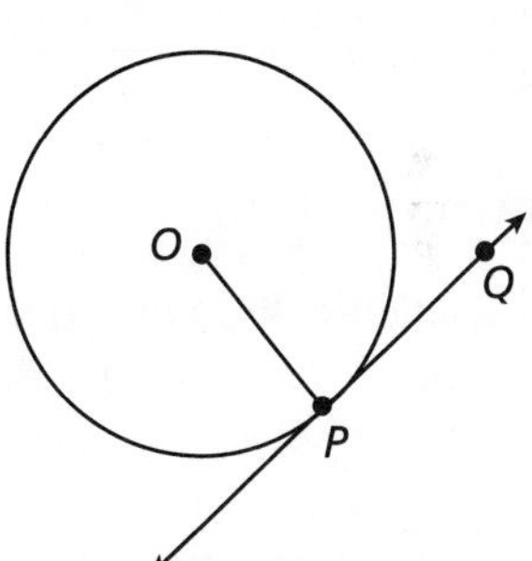

D Use the straightedge to draw the radius $\overline{OP}$.

E Use a protractor to measure $\angle OPQ$.

F Repeat the process, starting with a different circle.

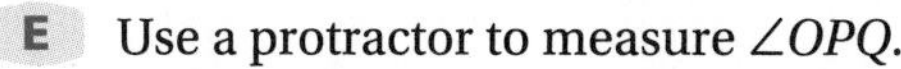

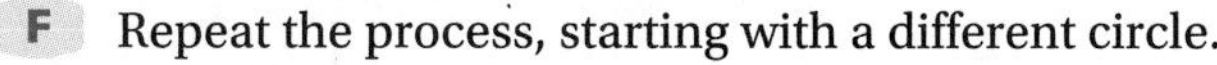

REFLECT

1a. Compare your findings with those of other students. Then make a conjecture: What can you say about the relationship between a tangent line and a radius to the point of tangency?

____

1b. Describe any inaccuracies related to the tools you used in the investigation.

____

____

You may have discovered the following theorem.

Tangent-Radius Theorem

If a line is tangent to a circle, then it is perpendicular to the radius drawn to the point of tangency.

Line m is tangent to circle C at point P, so $\overline{CP} \perp m$.

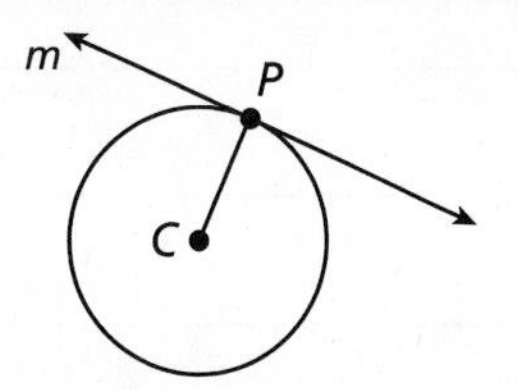

2 Prove the Tangent-Radius Theorem.

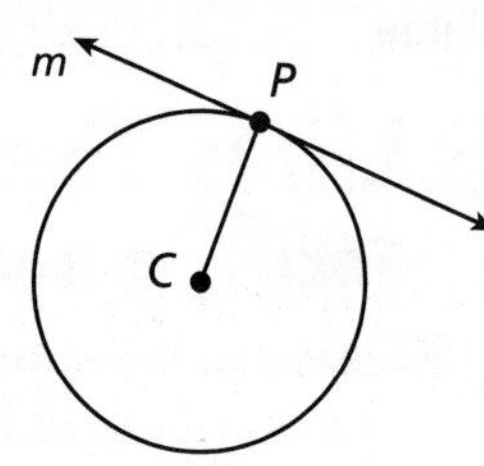

Given: Line m is tangent to circle C at point P.

Prove: $\overline{CP} \perp m$

Use an indirect proof. Assume that $\overline{CP}$ is *not* perpendicular to line m. Then it must be possible to draw $\overline{CX}$ so that $\overline{CX} \perp m$.

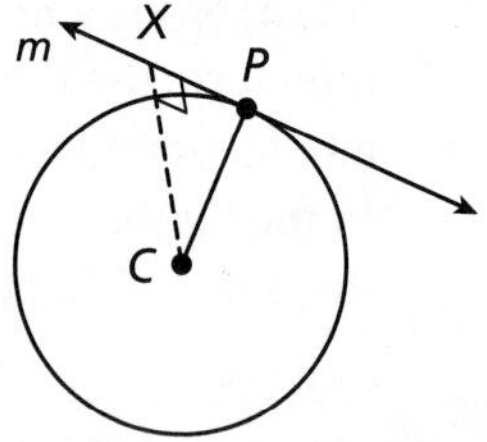

In this case, $\triangle CXP$ is a right triangle, so $CP > CX$ because

____

Because line m is a tangent line, it can intersect circle C at only one point, P, and all other points of line m are in the exterior of the circle. This means point X is in the exterior of the circle. So, you can conclude that $CP < CX$ because

____

This contradicts the fact that $CP > CX$. Therefore,

____

REFLECT

2a. In the figure, lines m and n are tangent lines to circle A. What can you say about quadrilateral $ABCD$? Explain.

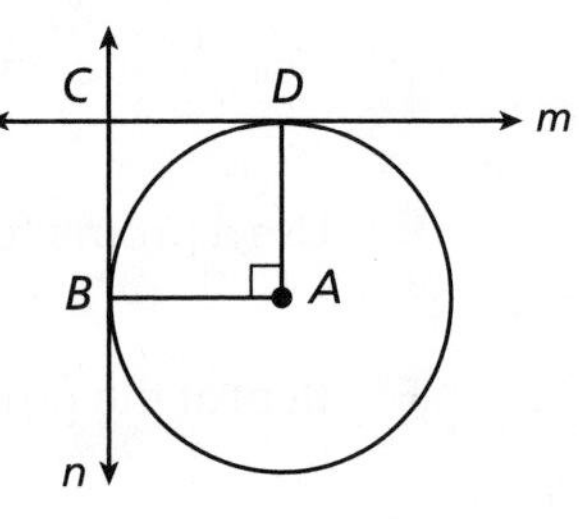

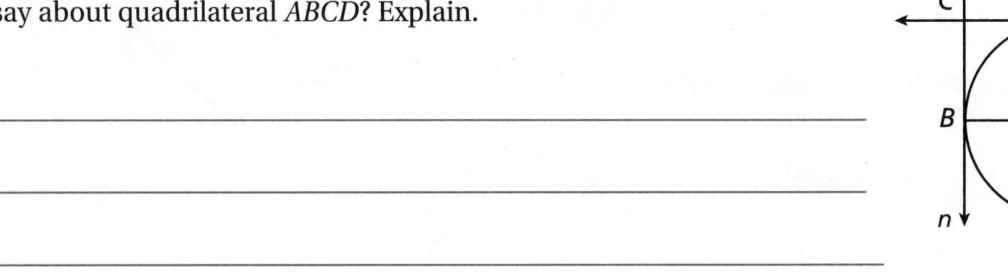

____

2b. Prove the converse of the Tangent-Radius Theorem: If a line is perpendicular to a radius of a circle at a point on the circle, then the line is a tangent to the circle. (*Hint:* Consider a circle C, point P on the circle, and line m perpendicular to $\overline{CP}$. Let Q be any point on line m other than P. Show that $CQ > CP$.)

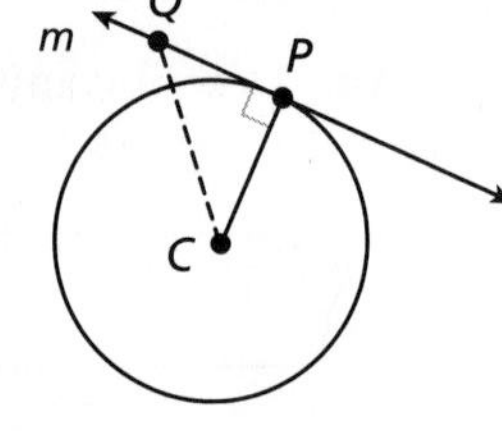

____

Name ____________________ Class ____________ Date __________ **12-1**

Additional Practice

In the diagram, $\overline{AB}$, $\overline{BC}$, $\overline{CD}$, and $\overline{DA}$ are tangent to circle *O* at their midpoints. Use the diagram for Exercises 1–4. For some exercises, you will need to draw on the diagram.

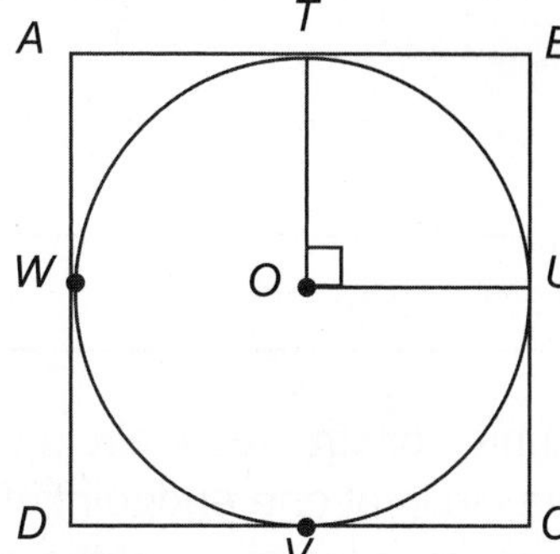

1. What is the measure of $\angle B$? What can you conclude about quadrilateral *OTBU*?

____

____

2. Use a straightedge to draw a radius to point *V*. What can you conclude about quadrilateral *OUCV*?

____

3. Use a straightedge to draw a radius to a point *W*. What can you conclude about quadrilaterals *WOVD* and *ATOW*?

____

4. Based on your answers to Exercises 1–3, what can you conclude about quadrilateral *ABCD*? Justify your answer.

____

____

____

____

____

____

____

____

5. Suppose a line is tangent to a circle. What theorem can you use to prove that the line is perpendicular to a diameter drawn to the point of tangency?

____

Problem Solving

1. In the stained glass window shown, six segments are tangent to a circle. Three diameters divide the circle into six panes. Explain how you know that any one of the diameters shown is perpendicular to two of the tangent segments shown.

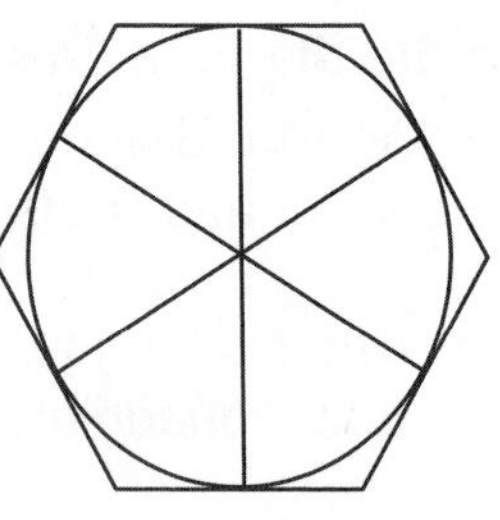

____

____

____

2. Annie constructed a circle and its diameter. She drew a line tangent to the circle at one endpoint of the diameter. Then she drew a line tangent to the circle at the other endpoint of the diameter She claims the two tangent lines are parallel. Do you agree? Why or why not?

____

____

____

____

Choose the best answer.

3. Maria drew a design for a company logo. Her design is based on the diagram shown at the right. In the diagram, $\overline{KM}$ is tangent to circle J and to circle L at point N. Point N is the midpoint of $\overline{KM}$ and $\overline{JL}$. If $JL = 4$ cm, what is the area of quadrilateral $JKLM$?

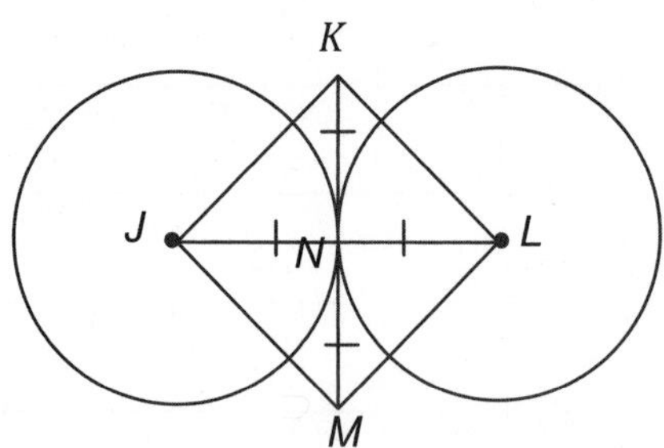

A 2 cm^2 C 4 cm^2

B 8 cm^2 D 16 cm^2

4. Paul also drew a design for a company logo. His design is based on the diagram shown at the right. In the diagram, $\overline{BD}$ is tangent to a half circle with radius AD at point D. If $AD = BD = x$ centimeters, and $\overline{DC}$ is three times as long as $\overline{AD}$, which expression represents the area of $\triangle ABC$?

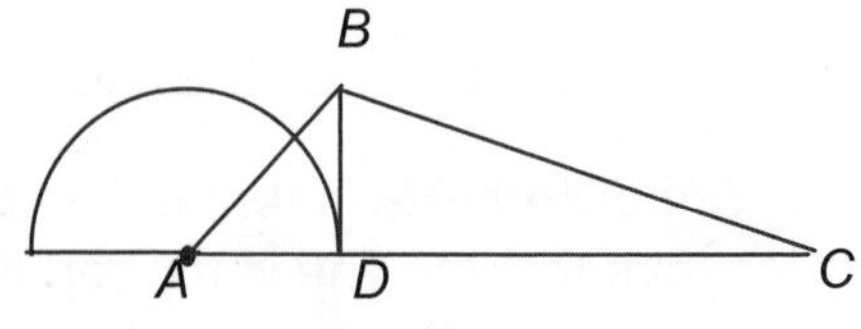

F $0.5x^2 \text{ cm}^2$ H $2x^2 \text{ cm}^2$

G $1.5x^2 \text{ cm}^2$ J $3x^2 \text{ cm}^2$

Name ______________________ Class ______________ Date ________

12-2

Arcs and Chords

Going Deeper

Essential question: *How are arcs and chords of circles associated with central angles?*

Video Tutor

MCC9–12.G.C.2

1 ENGAGE Introducing Angles and Arcs

In order to begin working with circles, it is helpful to introduce some vocabulary.

A **chord** is a segment whose endpoints lie on a circle. A **central angle** is an angle whose vertex is the center of a circle. An **inscribed angle** is an angle whose vertex lies on a circle and whose sides contain chords of the circle.

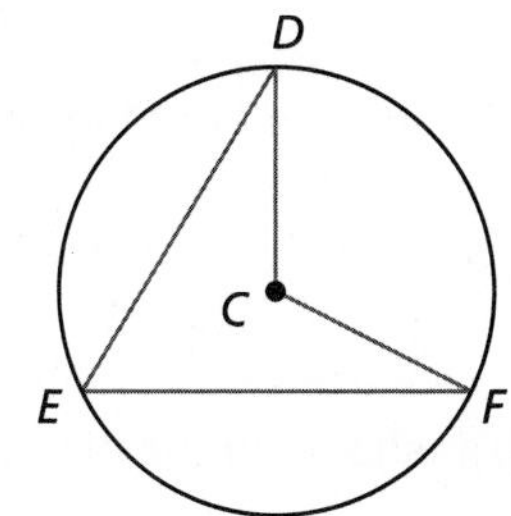

$\overline{DE}$ and $\overline{EF}$ are chords.
$\angle DCF$ is a central angle.
$\angle DEF$ is an inscribed angle.

An **arc** is a continuous portion of a circle consisting of two points on the circle, called the *endpoints* of the arc, and all the points of the circle between them. The table summarizes arc measurement and arc notation.

Arc	Measure/Notation	Figure
A **minor arc** is an arc whose points are on or in the interior of a central angle.	The measure of a minor arc is the measure of its central angle. $m\overset{\frown}{DF} = m\angle DCF$	$\overset{\frown}{DF}$ D C F
A **major arc** is an arc whose points are on or in the exterior of a central angle.	The measure of a major arc is 360° minus the measure of its central angle. $m\overset{\frown}{DEF} = 360° - m\angle DCF$	$\overset{\frown}{DEF}$ D C E F
A **semicircle** is an arc whose endpoints are the endpoints of a diameter.	The measure of a semicircle is 180°. $m\overset{\frown}{GHJ} = 180°$	$\overset{\frown}{GHJ}$ H J C G

REFLECT

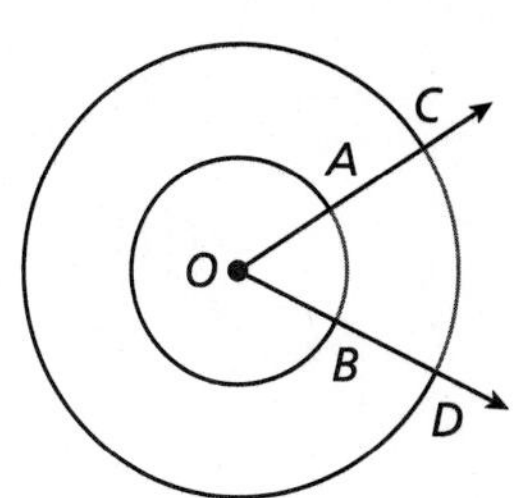

1a. Explain how $m\overset{\frown}{AB}$ compares to $m\overset{\frown}{CD}$.

____

1b. The minute hand of a clock sweeps out an arc as the time progresses from 12:05 to 12:20. What is the measure of the arc? Explain.

____

Two arcs of a circle are *adjacent arcs* if they share an endpoint. The following postulate states that you can add the measures of adjacent arcs.

Arc Addition Postulate

The measure of an arc formed by two adjacent arcs is the sum of the measures of the two arcs.

$m\overset{\frown}{ABC} = m\overset{\frown}{AB} + m\overset{\frown}{BC}$

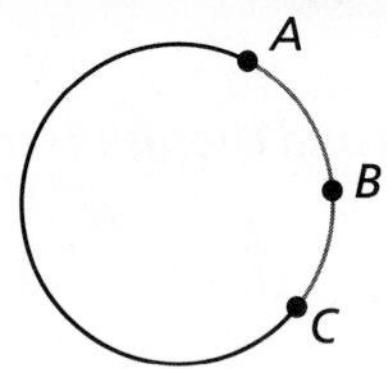

MCC9-12.G.C.2

2 EXPLORE Investigating Congruent Chords in a Circle

A Use a compass to draw a circle. Mark the center of the circle *C*.

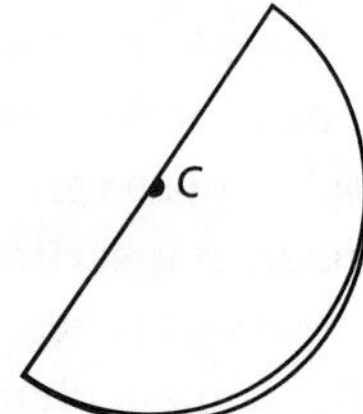

B Cut out the circle and fold it in half.

C Fold both halves to create a chord, as shown in the diagram.

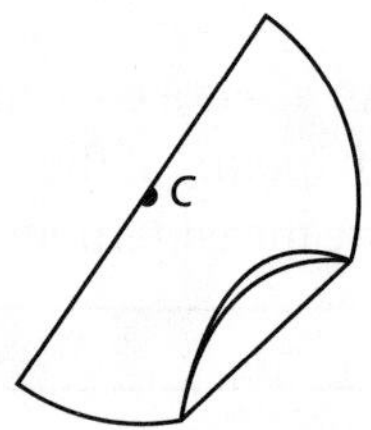

D Unfold the paper and use a straightedge to draw segments from the endpoints of the two folded chords to the center of the circle.

E Use a protractor to measure the central angles of the two chords. Record the measures.

Central angle of chord 1:

Central angle of chord 2:

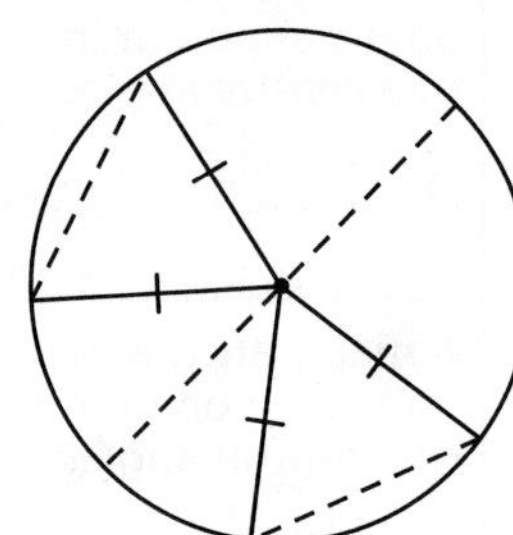

F What do you notice about the central angles?

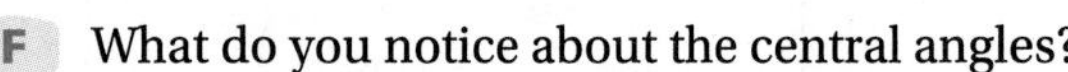

REFLECT

2a. Write a conjecture that your work in the Explore suggests.

Name ______________________ Class ______________ Date ____________ **12-2**

Additional Practice

Use the figure to find each of the following measurements. *A* is the center of the circle.

1. m$\overset{\frown}{CE}$ ______________
2. m∠*DAF* ______________
3. m$\overset{\frown}{EF}$ ______________
4. m$\overset{\frown}{BD}$ ______________
5. m∠*BAD* ______________
6. m$\overset{\frown}{EFD}$ ______________

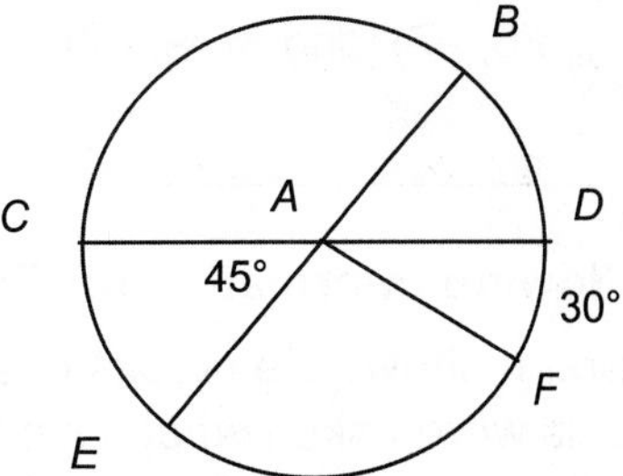

Find each measure.

7.

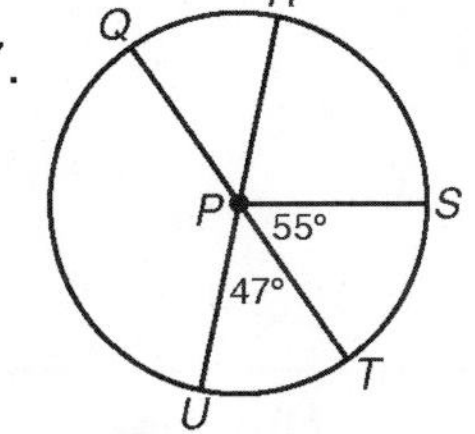

m$\overset{\frown}{QS}$ ____________

m$\overset{\frown}{RQT}$ ____________

8.

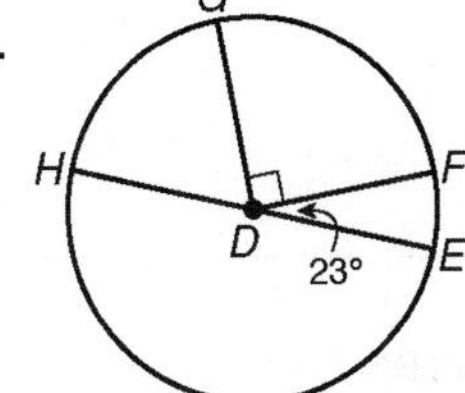

m$\overset{\frown}{HG}$ ____________

m$\overset{\frown}{FEH}$ ____________

9.

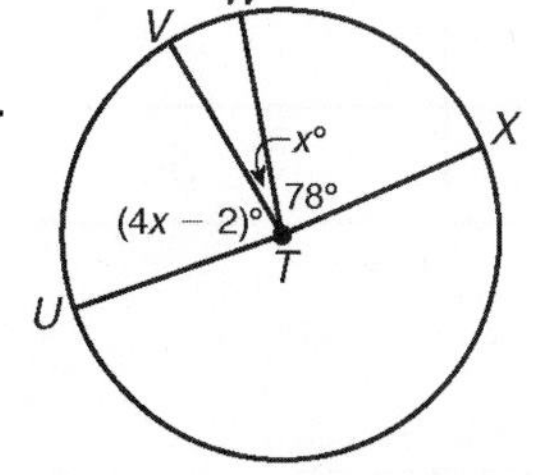

Find m∠*UTW*. ____________

10.

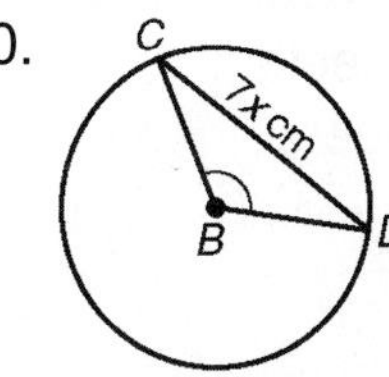

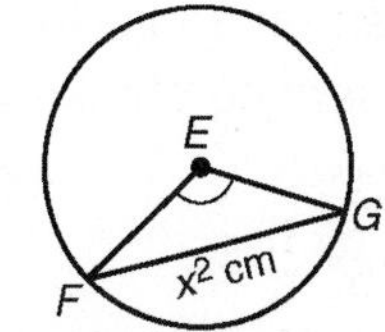

⊙*L* ≅ ⊙*E*, and ∠*CBD* ≅ ∠*FEG*.

Find *FG*. ____________

Problem Solving

1. Circle D has center (–2, –7) and radius 7. What is the measure, in degrees, of the major arc that passes through points $H(-2, 0)$, $J(5, -7)$, and $K(-9, -7)$?

____

2. A circle graph is composed of sectors with central angles that measure $3x°$, $3x°$, $4x°$, and $5x°$. What is the measure, in degrees, of the smallest minor arcs?

____

Use the following information for Exercises 3 and 4.

The circle graph shows the results of a survey in which teens were asked what says the most about them at school. Find each of the following.

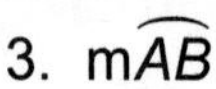

3. $m\widehat{AB}$

____

4. $m\angle APC$

____

Teens Surveyed

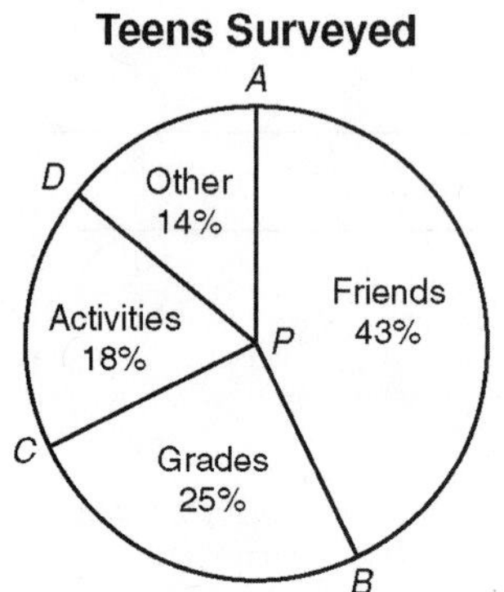

Use the table for Exercises 5–7. Choose the best answer.

5. Students were asked to name their favorite cafeteria food. The results of the survey are shown in the table. In a circle graph showing these results, which is closest to the measure of the central angle for the section representing chicken tenders?

   A 21°   C 83°
   B 75°   D 270°

Favorite Lunch	Number of Students
Pizza	108
Chicken tenders	75
Taco salad	90
Other	54

6. Which is the closest measure of the arc for the sector in the circle graph representing taco salad?

   F 59°   H 100°
   G 90°   J 180°

7. If the sectors for pizza and chicken tenders are adjacent in the circle graph, which is the closest measure for the arc that spans both sectors?

   A 100°   C 183°
   B 166°   D 201°

Name______________________ Class______________ Date__________

12-3

Sector Area and Arc Length

Going Deeper

Essential question: *How do you find the area of a sector of a circle, and how do you calculate arc length in a circle?*

MCC9–12.G.GMD.1

1 EXPLORE Developing a Formula for the Area of a Circle

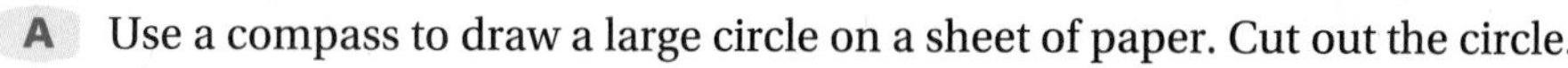

A Use a compass to draw a large circle on a sheet of paper. Cut out the circle.

B Fold the circle in half. Then fold the resulting semicircle in half. Then fold the resulting quarter-circle in half.

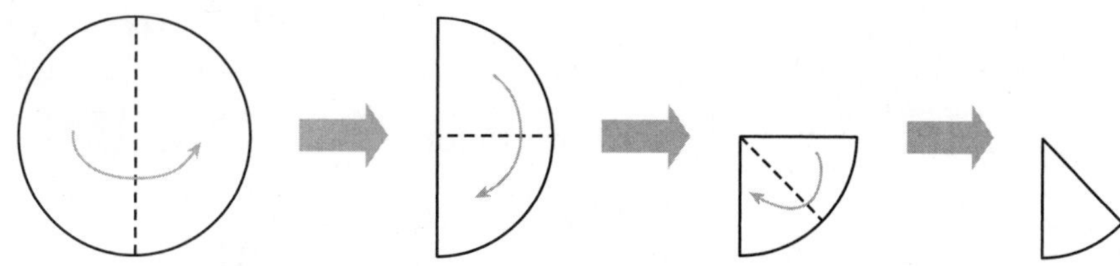

C Unfold the paper and cut along the folds to make 8 wedges.

D Rearrange the wedges as shown to make a shape that resembles a parallelogram.

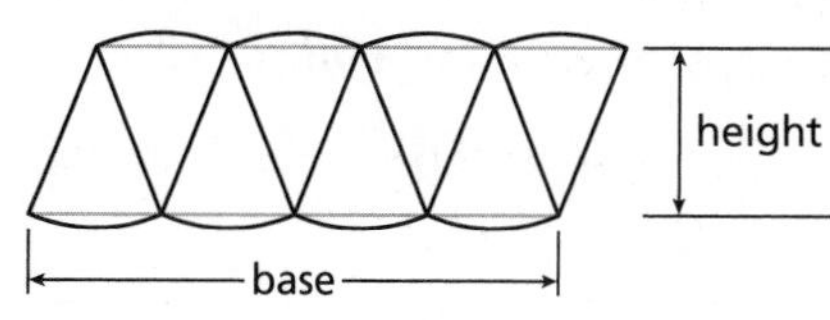

Assume the original circle has radius *r*. What is the approximate height of the parallelogram? __________

The base of the parallelogram can be approximated by half the circumference of the circle. Express the base in terms of *r*. __________

Recall that the area of a parallelogram is the base times the height. What is the approximate area of the parallelogram? __________

REFLECT

1a. What happens as you repeat the process, cutting the circle into more and more wedges each time?

____

____

1b. Make a conjecture: What do you think is the formula for the area *A* of a circle with radius *r*? Why?

____

____

____

Area of a Circle

The area A of a circle with radius r is given by $A = \pi r^2$.

A **sector** of a circle is a region bounded by two radii and their intercepted arc. A sector is named by the endpoints of the arc and the center of the circle. For example, the figure shows sector POQ.

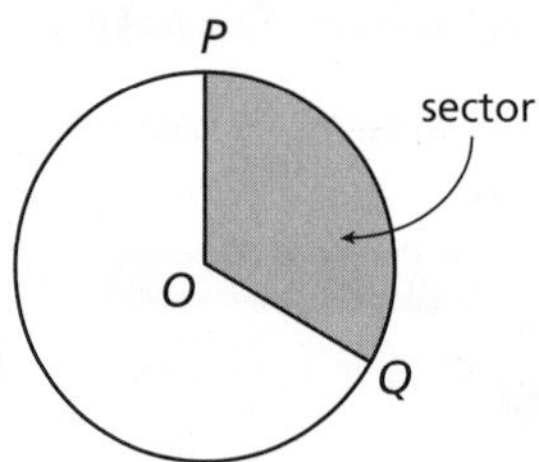

In the same way that you used proportional reasoning to find the length of an arc, you can use proportional reasoning to find the area of a sector.

MCC9–12.G.C.5

2 EXAMPLE Finding the Area of a Sector

Find the area of sector AOB. Express your answer in terms of π and rounded to the nearest tenth.

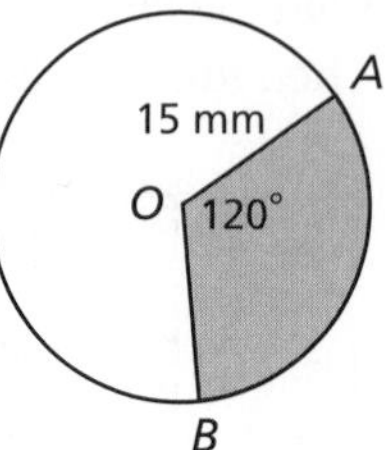

A First find the area of the circle.

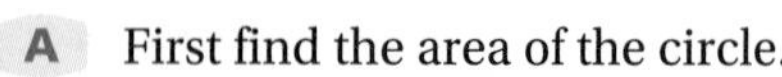

$A = \pi r^2 = \pi(\_\_\_\_\_\_\_\_)^2$ Substitute 15 for r.

$= \_\_\_\_\_\_\_\_$ Simplify.

B The entire circle is 360°, but $\angle AOB$ measures 120°. Therefore, the sector's area is $\frac{120}{360}$ or $\frac{1}{3}$ of the circle's area.

Area of sector $AOB = \frac{1}{3} \cdot \_\_\_\_\_\_\_\_$ The area is $\frac{1}{3}$ of the circle's area.

$= \_\_\_\_\_\_\_\_$ Simplify.

$= \_\_\_\_\_\_\_\_$ Use a calculator to evaluate. Then round.

So, the area of sector AOB is ________ or ________.

REFLECT

2a. How could you use the above process to find the area of a sector of the circle whose central angle measures $m°$?

____

____

2b. Make a conjecture: What do you think is the formula for the area of a sector with a central angle of $m°$ and radius r?

____

The proportional reasoning process you used in the example can be generalized. Given a sector with a central angle of $m°$ and radius r, the area of the entire circle is πr^2 and the area of the sector is $\frac{m}{360}$ times the circle's area. This gives the following formula.

Area of a Sector

The area A of a sector of a circle with a central angle of $m°$ and radius r is given by $A = \frac{m}{360} \cdot \pi r^2$.

Arc length is understood to be the distance along a circular arc measured in linear units (such as feet or centimeters). You can use proportional reasoning to find arc lengths.

MCC9–12.G.CO.1

3 EXAMPLE Finding Arc Length

Find the arc length of $\overset{\frown}{AB}$. Express your answer in terms of π and rounded to the nearest tenth.

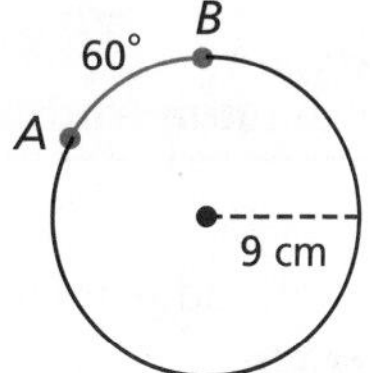

A First find the circumference of the circle.

$C = 2\pi r =$ ______ Substitute 9 for r.

B The entire circle is 360°, but $\overset{\frown}{AB}$ measures 60°. Therefore, the arc's length is $\frac{60}{360}$ or $\frac{1}{6}$ of the circumference.

Arc length of $\overset{\frown}{AB} = \frac{1}{6} \cdot$ ______ Arc length is $\frac{1}{6}$ of the circumference.

= ______ Multiply.

= ______ Use a calculator to evaluate. Then round.

So, the arc length of $\overset{\frown}{AB}$ is ______ or ______.

REFLECT

3a. How could you use the above process to find the length of an arc of the circle that measures $m°$?

______

______

The proportional reasoning process you used above can be generalized. Given a circle with radius r, its circumference is $2\pi r$ and the arc length s of an arc with measure $m°$ is $\frac{m}{360}$ times the circumference. This gives the following formula.

Arc Length

The arc length s of an arc with measure $m°$ and radius r is given by the formula $s = \frac{m}{360} \cdot 2\pi r$.

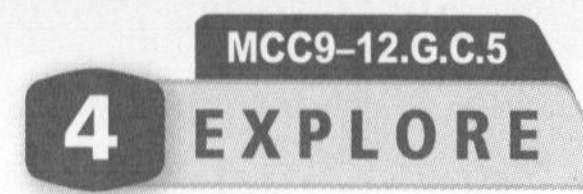

Investigating Arc Lengths in Concentric Circles

Consider a set of concentric circles with center O and radius 1, 2, 3, and so on. The central angle shown in the figure is a right angle and it cuts off arcs that measure 90°.

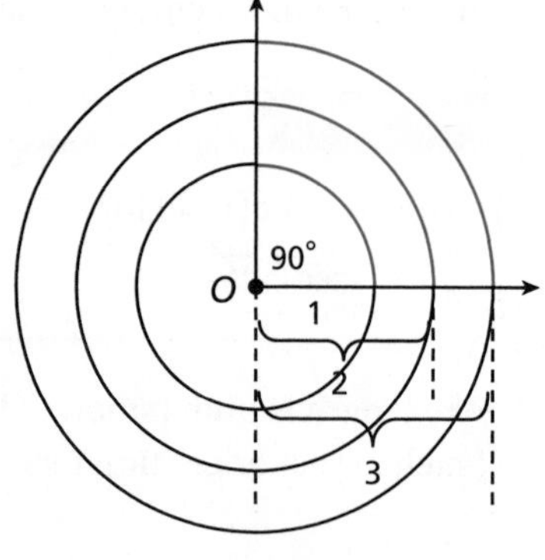

A For each value of the radius r listed in the table below, find the corresponding arc length. Write the length in terms of π and rounded to the nearest hundredth.

For example, when $r = 1$, the arc length is $\frac{90}{360} \cdot 2\pi(1) = \frac{1}{2}\pi \approx 1.57$.

Radius r	1	2	3	4	5
Arc length s in terms of π	$\frac{1}{2}\pi$				
Arc length s to nearest hundredth	1.57				

B Plot the ordered pairs from your table on the coordinate plane at right.

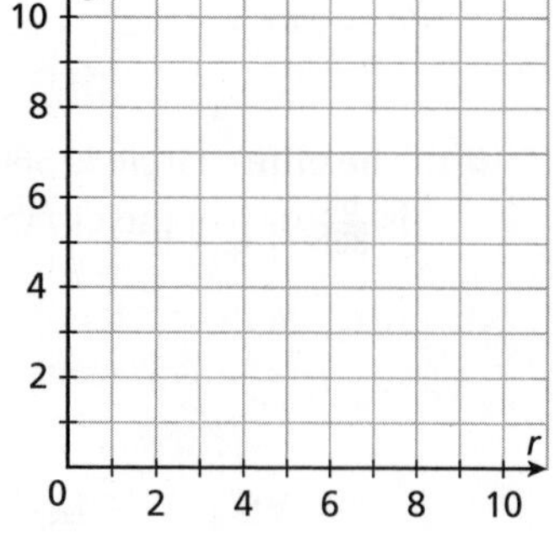

What do you notice about the points?

____

____

What type of relationship is the relationship between arc length and radius?

____

What is the constant of proportionality for this relationship?

____

REFLECT

4a. What happens to the arc length when you double the radius? How is this connected to the idea that all circles are similar?

____

____

As you discovered in the Explore, when the central angle is fixed at $m°$, the length of the arc cut off by the central angle is proportional to (or varies directly with) the radius. In fact, you can see that the formula for arc length is a proportional relationship when m is fixed.

$$s = \underbrace{\frac{m}{360} \cdot 2\pi}_{\text{constant of proportionality}} r$$

The constant of proportionality for the proportional relationship is $\frac{m}{360} \cdot 2\pi$. This constant of proportionality is defined to be the **radian measure** of the angle.

MCC9-12.G.C.5

5 EXAMPLE Converting to Radian Measure

Convert each angle measure to radian measure.

A 180° **B** 60°

A To convert 180° to radian measure, let $m = 180$ in the expression $\frac{m}{360} \cdot 2\pi$.

$180° = \frac{\square}{360} \cdot 2\pi$ radians — Substitute 180 for m.

$=$ ________ radians — Simplify.

B To convert 60° to radian measure, let $m = 60$ in the expression $\frac{m}{360} \cdot 2\pi$.

$60° = \frac{\square}{360} \cdot 2\pi$ radians — Substitute 60 for m.

$=$ ________ radians — Simplify.

REFLECT

5a. Explain why the radian measure for an angle of $m°$ is sometimes defined as the length of the arc cut off on a circle of radius 1 by a central angle of $m°$.

____

____

____

5b. Explain how to find the degree measure of an angle whose radian measure is $\frac{\pi}{4}$.

____

____

____

PRACTICE

Find the area of sector *AOB*. Express your answer in terms of π and rounded to the nearest tenth.

1.

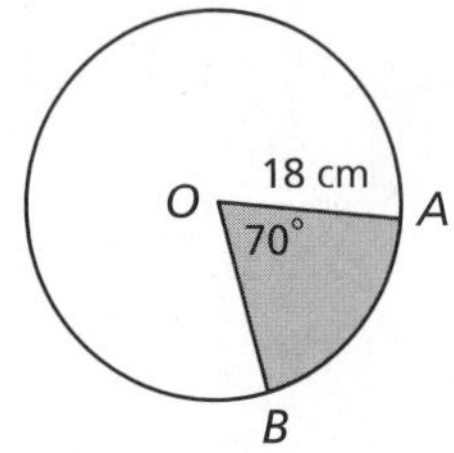

2.

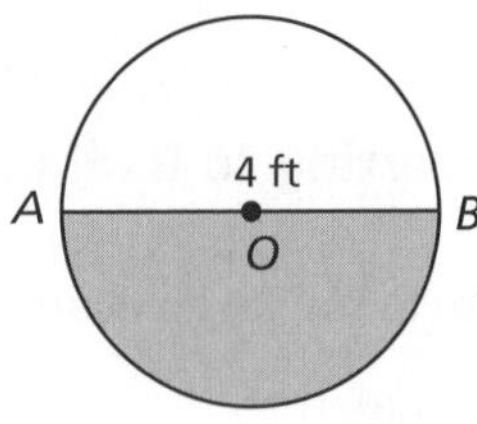

3.

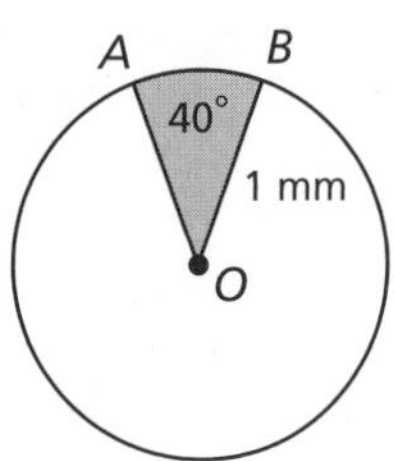

4.

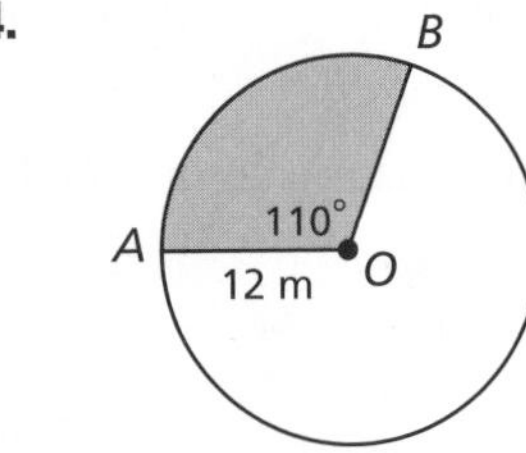

5.

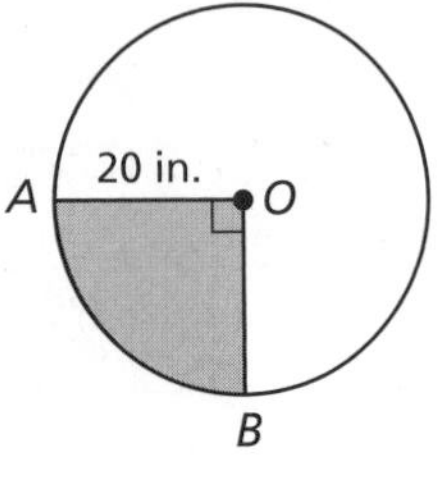

6.

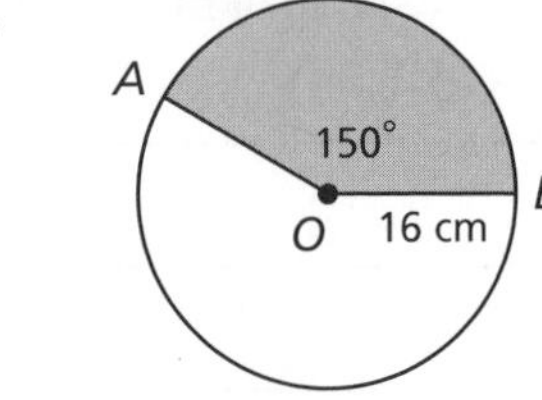

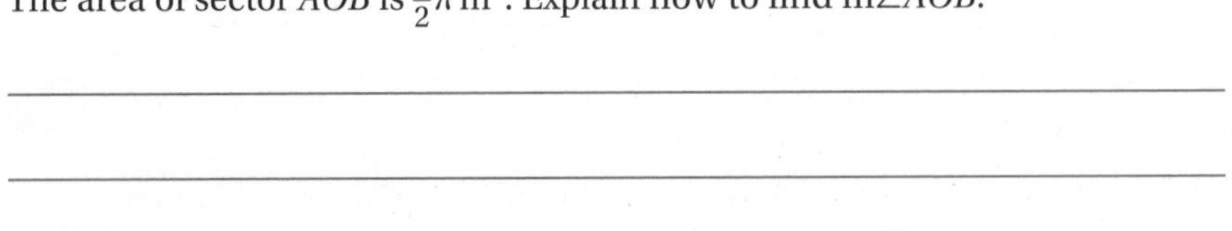

7. The area of sector AOB is $\frac{9}{2}\pi \text{m}^2$. Explain how to find m$\angle AOB$.

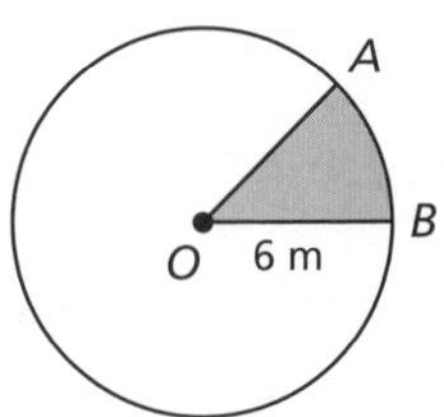

8. Error Analysis A student claims that when you double the radius of a sector while keeping the measure of the central angle constant, you double the area of the sector. Do you agree or disagree? Explain.

Find the arc length of $\overset{\frown}{AB}$. Express your answer in terms of π and rounded to the nearest tenth.

9.

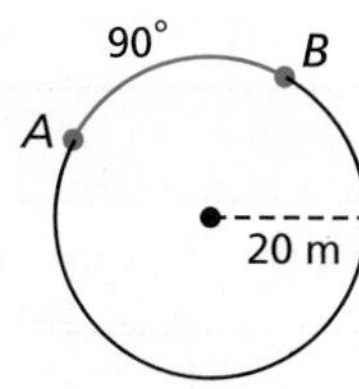

10.

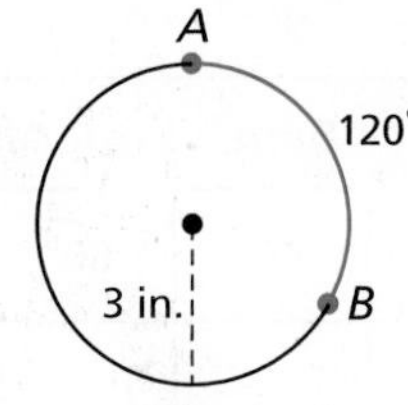

11.

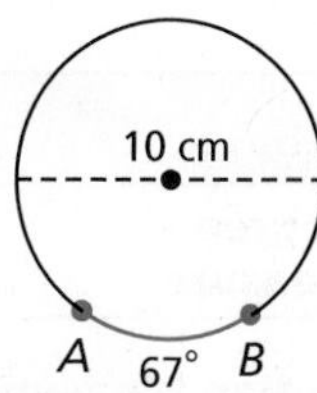

12.

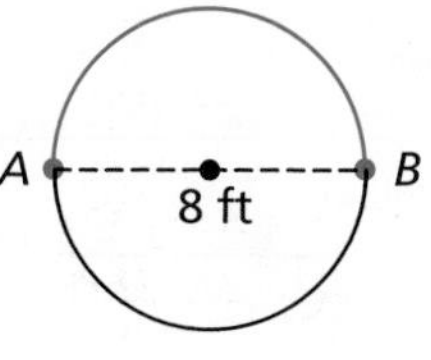

13.

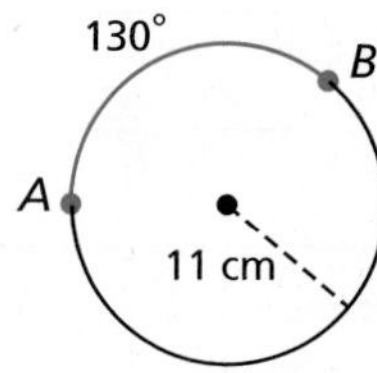

14.

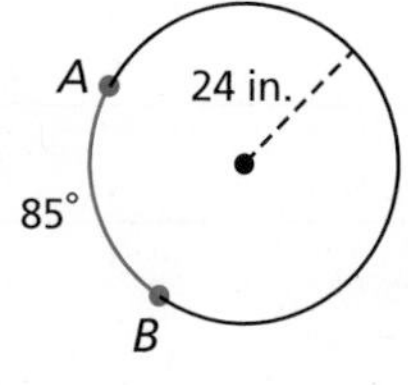

15. The minute hand of a clock is 4 inches long. To the nearest tenth of an inch, how far does the tip of the minute hand travel as the time progresses from 12:00 to 12:25?

16. Error Analysis A student was asked to find the arc length of $\overset{\frown}{PQ}$. The student's work is shown below. Explain the student's error and give the correct arc length.

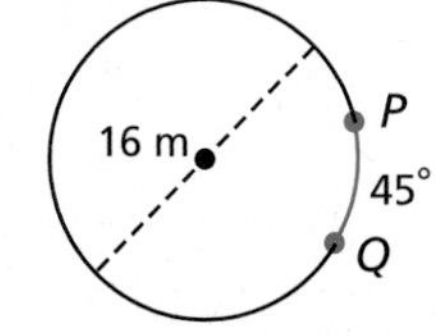

The entire circumference is $2\pi \cdot 16 = 32\pi$ and 45° is $\frac{1}{8}$ of the circle, so the arc length is $\frac{1}{8} \cdot 32\pi = 4\pi$ m.

17. It is convenient to know the radian measure for benchmark angles such as 0°, 30°, 45°, and so on. Complete the table by finding the radian measure for each of the given benchmark angles.

Benchmark Angles									
Degree Measure	0°	30°	45°	60°	90°	120°	135°	150°	180°
Radian Measure									

18. Explain how to convert a radian measure into degrees. Then use your method to find what 1 radian is in degrees. Round to the nearest tenth of a degree.

Name______________________ Class______________ Date__________

12-3

Additional Practice

Find the area of each sector. Give your answer in terms of π and rounded to the nearest hundredth.

1. 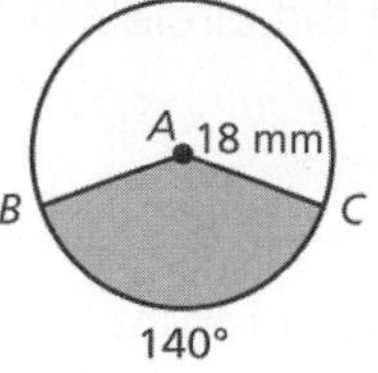

sector *BAC* ____________________

2. 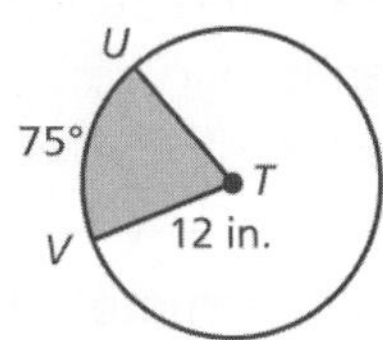

sector *UTV* ____________________

3. 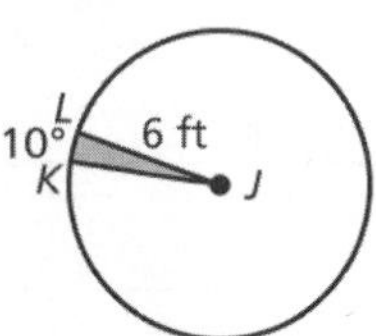

sector *KJL* ____________________

4. 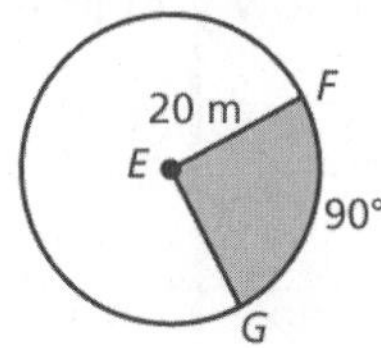

sector *FEG* ____________________

5. The speedometer needle in Ignacio's car is 2 inches long. The needle sweeps out a 130° sector during acceleration from 0 to 60 mi/h. Find the area of this sector. Round to the nearest hundredth. ____________

Find the area of each shaded sector to the nearest hundredth.

6. 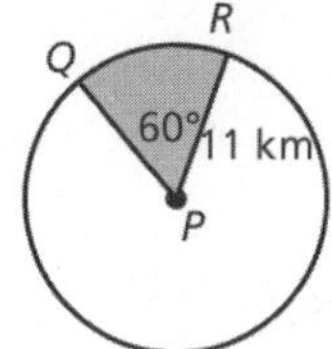

____

7. 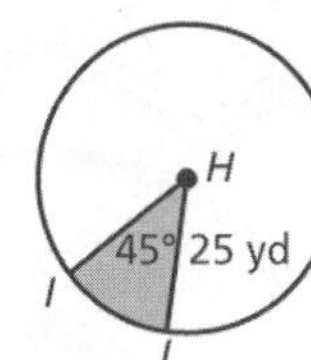

____

8. 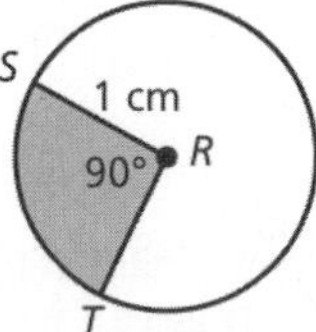

____

9. 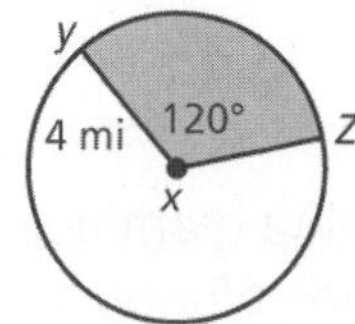

____

Find each arc length. Give your answer in terms of π and rounded to the nearest hundredth.

10. 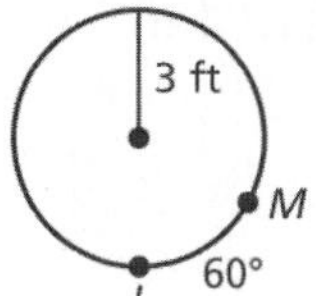

____

11. 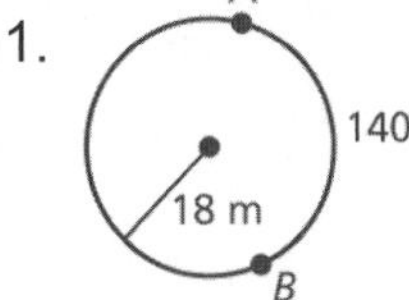

____

12. an arc with measure 45° in a circle with radius 2 mi ____________

13. an arc with measure 120° in a circle with radius 15 mm ____________

Problem Solving

1. A circle with a radius of 20 centimeters has a sector that has an arc measure of 105°. What is the area of the sector? Round to the nearest tenth.

2. A sector whose central angle measures 72° has an area of 16.2π square feet. What is the radius of the circle?

3. A circular wall clock has a diameter of 18 inches. If the hour and minute hand were extended to reach to the edge of the clock, what would be the area of the smaller of the two sectors formed by the hands at 2 o'clock? Round your answer to the nearest tenth of a square inch, and explain how you found your answer.

Choose the best answer.

4. The circular shelves in diagram are each 28 inches in diameter. The "cut-out" portion of each shelf is 90°. Approximately how much shelf paper is needed to cover both shelves?

   A 154 in^2
   B 308 in^2
   C 462 in^2
   D 924 in^2

5. Find the area of the shaded region. Round to the nearest tenth.

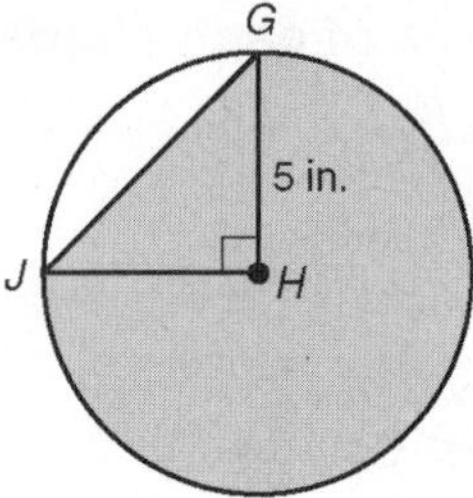

   F 8.2 in^2
   G 19.6 in^2
   H 71.4 in^2
   J 78.5 in^2

6. A semicircular garden with a diameter of 6 feet is to have 2 inches of mulch spread over it. To the nearest tenth, what is the volume of mulch that is needed?

   A 2.4 ft^3
   B 4.8 ft^3
   C 14.1 ft^3
   D 28.3 ft^3

7. A round cheesecake 12 inches in diameter and 3 inches high is cut into 8 equal-sized pieces. If five pieces have been taken, what is the approximate volume of the cheesecake that remains?

   F 42.4 in^3
   G 70.7 in^3
   H 127.2 in^3
   J 212.1 in^3

Name ______________________ Class ______________ Date ________

12-4

Inscribed Angles

Going Deeper

Essential question: *What is the relationship between central angles and inscribed angles in a circle?*

MCC9–12.G.C.2

1 EXPLORE Investigating Central Angles and Inscribed Angles

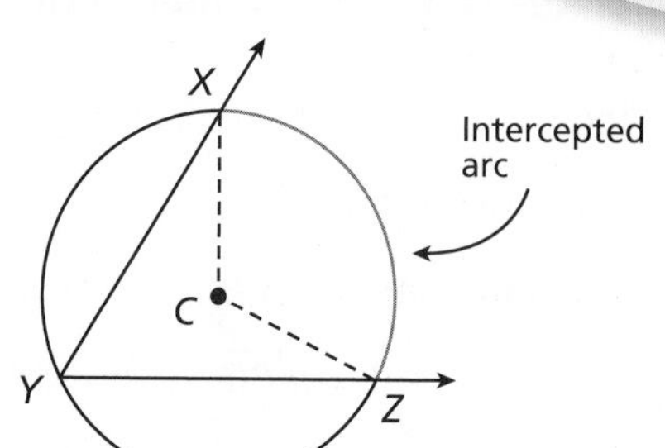

A Use a compass to draw a circle. Label the center C.

B Use a straightedge to draw an inscribed angle, $\angle XYZ$.

C Use the straightedge to draw the central angle, $\angle XCZ$.

D Use a protractor to measure the inscribed angle and the central angle. Use the measure of the central angle to determine the measure of the intercepted arc.

E Repeat the process four more times. Be sure to draw a variety of inscribed angles (acute, right, obtuse, passing through the center, etc.). Record your results in the table.

	Circle 1	Circle 2	Circle 3	Circle 4	Circle 5
Measure of Inscribed Angle					
Measure of Intercepted Arc					

REFLECT

1a. Compare your work with that of other students. Then make a conjecture: What is the relationship between the measure of an inscribed angle and the measure of its intercepted arc?

____

____

1b. Suppose an inscribed angle, $\angle XYZ$, measures $x°$. If $\angle XYZ$ is acute, what is the measure of its associated central angle, $\angle XCZ$? What if $\angle XYZ$ is obtuse?

____

1c. Draw a triangle inscribed in a circle so that the center of the circle lies in the interior of the triangle. Then draw the central angle associated with each inscribed angle of the triangle. What is the sum of the measures of the inscribed angles? What is the sum of the measures of the central angles?

____

____

You may have discovered the following relationship between an inscribed angle and its intercepted arc.

Inscribed Angle Theorem

The measure of an inscribed angle is half the measure of its intercepted arc.

$m\angle ADB = \frac{1}{2} m\widehat{AB}$

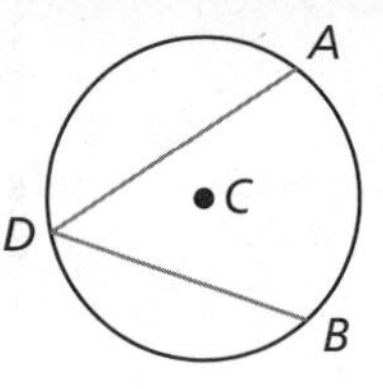

MCC9–12.G.C.2

2 EXAMPLE Finding Arc and Angle Measures

Find $m\widehat{BC}$, $m\widehat{BD}$, $m\angle DAB$, and $m\angle ABC$.

A Find $m\widehat{BC}$.

$m\angle BAC = \frac{1}{2} m\widehat{BC}$	Inscribed Angle Theorem
$2m\angle BAC = m\widehat{BC}$	Multiply both sides by 2.
$2 \cdot$ _____ $= m\widehat{BC}$	Substitute.
_____ $= m\widehat{BC}$	Multiply.

B By the Arc Addition Postulate, $m\widehat{BD} = m\widehat{BC} + m\widehat{CD} =$ _______ $+ 88° =$ _______ .

C By the Inscribed Angle Theorem, $m\angle DAB = \frac{1}{2} m\widehat{BD} = \frac{1}{2} \cdot$ _______ $=$ _______ .

D To find $m\angle ABC$, note that $\widehat{ADC}$ is a _____________ .

Therefore, $m\widehat{ADC} =$ _______ , and $m\angle ABC = \frac{1}{2} m\widehat{ADC} = \frac{1}{2} \cdot$ _______ $=$ _______ .

REFLECT

2a. Is it possible to find $m\widehat{DAB}$? If so, how? If not, why not?

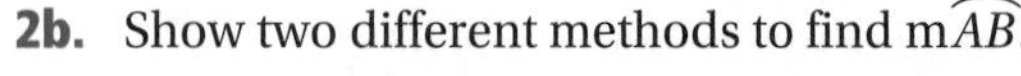

2b. Show two different methods to find $m\widehat{AB}$.

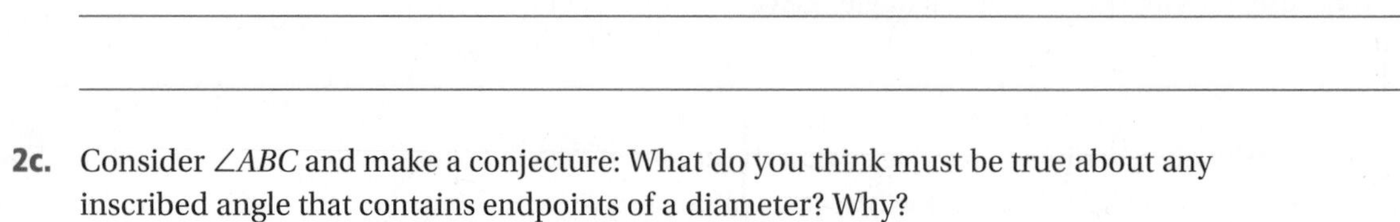

2c. Consider $\angle ABC$ and make a conjecture: What do you think must be true about any inscribed angle that contains endpoints of a diameter? Why?

The following theorem describes a key relationship between inscribed angles and diameters.

Theorem

The endpoints of a diameter lie on an inscribed angle if and only if the inscribed angle is a right angle.

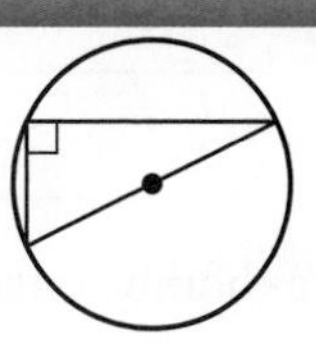

Another theorem that relies on the Inscribed Angle Theorem in its proof is shown below. It is a theorem about the measures of the angles in any quadrilateral that is inscribed in a circle.

Inscribed Quadrilateral Theorem

If a quadrilateral is inscribed in a circle, then its opposite angles are supplementary.

The converse of the Inscribed Quadrilateral Theorem is also true. Taken together, the theorem and its converse tell you that a quadrilateral can be inscribed in a circle *if and only if* its opposite angles are supplementary.

MCC9–12.G.C.3

3 PROOF Inscribed Quadrilateral Theorem

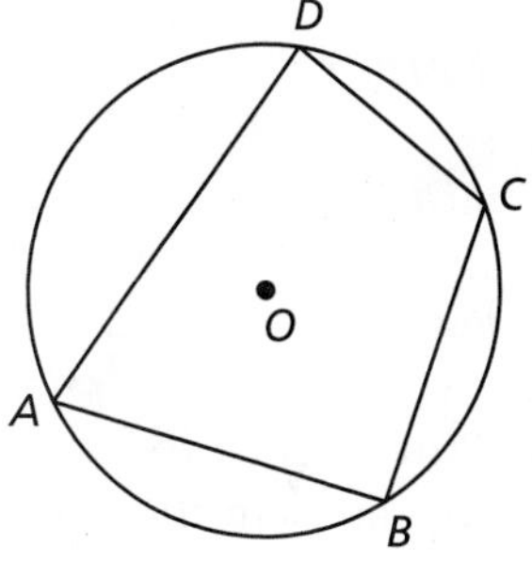

Given: Quadrilateral $ABCD$ is inscribed in circle O.

Prove: $\angle A$ and $\angle C$ are supplementary;
$\angle B$ and $\angle D$ are supplementary.

A $\overparen{BCD}$ and $\overparen{DAB}$ make a complete circle. Therefore,

$m\overparen{BCD} + m\overparen{DAB} =$ ___________.

B $\angle A$ is an inscribed angle and its intercepted arc is $\overparen{BCD}$; $\angle C$ is an inscribed angle and its intercepted arc is $\overparen{DAB}$. By the Inscribed Angle Theorem,

$m\angle A =$ ___________ and $m\angle C =$ ___________.

C So, $m\angle A + m\angle C =$ ____________________ Substitution

$=$ ____________________ Distributive Property

$=$ ____________________ Substitution

$=$ ____________________ Simplify.

This shows that $\angle A$ and $\angle C$ are supplementary. Similar reasoning shows that $\angle B$ and $\angle D$ are supplementary.

REFLECT

3a. What must be true about a parallelogram that is inscribed in a circle? Explain.

____

____

3b. What must be true about a rhombus that is inscribed in a circle? Explain.

____

____

____

PRACTICE

Use the figure to find each of the following.

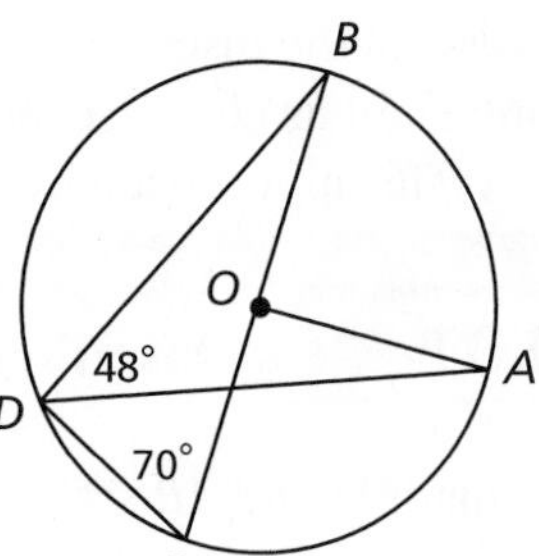

1. m$\overparen{BA}$ ______ **2.** m$\angle BOA$ ______

3. m$\overparen{AE}$ ______ **4.** m$\angle AOE$ ______

5. m$\overparen{BAE}$ ______ **6.** m$\angle BDE$ ______

7. m$\angle DBE$ ______ **8.** m$\overparen{DE}$ ______

9. m$\overparen{DB}$ ______ **10.** m$\overparen{ABD}$ ______

11. m$\angle EDA$ ______ **12.** m$\angle OAD$ ______

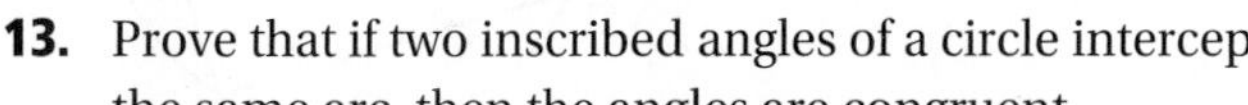

13. Prove that if two inscribed angles of a circle intercept the same arc, then the angles are congruent.

Given: $\angle ABC$ and $\angle ADC$ intercept $\overparen{AC}$.

Prove: $\angle ABC \cong \angle ADC$

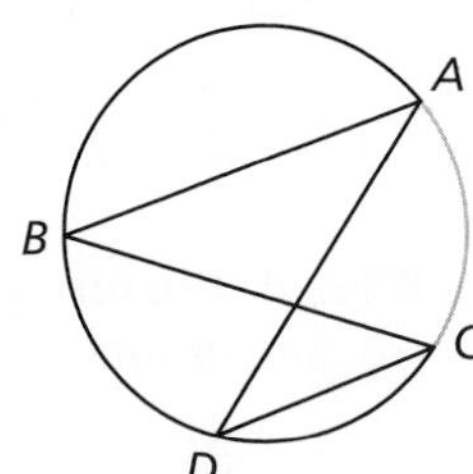

____

____

____

14. A carpenter's square is a tool that is used to draw right angles. Suppose you are building a toy car and you have a small circle of wood that will serve as a wheel. Explain how you can use the carpenter's square to find the center of the circle.

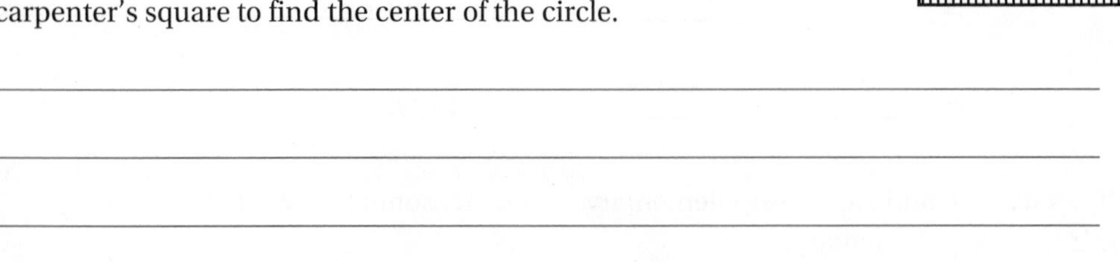

____

____

____

____

Name ________________ Class ________ Date ________

Additional Practice

Find each measure.

1. 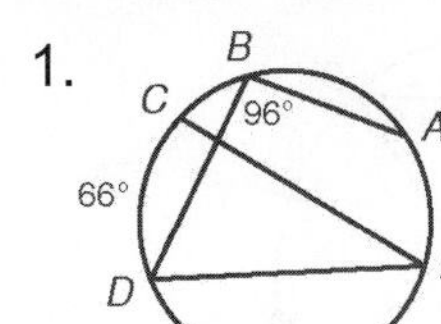

$m\angle CED =$ ________

$m\widehat{DEA} =$ ________

2. 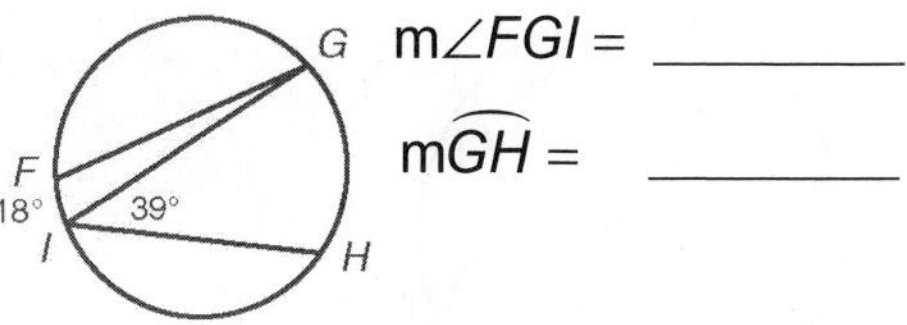

$m\angle FGI =$ ________

$m\widehat{GH} =$ ________

3. 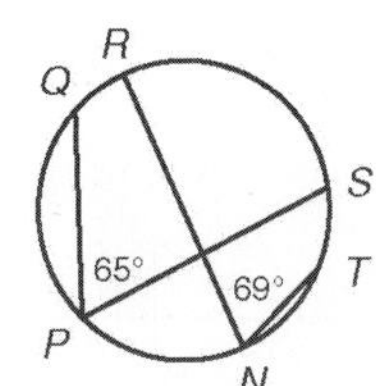

$m\widehat{QRS} =$ ________

$m\widehat{TSR} =$ ________

4. 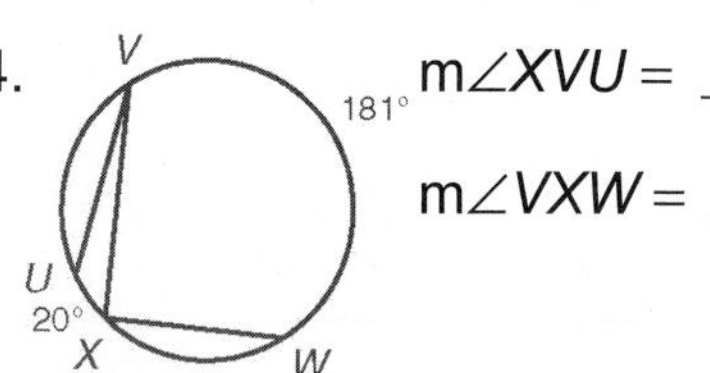

$m\angle XVU =$ ________

$m\angle VXW =$ ________

5. A circular radar screen in an air traffic control tower shows these flight paths. Find $m\angle LNK$. ________

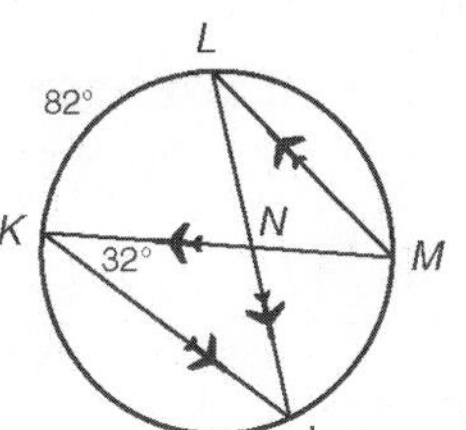

Find each value.

6. 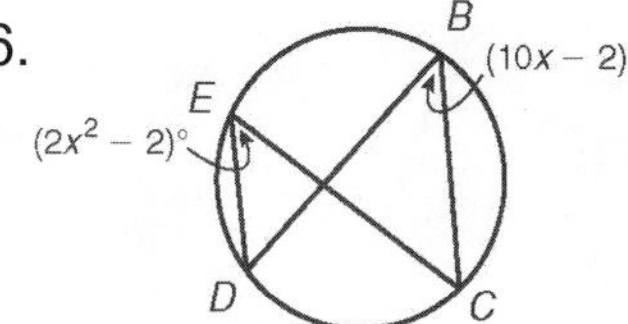

$m\angle CED =$ ________

7. 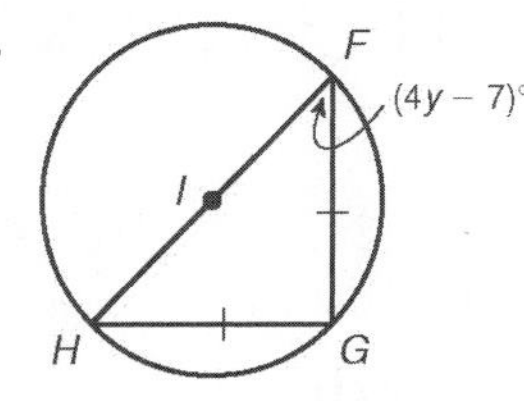

$y =$ ________

8. 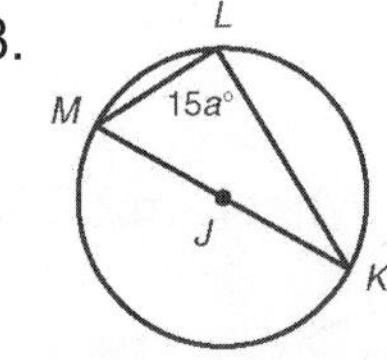

$a =$ ________

9. 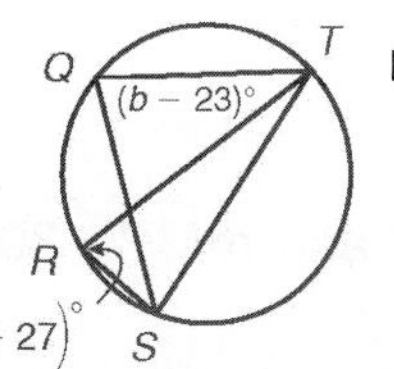

$m\angle SRT =$ ________

Find the angle measures of each inscribed quadrilateral.

10. 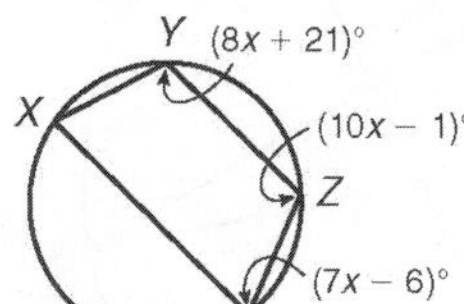

$m\angle X =$ ________

$m\angle Y =$ ________

$m\angle Z =$ ________

$m\angle W =$ ________

11. 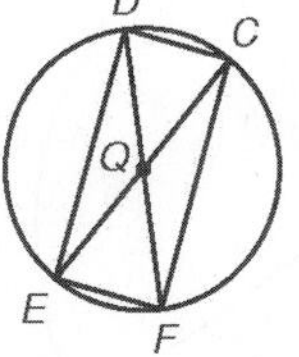

$m\angle C =$ ________

$m\angle D =$ ________

$m\angle E =$ ________

$m\angle F =$ ________

12. 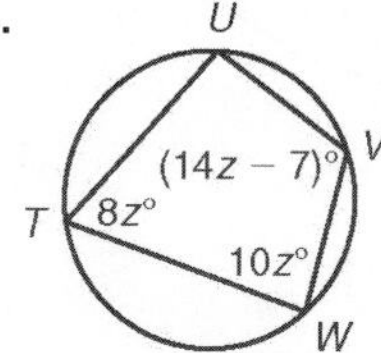

$m\angle T =$ ________

$m\angle U =$ ________

$m\angle V =$ ________

$m\angle W =$ ________

13. 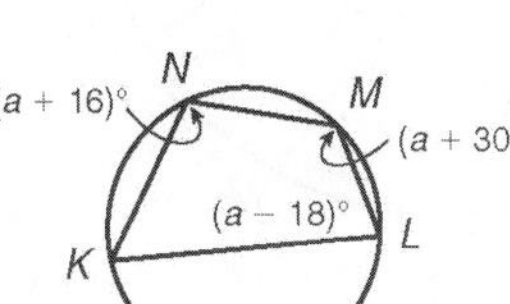

$m\angle K =$ ________

$m\angle L =$ ________

$m\angle M =$ ________

$m\angle N =$ ________

Problem Solving

1. Find $m\widehat{AB}$.

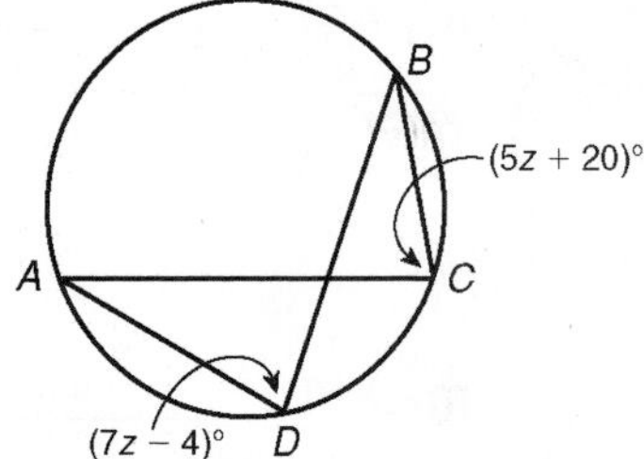

2. Find the angle measures of *RSTU*.

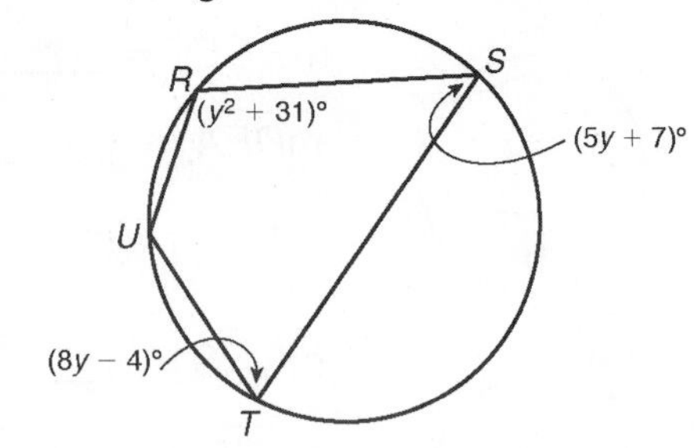

Choose the best answer.

Use the diagram of a floor tile for Exercises 3 and 4. Points *Q*, *R*, *S*, *T*, *U*, *V*, *W*, and *X* are equally spaced around ⊙*L*.

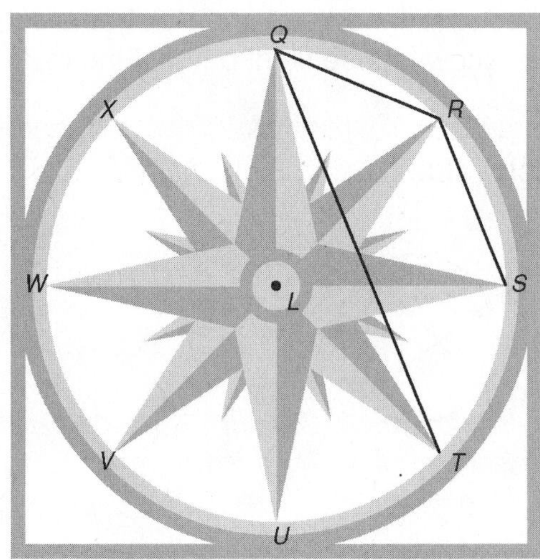

3. Find $m\angle RQT$.

A 15° C 45°

B 30° D 60°

4. Find $m\angle QRS$.

F 67.5° H 180°

G 135° J 270°

5. If $m\angle KLM = 20°$ and $m\widehat{MP} = 30°$, what is $m\angle KNP$?

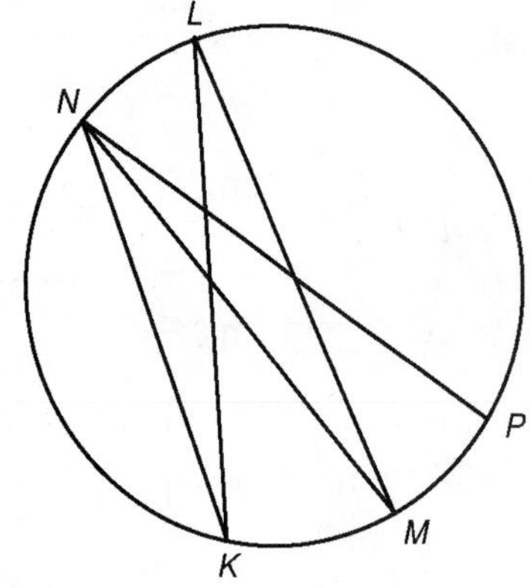

A 25° C 50°

B 35° D 70°

6. In ⊙*M*, $m\angle AMB = 74°$. What is $m\angle CDB$?

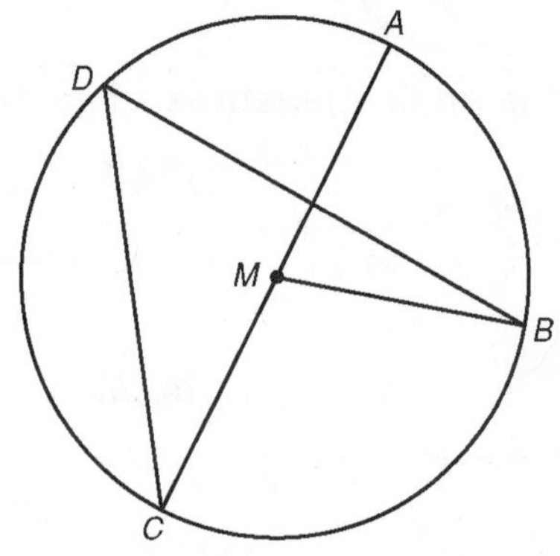

F 37° H 74°

G 53° J 106°

Name________________________ Class________________ Date__________

UNIT 3

Performance Tasks

MCC9-12.G.GMD.1
MCC9-12.G.GMD.3
MCC9-12.G.C.2

 **1.** A circular table has a diameter of 48 inches. A carpenter is remaking it into a square table. To the nearest tenth of an inch, what is the greatest possible side length of the square table? Explain.

 **2.** A moving company needs to replace a circular glass mirror that it broke during a move. The dimensions of a piece of the broken mirror are shown in the figure. What was the diameter of the original mirror? Round your answer to the nearest tenth of an inch.

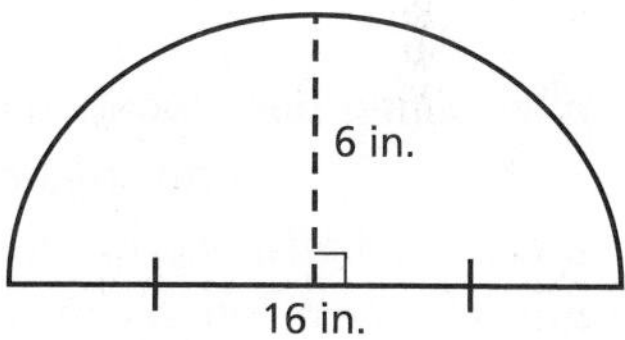

 **3.** Two congruent, cylindrical salt-and-pepper shakers fit snugly beside one another inside a rectangular prism box, as shown at right. The box is 7 centimeters wide, 14 centimeters long, and 10 centimeters high, and the shakers are upright. The shakers are the same height as the box.

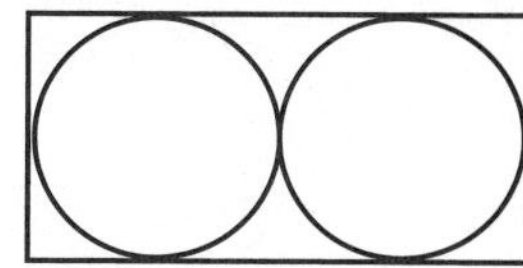

a. Find the radius of one shaker. Justify your answer.

b. After the shakers are put into the box, the remaining empty space is filled with shredded paper. What volume of shredded paper will be included in the box? Round your answer to the nearest cubic centimeter and show your work.

continued

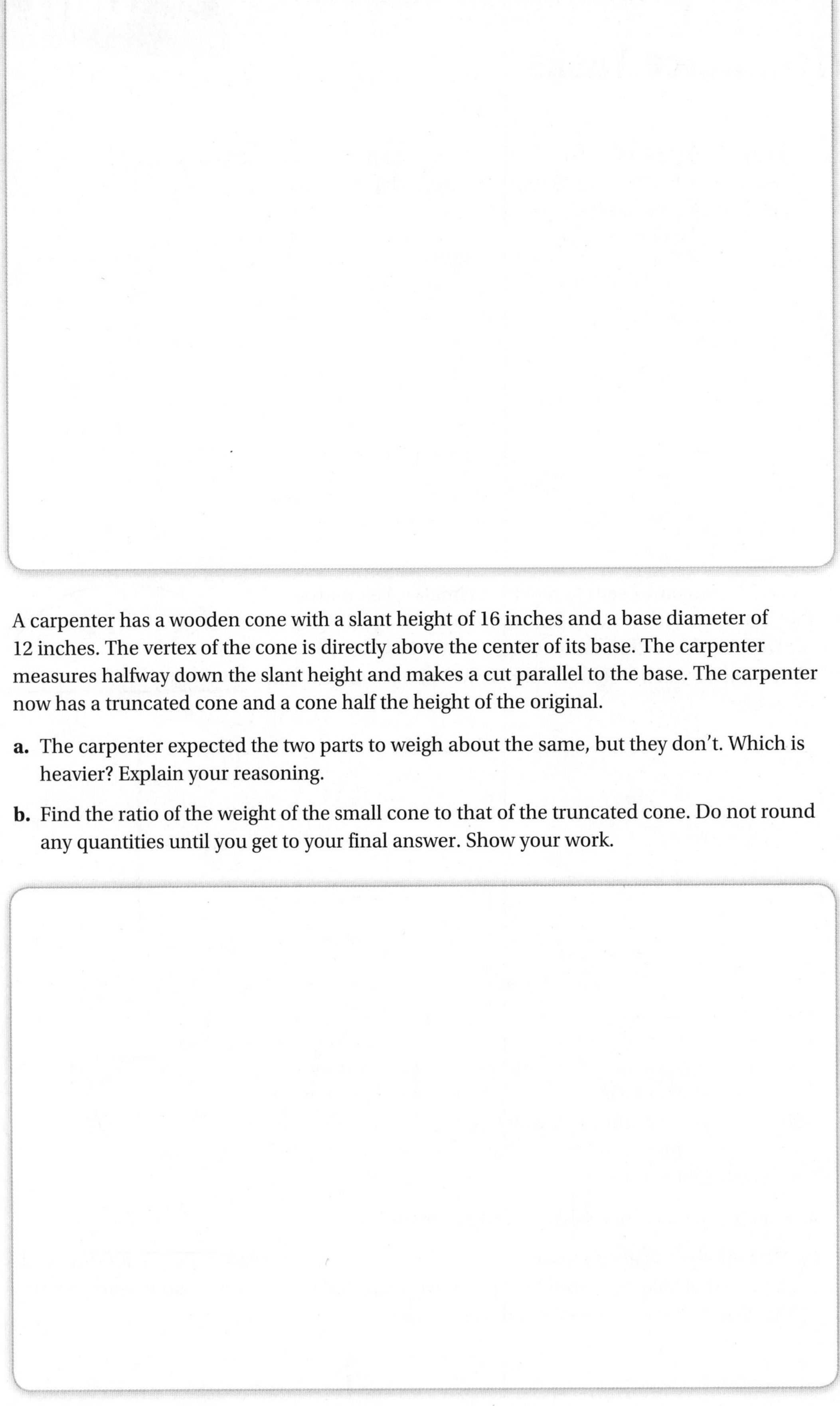

4. A carpenter has a wooden cone with a slant height of 16 inches and a base diameter of 12 inches. The vertex of the cone is directly above the center of its base. The carpenter measures halfway down the slant height and makes a cut parallel to the base. The carpenter now has a truncated cone and a cone half the height of the original.

a. The carpenter expected the two parts to weigh about the same, but they don't. Which is heavier? Explain your reasoning.

b. Find the ratio of the weight of the small cone to that of the truncated cone. Do not round any quantities until you get to your final answer. Show your work.

Name ______________________ Class ______________ Date __________

SELECTED RESPONSE

1. A wire frame in the shape of the cube is used to support a pyramid-shaped basket, as shown. The vertex of the pyramid lies in the same plane as a face of the cube. To the nearest tenth, what is the volume of the pyramid-shaped basket?

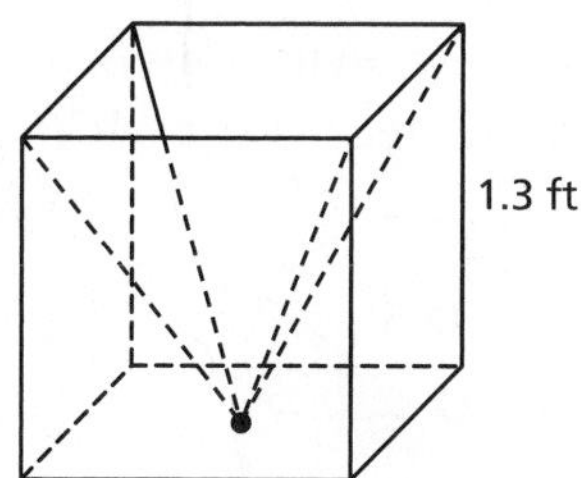

F. 0.7 ft^3 **H.** 2.2 ft^3

G. 1.7 ft^3 **J.** 2.3 ft^3

2. A food manufacturer sells yogurt in cone-shaped cups with the dimensions shown. To the nearest tenth, how many fluid ounces of yogurt does the cup hold? (*Hint:* 1 $cm^3 \approx 0.034$ fl oz)

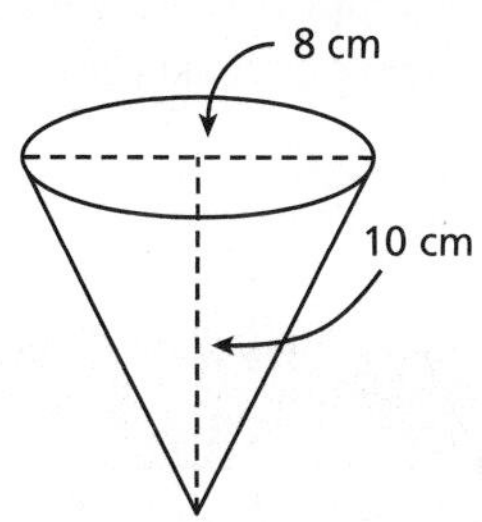

A. 0.6 fl oz **C.** 17.1 fl oz

B. 5.7 fl oz **D.** 22.8 fl oz

3. You want to design a cylindrical container for oatmeal that has a volume of 90 $in.^3$ You also want the height of the container to be 3.5 times the radius. To the nearest tenth, what should the radius of the container be?

F. 2.0 in. **H.** 3.0 in.

G. 2.9 in. **J.** 3.1 in.

4. $\overline{PR}$ and $\overline{QR}$ are tangents to circle C. Which expression represents $m\angle C$?

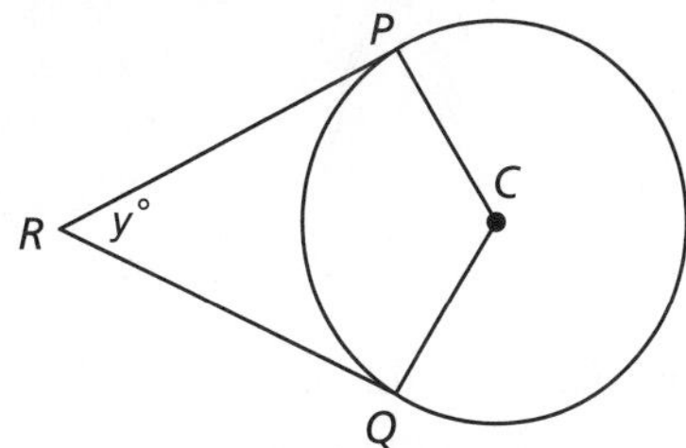

A. $(2y)°$ **C.** $(90 - y)°$

B. $(180 - y)°$ **D.** $\left(\frac{1}{2}y\right)°$

5. In circle O, $\angle ABC$ is an inscribed angle and $\overline{AC}$ is a diameter. Which of the following must be true?

F. $\angle ABC$ is an acute angle.

G. $\angle ABC$ is a right angle.

H. $\overline{AB}$ is a radius.

J. $\overline{AC} \perp \overline{BC}$

6. What is the radian measure of the angle whose degree measure is 20°?

A. $\frac{\pi}{20}$ **C.** $\frac{\pi}{9}$

B. $\frac{\pi}{18}$ **D.** $\frac{2\pi}{9}$

7. $\overline{JK}$ is a tangent to circle C. What is $m\widehat{KL}$?

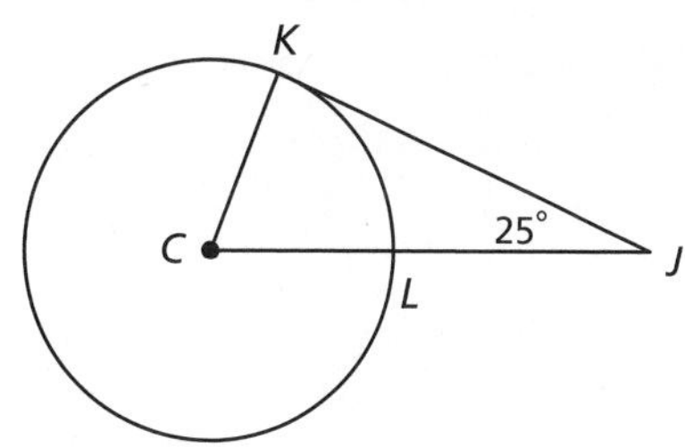

F. 25° **H.** 65°

G. 50° **J.** 130°

CONSTRUCTED RESPONSE

8. In order to develop and justify the formula for the volume of a cone, you begin with a given cone that has radius r and height h. You consider pyramids with regular polygonal bases that are inscribed in the cone.

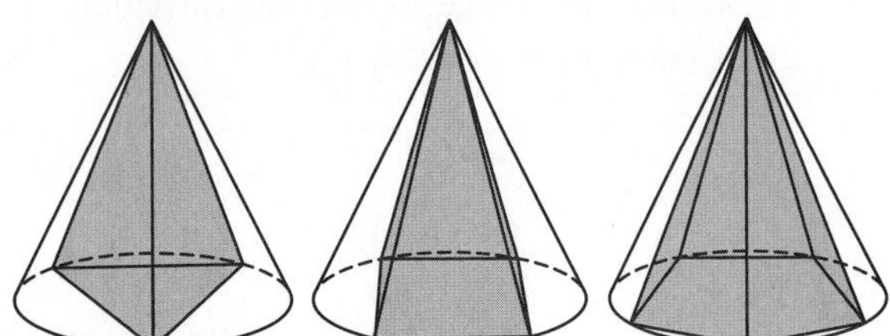

You show that when the inscribed pyramid has a base that is a regular n-gon, the volume of the pyramid is given by the following expression.

$$\frac{1}{3}r^2hn \sin\left(\frac{180^\circ}{n}\right) \cos\left(\frac{180^\circ}{n}\right)$$

Describe the remaining steps of the argument.

9. A spherical gas tank has the dimensions shown. When filled with butane, it provides 468,766 BTU. How many BTUs does one cubic foot of butane yield? Round to the nearest BTU.

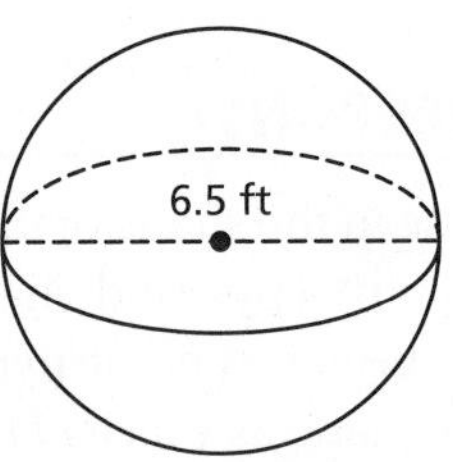

10. Write an expression in terms of m that you can use to find the area of sector AOB.

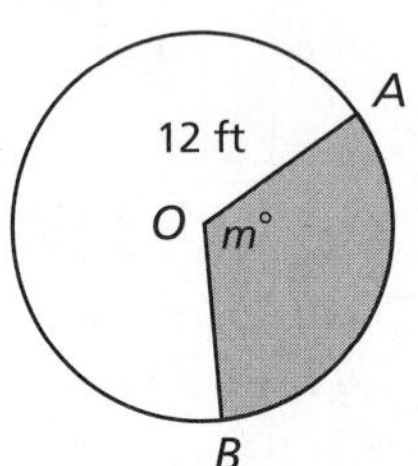

11. Using the figure below, Andrea discovers that the length of the arc intercepted by the 60° angle is proportional to the radius. What is the constant of proportionality for the relationship? Show your reasoning.

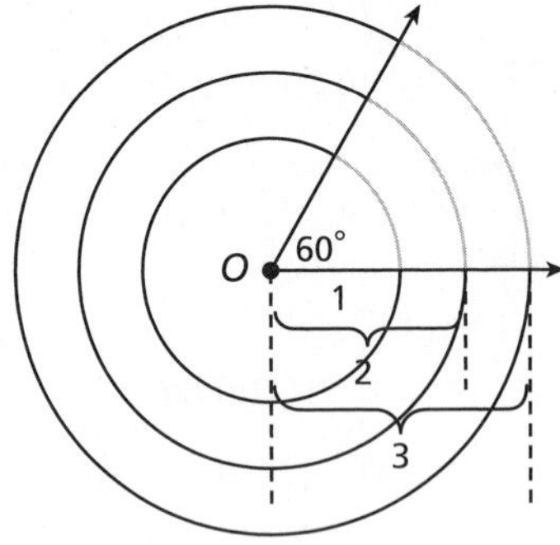

Extending the Number System

Unpacking the Standards

Understanding the standards and the vocabulary terms in the standards will help you know exactly what you are expected to learn in this unit.

GPS COMMON CORE **MCC9-12.N.CN.2**

Use the relation $i^2 = -1$ and the commutative, associative, and distributive properties to add, subtract, and multiply complex numbers.

Key Vocabulary

complex number *(número complejo)* Any number that can be written as $a + bi$, where a and b are real numbers and $i = \sqrt{-1}$.

What It Means For You

Whole numbers, integers, real numbers, and so on, are all members of a larger set called the complex numbers. You can use the same properties of operations with all of them.

EXAMPLE

$(4 + i)(3 - 2i)$

$= 4(3 - 2i) + i(3 + 2i)$	*Distributive Property*
$= 12 - 8i + 3i - 2i^2$	*Distributive Property*
$= 12 - 8i + 3i + 2$	$i^2 = -1$
$= (12 + 2) + (-8i + 3i)$	*Associative/ Commutative Properties*
$= 14 - 5i$	*Add real parts and imaginary parts.*

UNIT 4

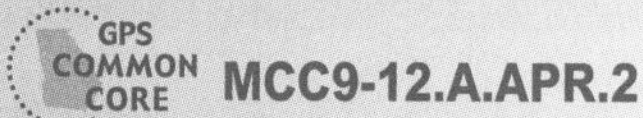

MCC9-12.A.APR.2

Know and apply the Remainder Theorem: For a polynomial $p(x)$ and a number a, the remainder on division by $x - a$ is $p(a)$, so $p(a) = 0$ if and only if $(x - a)$ is a factor of $p(x)$.

What It Means For You

You can use the Remainder Theorem to find factors of polynomials.

EXAMPLE

To check whether $(x - 2)$ is a factor of $P(x) = x^3 - 19x + 30$, find the value of $P(2)$. If $P(2) = 0$, then $(x - 2)$ is a factor of P by the Remainder Theorem. You can substitute as shown below, or use a shortcut called synthetic substitution.

$$P(x) = x^3 - 19x + 30$$

$$P(2) = 2^3 - 19(2) + 30$$

$$P(2) = 8 - 38 + 30$$

$$P(2) = 0$$

Because $P(2) = 0$, $(x - 2)$ is a factor of P.

You can instead divide $x^3 - 19x + 30$ by $(x - 2)$ to check that $(x - 2)$ is a factor, using either long division or synthetic division. You will find that $\frac{x^3 - 19x + 30}{x - 2} = x^2 + 2x - 15$ or $(x + 5)(x - 3)$.

UNIT 4

Key Vocabulary

absolute value of a complex number *(valor absoluto de un número complejo)* The absolute value of $a + bi$ is the distance from the origin to the point (a, b) in the complex plane and is denoted $|a + bi| = \sqrt{a^2 + b^2}$.

complex conjugate *(conjugado complejo)* The complex conjugate of any complex number $a + bi$, denoted $\overline{a + bi}$, is $a - bi$.

complex number *(número complejo)* Any number that can be written as $a + bi$, where a and b are real numbers and $i = \sqrt{-1}$.

complex plane *(plano complejo)* A set of coordinate axes in which the horizontal axis is the real axis and the vertical axis is the imaginary axis; used to graph complex numbers.

imaginary unit *(unidad imaginaria)* The unit in the imaginary number system, $\sqrt{-1}$.

imaginary number *(número imaginario)* The square root of a negative number, written in the form bi, where b is a real number and i is the imaginary unit, $\sqrt{-1}$. Also called a *pure imaginary number*.

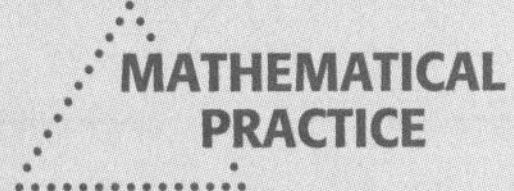

The Common Core Standards for Mathematical Practice describe varieties of expertise that mathematics educators at all levels should seek to develop in their students. Opportunities to develop these practices are integrated throughout this program.

1. **Make sense of problems and persevere in solving them.**
2. **Reason abstractly and quantitatively.**
3. **Construct viable arguments and critique the reasoning of others.**
4. **Model with mathematics.**
5. **Use appropriate tools strategically.**
6. **Attend to precision.**
7. **Look for and make use of structure.**
8. **Look for and express regularity in repeated reasoning.**

Name ______________________ Class ______________ Date __________

13-1

Complex Numbers and Roots

Going Deeper

Essential question: *What is a complex number?*

MCC9–12.N.CN.1

1 EXPLORE Understanding Complex Numbers

Video Tutor

Consider the quadratic equations $x^2 - 1 = 0$ and $x^2 + 1 = 0$. You can solve the equations using square roots.

$$x^2 - 1 = 0 \qquad x^2 = 1 \qquad x = \pm\sqrt{1} = \pm 1$$

$$x^2 + 1 = 0 \qquad x^2 = -1 \qquad x = \pm\sqrt{-1}$$

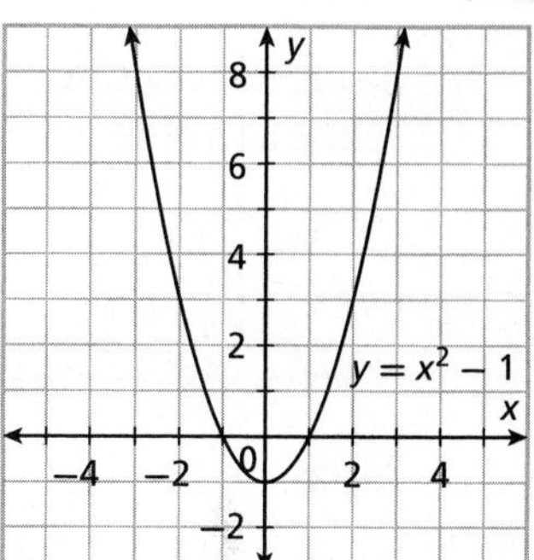

A The first equation has two solutions, 1 and −1. The second equation also has two solutions, $\sqrt{-1}$ and $-\sqrt{-1}$. Which of these four solutions are real numbers? ______________________

B The graphs of $y = x^2 - 1$ and $y = x^2 + 1$ are shown. How do the graphs confirm your answer to part **A**?

____

____

____

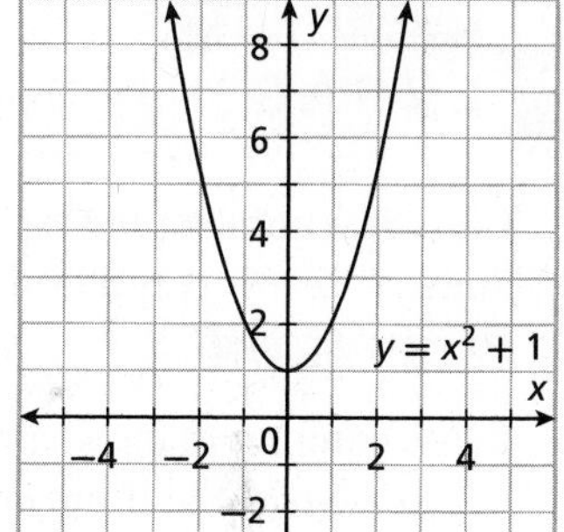

When the graph of a quadratic function $f(x)$ does not cross the x-axis, the solutions of $f(x) = 0$ involve the *imaginary unit i.*

C Previously you have used the Product Property $\sqrt{ab} = \sqrt{a} \cdot \sqrt{b}$ to simplify square roots of nonnegative numbers. Now extend the property to situations where $a = -1$ or $b = -1$. Simplify the following square roots by writing them in terms of the so-called **imaginary unit** i, which equals $\sqrt{-1}$.

$$\sqrt{-2} = \sqrt{-1 \cdot 2} = \sqrt{-1} \cdot \sqrt{\quad} = i\sqrt{2} \qquad \sqrt{-4} = \sqrt{\qquad} = \sqrt{4} \cdot \sqrt{-1} = 2i$$

A **complex number** is a number that can be written in the form $a + bi$, where a and b are real numbers and $i = \sqrt{-1}$. The set of real numbers is a subset of the complex numbers $\mathbb{C}$. Every complex number has a real part a and an imaginary part b.

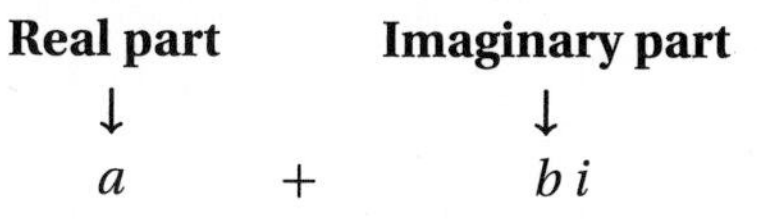

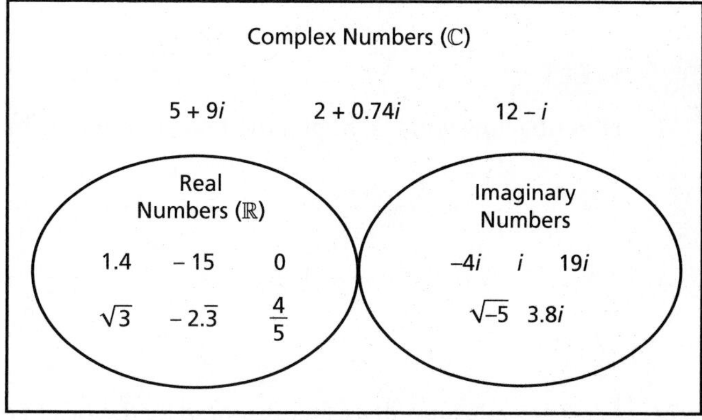

Real numbers are complex numbers where $b = 0$. Imaginary numbers are complex numbers where $a = 0$ and $b \neq 0$. These are sometimes called **pure imaginary numbers**.

The complex numbers that are neither real nor imaginary, such as $5 + 9i$, are called *nonreal numbers*. In general, the nonreal numbers $a + bi$ are those in which both $a \neq 0$ and $b \neq 0$.

REFLECT

1a. How many real solutions does $x^2 + 4 = 0$ have? How many nonreal solutions? Explain.

____

1b. What is the value of i^2? Explain.

____

1c. Using just the three set names shown in the Venn diagram on the previous page, name all sets to which each of the following numbers belong.

$1 - 2i$ ____

$-2i$ ____

-2 ____

MCC9–12.N.CN.1

2 ENGAGE The Complex Plane

Every real number corresponds to a point on the real number line. Similarly, every complex number corresponds to a point in the **complex plane**.

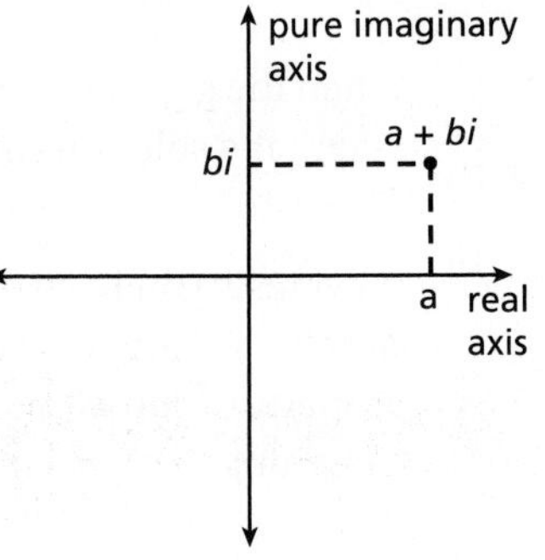

In the complex plane, real numbers are represented on a horizontal axis called the *real axis*. Pure imaginary numbers are represented on a vertical axis called the *pure imaginary* axis. Complex numbers that are neither real numbers nor pure imaginary numbers are represented in the plane formed by these axes.

It is important to recognize that the complex plane is not the same as the *x*-*y* coordinate plane that you are familiar with. In the *x*-*y* plane, real numbers are represented on both the *x*-axis and the *y*-axis.

REFLECT

2a. Describe how you would plot the following points in the complex plane.

7 ____

$-4i$ ____

$-6 + 2i$ ____

2b. What complex number is represented by the origin of the complex plane?

____

The **complex conjugate** of any real number $a + bi$ is the complex number $a - bi$.

MCC9–12.N.CN.1

3 EXAMPLE Finding Complex Conjugates

Find each complex conjugate.

A $3 + 5i$ **B** $-6 - i$ **C** 12 **D** $-2i$

REFLECT

3a. What is the conjugate of the conjugate of a complex number $a + bi$? Explain.

MCC9–12.N.CN.1

4 EXPLORE Graphing Complex Conjugates

A Use the quadratic formula to solve $x^2 - 4x + 5 = 0$.

$$x_1 = \frac{-\square + \sqrt{\square^2 - 4 \bullet \square \bullet \square}}{2 \bullet \square} \qquad x_2 = \frac{-\square - \sqrt{\square^2 - 4 \bullet \square \bullet \square}}{2 \bullet \square}$$

$$= \frac{\square + \sqrt{\square}}{\square} \qquad = \frac{\square - \sqrt{\square}}{\square}$$

$$= \square + i \qquad = \square - i$$

B Graph the solutions on the complex plane.

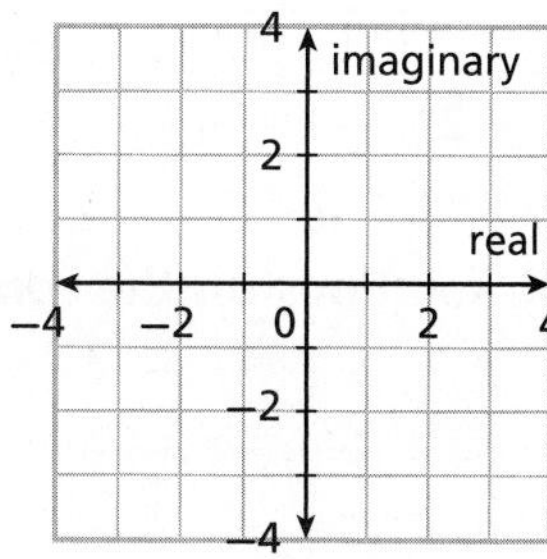

REFLECT

4a. Why are nonreal roots of a quadratic equation complex conjugates?

4b. Describe the locations of the graphs of a complex number and its conjugate relative to the real axis. Explain why the relationship exists.

PRACTICE

Write each number in its proper location in the Venn diagram.

1. $3 + i$

2. -17

3. $\sqrt{7}$

4. $9i$

5. $-6 - 5i$

6. $-\frac{7}{8}$

7. 6.492

8. $-\sqrt{-25}$

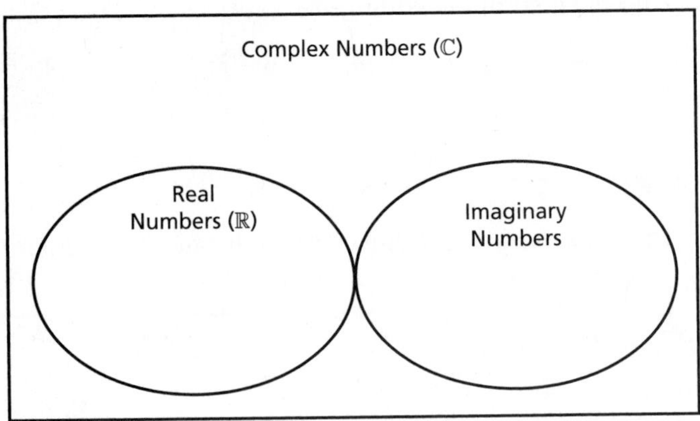

Write the square roots of each number in terms of *i*.

9. -9 ____ and ____

10. -7 ____ and ____

11. -1 ____ and ____

12. -100 ____ and ____

Solve.

13. $x^2 - 16 = 0$ ____ and ____

14. $x^2 + 16 = 0$ ____ and ____

15. $x^2 - 5 = 0$ ____ and ____

16. $x^2 + 5 = 0$ ____ and ____

Find each complex conjugate.

17. $7 - 2i$ ____

18. 9 ____

19. $6i$ ____

20. $-8i$ ____

21. $-1 - 9i$ ____

22. $12 + 5i$ ____

Solve. Then graph the solutions on the complex plane.

23. $x^2 + 2x + 5 = 0$

$x =$ ____

$x =$ ____

24. $x^2 - 6x + 13 = 0$

$x =$ ____

$x =$ ____

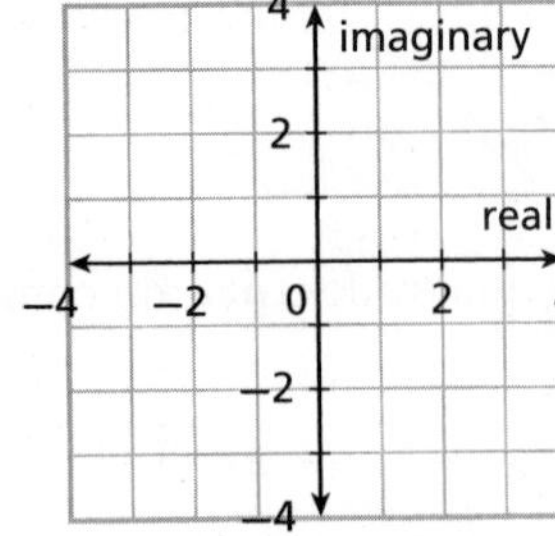

Name________________________ Class______________ Date______________

13-1

Additional Practice

Express each number in terms of *i*.

1. $\sqrt{-32}$

2. $2\sqrt{-18}$

3. $\sqrt{-\frac{1}{9}}$

Solve each equation.

4. $3x^2 + 81 = 0$

5. $4x^2 = -28$

6. $\frac{1}{4}x^2 + 12 = 0$

7. $6x^2 = -126$

Find the values of *x* and *y* that make each equation true.

8. $2x - 20i = 8 - (4y)i$

9. $5i - 6x = (10y)i + 2$

Find the zeros of each function.

10. $f(x) = x^2 - 2x + 4$

11. $g(x) = x^2 + 6x + 14$

Find each complex conjugate.

12. $i - 3$

13. $3i - 4$

14. $11i$

Solve.

15. The impedance of an electrical circuit is a way of measuring how much the circuit impedes the flow of electricity. The impedance can be a complex number. A circuit is being designed that must have an impedance that satisfies the function $f(x) = 2x^2 - 12x + 40$, where x is a measure of the impedance. Find the zeros of the function.

Problem Solving

At a carnival, a new attraction allows contestants to jump off a springboard onto a platform to be launched vertically into the air. The object is to ring a bell located 20 feet overhead. The distance from the bell in feet is modeled by the function $dt = 16t^2 - bt + 20$, where t is the time in seconds after leaving the platform, and b is the takeoff velocity from the platform.

1. Kate watches some of the contestants. She theorizes that if the platform launches a contestant with a takeoff velocity of at least 32 feet per second, the contestant can ring the bell.
   a. Find the zeros for the function using 32 feet per second as the takeoff velocity. ________________
   b. Is Kate's theory valid? Explain.

____

2. Mirko suggests they vary the value of b and determine for which values of b the roots are real.
   a. Complete the table to show the roots for different values of b.
   b. For which values of b in the table are the roots real?

____

   c. What difference does it make if the roots are real?

b	Function	Roots
24	$d(t) = 16t^2 - 24t + 20$	
32	$d(t) = 16t^2 - \_\_t + 20$	
40	$d(t) = 16t^2 - \_\_t + 20$	
48	$d(t) = 16t^2 - \_\_t + 20$	

____

3. Using the results from the table, and the function, estimate the minimum takeoff velocity needed for a contestant to be able to ring the bell. ________________

Choose the letter for the best answer.

4. Mirko suggests using four bells at heights of 15, 20, 25, and 30 feet from the platform. How many of the bells can a contestant reach if the takeoff velocity is 32 feet per second?

   A 3 C 1
   B 2 D 0

5. At what height must a bell be placed for a contestant to reach it with a takeoff velocity of 48 feet per second?

   A 20 feet or less
   B 25 feet or less
   C 30 feet or less
   D 36 feet or less

Name ______________________ Class ______________ Date ________

13-2

Operations with Complex Numbers

Going Deeper

Video Tutor

Essential question: *How do you add, subtract, and multiply complex numbers?*

To add or subtract complex numbers, add or subtract their real parts and add or subtract their nonreal parts. You can use the distributive property to add or subtract the nonreal parts. For instance, $3i + 2i = (3 + 2)i = 5i$.

MCC9–12.N.CN.2

1 EXAMPLE Adding and Subtracting Complex Numbers

A $(8 + 3i) + (7 + 5i) = (\square + \square) + (\square + \square)$ Collect real parts, and collect nonreal parts.

$= \square + \square$ Add real parts, and add nonreal parts.

B $(8 + 3i) - (7 + 3i) = (\square - \square) + (\square - \square)$ Collect real parts, and collect nonreal parts.

$= \square + (\square)$ Subtract real parts, and subtract nonreal parts.

$= \square - \square$ Write the number without parentheses.

REFLECT

1a. Give an example of two complex numbers whose sum is a real number. Find the sum of the numbers.

____

1b. Give an example of two complex numbers whose sum is an imaginary number. Find the sum of the numbers.

____

1c. What properties (extended to nonreal numbers) allow you to collect the real parts and nonreal parts of two complex numbers being added?

____

To multiply two complex numbers, use the distributive property to multiply each part of one of the numbers with each part of the other. Then simplify by using the fact that $i^2 = -1$ and combining like terms. The general multiplication pattern is shown below.

$$(a + bi)(c + di) = ac + adi + bci + bdi^2$$

MCC9-12.N.CN.2

2 EXAMPLE Multiplying Complex Numbers

A $(5 + 3i)(9 + 8i) = 45 + \square + \square + 24i^2$ Multiply.

$= 45 + \square + \square + 24(-1)$ $i^2 = -1$

$= 21 + \square$ Combine like terms.

B $(8 + 12i)(4 - 2i) = \square - 16i + 48i + (\square)$ Multiply.

$= \square + 32i + \square$ $i^2 = -1$

$= \square + 32i$ Combine like terms.

REFLECT

2a. How is multiplying $(5 + 3i)(9 + 8i)$ like multiplying $(5 + 3x)(9 + 8x)$? How is it different?

____

____

____

____

2b. What is the product of $a + bi$ and $a - bi$ where a and b are real numbers, $a \neq 0$, and $b \neq 0$? Classify the product as a real number or a nonreal number. Explain.

____

____

____

2c. What is the square of $a + bi$ where a and b are real numbers, $a \neq 0$, and $b \neq 0$? Classify the square as a real number, an imaginary number, or neither.

____

____

____

2d. If you multiply a nonzero real number and a nonreal number, is the product real or nonreal? Explain.

____

____

Let $z = a + bi$ be a complex number. The **conjugate** of z is $\bar{z} = a - bi$. For example, the conjugate of $4 + 7i$ is $4 - 7i$.

MCC9–12.N.CN.3(+)

3 EXPLORE Finding Products of Complex Numbers and Their Conjugates

A Complete the table.

z	$\bar{z}$	$z \cdot \bar{z}$
$4 + 7i$		
$5 - 2i$		
$3i$		
-6		

B Generalize the results: If $z = a + bi$, then in terms of a and b,
$z \cdot \bar{z} = (a + bi)(a - bi) = a^2 - (bi)^2 = a^2 - b^2i^2 = a^2 - b^2(-1) =$ __________.

REFLECT

3a. Is the product $z \cdot \bar{z}$ a real number or an nonreal number? Explain.

____

____

MCC9–12.N.CN.3(+)

4 ENGAGE Understanding the Absolute Value of a Complex Number

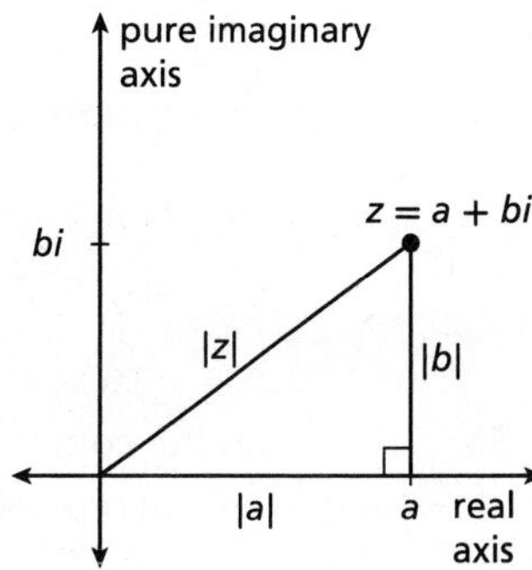

A complex number can be represented by a point in the *complex plane* having real numbers on its horizontal axis and pure imaginary numbers on its vertical axis. If $z = a + bi$, then the coordinates of the point representing z are (a, bi).

For any complex number not on one of the axes, you can draw a right triangle as shown. The lengths of the legs are the real numbers $|a|$ and $|b|$. The **absolute value** of the complex number z, written as $|z|$, is the length of the hypotenuse. The absolute value of z is also called the *modulus* of z.

For the special case of $z = a + 0i$, the graph of z is a point on the real axis, and $|z| = |a|$. Similarly, for the special case of $z = 0 + bi$, the graph of z is a point on the pure imaginary axis, and $|z| = |b|$.

REFLECT

4a. If $z = a + bi$, use the Pythagorean Theorem to express $|z|$ in terms of a and b. (Note that $|a|^2$ can simply be written as a^2 and $|b|^2$ as b^2.)

____

____

4b. Show that the formula you wrote for Question 2a also applies to the special cases $z = a + 0i$ and $z = 0 + bi$. Use the fact that if x is a real number, then $\sqrt{x^2} = |x|$.

____

____

____

4c. How is $|z|$ related to $z \cdot \overline{z}$?

____

Comparing Absolute Values The set of real numbers is an *ordered set* because for any two real numbers a and b, you can determine whether $a < b$, $a = b$, or $a > b$. The set of complex numbers, however, is not an ordered set. For instance, you cannot compare the numbers $3 + 4i$ and $1 - 5i$ other than to say that they are not equal.

Because the absolute value of a complex number is a real number, you *can* compare the absolute values of two complex numbers. Just as you can interpret the absolute value of a real number geometrically as the number's distance from 0 on the real number line, you can interpret the absolute value of a complex number geometrically as the number's distance from the origin of the complex plane.

MCC9–12.N.CN.3(+)

5 EXAMPLE Comparing Absolute Values of Complex Numbers

Compare the absolute values of $3 + 4i$ and $1 - 5i$.

A Find each absolute value.

$|3 + 4i| = \sqrt{\square^2 + \square^2} = \sqrt{\square} = \square$

$|1 - 5i| = \sqrt{\square^2 + (\square)^2} = \sqrt{\square}$

B Compare the absolute values.

$|3 + 4i|$ $\square$ $|1 - 5i|$ because ______________.

REFLECT

5a. What does the comparison of $|3 + 4i|$ and $|1 - 5i|$ tell you about the points in the complex plane representing $3 + 4i$ and $1 - 5i$?

____

____

____

5b. In part A you found that $|3 + 4i| = 5$. Give three other complex numbers that have an absolute value of 5.

____

____

Dividing Complex Numbers To divide two complex numbers $a + bi$ and $c + di$, express the quotient as $\frac{a + bi}{c + di}$. You can write this fraction as a single complex number by multiplying the numerator and denominator by the conjugate of the denominator and then simplifying.

MCC9–12.N.CN.3(+)

6 EXAMPLE Dividing Complex Numbers

Divide.

A $\frac{6 - 4i}{2i} = \frac{6 - 4i}{2i} \cdot \frac{\square}{\square}$

Multiply the numerator and denominator by the conjugate of the denominator.

$= \frac{\square}{\square}$

Multiply the numerators, and multiply the denominators. Simplify each product.

$= \square$

Write in the form $a + bi$.

B $\frac{10 - 15i}{2 + i} = \frac{10 - 15i}{2 + i} \cdot \frac{\square}{\square}$

Multiply the numerator and denominator by the conjugate of the denominator.

$= \frac{\square}{\square}$

Multiply the numerators, and multiply the denominators. Simplify each product.

$= \square$

Write in the form $a + bi$.

C $\frac{1}{2 + 2i} = \frac{1}{2 + 2i} \cdot \frac{\square}{\square}$

Multiply the numerator and denominator by the conjugate of the denominator.

$= \frac{\square}{\square}$

Multiply the numerators, and multiply the denominators. Simplify each product.

$= \square$

Write in the form $a + bi$.

REFLECT

6a. How can you use multiplication to check the quotient that you obtain when you divide one complex number by another? Illustrate this procedure using the quotient from part A.

____

____

6b. Find the absolute values of the dividend, the divisor, and the quotient in part A. How are these absolute values related?

____

____

____

PRACTICE

Add or subtract.

1. $10i - 2i$ ____________

2. $9i - (13 + 7i)$ ____________

3. $(9 - 8i) - (6 - 4i)$ ____________

4. $(3 + 15i) - (-5 + i)$ ____________

Multiply.

5. $-2(1 - 3i)$ ____________

6. $5i(-5 + 2i)$ ____________

7. $(4 - 8i)(5 - 6i)$ ____________

8. $(5 + 4i)(3 + 9i)$ ____________

9. $(1 + 2i)^2$ ____________

10. $(2 - i)^2$ ____________

11. Find the values i^1, i^2, i^3, and i^4. Use these to find the product $i^{18} \cdot i^{23}$ two ways: (1) by simplifying each power before multiplying, and (2) by using the product of powers property and then simplifying.

____

____

Find the absolute value of each complex number.

12. $4 + 3i$ ____________

13. $5i$ ____________

14. $-3 - 2i$ ____________

Compare the absolute values of each pair of complex numbers.

15. $1 + 2i, 2 - i$ ____________

16. $7 - 2i, 6 + 4i$ ____________

Divide.

17. $\frac{-3 - 2i}{i}$ ____________

18. $\frac{8 - 12i}{5 + 3i}$ ____________

19. $\frac{5 + 2i}{3 + 6i}$ ____________

20. For a complex number z, compare $|z|$ and $|\bar{z}|$. Explain the relationship two ways: using algebra and using a geometric interpretation.

____

____

____

____

21. For a real number a, $|a| = |-a|$. Show that this property also applies to a complex number and its opposite.

____

____

Name________________ Class__________ Date__________

Additional Practice

Graph each complex number.

1. -6
2. $4i$
3. $6 + 7i$
4. $-8 - 5i$
5. $-3i$

Imaginary axis

Real axis

Find each absolute value.

6. $|4 + 2i|$ ________

7. $|5 - i|$ ________

8. $|-3i|$ ________

Add or subtract. Write the result in the form *a* + *bi*.

9. $(-1 + 2i) + (6 - 9i)$ ________

10. $(3 - 3i) - (4 + 7i)$ ________

11. $(-5 + 2i) + (-2 + 8i)$ ________

Multiply. Write the result in the form *a* + *bi*.

12. $3i(2 - 3i)$ ________

13. $(4 + 5i)(2 + i)$ ________

14. $(-1 + 6i)(3 - 2i)$ ________

Simplify.

15. $\dfrac{2 + 4i}{3i}$ ________

16. $\dfrac{3 + 2i}{4 + i}$ ________

17. $2i^{11}$ ________

Solve.

18. In electronics, the total resistance to the flow of electricity in a circuit is called the impedance, Z. Impedance is represented by a complex number. The total impedance in a series circuit is the sum of individual impedances. The impedance in one part of a circuit is $Z_1 = 3 + 4i$. In another part of a circuit, the impedance is $Z_1 = 5 - 2i$. What is the total impedance of the circuit?

____

Problem Solving

Hannah and Aoki are designing fractals. Aoki recalls that many fractals are based on the Julia Set, whose formula is $Z_{n+1} = (Z_n)^2 + c$, where c is a constant. Hannah suggests they make their own fractal pattern using this formula, where $c = 1$ and $Z_1 = 1 + 2i$.

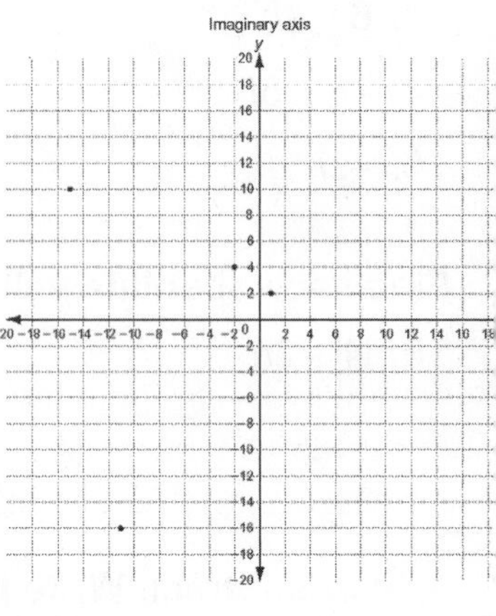

1. Complete the table to show values of n and Z_n.

n	$Z_{n+1} = (Z_n)^2 + c$	Z_n
0	$Z_1 = 1 + 2i$	$Z_1 = 1 + 2i$
1	$Z_2 = (1 + 2i)^2 + 1$	$Z_2 =$
2	$Z_3 = (\_\_\_\_\_\_\_\_\_\_)^2 + 1$	$Z_3 =$
3	$Z_4 = (\_\_\_\_\_\_\_\_\_\_)^2 + 1$	$Z_4 =$

2. Four points are shown on the complex plane. Which point is not part of the fractal pattern they have created? Explain.

Choose the letter for the best answer.

3. Aoki creates a second pattern by changing the value of c to 3. What happens to Z_n as n increases?
   - A The imaginary part is always twice the real part.
   - B The real and imaginary parts become equal.
   - C The real part becomes zero.
   - D The imaginary part becomes zero.

4. Hannah changes the formula to $Z_{n+1} = \frac{1}{(Z_n)^2} + c$. Leaving $c = 1$ and $Z_1 = 1 + 2i$, what is the value of Z_2?
   - A $0.48 - 0.16i$
   - B $0.88 - 0.16i$
   - C $1.2 - 0.4i$
   - D $2.2 - 0.4i$

5. Aoki takes Hannah's new formula, leaves $c = 1$, and sets $Z_1 = \frac{1}{1+2i}$. What is the value of Z_3?
   - A $Z_3 = -11 - 16i$
   - B $Z_3 = 2 + 2i$
   - C $Z_3 = 0.48 - 0.16i$
   - D $Z_3 = 147.4 + i$

6. Hannah reverts to $Z_{n+1} = (Z_n)^2 + c$. She sets $Z_1 = i$ and $c = i$. Which statement is NOT true?
   - A Z_n flip-flops between $(-1 + i)$ and $(-i)$.
   - B The coefficient of i never reaches 2.
   - C The imaginary part becomes zero.
   - D On a graph $Z_1 - Z_3$ create a triangle.

Name_______________ Class_______________ Date_______________

UNIT 4

Performance Tasks

GPS COMMON CORE

MCC9-12.N.CN.1
MCC9-12.N.CN.2
MCC9-12.N.CN.3(+)

★ **1.** Give an argument that a complex number, $a + bi$, multiplied by its conjugate, always results in a real number.

 **2.** Simplify $\frac{-2 + 2i}{5 + 3i}$.

3. Write an expression that is equivalent to $(3 - 2i)^2$.

4. Petra must determine for what positive values of y the expression $\sqrt[51]{y^{17}}$ is greater than 8. Explain how she can find the values, then simplify the problem by rewriting the radical using a rational exponent.

Name ______________________ Class ______________ Date __________

SELECTED RESPONSE

1. What is the definition of a complex number?

A. A number of the form $a + bi$ where a and b are real

B. A number of the form $a + bi$ where $a = 0$ and b is real

C. A number of the form $a + bi$ where a is real and $b = 0$

D. A number of the form $a + bi$ where $a = 0$, b is real, and $b \neq 0$

2. What is the simplified form of the product $(-4 + 2i)(3 - 9i)$?

F. $6 - 42i$ **H.** $6 + 42i$

G. $-30 - 42i$ **J.** $-6 + 42i$

3. What is the conjugate of $2 - 3i$?

A. $-2 - 3i$ **C.** $3 + 2i$

B. $2 + 3i$ **D.** $3 - 2i$

4. What is the simplified form of the quotient $\frac{1 - 4i}{-2 + i}$?

F. $-2 + \frac{7}{3}i$ **H.** $\frac{2}{3} + 3i$

G. $-\frac{6}{5} + \frac{7}{5}i$ **J.** $\frac{2}{5} + \frac{9}{5}i$

5. What is $|-1 - i|$?

A. $1 + i$ **C.** $\sqrt{2}$

B. 1 **D.** 0

6. Solve the equation $2x^2 + 18 = 0$.

F. $x = 3 \pm i$ **H.** $x = \pm 3i$

G. $x = \pm 3$ **J.** $x = \pm 3 + i$

7. Find the zeros of the function $f(x) = x^2 + 6x + 18$.

A. $x = 3i$ or $-3i$ **C.** $x = -3 + 3i$

B. $x = -3 + 3i$ or $-3 - 3i$ **D.** $x = -6 + 3i$ or $-6 - 3i$

8. Find the complex conjugate of $3i + 4$.

F. $-4 - 3i$ **H.** $4 + 3i$

G. $-4 + 3i$ **J.** $4 - 3i$

CONSTRUCTED RESPONSE

9. Graph the complex number $4 + 2i$.

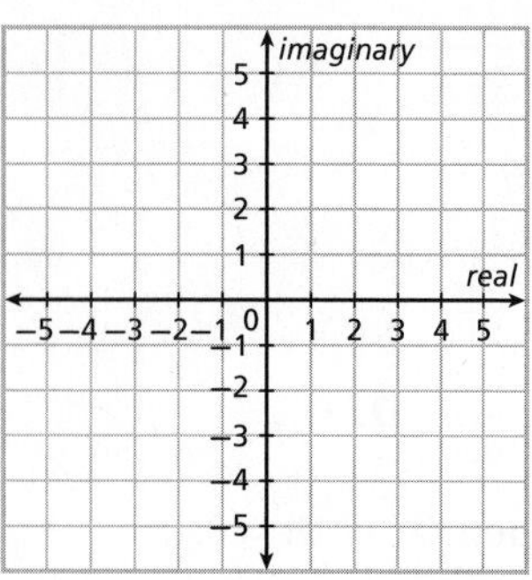

10. Graph the complex number $-5 + i$.

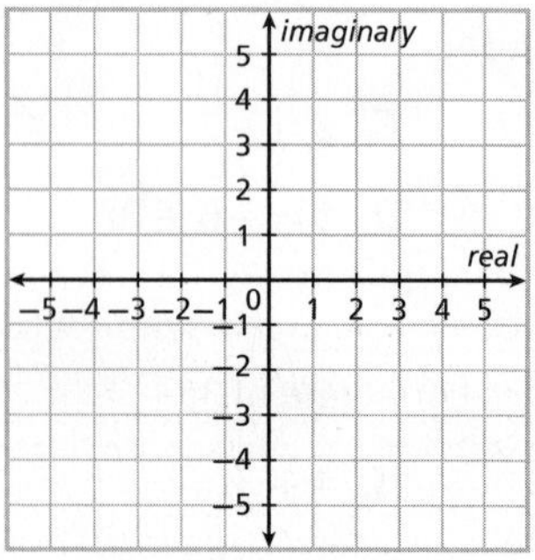

11. Find $(-3 + 6i) + (-4 - 2i)$ by graphing on the complex plane.

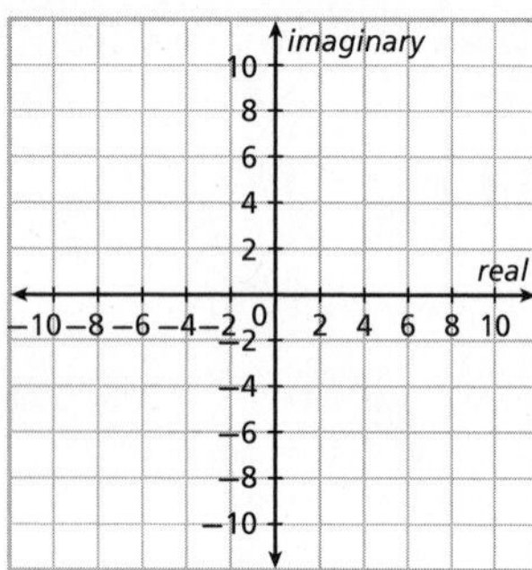

12. Consider the equation $x^2 - 4x + 5 = 0$.

a. Without solving the equation, tell whether it has real or imaginary solutions. Explain how you know.

b. What are the solutions of the equation?

c. Evaluate $x^2 - 4x + 5$ for each solution. Show your results each time you perform an operation (squaring, multiplying, subtracting, and adding). What can you conclude?

Quadratic Functions

GPS COMMON CORE

Unpacking the Standards

Understanding the standards and the vocabulary terms in the standards will help you know exactly what you are expected to learn in this unit.

GPS COMMON CORE **MCC9-12.A.SSE.2**

Use the structure of an expression to identify ways to rewrite it.

Key Vocabulary

expression *(expresión)* A mathematical phrase that contains operations, numbers, and/or variables.

UNIT 5

What It Means For You

You will learn to *factor* expressions, which means you will rewrite them as a product of two or more expressions. Being able to recognize patterns will help you decide which method to use.

EXAMPLE **Factor $x^2 + 7x + 6$**

The algebra tiles below show that $x^2 + 7x + 6 = (x + 1)(x + 6)$.

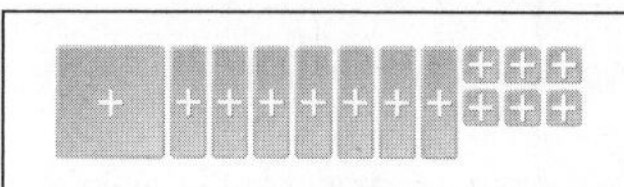

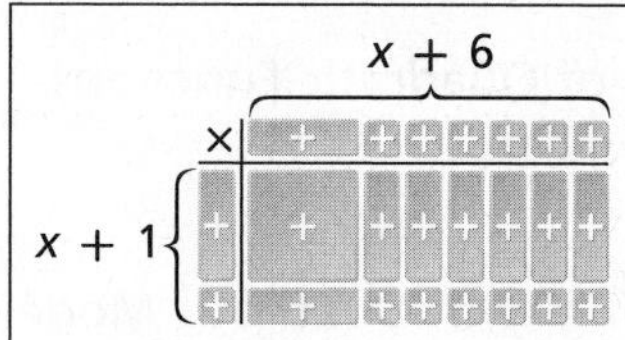

EXAMPLE **Factor $6x^2 - 11x + 3$**

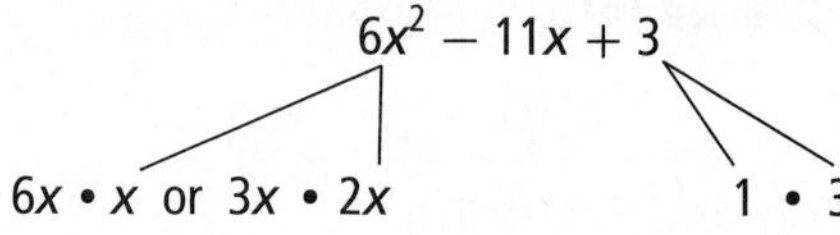

Guess and check: $(6x - 1)(x - 3) = 6x^2 - 18x - x + 3$

$= 6x^2 - 19x + 3$ ✗

Guess and check: $(3x - 1)(2x - 3) = 6x^2 - 9x - 2x + 3$

$= 6x^2 - 11x + 3$ ✓

EXAMPLE **Factor $x^2 - 49$**

Use the difference of two squares pattern:

$$a^2 - b^2 = (a + b)(a - b)$$

$$x^2 - 49 = (x + 7)(x - 7)$$

MCC9-12.F.IF.7a

Graph … quadratic functions and show intercepts, maxima, and minima.

Key Vocabulary

quadratic function *(función cuadrática)* A function that can be written in the form $f(x) = ax^2 + bx + c$, where a, b, and c are real numbers and $a \neq 0$, or in the form $f(x) = a(x - h)^2 + k$, where a, h, and k are real numbers and $a \neq 0$.

***x*-intercept** *(intersección con el eje x)* The *x*-coordinate(s) of the point(s) where a graph intersects the *x*-axis.

***y*-intercept** *(intersección con el eje y)* The *y*-coordinate(s) of the point(s) where a graph intersects the *y*-axis.

maximum/minimum value of a function *(máximo/mínimo de una función)* The *y*-value of the highest/lowest point on the graph of the function.

What It Means For You

The graph of a quadratic function has key features that are helpful when interpreting a real-world quadratic model: the intercepts and the maximum or minimum value.

EXAMPLE Graph of $y = x^2 + 2x - 3$

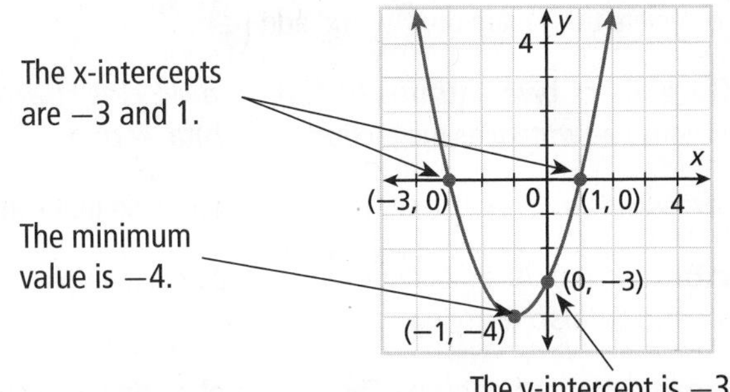

GPS COMMON CORE

MCC9-12.F.BF.3

Identify the effect on the graph of replacing $f(x)$ by $f(x) + k$, $k\,f(x)$, $f(kx)$, and $f(x + k)$ for specific values of k (both positive and negative); …

Key Vocabulary

function notation *(notación de función)* If x is the independent variable and y is the dependent variable, then the function notation for y is $f(x)$, read "f of x," where f names the function.

What It Means For You

You can change a function by adding or multiplying by a constant. The result will be a new function that is a transformation of the original function.

EXAMPLE Compression and Stretch/Reflection of $f(x)$

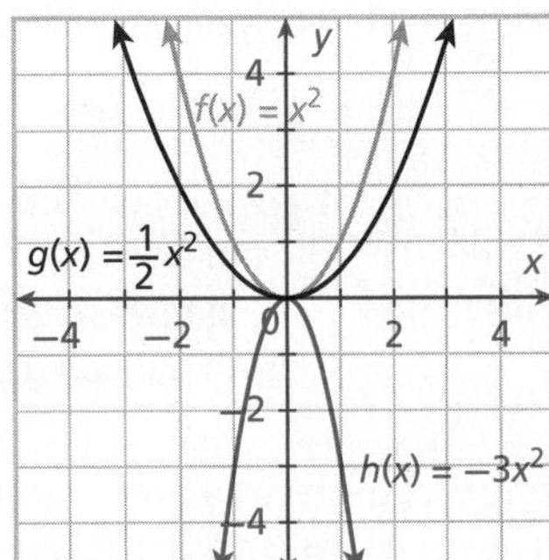

UNIT 5

UNIT 5

Key Vocabulary

binomial *(binomio)* A polynomial with two terms.

completing the square *(completar el cuadrado)* A process used to form a perfect-square trinomial. To complete the square of $x^2 + bx$, add $\left(\frac{b}{2}\right)^2$.

difference of two squares *(diferencia de dos cuadrados)* A polynomial of the form $a^2 - b^2$, which may be written as the product $(a + b)(a - b)$.

expression *(expresión)* A mathematical phrase that contains operations, numbers, and/or variables.

factor *(factor)* A number or expression that is multiplied by another number or expression to get a product. *See also* factoring.

factoring *(factorización)* The process of writing a number or algebraic expression as a product.

monomial *(monomio)* A number or a product of numbers and variables with whole-number exponents, or a polynomial with one term.

perfect-square trinomial *(trinomio cuadrado perfecto)* A trinomial whose factored form is the square of a binomial. A perfect-square trinomial has the form $a^2 - 2ab + b^2 = (a - b)^2$ or $a^2 + 2ab + b^2 = (a + b)^2$.

polynomial *(polinomio)* A monomial or a sum or difference of monomials.

quadratic equation *(ecuación cuadrática)* An equation that can be written in the form $ax^2 + bx + c = 0$, where a, b, and c are real numbers and $a \neq 0$.

Quadratic Formula *(fórmula cuadrática)* The formula $x = \frac{-b \pm \sqrt{b^2 - 4ac}}{2a}$ which gives solutions, or roots, of equations in the form $ax^2 + bx + c = 0$, where $a \neq 0$.

quadratic function *(función cuadrática)* A function that can be written in the form $f(x) = ax^2 + bx + c = 0$, where a, b, and c are real numbers and $a \neq 0$, or in the form $f(x) = a(x - h)^2 + k$, where a, h, and k are real numbers and $a \neq 0$.

trinomial *(trinomio)* A polynomial with three terms.

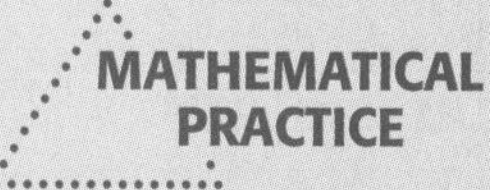

The Common Core Standards for Mathematical Practice describe varieties of expertise that mathematics educators at all levels should seek to develop in their students. Opportunities to develop these practices are integrated throughout this program.

1. **Make sense of problems and persevere in solving them.**
2. **Reason abstractly and quantitatively.**
3. **Construct viable arguments and critique the reasoning of others.**
4. **Model with mathematics.**
5. **Use appropriate tools strategically.**
6. **Attend to precision.**
7. **Look for and make use of structure.**
8. **Look for and express regularity in repeated reasoning**

Name ____________________ Class ____________ Date ________

14-1

Factoring $x^2 + bx + c$

Going Deeper

Essential question: *How can you factor $x^2 + bx + c$?*

Video Tutor

MCC9-12.A.SSE.2

1 ENGAGE Factoring Trinomials

You know how to multiply binomials: for example, $(x + 3)(x - 5) = x^2 - 2x - 15$. In this lesson, you will learn how to reverse this process and factor trinomials.

There are several important things you should remember from multiplying binomials.

- Using FOIL, the constant term in the trinomial is a result of multiplying the *last* terms in the two binomials.
- Using FOIL, the x-term results from adding the products of the *outside* terms and *inside* terms.

You can factor $x^2 + 10x + 21$ by working FOIL backward. Both signs in the trinomial are plus signs, so you know both binomials are of the form x *plus something*. Therefore, you can set up the factoring as shown below.

$$x^2 + 10x + 21 = (x + \boxed{?})(x + \boxed{?})$$

To find the constant terms in the binomials, use the information above and follow the steps below.

1) The constant term in the trinomial, 21, is the product of the last terms in the two binomials. Factor 21 into pairs. The factor pairs are shown in the table at the right.
2) The correct factor pair is the one whose sum is the coefficient of x in the trinomial.
3) Complete the binomial expression with the appropriate numbers.

$$x^2 + 10x + 21 = \left(x + \quad\right)\left(x + \quad\right)$$

Factors of 21	Sum of Factors
1 and 21	22
3 and 7	10 ✓

REFLECT

1a. You want to factor $x^2 - 6x + 8$. What factoring pattern would you set up to begin the process? Explain.

____

____

1b. You want to factor $x^2 - 2x - 15$. What factoring pattern would you set up to begin the process? Explain. Would this pattern also work for $x^2 + 2x - 15$? Explain.

1c. Use factoring patterns to factor $x^2 + 8x + 16$ and $x^2 - 6x + 9$. What do you notice about the factored forms? What special type of trinomials are $x^2 + 8x + 16$ and $x^2 - 6x + 9$?

MCC9–12.A.SSE.2

2 EXAMPLE Factoring Trinomials

A **Factor $x^2 + 3x - 10$.**

The constant is negative, so you know one binomial will have a subtraction sign.

$$x^2 + 3x - 10 = (x + \boxed{?})(x - \boxed{?})$$

Complete the table at the right. Note that you are finding the factors of −10, not 10. Since the coefficient of x is positive, the factor with the greater absolute value will be positive (and the other factor will be negative).

Factors of −10	Sum of Factors
−1 and 10	

$$x^2 + 3x - 10 = (x + \quad)(x - \quad)$$

B **Factor $x^2 - 8x - 48$.**

The constant is negative, so you know one binomial will have a subtraction sign.

$$x^2 - 8x - 48 = (x + \boxed{?})(x - \boxed{?})$$

Complete the table at the right. Since the coefficient of x is negative, the factor with the greater absolute value will be negative (and the other factor will be positive).

Factors of −48	Sum of Factors
1 and −48	
2 and	

$$x^2 - 8x - 48 = (x + \quad)(x - \quad)$$

REFLECT

2a. Complete the table below. Assume that *b*, *c*, *p*, and *q* are positive numbers.

Trinomial	Form of Binomial Factors
$x^2 + bx + c$	$(x \;\square\; p)(x \;\square\; q)$
$x^2 - bx + c$	$(x \;\square\; p)(x \;\square\; q)$
$x^2 - bx - c$ or $x^2 + bx - c$	$(x \;\square\; p)(x \;\square\; q)$

For the last row in the table, explain how to determine which factor contains a + sign and which factor contains a − sign.

____

____

____

PRACTICE

Complete the factorization of the polynomial.

1. $t^2 + 6t + 5 = (t + 5)(t + \square)$

2. $z^2 - 121 = (z + 11)(z \;\square\; \square)$

3. $d^2 + 5d - 24 = (d + \square)(d - \square)$

4. $x^4 - 4 = (x^2 + \square)(\square - 2)$

Factor the polynomial.

5. $y^2 + 3y - 4$

____

6. $x^2 - 2x + 1$

____

7. $p^2 - 2p - 24$

____

8. $g^2 - 100$

____

9. $z^2 - 7z + 12$

____

10. $q^2 + 25q + 100$

____

11. $m^2 + 8m + 16$

____

12. $n^2 - 10n - 24$

____

13. $x^2 + 25x$

____

14. $y^2 - 13y - 30$

____

Factor the polynomial.

15. $z^2 - 9$

16. $p^2 + 3p - 54$

17. $x^2 + 11x - 42$

18. $g^2 - 14g - 51$

19. $n^2 - 81$

20. $y^2 - 25y$

21. $x^2 + 11x + 30$

22. $x^2 - x - 20$

23. $x^2 + 6x - 7$

24. $x^2 + 2x + 1$

Name ____________________ Class ____________ Date ________ 14-1

Additional Practice

Factor each trinomial.

1. $x^2 + 7x + 10$ ____________
2. $x^2 + 9x + 8$ ____________
3. $x^2 + 13x + 36$ ____________
4. $x^2 + 9x + 14$ ____________
5. $x^2 + 7x + 12$ ____________
6. $x^2 + 9x + 18$ ____________
7. $x^2 - 9x + 18$ ____________
8. $x^2 - 5x + 4$ ____________
9. $x^2 - 9x + 20$ ____________
10. $x^2 - 12x + 20$ ____________
11. $x^2 - 11x + 18$ ____________
12. $x^2 - 12x + 32$ ____________
13. $x^2 + 7x - 18$ ____________
14. $x^2 + 10x - 24$ ____________
15. $x^2 + 2x - 3$ ____________
16. $x^2 + 2x - 15$ ____________
17. $x^2 + 5x - 6$ ____________
18. $x^2 + 5x - 24$ ____________
19. $x^2 - 5x - 6$ ____________
20. $x^2 - 2x - 35$ ____________
21. $x^2 - 7x - 30$ ____________
22. $x^2 - x - 56$ ____________
23. $x^2 - 2x - 8$ ____________
24. $x^2 - x - 20$ ____________
25. Factor $n^2 + 5n - 24$. Show that the original polynomial and the factored form describe the same sequence of numbers for $n = 0, 1, 2, 3,$ and 4.

____

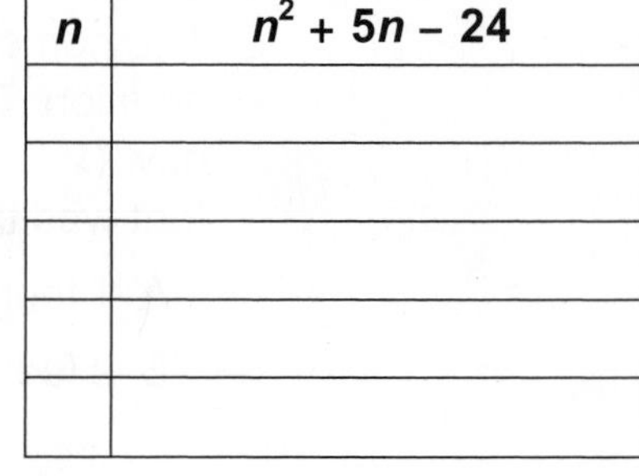

n	$n^2 + 5n - 24$

n	

Problem Solving

Write the correct answer.

1. A plot of land is rectangular and has an area of $x^2 - 5x - 24$ m^2. The length is $x + 3$ m. Find the width of the plot.

____

____

2. An antique Persian carpet has an area of $(x^2 + x - 20)$ ft^2 and a length of $(x + 5)$ feet. The rug is displayed on a wall in a museum. The wall has a width of $(x + 2)$ feet and an area of $(x^2 + 17x + 30)$ ft^2. Write expressions for the length and width of both the rug and wall. Then find the dimensions of the rug and the wall if $x = 20$ feet.

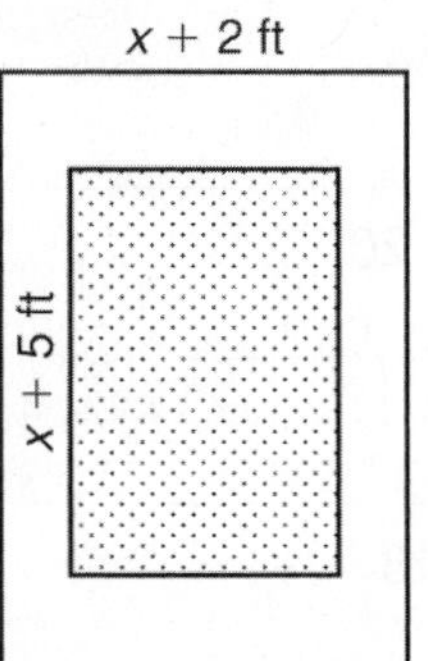

____

____

3. The area of a poster board is $x^2 + 3x - 10$ inches. The width is $x - 2$ inches.

   a. Write an expression for the length of the poster board.

   ____

   b. Find the dimensions of the poster board when $x = 14$.

   ____

   c. Write a polynomial for the area of the poster board if one inch is removed from each side.

   ____

The figure shows the plans for an addition on the back of a house. Use the figure to answer questions 4–6. Select the best answer.

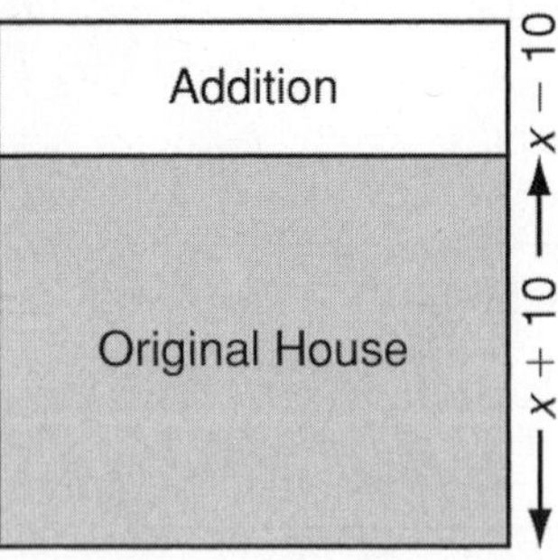

4. The area of the addition is $(x^2 + 10x - 200)$ ft^2. What is its length?

   A $(x - 20)$ feet

   B $(x - 2)$ feet

   C $(x + 2)$ feet

   D $(x + 20)$ feet

5. What is the area of the original house?

   F $(x^2 - 10x - 200)$ ft^2

   G $(x^2 + 8x - 20)$ ft^2

   H $(x^2 + 12x + 200)$ ft^2

   J $(x^2 + 30x + 200)$ ft^2

6. The homeowners decide to extend the addition. The area with the addition is now $(x^2 + 12x - 160)$ ft^2. By how many feet was the addition extended?

   A 1 foot

   B 2 feet

   C 3 feet

   D 4 feet

Name ______________________ Class ______________ Date __________

14-2

Video Tutor

Factoring $ax^2 + bx + c$

Going Deeper

Essential question: *How can you factor $ax^2 + bx + c$?*

You have learned how to factor $ax^2 + bx + c$ when $a = 1$ by identifying the correct pair of factors of c whose sum is b. But what if the coefficient of x^2 is not 1?

First, review binomial multiplication. The product $(2x + 5)(3x + 2)$ is found by using FOIL.

$$(2x + 5)(3x + 2) = \underset{\mathbf{F}}{6x^2} + \underset{\mathbf{O}}{4x} + \underset{\mathbf{I}}{15x} + \underset{\mathbf{L}}{10} = 6x^2 + 19x + 10$$

F The product of the coefficients of the **first** terms is a.

O, **I** } The sum of the coefficients of the **outer** and **inner** products is b.

L The product of the **last** terms is c.

To factor $ax^2 + bx + c$, you need to reverse this process. Start by listing the possible factor pairs of a and c. Then use trial and error to find a sum of b for the outer and inner products.

MCC9–12.A.SSE.2

1 EXAMPLE Factoring $ax^2 + bx + c$

Factor $5n^2 + 11n + 2$.

A First list the possible factor pairs for both a and c. All of the signs of the terms are positive, so the factors of a and c must all be positive.

The only factor pair for a is _____, _____. The only factor pair for c is _____, _____.

B Choose the arrangement of the factor pairs that makes $b = 11$. Check your result by multiplying.

$$5n^2 + 11n + 2 = (\square n + \square)(\square n + \square)$$

REFLECT

1a. What other arrangement of factor pairs is possible for a and c? What is the resulting product, and how is it different from $5n^2 + 11n + 2$?

____

1b. If a is positive, b is negative, and c is positive, what are the signs of the factors of a and c that you are looking for?

____

1c. If a is positive, b is negative, and c is negative, what are the signs of the factors of a and c that you are looking for?

____

If a and c have a lot of factors, there are many possible arrangements. One way to quickly check each arrangement is shown below, using the trinomial $5n^2 + 11n + 2$. List the factor pairs of a and c vertically, then multiply diagonally, and add.

Factors of a	Factors of c		Inner and Outer products
1	2	=	10
5	1	=	1
			11 ← Sum

If the sum is correct, the factors are read across: $(1n + 2)$ and $(5n + 1)$.

MCC9-12.A.SSE.2

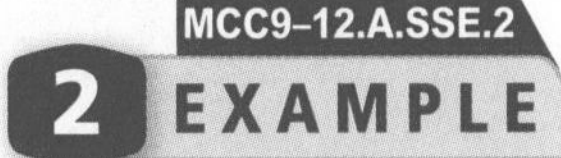

2 EXAMPLE Factoring $ax^2 + bx + c$

Factor $6x^2 - 13x - 8$.

A First list the possible factor pairs for both a and c. Because c is negative, one of the factors of c must be positive, and the other must be negative.

The factor pairs for a are: ____, ____ and ____, ____.

The factor pairs for c are: ____, ____; ____, ____; ____, ____; ____, ____.

B Choose the arrangement of factor pairs that makes $b = -13$. Each factor pair of a can be arranged in two ways with each factor pair of c, so there are 16 possible arrangements. Three are shown below.

1	1 =	____	2	2 =	____	2	1 =	____
6	−8 =	____	3	−4 =	____	3	−8 =	____
		____			____			____

$$6x^2 - 13x - 8 = (\quad x + \quad)(\quad x - \quad)$$

REFLECT

2a. If you know the factors of $6x^2 - 13x - 8$, how could you easily factor $6x^2 + 13x - 8$?

____

2b. What fact about the sign of the sum can you use so that you need to test at most half of the possible arrangements?

____

____

PRACTICE

Factor.

1. $2x^2 + 15x + 7$

2. $7z^2 - 30z + 27$

3. $8x^2 - 10x - 3$

4. $30d^2 + 7d - 15$

5. $10g^2 + 23g + 12$

6. $5y^2 - 2y - 7$

7. $2n^2 - 11n + 15$

8. $6a^2 + 7a - 10$

9. $12x^2 - x$

10. $9z^2 - 25$

11. $36h^2 - 12h + 1$

12. $3n^2 - 20n + 12$

13. $9x^2 + 12x + 4$

14. $4y^2 + y - 18$

To factor a polynomial of the form $ax^2 + bx + c$ where a is negative, you first factor out −1 from all the terms. Factor each polynomial.

15. $-6x^2 + 11x + 10$

16. $-3x^2 + 5x + 22$

17. $-4x^2 - 12x + 7$

18. $-8x^2 + 6x + 9$

19. $-6x^2 + 7x + 5$

20. $-6x^2 - 25x + 9$

21. $-5x^2 + 17x - 6$

22. $-15x^2 + 2x + 8$

23. A dolphin bounces a ball off its nose at an initial upward velocity of 6 m/s to a trainer lying on a 1-meter high platform. The polynomial $-5t^2 + 6t - 1$ models the ball's height (in meters) above the platform.

a. Factor the polynomial.

____

b. When $t = 0$, what is the value of the polynomial? What does this value mean in the context of the situation?

____

____

c. For what values on t does the polynomial equal 0?

$t =$ __________ or $t =$ __________

d. Explain the two values for t in the context of the situation.

____

____

____

Name ________________ Class ________________ Date ________________

14-2

Additional Practice

Factor each trinomial.

1. $2x^2 + 13x + 15$ ________________
2. $3x^2 + 10x + 8$ ________________
3. $4x^2 + 24x + 27$ ________________
4. $5x^2 + 21x + 4$ ________________
5. $4x^2 + 11x + 7$ ________________
6. $6x^2 - 23x + 20$ ________________
7. $7x^2 - 59x + 24$ ________________
8. $3x^2 - 14x + 15$ ________________
9. $8x^2 - 73x + 9$ ________________
10. $2x^2 + 11x - 13$ ________________
11. $3x^2 + 2x - 16$ ________________
12. $2x^2 + 17x - 30$ ________________
13. $8x^2 + 29x - 12$ ________________
14. $11x^2 + 25x - 24$ ________________
15. $9x^2 - 3x - 2$ ________________
16. $12x^2 - 7x - 12$ ________________
17. $9x^2 - 49x - 30$ ________________
18. $6x^2 + x - 40$ ________________
19. $-12x^2 - 35x - 18$ ________________
20. $-20x^2 + 29x - 6$ ________________
21. $-2x^2 + 5x + 42$ ________________
22. The area of a rectangle is $20x^2 - 27x - 8$. The length is $4x + 1$. What is the width? ________________

Problem Solving

Write the correct answer.

1. A rectangular painting has an area of $(2x^2 + 8x + 6)$ cm^2. Its length is $(2x + 2)$ cm. Find the width of the painting.

2. A ball is kicked straight up into the air. The height of the ball in feet is given by the expression $-16t^2 + 12t + 4$, where t is time in seconds. Factor the expression. Then find the height of the ball after 1 second.

3. Instructors led an exercise class from a raised rectangular platform at the front of the room. The width of the platform was $(3x - 1)$ feet and the area was $(9x^2 + 6x - 3)$ ft^2. Find the length of this platform. After the exercise studio is remodeled, the area of the platform will be $(9x^2 + 12x + 3)$ ft^2. By how many feet will the width of the platform change?

4. A clothing store has a rectangular clearance section with a length that is twice the width w. During a sale, the section is expanded to an area of $(2w^2 + 19w + 35)$ ft^2. Find the amount of the increase in the length and width of the clearance section.

Select the best answer.

5. The area of a soccer field is $(24x^2 + 100x + 100)$ m^2. The width of the field is $(4x + 10)$ m. What is the length?

   A $(3x + 10)$ m C $(6x + 10)$ m

   B $(6x + 1)$ m D $(8x + 2)$ m

6. A square parking lot has an area of $(4x^2 + 20x + 25)$ ft^2. What is the length of one side of the parking lot?

   F $(2x + 5)$ ft H $(5x + 4)$ ft

   G $(2x + 10)$ ft J $(5x + 2)$ ft

7. For a certain college, the number of applications received after x recruiting seminars is modeled by the polynomial $3x^2 + 490x + 6000$. What is this expression in factored form?

   A $(3x - 40)(x - 150)$

   B $(3x + 40)(x + 150)$

   C $(3x - 30)(x - 200)$

   D $(3x - 30)(x + 200)$

8. Jin needs to fence in his rectangular backyard. The fence will have one long section away from, but parallel to, the length of his house and two shorter sides connecting that section to the house. The length of Jin's house is $(3x + 4)$ yd and the area of his backyard is $(9x^2 + 15x + 4)$ yd^2. How many yards of fencing will Jin need?

   F $(6x + 2)$ yd H $(9x + 9)$ yd

   G $(9x + 6)$ yd J $(12x + 10)$ yd

Name ________________ Class ________________ Date ________

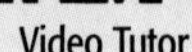

14-3

Factoring Special Products

Connection: Area

Essential question: *How can you represent factoring special products geometrically?*

Recall that perfect square trinomials and the difference of two squares are special polynomials.

1 EXPLORE

Representing the Factoring of a Perfect Square Trinomial

Use area models to factor $a^2 + 2ab + b^2$.

A Finish labeling this model of $a^2 + 2ab + b^2$. Use a and b.

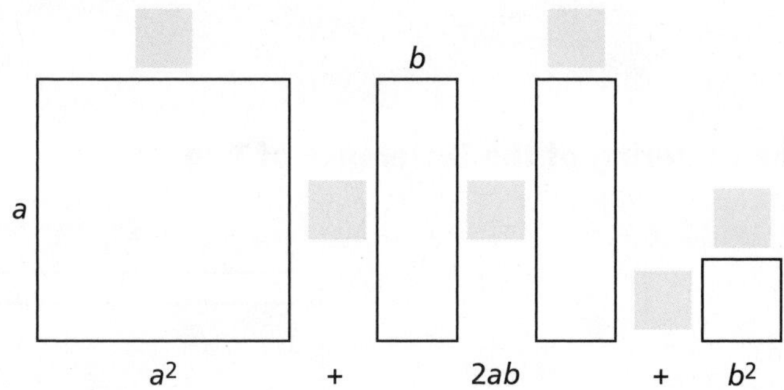

B Draw dashed lines inside the square below to show how the squares and rectangles from Step A could be placed together to form a larger square. Label the dimension of each part of the length and width of the larger square.

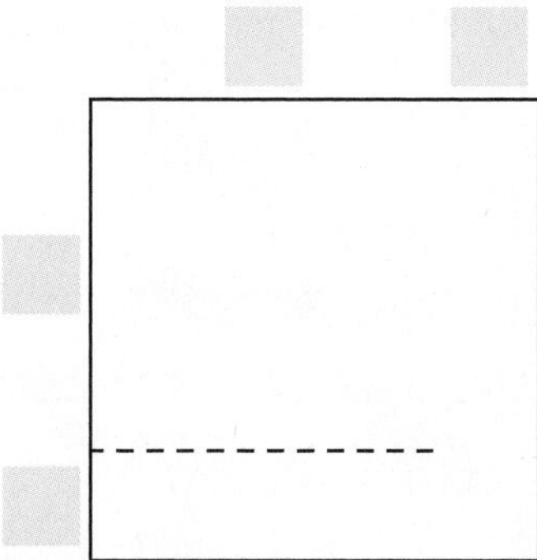

C Use the dimensions of the square in Step B to write the area of the square in Step B.

$A = ($__________$)($__________$)$

D Because the square has the same area as the model of the polynomial, the factorization of $a^2 + 2ab + b^2$ is ________________.

REFLECT

1a. How does the model at the right show that the factorization of $a^2 - 2ab + b^2$ is $(a - b)(a - b)$?

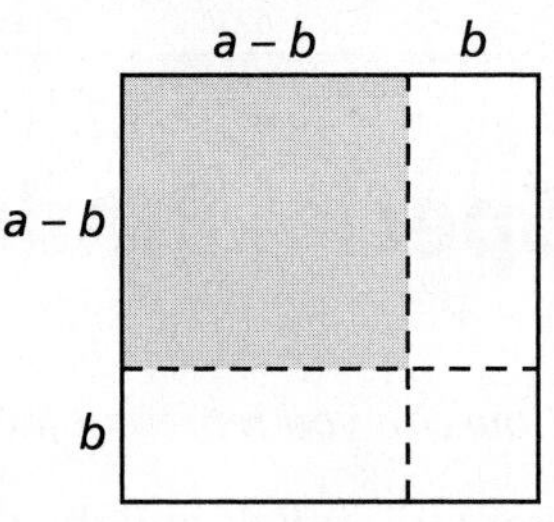

MCC9–12.A.SSE.2

2 EXPLORE Representing the Factoring of the Difference of Two Squares

Use area models to factor $a^2 - b^2$.

A Finish labeling this model of $a^2 - b^2$. Use a and b.

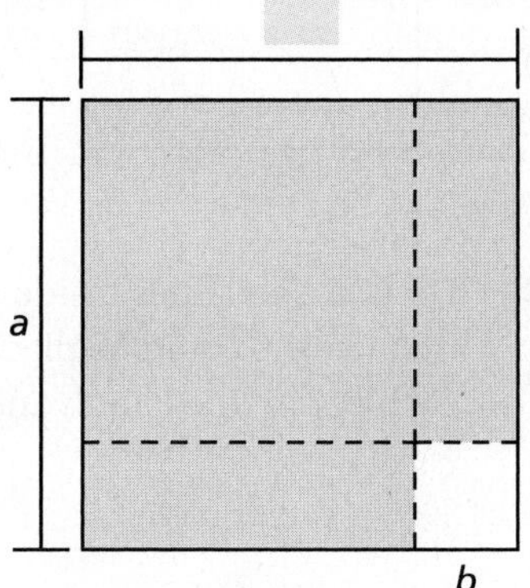

B Make a drawing that shows the shaded parts of the model arranged to show a rectangle. Label each segment of the length and width of the rectangle.

C What is the length of the longer side of the rectangle? Explain.

____

What is the length of the shorter side of the rectangle? ________

What is the area of the rectangle? (________)(________)

D Because the rectangle has the same area as the model of the polynomial, the factorization of $a^2 - b^2$ is ______________.

Name ______________________ Class ______________ Date ____________

14-3

Additional Practice

Determine whether each trinomial is a perfect square. If so, factor it. If not, explain why.

1. $x^2 + 6x + 9$

____

2. $4x^2 + 20x + 25$

____

3. $36x^2 - 24x + 16$

____

4. $9x^2 - 12x + 4$

____

5. A rectangular fountain in the center of a shopping mall has an area of $(4x^2 + 12x + 9)$ ft^2. The dimensions of the fountain are of the form $cx + d$, where c and d are whole numbers. Find an expression for the perimeter of the fountain. Find the perimeter when $x = 2$ ft.

____

Determine whether each binomial is the difference of perfect squares. If so, factor it. If not, explain why.

6. $x^2 - 16$

____

7. $9b^4 - 200$

____

8. $1 - m^6$

____

9. $36s^2 - 4t^2$

____

10. $x^2y^2 + 196$

____

Problem Solving

Write the correct answer.

1. A rectangular fountain has an area of $(16x^2 + 8x + 1)$ ft^2. The dimensions of the rectangle have the form $ax + b$, where a and b are whole numbers. Write an expression for the perimeter of the fountain. Then find the perimeter when $x = 2$ feet.

____

____

2. A square tabletop has an area of $(9x^2 - 90x + 225)$ cm^2. The dimensions of the tabletop have the form $cx - d$, where c and d are whole numbers. Write an expression for the perimeter of the tabletop. Then find the perimeter when $x = 25$ centimeters.

____

____

3. The floor plan of a daycare center is shown.

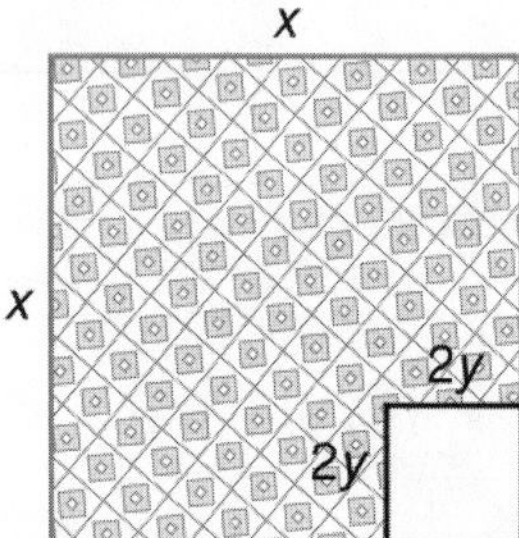

The arts and crafts area in the lower right corner is not carpeted. The rest of the center is carpeted. Write an expression, in factored form, for the area of the floor that is carpeted.

____

4. A plate with a decorative border is shown.

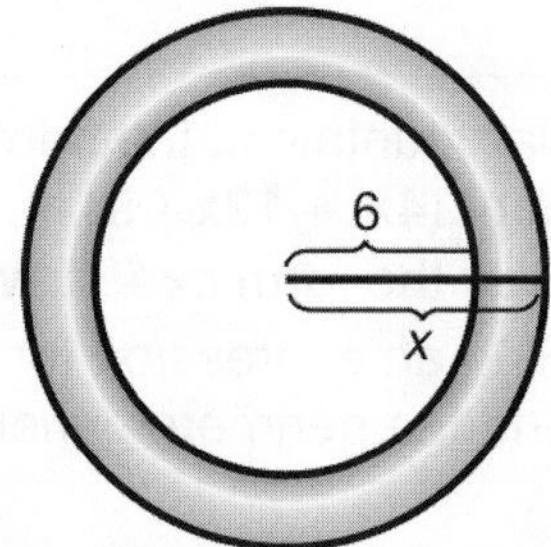

Write an expression, in factored form, for the area of the border. (*Hint:* First factor out the GCF.)

____

Nelson is making open top boxes by cutting out corners from a sheet of cardboard, folding the edges up, and then taping them together. Select the best answer.

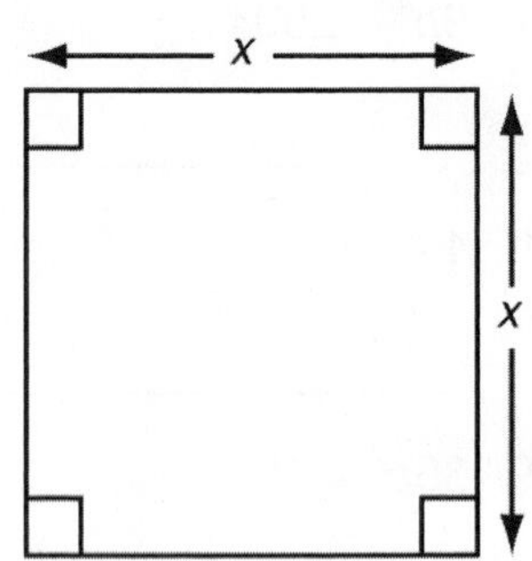

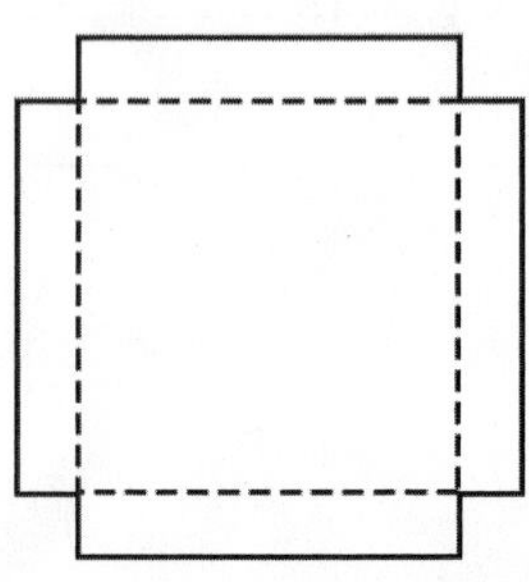

5. Nelson cut corners so that each corner was a square with side lengths of 4. What is the total area of the remaining piece of cardboard?

A $x^2 - 8x + 16$ C $x^2 - 16x + 64$

B $x^2 + 8x + 16$ D $x^2 + 16x + 64$

6. What are the dimensions of the square corners if the total remaining area is $x^2 - 4x + 4$?

F 1 by 1 H 4 by 4

G 2 by 2 J 8 by 8

Name_______________ Class_______________ Date_______________

15-1

Using Transformations to Graph Quadratic Functions

Extension: Graphing Quadratic Functions in Vertex Form

Essential question: *How can you graph the function $f(x) = a(x - h)^2 + k$?*

MCC9–12.F.BF.3

1 ENGAGE — Understanding Vertex Form

The **vertex form** of a quadratic function is $f(x) = a(x - h)^2 + k$. The vertex of the graph of a quadratic function in vertex form is (h, k).

$$f(x) = a(x - h)^2 + k$$

- a indicates a vertical stretch or shrink and/or a reflection across the x-axis.
- h indicates a horizontal translation.
- k indicates a vertical translation.

A **zero of a function** is an input value x that makes the output value $f(x)$ equal 0. You can estimate the zeros of a quadratic function by observing where the graph crosses the x-axis.

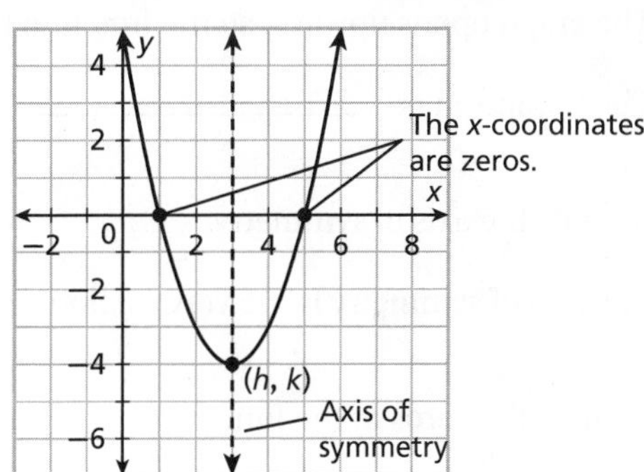

REFLECT

1a. For the function $f(x) = 2(x - 3)^2 + 1$, what are the values of a, h, and k? What do each of these values indicate about the graph of the function?

____

____

____

1b. Explain why the vertex of the graph of a quadratic function in vertex form is (h, k).

____

____

1c. If you estimate a zero of a quadratic function from a graph, how could you use algebra to check your answer?

____

____

MCC9–12.F.IF.7a

2 EXAMPLE Graphing $f(x) = a(x - h)^2 + k$

Graph the function $f(x) = 2(x + 1)^2 - 2$. Identify the vertex, minimum or maximum, axis of symmetry, and zeros of the function.

A Identify and graph the vertex.

$h =$

$k =$

The vertex of the graph is ________________.

B Identify the coordinates of points to the left and right of the vertex.

x	−3	−2	0	1
$f(x)$				

C Graph the points and connect them with a smooth curve.

D Identify the minimum or maximum.

The graph opens upward, so the function has a ________________.

The minimum is ________________.

E Identify the axis of symmetry.

The axis of symmetry is the vertical line $x =$ ________________.

F Identify the zeros of the function.

The graph appears to cross the x-axis at the points ________________ and ________________, so the zeros of the function appear to be ____________ and ____________.

REFLECT

2a. How could you use the value of a to determine whether the function $f(x) = 2(x + 1)^2 - 2$ has a minimum or a maximum?

____

____

2b. How could you use the table in part B to confirm that you correctly identified the zeros of the function from its graph?

____

____

MCC9–12.F.BF.3

3 EXAMPLE Writing Equations in Vertex Form

Write the vertex form of the quadratic function whose graph is shown.

A Use the vertex of the graph to identify the values of h and k.

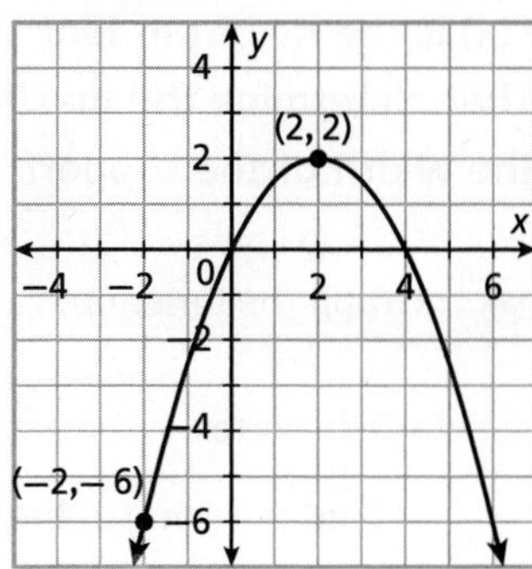

The vertex of the graph is ________.

$h =$ ☐

$k =$ ☐

Substitute the values of h and k into the vertex form:

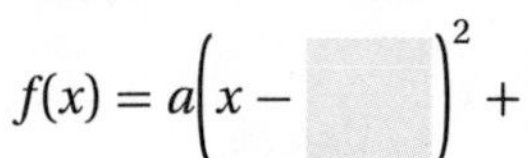

$f(x) = a\left(x - \square\right)^2 + \square$

B Use the point $(-2, -6)$ to identify the value of a.

$f(x) = a(x-2)^2 + 2$	Vertex form
$\square = a\left(\square - 2\right)^2 + 2$	Substitute −6 for $f(x)$ and −2 for x.
$-6 = a\left(\square\right) + 2$	Simplify.
$\square = a(16)$	Subtract 2 from both sides.
$\square = a$	Divide both sides by 16.

Substitute the value of a into the vertex form:

$f(x) = \square\,(x-2)^2 + 2$

So, the vertex form of the function shown in the graph is

________________________.

REFLECT

3a. How can you tell by looking at the graph that the value of a is negative?

____

____

____

3b. Describe the graph of the given function as a transformation of the parent quadratic function.

____

____

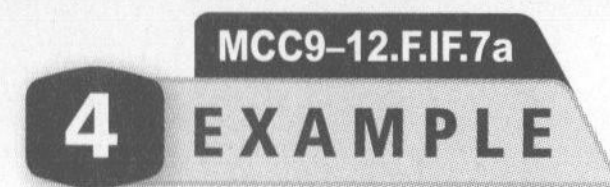

4 EXAMPLE Modeling Quadratic Functions in Vertex Form

The shape of a bridge support can be modeled by $f(x) = -\frac{1}{600}(x - 300)^2 + 150$, where x is the horizontal distance in feet from the left end of the bridge and $f(x)$ is the height in feet above the bridge deck. Sketch a graph of the support. Then determine the maximum height of the support above the bridge deck and the width of the support at the level of the bridge deck.

A Graph the function.

- The vertex of the graph is ________.
- Find the point at the left end of the support ($x = 0$).

  Since $f(0) =$ ______, the point ______ represents the left end.

- Use symmetry to find the point at the right end of the support.

  Since the left end is 300 feet to the left of the vertex, the right end will be 300 feet to the right of the vertex.

  The point ______ represents the right end.

- Find two other points on the support.

  $(120, \ \ )$ and $(480, \ \ )$

- Sketch the graph.

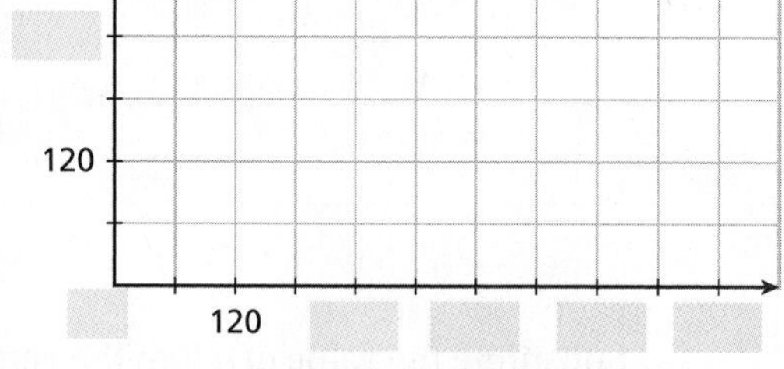

B Determine the maximum height of the support.

The maximum of the function is ______.

So, the maximum height of the bridge support is ______ feet.

C Determine the width of the bridge support at the level of the bridge deck.

The distance from the left end to the right end is ______ feet.

So, the width is ______ feet at the level of the bridge deck.

REFLECT

4a. Explain how you know that the y-coordinate of the right end of the support is 0.

______

______

4b. What does the vertex represent in this situation?

______

______

PRACTICE

Graph each quadratic function. Identify the vertex, minimum or maximum, axis of symmetry, and zeros of the function.

1. $f(x) = -2x^2 + 8$

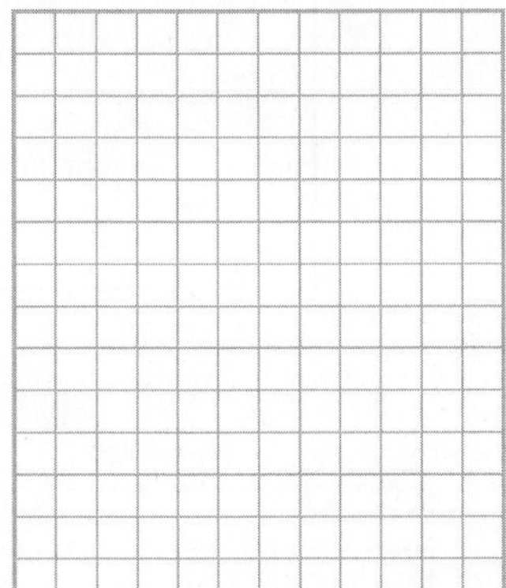

2. $f(x) = (x - 2)^2 - 4$

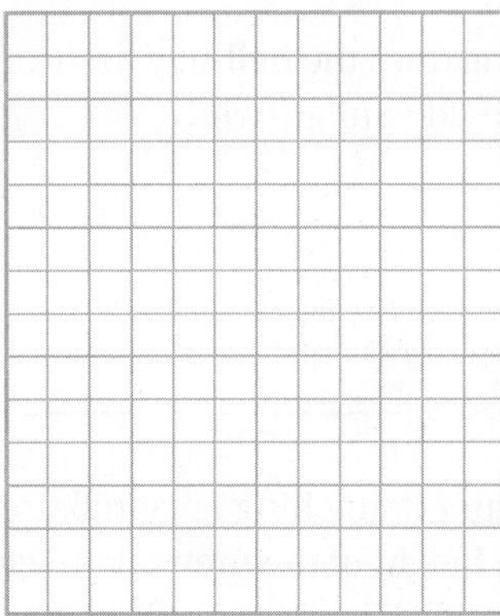

3. $f(x) = -(x + 4)^2 + 1$

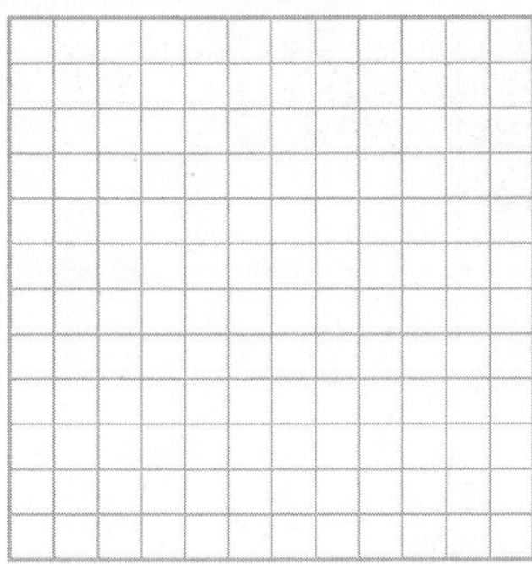

4. $f(x) = \frac{1}{3}(x - 2)^2 - 3$

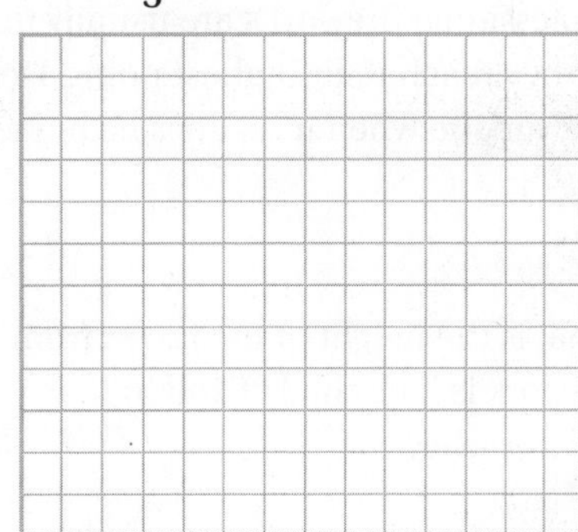

Write the vertex form of each quadratic function.

5.

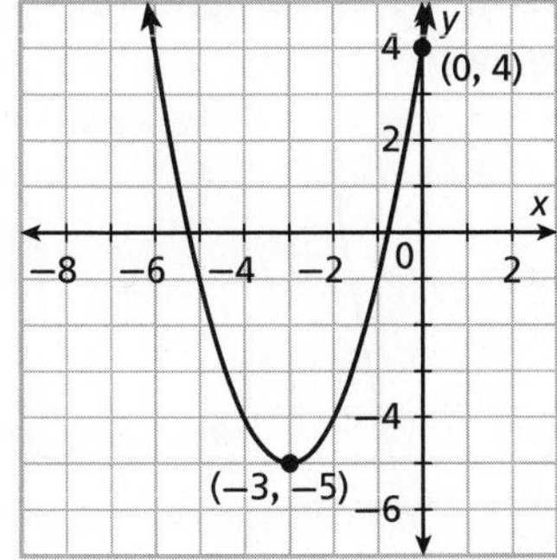

6.

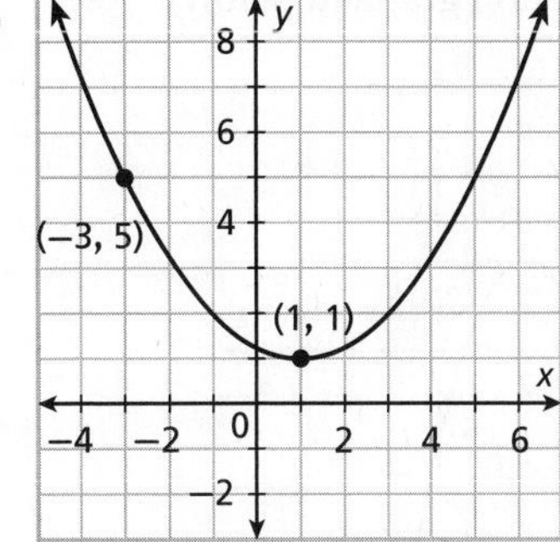

7. The function $f(x) = -16(x - 1)^2 + 16$ gives the height in feet of a football x seconds after it is kicked from ground level.

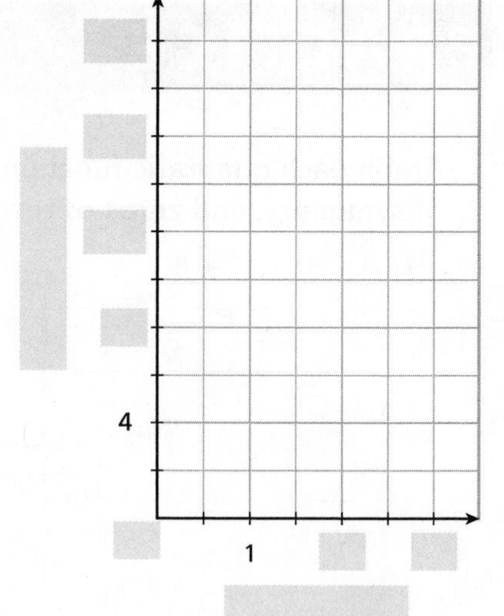

a. Sketch a graph of the function.

b. What is the maximum height that the ball reaches?

____

c. How long does the ball stay in the air? Explain how you determined your answer.

____

____

____

8. A technician is launching an aerial firework from a tower. The height of the firework in feet is modeled by the function $f(x) = -16(x - 3)^2 + 256$ where x is the time in seconds after the firework is launched.

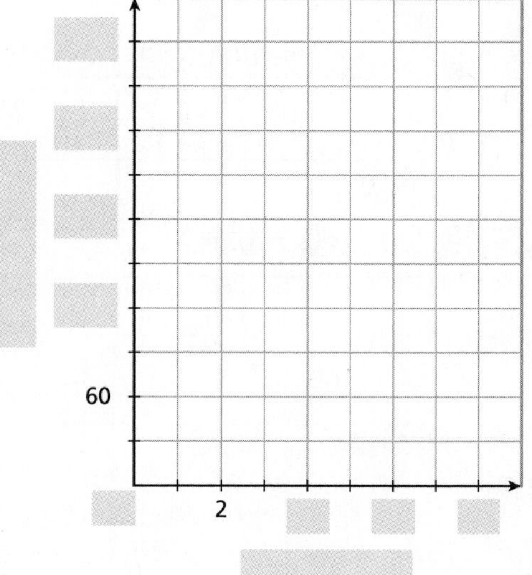

a. Sketch a graph of the function.

b. Professional fireworks are usually timed to explode as they reach their highest point. How high will the firework be when it reaches its highest point?

____

c. What is the height of the tower from which the firework is launched? Explain how you determined your answer.

____

____

9. Which quadratic function has a greater maximum: the function $f(x) = -(x - 5)^2 + 4$ or the function graphed below?

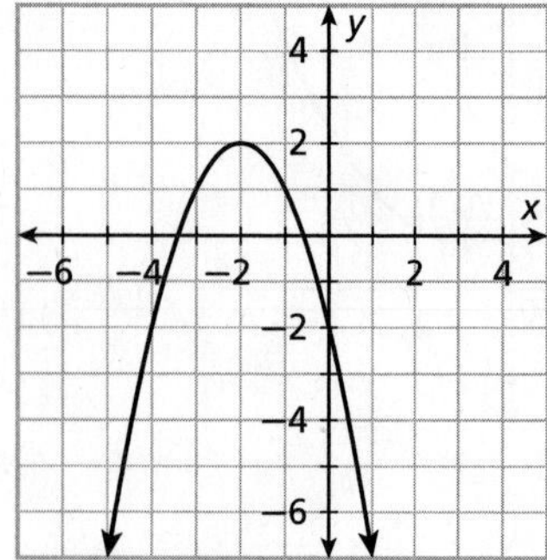

____

10. Which quadratic function has a lesser minimum: a function whose graph has a vertex at $(-5, -1)$ or the function graphed below?

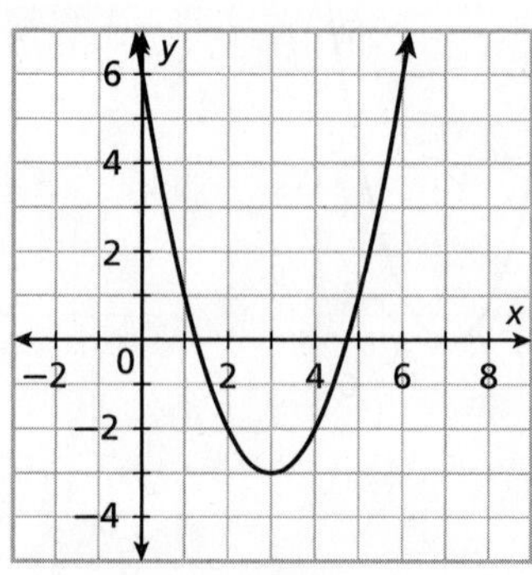

____

Name______________ Class______________ Date______________

15-1

Additional Practice

Graph the function by using a table.

1. $f(x) = x^2 + 2x - 1$

x	$f(x) = x^2 + 2x - 1$	$(x, f(x))$
−2		
−1		
0		
1		
2		

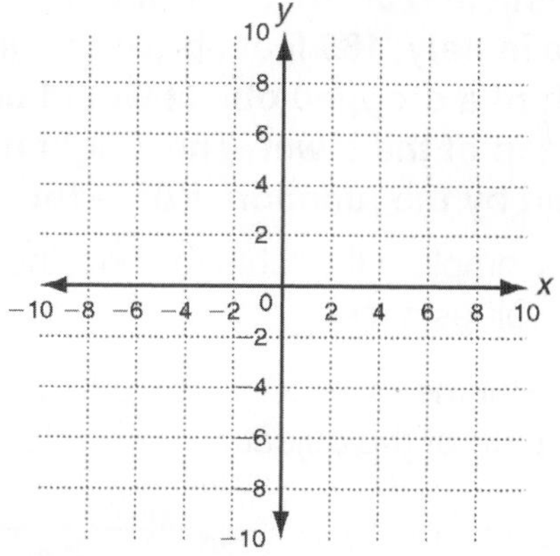

Using the graph of $f(x) = x^2$ as a guide, describe the transformations, and then graph each function. Label each function on the graph.

2. $h(x) = (x - 2)^2 + 2$

____

3. $h(x) = -(3x)^2$

____

4. $h(x) = \left(\frac{1}{2}x\right)^2$

____

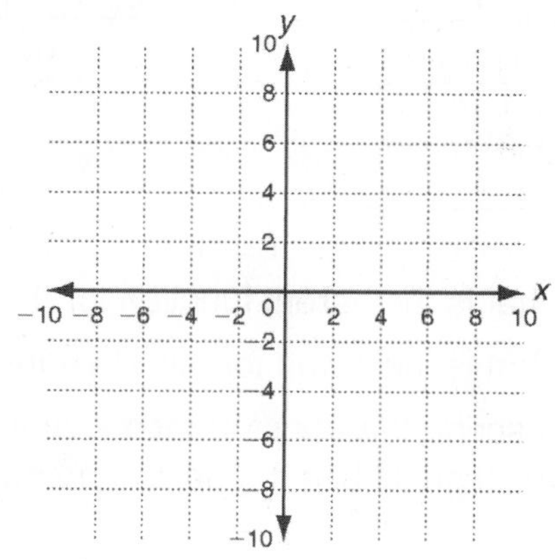

Use the description to write a quadratic function in vertex form.

5. The parent function $f(x) = x^2$ is reflected across the x-axis, horizontally stretched by a factor of 3 and translated 2 units down to create function g.

____

6. A ball dropped from the top of tower A can be modeled by the function $h(t) = -9.8t^2 + 400$, where t is the time after it is dropped and $h(t)$is its height at that time. A ball dropped from the top of tower B can be modeled by the function $h(t) = -9.8t^2 + 200$. What transformation describes this change? What does this transformation mean?

____

Problem Solving

Christa and Jelani are standing at the top of the Leaning Tower of Pisa in Italy, 185 feet above the ground. Jelani wonders what the path of a dropped object would be as it falls to the ground from the top of the tower. The height of an object after *t* seconds is given by the function, $f(t) = -16t^2 + 185$.

1. Complete the table to show the height, $f(t)$, of the object for different values of t.

2. Plot the ordered pairs from the table and draw the graph to show the path of the object.

Time (t)	$f(t) = -16t^2 + 185$	$(t, f(t))$
0	$f(0) = -16(0)^2 + 185$	
1	$f(1) = -16(1)^2 + 185$	
2		
3		
4		

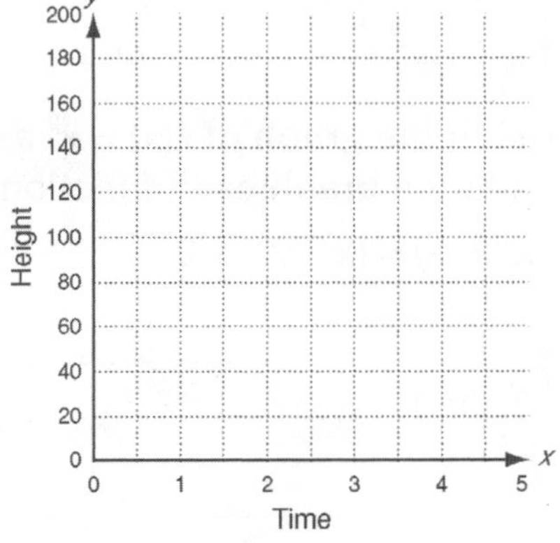

3. What is the parent function for the graph? ______________

4. What is the name for this U-shaped curve? ______________

5. Describe the transformations of the parent function into $f(t) = -16t^2 + 185$, which describes the path of an object falling from 185 feet.

____

Choose the letter for the best answer.

6. Mario dropped a wrench from the top of a sailboat mast 58 feet high. Which function describes the path of the falling wrench?

   A $f(t) = 16(t - 58)^2 - 185$

   B $f(t) = -16(t - 58)^2 + 185$

   C $f(t) = 16t^2 - 58$

   D $f(t) = -16t^2 + 58$

7. Delle wants to transform the parent function $f(t) = t^2$ into $f(t) = -4(t - 0.6)^2 + 6$. Which is NOT a step in that transformation?

   A Translation 6 units up

   B Translation 0.6 unit left

   C Reflection across the x-axis

   D Vertical stretch by a factor of 4

Name______________________ Class______________ Date__________

15-2

Video Tutor

Properties of Quadratic Functions in Standard Form

Going Deeper

Essential question: *How is the structure of a quadratic equation related to the structure of the parabola it describes?*

The standard form of a quadratic function is $f(x) = ax^2 + bx + c$, where a, b and c are constants and $a \neq 0$. The graph of a quadratic function is a parabola.

MCC9–12.F.IF.7a

1 EXPLORE Find the Axis of Symmetry and Vertex from a Graph

Find the axis of symmetry and vertex by graphing.

A Complete the table of values below. Sketch the graph of $y = x^2 - 4x + 5$.

x	$y = x^2 - 4x + 5$
0	
1	
2	
3	
4	

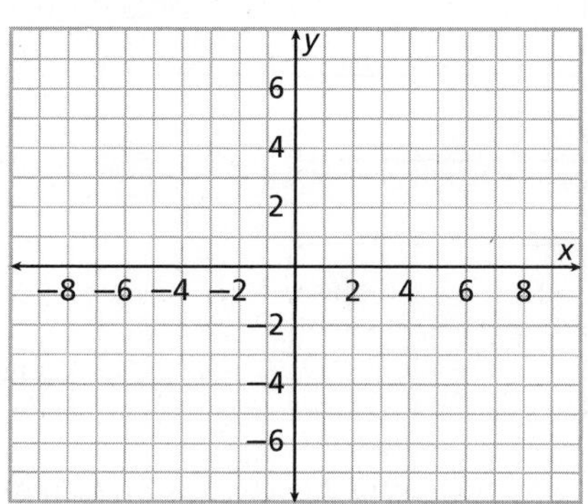

What is the axis of symmetry of the parabola? ____________

What is the vertex of the parabola? ____________

What is the y-intercept of the parabola? ____________

In which direction does the parabola open? ____________

B Complete the table of values below. Sketch the graph of $y = 2x^2 + 4x + 1$.

x	$y = 2x^2 + 4x + 1$
−3	
−2	
−1	
0	
1	

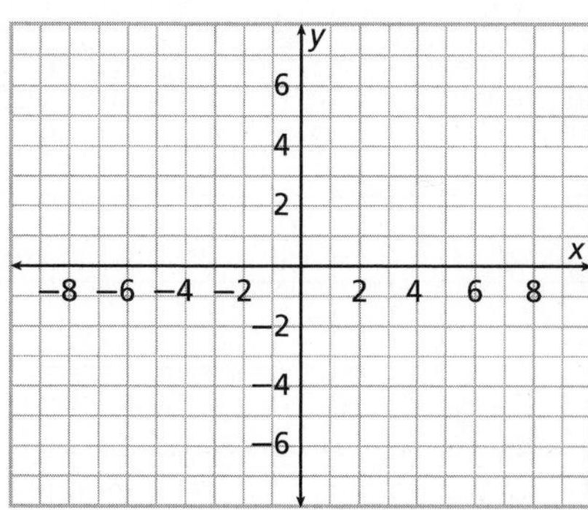

What is the axis of symmetry of the parabola? ____________

What is the vertex of the parabola? ____________

What is the y-intercept of the parabola? ____________

In which direction does the parabola open? ____________

REFLECT

1. How is the equation of the axis of symmetry related to coefficients a and b in Part A? How is the equation of the axis of symmetry related to coefficients a and b in Part C? Write a rule for the equation of the axis of symmetry based on the values of a and b.

MCC9–12.F.IF.7

2 EXAMPLE Find the Axis of Symmetry and Vertex from a Table

A Complete the table of values below.

x	$y = x^2 + x + 2$
−2	
−1	
0	
1	
2	

B Between which two x-values is the axis of symmetry located? ____________

What is the axis of symmetry of the parabola? ____________

How did you find the axis of symmetry?

How can you find the vertex of the parabola once you know the axis of symmetry?

What is the vertex of the parabola? ________________

REFLECT

2a. How might you find the axis of symmetry of a parabola if you are given a table of values?

____

____

2b. Why is the axis of symmetry halfway between two points on the parabola that have the same y-value?

____

____

PRACTICE

Complete the table of values and sketch the graph. Identify the axis of symmetry, vertex, and y-intercept of each parabola.

1. $y = x^2 + 6x - 1$

x	$y = x^2 + 6x - 1$
−5	
−4	
−3	
−2	
−1	

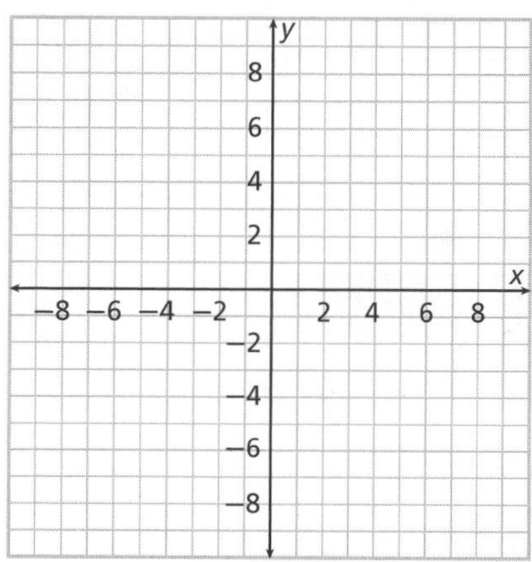

Axis of symmetry: ______________

Vertex: ______________

y-intercept: ______________

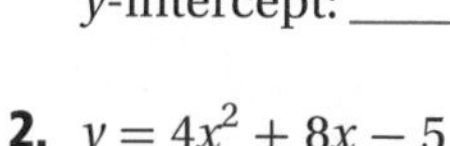

2. $y = 4x^2 + 8x - 5$

x	$y = 4x^2 + 8x - 5$
−3	
−2	
−1	
0	
1	

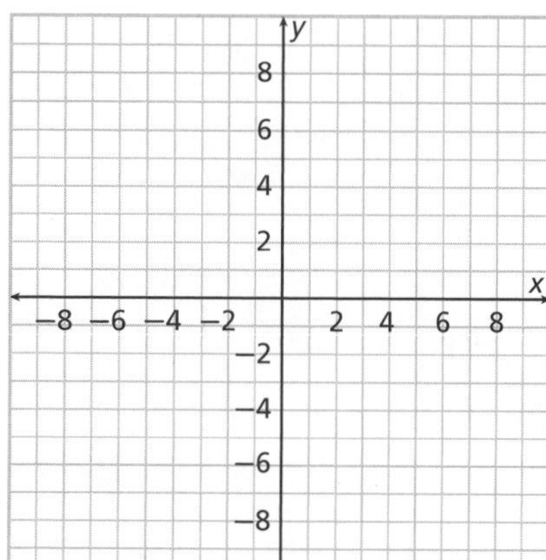

Axis of symmetry: ______________

Vertex: ______________

y-intercept: ______________

Complete the table of values. Identify the axis of symmetry, vertex, and *y*-intercept of each parabola.

3. $y = -2x^2 + 2x + 1$

x	$y = -2x^2 + 2x + 1$
−2	
−1	
0	
1	
2	

Axis of symmetry: ____________

Vertex: ____________

y-intercept: ____________

4. $y = x^2 + 3x - 2$

x	$y = x^2 + 3x - 2$
−4	
−3	
−2	
−1	
0	

Axis of symmetry: ____________

Vertex: ____________

y-intercept: ____________

5. $y = -x^2 - x - 4$

x	$y = -x^2 - x - 4$
−3	
−2	
−1	
0	
1	

Axis of symmetry: ____________

Vertex: ____________

y-intercept: ____________

Name ______________________ Class ______________ Date ____________

Additional Practice

Identify the axis of symmetry for the graph of each function.

1. $g(x) = x^2 - 4x + 2$
2. $h(x) = -8x^2 + 12x - 11$
3. $k(x) = -4(x + 3)^2 + 9$

________________ ________________ ________________

For each function, (a) determine whether the graph opens upward or downward, (b) find the axis of symmetry, (c) find the vertex, and (d) find the *y*-intercept. Then graph the function.

4. $f(x) = -x^2 + 3x + 1$
   a. Upward or downward ________________
   b. Axis of symmetry ________________
   c. Vertex ________________
   d. *y*-intercept ________________
5. $g(x) = 2x^2 + 4x - 2$
   a. Upward or downward ________________
   b. Axis of symmetry ________________
   c. Vertex ________________
   d. *y*-intercept ________________

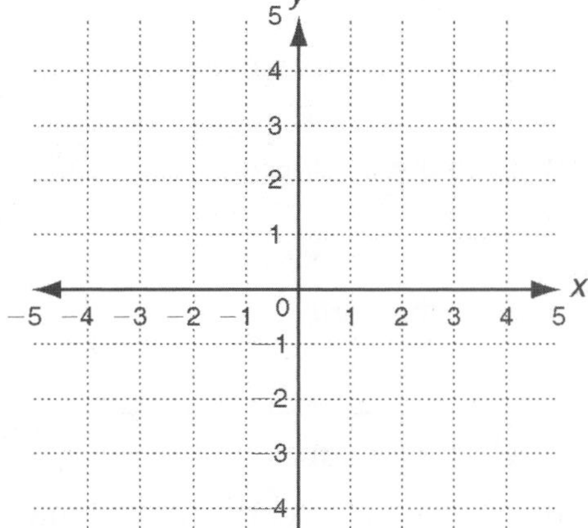

Find the minimum or maximum value of each function. Then state the domain and range of the function.

6. $g(x) = x^2 - 2x + 1$
7. $h(x) = -5x^2 + 15x - 3$

________________________ ________________________

Solve.

8. A record label uses the following function to model the sales of a new release.

$$a(t) = -90t^2 + 8100t$$

The number of albums sold is a function of time, *t*, in days. On which day were the most albums sold? What is the maximum number of albums sold on that day?

____

Problem Solving

Kim wants to buy a used car with good gas mileage. He knows that the miles per gallon, or mileage, varies according to various factors, including the speed. He finds that highway mileage for the make and model he wants can be approximated by the function $f(s) = -0.03s^2 + 2.4s - 30$, where *s* is the speed in miles per hour. He wants to graph this function to estimate possible gas mileages at various speeds.

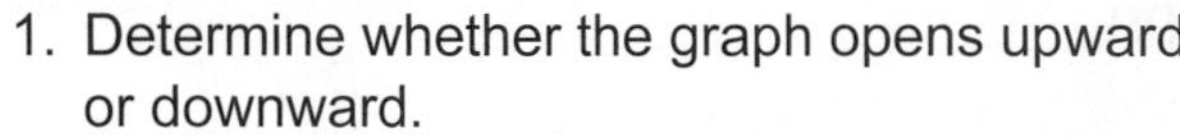

1. Determine whether the graph opens upward or downward. ________________

2. Identify the axis of symmetry for the graph of the function. ________________

3. Find the *y*-intercept.

   ____

4. Find the vertex.

   ____

5. Graph the function.

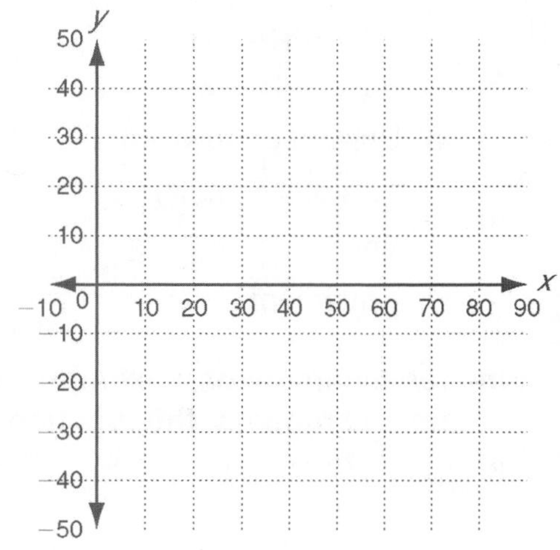

6. a. Does the curve have a maximum or a minimum value?

   ____

   b. What is the value of the *y*-coordinate at the maximum or minimum?

   ____

   c. Explain what this point means in terms of gas mileage.

   ____

A ball is hit into the air from a height of 4 feet. The function $g(t) = -16t^2 + 120t + 4$ can be used to model the height of the ball where *t* is the time in seconds after the ball is hit. Choose the letter for the best answer.

7. About how long is the ball in the air?

   A 3.5 seconds

   B 3.75 seconds

   C 7 seconds

   D 7.5 seconds

8. What is the maximum height the ball reaches?

   A 108 feet

   B 124 feet

   C 229 feet

   D 394 feet

Name ______________________ Class ______________ Date __________

15-3

Curve Fitting with Quadratic Models

Focus on Modeling

Essential question: *How can you model changes in revenue from season-ticket sales using a quadratic function?*

Video Tutor

A community theater currently sells 200 season tickets at \$50 each. In order to increase its season-ticket revenue without increasing the number of season tickets that it sells, the theater surveys its season-ticket holders to see if they would be willing to pay more. The survey finds that for every \$5 increase in the price of a season ticket, the theater would lose 10 season-ticket holders. What action, if any, should the theater take to increase revenue?

1 Create a revenue function from the survey information.

A Let n be the number of \$5 price increases in the cost of a season ticket. Write an expression for the cost of a season ticket after n price increases.

____

B Write an expression for the number of season-ticket holders after n price increases.

____

C The revenue generated from season-ticket sales is given below in words. Use this verbal model and your expressions from steps 1A and 1B to write an algebraic rule for the revenue function $R(n)$.

Revenue from season tickets	=	Number of season-ticket holders	·	Price of a season ticket

$R(n) =$ ______________________________

D As a check on your function rule, find the value of $R(0)$. Tell what this number represents and whether it agrees with the problem statement.

____

REFLECT

1a. What units are associated with the expressions that you wrote in steps 1A and 1B?

____

1b. When you multiply the units for the expressions, what units do you get for the revenue? Are they the units you expect?

____

2 Determine the domain of the revenue function.

A Because n is the number of $5 price increases in the cost of a season ticket, you might think that the domain of the revenue function $R(n)$ is the set of whole numbers. However, given that increases in price result in losses of customers, what eventually happens to the number of season-ticket holders as n increases?

____

B Determine a constraint on the values of n. That is, write and solve an inequality that represents an upper bound on the values of n.

____

C State a reasonable domain for the revenue function.

____

REFLECT

2. When the value of n reaches its upper bound, what will happen to the value of $R(n)$? Why?

____

3 Graph the revenue function.

A Complete the tables of values for the revenue function.

n	$R(n)$
0	10,000
1	
2	
3	
4	
5	
6	
7	
8	
9	
10	

n	$R(n)$
11	
12	
13	
14	
15	
16	
17	
18	
19	
20	

B Graph the revenue function. Be sure to label the axes with the quantities they represent and indicate the axis scales by showing numbers for some grid lines.

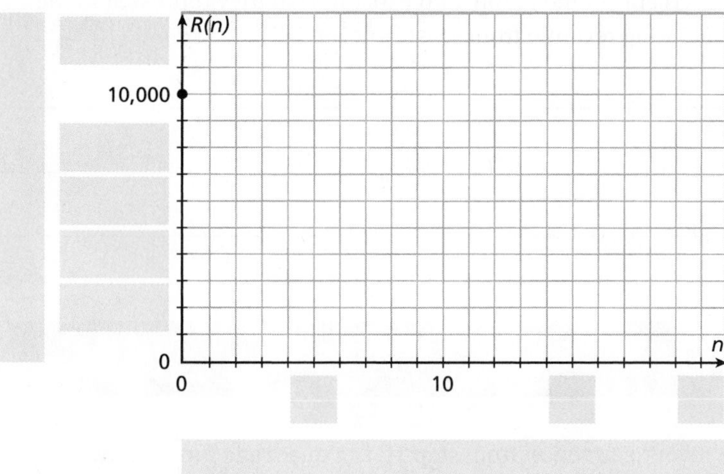

REFLECT

3. Enter the revenue function on a graphing calculator. Set the viewing window to match that of the grid above, then graph the function. Is your graph identical to the one on the graphing calculator? If not, describe and explain any differences. Which graph is correct, and why?

____

____

____

4 Analyze the revenue function.

A For what values of n does $R(n)$ increase? For what values of n does $R(n)$ decrease?

____

B At what value of n does $R(n)$ take on its maximum value? What is the maximum value?

____

C Write a brief paragraph describing what action the theater should take to maximize revenue. Include what happens to the number of season-ticket holders as well as the season-ticket price.

____

____

____

REFLECT

4. Identify the intercepts of the graph, and explain what they represent in the context of generating revenue from season-ticket sales.

EXTEND

1. Show that the revenue function from step 1C is a quadratic function by multiplying the two factors and collecting like terms to obtain a function of the form $R(n) = an^2 + bn + c$ where a, b, and c are constants.

2. A quadratic function $f(x) = ax^2 + bx + c$ has a maximum value at $x = -\frac{b}{2a}$ if $a < 0$ or a minimum value at $x = -\frac{b}{2a}$ if $a > 0$. Confirm that this property is true for the rewritten revenue function from Exercise 1.

3. Complete the square on the rewritten revenue function from Exercise 1 to obtain a function of the form $R(n) = a(n - h)^2 + k$ where a, h, and k are constants. Using this vertex form, identify the vertex of the graph of $R(n)$ and check to see whether it agrees with your answers for step 4B.

4. When graphing the revenue function in step 3B, you may have noticed that $R(0) = R(10)$, $R(1) = R(9)$, $R(2) = R(8)$, $R(3) = R(7)$, and $R(4) = R(6)$. Use the rewritten revenue function from Exercise 3 to explain those observations.

5. Using your tables of values from step 3A, calculate the rate of change in $R(n)$ for consecutive values of n. (The rate of change in $R(n)$ is given by the fraction $\frac{\text{change in } R(n)}{\text{change in } n}$, but because the values of n are consecutive whole numbers, the change in n is always 1 and the rate of change in $R(n)$ is just the change in $R(n)$.) Describe what happens to the rates of change in $R(n)$, and relate them to your answers to the questions in step 4A.

n	*R(n)*	Change in *R(n)*
0	10,000	—
1		
2		
3		
4		
5		
6		
7		
8		
9		
10		

n	*R(n)*	Change in *R(n)*
11		
12		
13		
14		
15		
16		
17		
18		
19		
20		

6. Rather than maximize season-ticket revenue, suppose the theater wants to increase the current revenue by just 8%. Using the revenue function from step 1C, write and solve a quadratic equation, and interpret the solution(s).

7. Predict what would happen to revenue if the theater lost fewer than 10 season-ticket holders for every $5 increase in the price of a ticket. Then check your prediction by creating and analyzing a model for the situation.

Name ______________________ Class ____________ Date ____________

15-3

Additional Practice

Determine whether each data set could represent a quadratic function. Explain.

1.

x	–1	0	1	2	3
y	35	22	11	2	–5

____

2.

x	–2	0	2	4	6
y	18	10	6	2	1

____

Write a quadratic equation that fits each set of points.

3. (0, –8), (2, 0), and (–3, –5)

4. (–1, –16), (2, 5), and (5, 8)

5. (–2, 6), (0, –6), and (3, –9)

6. (1, 4), (–2, 13), and (0, 3)

Solve.

7. The data table shows the energy, *E,* of a certain object in joules at a given velocity, *v,* in meters per second.

Energy (joules)	4.5	12.5	24.5	40.5
Velocity (m/s)	1.5	2.5	3.5	4.5

a. Find the quadratic relationship between the energy and velocity of the object. ____________

b. What is the energy of an object with a speed of 5 m/s? ____________

c. What is the velocity of the object if the energy is 128 joules? ____________

Problem Solving

Ellen and Kelly test Ellen's new car in an empty parking lot. They mark a braking line where Ellen applies the brakes. Kelly then measures the distance from that line to the place where Ellen stops, for speeds from 5 miles per hour to 25 miles per hour.

Brake Test					
Speed (mi/h)	5	10	15	20	25
Stopping Distance (ft)	7	17	30	46	65

1. Ellen wants to know the stopping distance at 60 miles per hour. She cannot drive the car at this speed in the parking lot, so they decide to try curve fitting, using the data they have collected.
   a. Can you use a quadratic function to represent the data in the table? Explain how you know.

   ____

   b. Use three points to write a system of equations to find a, b, and c in $f(x) = ax^2 + bx + c$. ____________

   c. Use any method to solve 3 equations with 3 variables. Find the values for a, b, and c. ____________

   d. Write the quadratic function that models the stopping distance of Ellen's car. ____________

   e. What is the stopping distance of Ellen's car at 60 miles per hour? ____________

The table shows the sizes and prices of decorative square patio tiles. Choose the letter for the best answer.

Patio Tiles Sale					
Side Length (in.)	6	9	12	15	18
Price Each ($)	1.44	3.24	5.76	9.00	12.96

2. What quadratic function models the price of the patio tiles?
   A $P(x) = 0.4x^2$
   B $P(x) = 0.04x^2$
   C $P(x) = 0.04x^2 + 0.4x$
   D $P(x) = 0.04x^2 + x + 0.4$

3. What is the second difference constant for the data in the table?
   A 1.44
   B 1.08
   C 0.72
   D 0.36

Name_________________________ Class_______________ Date___________

16-1

Solving Quadratic Equations by Graphing and Factoring

Extension: Intercept Form

Essential question: *How do you determine where the graph of a quadratic function crosses the x-axis?*

Video Tutor

PREP FOR MCC9–12.F.IF.8

1 EXPLORE Writing Different Forms of Quadratic Expressions

Write the expression in the form described.

A Rewrite $(x + 2)(x + 5)$ in standard form by multiplying.

$(x + 2)(x + 5)$	Write the original expression.
$(x + 2)x + (x + 2)\square$	Distribute $(x + 2)$.
$x(x) + x(2) + 5(x) + 5(\square)$	Distibute x and distribute 5.
$x^2 + 2x + \square + \square$	Multiply.
$x^2 + \square + 10$	Combine like terms.

So, $(x + 2)(x + 5)$ is equivalent to ____________.

B Rewrite $x^2 - 3x - 4$ in factored form by factoring.

- You can factor a quadratic trinomial of the form $x^2 + bx + c$ by looking for factors of c whose sum is b.

  In the given expression, $b =$ ______ and $c =$ ______.

  So, look for factors of ______ whose sum is ______.

- Complete the table.

  The factors needed are ______ and ______.

Factors of –4	Sum
4 and –1	3
2 and –2	
1 and	

- Rewrite the given expression as a product of binomial factors with 1 and –4 as constants.

  $(x + \square)(x - \square)$

So, $x^2 - 3x - 4$ is equivalent to ____________.

REFLECT

1a. Describe the product you get when you multiply two linear binomials of the form $(x + p)$ and $(x + q)$ where p and q are constants.

____

____

REFLECT

1b. In part B, how could you check that you factored the given expression correctly?

____

____

The **intercept form** of a quadratic function is $f(x) = a(x - p)(x - q)$. The values of p and q are the x-intercepts of the function's graph, or the zeros of the function.

You can multiply to change a quadratic function in intercept form to standard form, and you can factor to change a quadratic function in standard form to intercept form.

MCC9–12.F.IF.8a

2 EXAMPLE Graphing $f(x) = a(x - p)(x - q)$

Write each function in intercept form. Identify the x-intercepts and vertex of the function's graph. Then graph the function.

A $f(x) = x^2 - 8x + 12$

- Write the function in intercept form by factoring the trinomial.

  $f(x) = \left(x - \square\right)\left(x - \square\right)$ Factor the trinomial.

- Identify the x-intercepts.

  The x-intercepts are ________ and ________.

  So, the graph includes the points (2, 0) and $\left(\square, 0\right)$.

- Identify the vertex.

  Based on the symmetry of the parabola, the x-coordinate of the vertex must be halfway between the x-coordinates of the points (2, 0) and (6, 0).

  The x-coordinate of the vertex is $\frac{2+6}{2} = \square$.

  Substitute this value of x into the function rule to find the y-coordinate of the vertex.

  $f(4) = \left(\square - 2\right)\left(\square - 6\right)$ Substitute 4 for x.

  $f(4) = \left(\square\right)\left(\square\right)$ Simplify the factors.

  $f(4) = \square$ Multiply.

  So, the vertex is $\left(\square, \square\right)$.

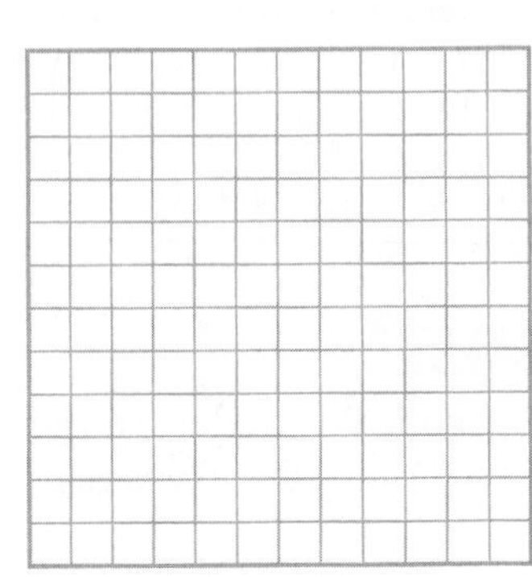

- Graph the function using the x-intercepts and the vertex.

B $f(x) = -\frac{1}{3}x^2 + \frac{4}{3}x + \frac{5}{3}$

- Write the function in intercept form by factoring the trinomial.

$f(x) = -\frac{1}{3}\left(x^2 - \square x - \square\right)$ Factor out $-\frac{1}{3}$ so that the coefficient of x^2 is 1.

$f(x) = -\frac{1}{3}\left(x - \square\right)\left(x + \square\right)$ Factor the trinomial.

- Identify the x-intercepts.

The x-intercepts are __________ and __________.

So, the graph includes the points $\left(\square, 0\right)$ and $\left(\square, 0\right)$.

- Identify the vertex.

The x-coordinate of the vertex must be halfway between the x-coordinates of the points (5, 0) and $\left(\square, 0\right)$.

The x-coordinate of the vertex is 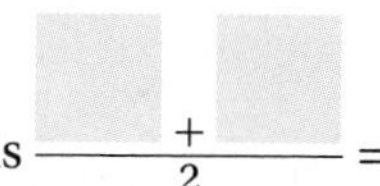 $\frac{\square + \square}{2} = \square$.

Substitute this value of x into the function rule to find the y-coordinate of the vertex.

$f(2) = -\frac{1}{3}\left(\square - 5\right)\left(\square + 1\right)$ Substitute 2 for x.

$f(2) = -\frac{1}{3}\left(\square\right)\left(\square\right)$ Simplify the factors.

$f(2) =$ 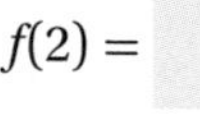 Multiply.

So, the vertex is $\left(\square, \square\right)$.

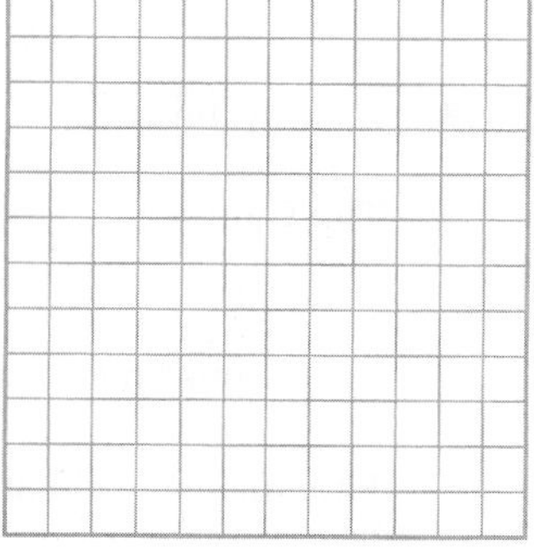

- Graph the function using the x-intercepts and the vertex.

REFLECT

2a. Describe another way that you could have found the vertex of the graph of the function in part A.

____

____

2b. In part B, how could you tell that the parabola opens downward by looking at the standard form of the quadratic function?

____

____

2c. A student claims that you can find the x-coordinate of the vertex of the graph of a quadratic function by averaging the values of p and q from the intercept form of the function. Is the student's claim correct? Explain.

____

____

____

MCC9–12.F.IF.8a

3 EXAMPLE Writing a Quadratic Model in Intercept Form

The cross-sectional shape of the archway of a bridge is modeled by the function $f(x) = -0.5x^2 + 2x$, where $f(x)$ is the height in meters of a point on the arch and x is the distance in meters from the left end of the arch's base. How wide is the arch at its base? Will a wagon that is 2 meters wide and 1.75 meters tall fit under the arch?

A Write the function in intercept form.

$f(x) = -0.5\left(x^2 - \boxed{}\,x\right)$ — Factor out -0.5 so that the coefficient of x^2 is 1.

$f(x) = -0.5(x)\left(x - \boxed{}\right)$ — Factor the binomial.

$f(x) = -0.5(x - 0)\left(x - \boxed{}\right)$ — Write the intercept form.

B Identify the x-intercepts and the vertex.

The x-intercepts are ________ and ________.

The x-coordinate of the vertex is $\dfrac{\boxed{} + \boxed{}}{2} = \boxed{}$.

Find the y-coordinate of the vertex.

$f(2) = -0.5\left(\boxed{} - 0\right)\left(\boxed{} - 4\right)$ — Substitute 2 for x.

$f(2) = -0.5\left(\boxed{}\right)\left(\boxed{}\right) = \boxed{}$ — Simplify.

The vertex is $\left(\boxed{}, \boxed{}\right)$.

C Graph the function using the x-intercepts and the vertex.

D Use the graph to solve the problem.

The width of the arch at its base is ________ meters.
Sketch the wagon on your graph. Will the wagon fit under the arch? Explain.

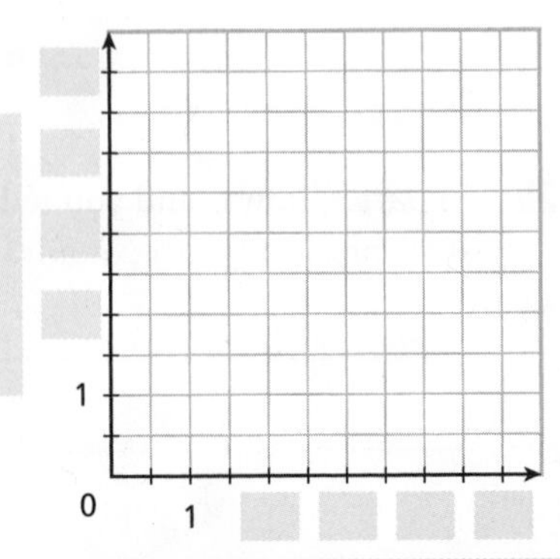

____

____

REFLECT

3a. What do the x-intercepts represent in this situation?

3b. Explain how you used the graph to find the width of the arch at its base.

3c. Explain how you modeled the shape of the wagon on the graph.

3d. What are the x-coordinates of the left and right sides of the model of the wagon? Evaluate the function modeling the arch for these x-values. Do the results verify your conclusion about whether the wagon will fit under the arch? Explain.

PRACTICE

Write each function in intercept form. Identify the x-intercepts and vertex of the function's graph. Then graph the function.

1. $f(x) = x^2 + 6x + 5$

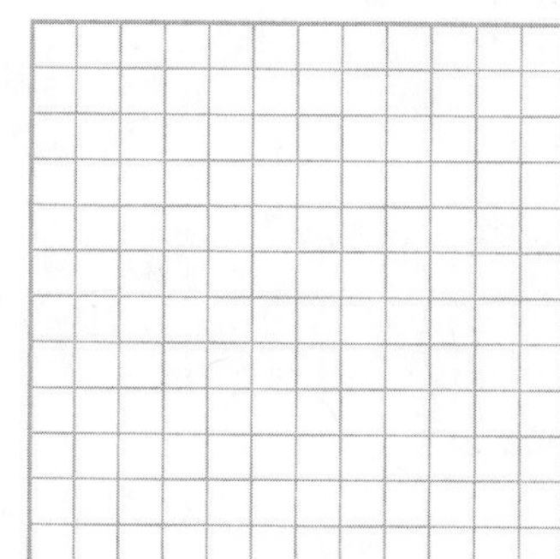

2. $f(x) = x^2 - 2x - 8$

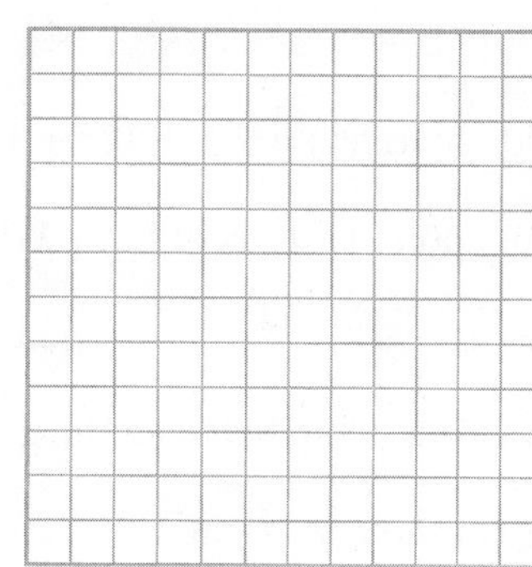

Write each function in intercept form. Identify the x-intercepts and vertex of the function's graph. Then graph the function.

3. $f(x) = 2x^2 - 8x + 6$

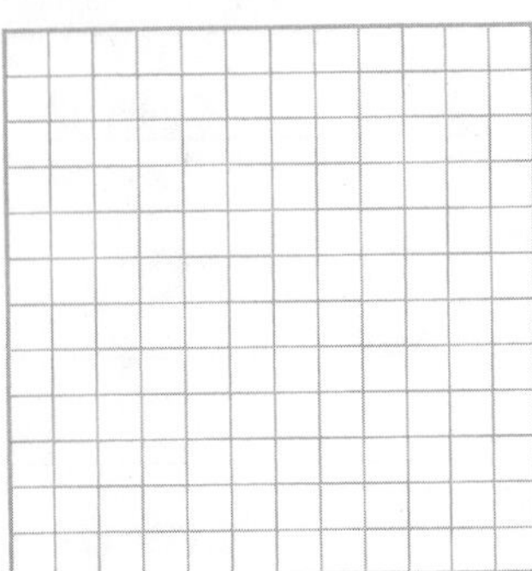

4. $f(x) = -3x^2 + 24x - 45$

5. In a football game, Tony attempts to kick a field goal at a distance of 40 yards from the goal post. The path of the kicked football is given by the equation $y = -0.02x^2 + 0.9x$ where x is the horizontal distance in yards and y is the vertical distance in yards.

a. Write the equation in intercept form.

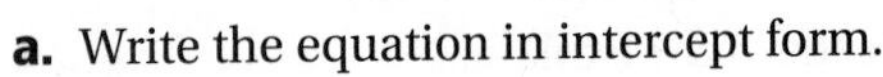

b. Identify the x-intercepts and the vertex.

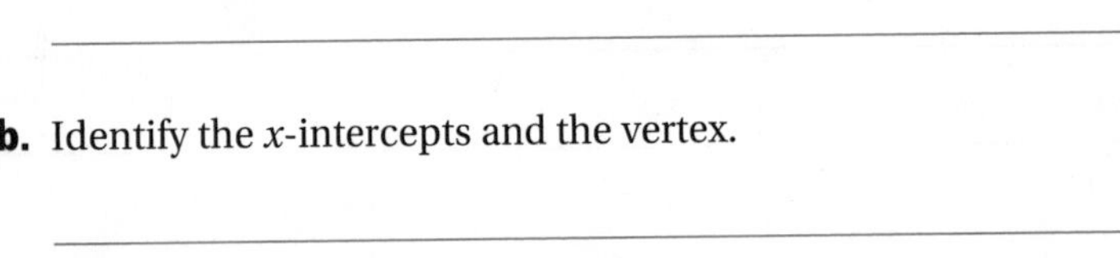

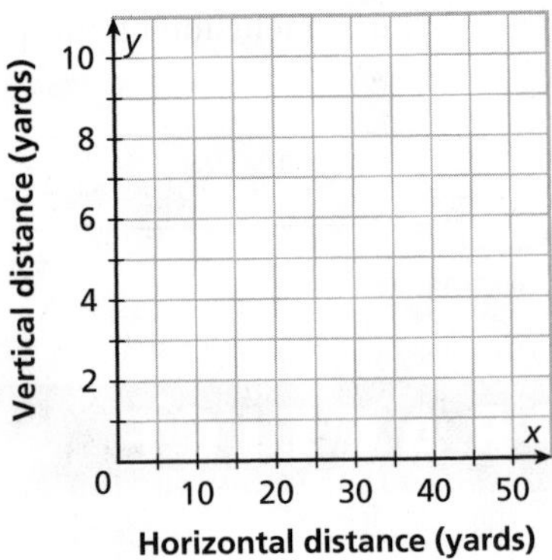

c. Graph the equation in the first quadrant.

d. The horizontal bar of the goal post is 10 feet above the ground. Does the ball go over the bar? Explain.

6. Consider the function $f(x) = 2x^2 + 12x + 18$.

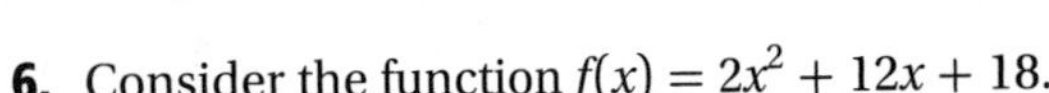

a. Write the function in intercept form. What is the relationship between p and q?

b. What is the relationship between the graph's x-intercepts and its vertex? Explain.

c. What is the vertex form of a quadratic function if $p = q$ in the intercept form of the function?

Name________________________ Class______________ Date__________

16-1

Additional Practice

Find the zeros of each function by using a graph and a table.

1. $f(x) = x^2 + 5x + 6$

x	–4	–3	–2	–1	0
$f(x)$					

____

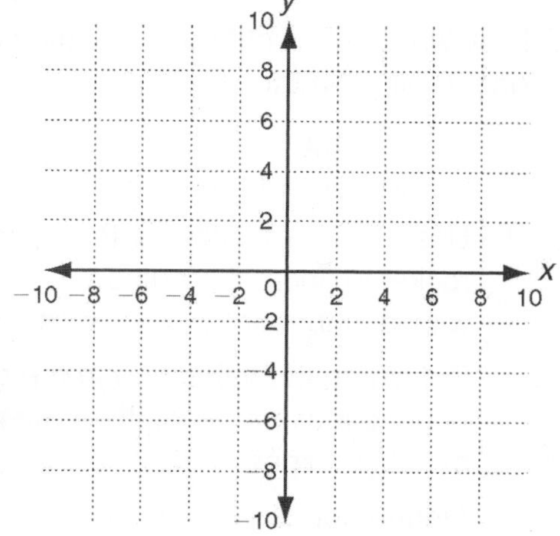

2. $g(x) = -x^2 + 4x + 5$

x	–2	0	2	4	6
$f(x)$					

____

Find the zeros of each function by factoring.

3. $h(x) = -x^2 - 6x - 9$

4. $f(x) = 2x^2 + 9x + 4$

5. $g(x) = x^2 + x - 20$

________________________ ________________________ ________________________

Find the roots of each equation by factoring.

6. $12x = 9x^2 + 4$

7. $16x^2 = 9$

________________________ ________________________

Write a quadratic function in standard form for each given set of zeros.

8. –2 and 7

9. 1 and –8

________________________ ________________________

Solve.

10. The quadratic function that approximates the height of a javelin throw is $h(t) = -0.08t^2 + 4.48$, where t is the time in seconds after it is thrown and h is the javelin's height in feet. How long will it take for the javelin to hit the ground?

____

Problem Solving

Erin and her friends launch a rocket from ground level vertically into the air with an initial velocity of 80 feet per second. The height of the rocket, $h(t)$, after t seconds is given by $h(t) = -16t^2 + 80t$.

1. They want to find out how high they can expect the rocket to go and how long it will be in the air.

   a. Use the standard form $f(x) = ax^2 + bx + c$ to find values for a, b, and c. ______________________

   b. Use the coordinates for the vertex of the path of the rocket to find t, the number of seconds the rocket will be in the air before it starts its downward path. ______________________

   c. Substitute the value for t in the given function to find the maximum height of the rocket. How high can they expect their rocket to go? ______________________

   d. Megan points out that the rocket will have a height of zero again when it returns to the ground. How long will the rocket stay in the air? ______________________

2. Megan gets ready to launch the same rocket from a platform 21 feet above the ground with the same initial velocity. How long will the rocket stay in the air this time?

   a. Write a function that represents the rocket's path for this launch. ______________________

   b. Factor the corresponding equation to find the values for t when h is zero. ______________________

   c. Erin says that the roots of the equation are $t = 5.25$ and $t = -20.25$ and that the rocket will stay in the air 5.5 seconds. Megan says she is wrong. Who is correct? How do you know?

   ____

   ____

Choose the letter for the best answer.

3. Which function models the path of a rocket that lands 3 seconds after launch?

   A $h(t) = -16t^2 + 32t + 48$

   B $h(t) = -16t^2 + 32t + 10.5$

   C $h(t) = -16t^2 + 40t + 48$

   D $h(t) = -16t^2 + 40t + 10.5$

4. Megan reads about a rocket whose path can be modeled by the function $h(t) = -16t^2 + 100t + 15$. Which could be the initial velocity and launch height?

   A 15 ft/s; 100 ft off the ground

   B 16 ft/s; 100 ft off the ground

   C 100 ft/s; 15 ft off the ground

   D 171 ft/s; 15 ft off the ground

Name ______________________ Class ______________ Date ________

16-2

Completing the Square

Connection: Vertex Form of Quadratic Equations

Essential question: *How do you convert quadratic functions to vertex form, $f(x) = a(x - h)^2 + k$?*

Video Tutor

MCC9–12.F.IF.8

1 EXPLORE Writing Quadratic Functions in Different Forms

Write the quadratic function in the form described.

A Write the function $f(x) = 2(x - 4)^2 + 3$ in the form $f(x) = ax^2 + bx + c$.

$f(x) = 2(x - 4)^2 + 3$

$f(x) = 2\left(x^2 - \square + \square\right) + 3$ Multiply to expand $(x - 4)^2$.

$f(x) = 2(x^2) - \square(8x) + \square(16) + 3$ Distribute 2.

$f(x) = 2x^2 - \square + \square + 3$ Multiply.

$f(x) = 2x^2 - 16x + \square$ Combine like terms.

So, $f(x) = 2(x - 4)^2 + 3$ is equivalent to ______________________.

B Write the function $f(x) = x^2 + 6x + 4$ in vertex form.

Recall that the vertex form of a quadratic function is $f(x) = a(x - h)^2 + k$. Write the given function in vertex form by completing the square.

$f(x) = x^2 + 6x + 4$

$f(x) = \left(x^2 + 6x + \square\right) + 4 - \square$ Set up for completing the square.

$f(x) = (x^2 + 6x + 9) + 4 - 9$ Add a constant so the expression inside the parentheses is a perfect square trinomial. Subtract the constant to keep the equation balanced.

$f(x) = \left(x + \square\right)^2 + 4 - 9$ Write $(x^2 + 6x + 9)$ as a binomial squared.

$f(x) = (x + 3)^2 - \square$ Combine like terms.

So, $f(x) = x^2 + 6x + 4$ is equivalent to ______________________.

REFLECT

1a. In part A, how does the value of a of the function in vertex form compare with the value of a when the function is in the form $f(x) = ax^2 + bx + c$?

____

1b. In part B, how could you check that you found the vertex form of the quadratic equation correctly?

____

____

1c. Describe how to complete the square for the quadratic expression $x^2 + 8x + \square$.

____

____

The **standard form** of a quadratic equation is $f(x) = ax^2 + bx + c$. Any quadratic function in standard form can be written in vertex form, and any quadratic function in vertex form can be written in standard form.

MCC9–12.F.IF.8a

2 EXAMPLE Graphing by Completing the Square

Graph the function by first writing it in vertex form. Then give the maximum or minimum of the function and identify its zeros.

A $f(x) = x^2 - 8x + 12$

- Write the function in vertex form.

$f(x) = \left(x^2 - 8x + \square\right) + 12 - \square$ Set up for completing the square.

$f(x) = \left(x^2 - 8x + \square\right) + 12 - \square$ Add a constant to complete the square. Subtract the constant to keep the equation balanced.

$f(x) = \left(x - \square\right)^2 + 12 - 16$ Write the expression in parentheses as a binomial squared.

$f(x) = (x - 4)^2 - \square$ Combine like terms.

- Sketch a graph of the function.

The vertex is __________.

Two points to the left of the vertex are $\left(2, \square\right)$ and $\left(3, \square\right)$.

Two points to the right of the vertex are $\left(5, \square\right)$ and $\left(6, \square\right)$.

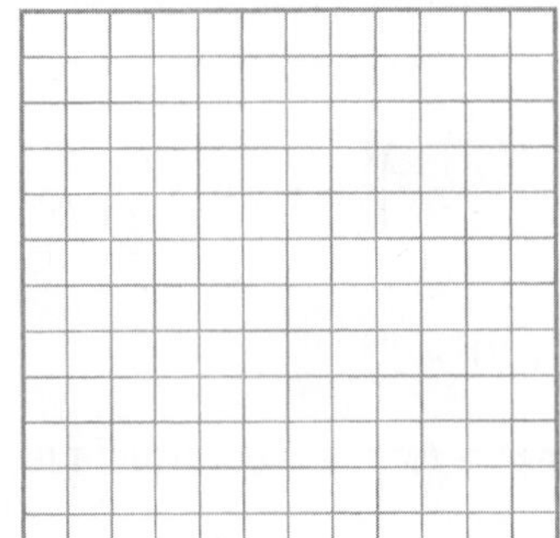

- Describe the function's properties.

The minimum is __________.

The zeros are __________ and __________.

B $f(x) = -2x^2 - 12x - 16$

- Write the function in vertex form.

$f(x) = \boxed{}(x^2 + 6x) - 16$

Factor the variable terms so that the coefficient of x^2 is 1.

$f(x) = -2\left(x^2 + 6x + \boxed{}\right) - 16 - \boxed{}$

Set up for completing the square.

$f(x) = -2\left(x^2 + 6x + \boxed{}\right) - 16 - (-2)\boxed{}$

Complete the square. Since the constant is multiplied by −2, subtract the product of −2 and the constant to keep the equation balanced.

$f(x) = -2\left(x + \boxed{}\right)^2 - 16 - (-2)9$

Write the expression in parentheses as a binomial squared.

$f(x) = -2(x + 3)^2 - 16 - \left(\boxed{}\right)$

Simplify (−2)9.

$f(x) = -2(x + 3)^2 + \boxed{}$

Combine like terms.

- Sketch a graph of the function.

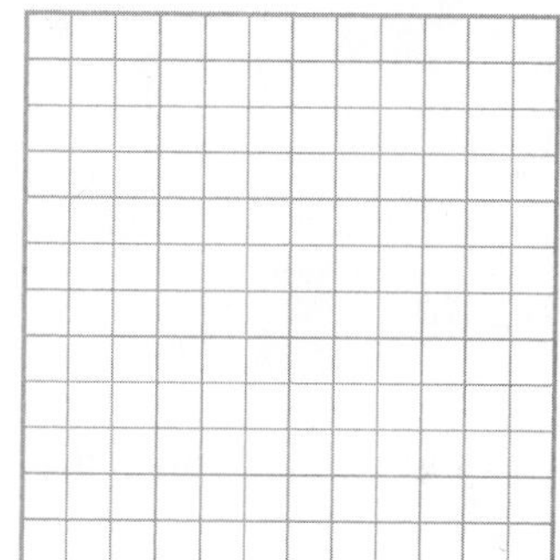

The vertex is ______.

Two points to the left of the vertex are

$\left(-5, \boxed{}\right)$ and $\left(-4, \boxed{}\right)$.

Two points to the right of the vertex are

$\left(-2, \boxed{}\right)$ and $\left(-1, \boxed{}\right)$.

- Describe the function's properties.

The maximum is ______.

The zeros are ______ and ______.

REFLECT

2a. How do you keep the equation of a quadratic function balanced when completing the square?

______

______

2b. In part B, why do you factor out −2 from the variable terms before completing the square?

______

______

2c. Why might the vertex form of a quadratic equation be more useful in some situations than the standard form?

____

____

____

MCC9–12.F.IF.8a

3 EXAMPLE Modeling Quadratic Functions in Standard Form

The function $h(t) = -16t^2 + 64t$ gives the height h in feet of a golf ball t seconds after it is hit. The ball has a height of 48 feet after 1 second. Use the symmetry of the function's graph to determine the other time at which the ball will have a height of 48 feet.

A Write the function in vertex form.

$h(t) = \square(t^2 - 4t)$ — Factor so that the coefficient of t^2 is 1.

$h(t) = -16\left(t^2 - 4t + \square\right) - (-16)\square$ — Complete the square and keep the equation balanced.

$h(t) = -16\left(t - \square\right)^2 - (-16)4$ — Write the expression in parentheses as a binomial squared.

$h(t) = -16(t - 2)^2 + \square$ — Simplify.

B Use symmetry to sketch a graph of the function and solve the problem.

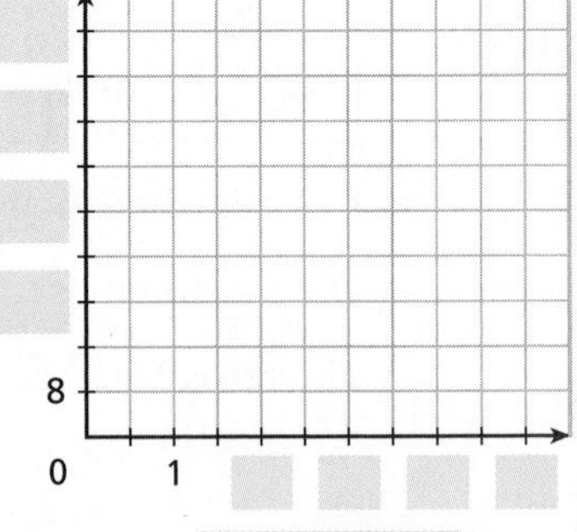

The vertex is ____________.

The point $\left(0, \square\right)$ is on the graph.

This point is 2 units to the left of the vertex. Based on symmetry, there is a point 2 units to the right of the vertex with the same y-coordinate at $\left(\square, 0\right)$.

The point (1, 48) is on the graph. Based on symmetry, the point $\left(\square, 48\right)$ is also on the graph.

So, the ball will have a height of 48 feet after 1 second and again after ________ seconds.

REFLECT

3a. How can you check your answer to the problem?

____

____

3b. What is the maximum height that the ball reaches? How do you know?

3c. If you know the coordinates of a point to the left of the vertex of the graph of a quadratic function, how can you use symmetry to find the coordinates of another point on the graph?

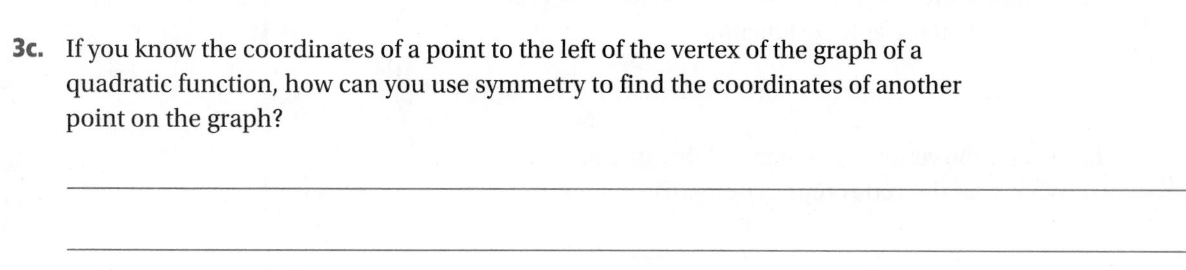

PRACTICE

Graph each function by first writing it in vertex form. Then give the maximum or minimum of the function and identify its zeros.

1. $f(x) = x^2 - 6x + 9$

2. $f(x) = x^2 - 2x - 3$

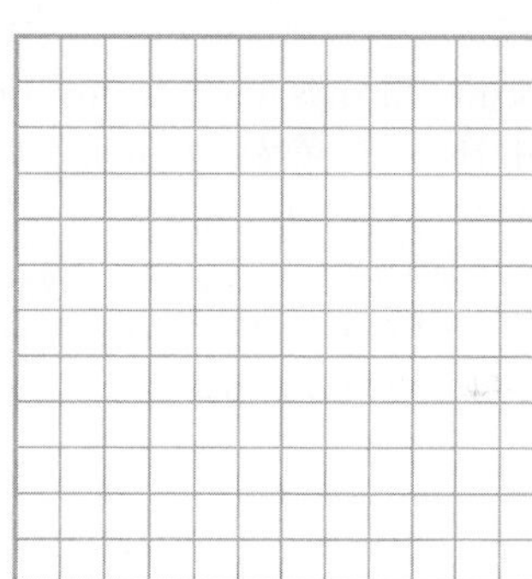

3. $f(x) = -7x^2 - 14x$

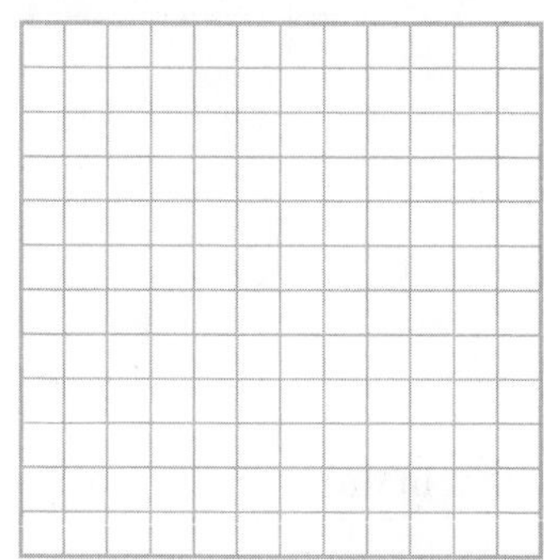

4. $f(x) = 3x^2 - 12x + 9$

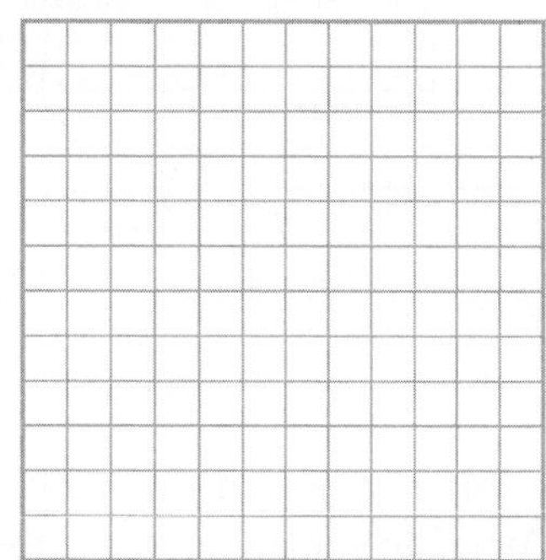

5. A company is marketing a new toy. The function $s(p) = -50p^2 + 3000p$ models how the total sales s of the toy, in dollars, depend on the price p of the toy, in dollars.

a. Complete the square to write the function in vertex form and then graph the function.

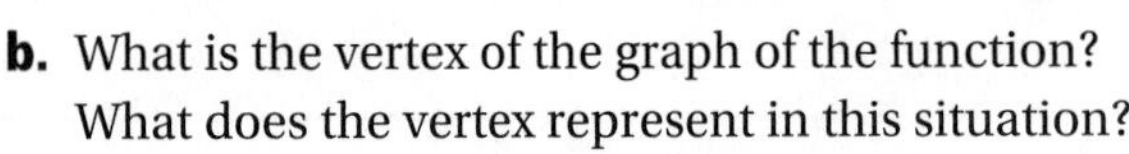

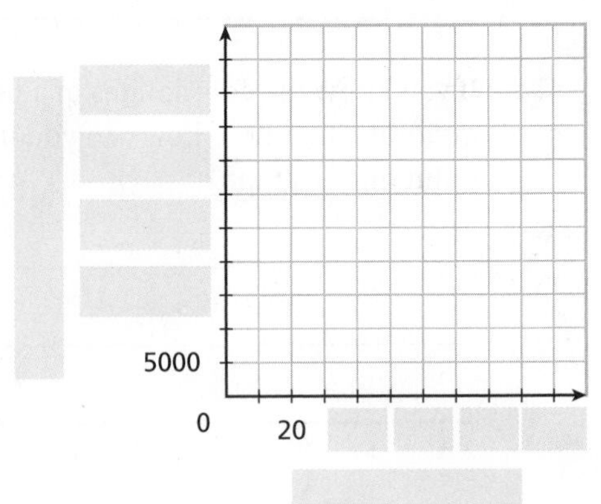

b. What is the vertex of the graph of the function? What does the vertex represent in this situation?

c. The model predicts that total sales will be $40,000 when the toy price is $20. At what other price does the model predict that total sales will be $40,000? Use the symmetry of the graph to support your answer.

6. A circus performer throws a ball from a height of 32 feet. The model $h(t) = -16t^2 + 16t + 32$ gives the height of the ball in feet t seconds after it is thrown.

a. Complete the square to write the function in vertex form and then graph the function.

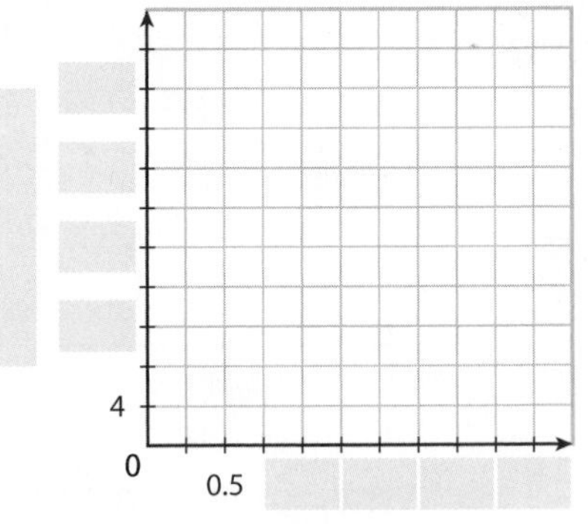

b. What is the maximum height that the ball reaches?

c. What is a reasonable domain of the function? Explain.

d. What is the y-intercept of the function's graph? What does it represent in this situation? What do you notice about the y-intercept and the value of c when the function is written in standard form?

Name________________________ Class______________ Date____________ 16-2

Additional Practice

Solve each equation.

1. $2x^2 - 6 = 42$ ________________
2. $x^2 - 14x + 49 = 18$ ________________

Complete the square for each expression. Write the resulting expression as a binomial squared.

3. $x^2 - 4x +$ _____ ________________
4. $x^2 + 12x +$ _____ ________________

Solve each equation by completing the square.

5. $2d^2 = 8 + 10d$ ________________
6. $x^2 + 2x = 3$ ________________
7. $-3x^2 + 18x = -30$ ________________
8. $4x^2 = -12x + 4$ ________________

Write each function in vertex form, and identify its vertex.

9. $f(x) = x^2 - 6x - 2$ ________________
10. $f(x) = x^2 - 4x + 1$ ________________
11. $h(x) = 3x^2 - 6x - 15$ ________________
12. $f(x) = -2x^2 - 16x + 4$ ________________

Solve.

13. Nathan made a triangular pennant for the band booster club. The area of the pennant is 80 square feet. The base of the pennant is 12 feet shorter than the height.

    a. What are the lengths of the base and height of the pennant?

    ____

    b. What are the dimensions of the pennant if the base is only 6 feet shorter than the height?

    ____

Problem Solving

Sean and Mason run out of gas while fishing from their boat in the bay. They set off an emergency flare with an initial vertical velocity of 30 meters per second. The height of the flare in meters can be modeled by $h(t) = -5t^2 + 30t$, where t represents the number of seconds after launch.

1. Sean thinks the flare should reach at least 15 meters to be seen from the shore. They want to know how long the flare will take to reach this height.
   a. Write an equation to determine how long it will take the flare to reach 15 meters. ____________________
   b. Simplify the function so you can complete the square. ____________________
   c. Solve the equation by completing the square. ____________________
   d. Mason thinks that the flare will reach 15 meters in 5.4 seconds. Is he correct? Explain.

   ____

   e. Sean thinks the flare will reach 15 meters sooner, but then the flare will stay above 15 meters for about 5 seconds. Is he correct? Explain.

   ____

2. Sean wants to know how high the flare will reach above the surface of the water.
   a. Write the function in vertex form, factoring so the coefficient of t^2 is 1. ____________________
   b. Complete the square using the vertex form of the function. ____________________
   c. How high will the flare reach? ____________________

Choose the letter for the best answer.

3. Use the vertex form of the function to determine how long after firing the flare it will reach its maximum height.

   A 3 s

   B 5 s

   C 9 s

   D 15 s

4. The boys fire a similar flare from the deck 5 meters above the water level. Which statement is correct?

   A The flare will reach 45 m in 3 s.

   B The flare will reach 50 m in 3 s.

   C The flare will reach 45 m in 3.5 s.

   D The flare will reach 50 m in 3.5 s.

Name ______________________ Class ______________ Date ________

16-3

Video Tutor

The Quadratic Formula

Going Deeper

Essential question: *When does a quadratic equation have nonreal solutions, and how do you find them?*

MCC9–12.A.REI.4b

1 ENGAGE Revisiting the Quadratic Formula

You have solved quadratic equations of the form $ax^2 + bx + c = 0$, where the coefficients a, b, and c are real numbers and $a \neq 0$, in several ways. One way was by using the *quadratic formula*:

$$x = \frac{-b \pm \sqrt{b^2 - 4ac}}{2a}$$

The radical $\sqrt{b^2 - 4ac}$ has meaning in the real number system only if the radicand $b^2 - 4ac$ is nonnegative. The radicand determines the number of real solutions and for this reason is called the *discriminant* for the quadratic equation. The table below summarizes the possible numbers of real solutions of a quadratic equation.

Value of Discriminant	Number of Real Solutions
$b^2 - 4ac > 0$	Two real solutions: $x = \frac{-b + \sqrt{b^2 - 4ac}}{2a}$ and $x = \frac{-b - \sqrt{b^2 - 4ac}}{2a}$
$b^2 - 4ac = 0$	One real solution: $x = -\frac{b}{2a}$
$b^2 - 4ac < 0$	No real solutions

When you solve a quadratic equation in the complex number system, where the radical $\sqrt{b^2 - 4ac}$ has meaning no matter what the value of the radicand is, the equation always has solutions. The table below summarizes the possible numbers of complex solutions of a quadratic equation.

Value of Discriminant	Number of Complex Solutions
$b^2 - 4ac > 0$	Two real solutions
$b^2 - 4ac = 0$	One real solution
$b^2 - 4ac < 0$	Two nonreal solutions

The table below gives three simple quadratic equations having different numbers and types of complex solutions.

Equation	Value of Discriminant	Solutions
$x^2 - 1 = 0$	$0^2 - 4(1)(-1) = 4$	$x = \pm 1$ (two real solutions)
$x^2 = 0$	$0^2 - 4(1)(0) = 0$	$x = 0$ (one real solution)
$x^2 + 1 = 0$	$0^2 - 4(1)(1) = -4$	$x = \pm i$ (two nonreal solutions)

REFLECT

1a. Use the discriminant to explain why the equation $x^2 + 2x - 3 = 0$ has two real solutions while the equation $x^2 + 2x + 3 = 0$ has no real solutions.

____

____

1b. For what value of c does the equation $x^2 + 2x + c = 0$ have exactly one real solution? Explain.

____

MCC9–12.N.CN.7

2 EXAMPLE Finding the Complex Solutions of a Quadratic Equation

Tell whether the solutions of $x^2 + 4 = 0$ are real or imaginary. Then find the solutions.

A Use the discriminant to determine the number and type of solutions.

$b^2 - 4ac = \square^2 - 4(\square)(\square) = \square$

Because $b^2 - 4ac$ $\square$ 0, there are two ______________ solutions.

B Use the quadratic formula to solve the equation.

$x = \dfrac{-b \pm \sqrt{b^2 - 4ac}}{2a}$ Write the quadratic formula.

$= \dfrac{-\square \pm \sqrt{\square}}{2(\square)}$ Substitute values. For the radicand $b^2 - 4ac$, use the value from part A.

$=$  Simplify the numerator, and simplify the denominator.

$=$  Simplify the fraction.

REFLECT

2a. Describe how you can check the solutions of a quadratic equation. Use the method to check the solutions of $x^2 + 4 = 0$.

____

____

2b. Why is it important to write a quadratic equation in the form $ax^2 + bx + c = 0$ before identifying the values of a, b, and c? For instance, why should you write $x^2 = -4$ as $x^2 + 4 = 0$ before using the quadratic formula to solve the equation?

____

____

____

MCC9–12.N.CN.7

3 EXAMPLE Finding the Complex Solutions of a Quadratic Equation

Tell whether the solutions of $x^2 - 4x + 13 = 0$ are real or imaginary. Then find the solutions.

A Use the discriminant to determine the number and type of solutions.

$b^2 - 4ac = (\quad)^2 - 4(\quad)(\quad) = \quad$

Because $b^2 - 4ac$ ___ 0, there are two ______________ solutions.

B Use the quadratic formula to solve the equation.

$x = \frac{-b \pm \sqrt{b^2 - 4ac}}{2a}$ Write the quadratic formula.

$= \frac{-(\quad) \pm \sqrt{\quad}}{2(\quad)}$ Substitute values. For the radicand $b^2 - 4ac$, use the value from part A.

$= \frac{\quad}{\quad}$ Simplify the numerator, and simplify the denominator.

$= \quad$ Simplify the fraction.

C One of the solutions is $x_1 = 2 + 3i$. Check this solution by substituting it into the equation to see if it produces a true statement.

$x^2 - 4x + 13 = (\quad)^2 - 4(\quad) + 13$ Substitute.

$= (\quad) - 4(\quad) + 13$ Square.

$= (\quad) + (\quad) + 13$ Multiply.

$= \quad$ Simplify.

REFLECT

3a. Describe what will change in each step of the check in part C when you substitute the other solution, x_2.

____

____

3b. Does the equation $x^2 + 4x + 13 = 0$ have the *same number and type of solutions* as $x^2 - 4x + 13 = 0$? Does it have the *same solutions*? Explain.

____

____

3c. Use the solutions x_1 and x_2 to write the expression $(x - x_1)(x - x_2)$. Multiply the binomials. What do you notice?

____

____

PRACTICE

Find the number and type of solutions of each equation.

1. $x^2 - 9 = 0$

2. $x^2 + 16 = 0$

3. $x^2 = 0$

4. $x^2 - 2x + 4 = 0$

5. $x^2 - 10x + 25 = 0$

6. $x^2 - 3x - 10 = 0$

7. $x^2 + 12x = -36$

8. $2x^2 + 5 = -3x$

9. $3x^2 = 7 - 4x$

Find the complex solutions of each equation.

10. $x^2 + 49 = 0$

11. $x^2 + 5 = 0$

12. $4x^2 + 9 = 0$

13. $x^2 - 2x + 2 = 0$

14. $x^2 - 6x + 13 = 0$

15. $x^2 + 10x + 29 = 0$

16. $5x^2 - 2x + 1 = 0$

17. $9x^2 + 12x + 5 = 0$

18. $2x^2 - 6x + 7 = 0$

19. Multiplying the binomials in $(x - x_1)(x - x_2)$ gives $x^2 - (x_1 + x_2)x + x_1x_2$.

a. Explain why x_1 and x_2 are solutions of the equation $(x - x_1)(x - x_2) = 0$ as well as the equation $x^2 - (x_1 + x_2)x + x_1x_2 = 0$.

b. For the equation $x^2 - (x_1 + x_2)x + x_1 x_2 = 0$, how is the coefficient of the x-term related to the equation's solutions? How is the constant term related to the solutions?

c. Describe a quick way to check the solutions x_1 and x_2 of an equation in the form $x^2 + bx + c = 0$. Then check to see if $x_1 = 2 + i$ and $x_2 = 2 - i$ are solutions of the equation $x^2 - 4x + 5 = 0$.

Name ____________________ Class ____________ Date ________ 16-3

Additional Practice

Find the zeros of each function by using the Quadratic Formula.

1. $f(x) = x^2 + 10x + 9$
2. $g(x) = 2x^2 + 4x - 12$

_______________ _______________

3. $h(x) = 3x^2 - 3x + \frac{3}{4}$
4. $f(x) = x^2 + 2x - 3$

_______________ _______________

5. $g(x) = 2x^2 + 3x + 1$
6. $g(x) = x^2 + 5x - 3$

_______________ _______________

Find the type and number of solutions for each equation.

7. $x^2 - 3x = -8$
8. $x^2 + 4x = -3$
9. $2x^2 - 12x = -18$

_______________ _______________ _______________

Solve.

10. A newspaper delivery person in a car is tossing folded newspapers from the car window to driveways. The speed of the car is 30 feet per second, and the driver does not slow down. The newspapers are tossed horizontally from a height of 4 feet above the ground. The height of the papers as they are thrown can be modeled by $y = -16t^2 + 4$, and the distance they travel to the driveway is $d = 30t$.

   a. How long does it take for a newspaper to land?

   ____

   b. From how many feet before the driveway must the papers be thrown?

   ____

   c. The delivery person starts to throw the newspapers at an angle and the height of the papers as they travel can now be modeled by $y = -16t^2 + 12t + 4$. How long does it take the papers to reach the ground now?

   ____

Problem Solving

In a shot-put event, Jenna tosses her last shot from a position of about 6 feet above the ground with an initial vertical and horizontal velocity of 20 feet per second. The height of the shot is modeled by the function $h(t) = -16t^2 + 20t + 6$, where t is the time in seconds after the toss. The horizontal distance traveled after t seconds is modeled by $d(t) = 20t$.

1. Jenna wants to know the exact distance the shot travels at a velocity of 20 feet per second.

   a. Use the Quadratic Formula $t = \frac{-b \pm \sqrt{b^2 - 4ac}}{2a}$ to solve the height function for t. ________________

   b. Use the value for t and the distance function to find the distance her shot travels. ________________

2. Jenna is working to improve her performance. She makes a table to show how the horizontal distance varies with velocity. Complete the table.

	Velocity (ft/s)	Formula	Time (s)	Distance (ft)
a.	22	$t = \frac{-22 \pm \sqrt{(22)^2 - 4(-16)(6)}}{2(-16)}$		
b.	25			
c.	28			

Jenna has not reached her full potential yet. Her goal is to toss the shot from a height of 6 feet 6 inches with a vertical and horizontal velocity of 30 feet per second. Choose the letter for the best answer.

3. If she achieves her goal, how long will her shot stay in the air?

   A 1.65 s

   B 1.87 s

   C 2.07 s

   D 2.27 s

4. If she achieves her goal, what horizontal distance will the shot travel?

   A 41.4 ft

   B 56.1 ft

   C 62.1 ft

   D 68.1 ft

Name ______________________ Class ______________ Date ________

16-4

Nonlinear Systems

Going Deeper

Essential question: *How can you solve a system of equations when one equation is linear and the other is quadratic?*

To estimate the solution to a system of equations, you can graph both equations on the same coordinate plane and find the intersection points. Or you can solve the equations algebraically using substitution or elimination.

MCC9–12.A.REI.7

1 EXAMPLE Solving by Graphing and Algebraically

Solve the system of equations.

$$f(x) = -8x + 48$$
$$g(x) = -2(x - 2)^2 + 32$$

A Solve the system of equations by graphing.

Start by graphing the quadratic function. The vertex is (___ , ___). Describe the transformation of the parent quadratic function that produces the graph of $g(x)$.

____

____

To make the graph more accurate, plot the points where the x-intercepts occur. The x-intercepts are the solutions of the equation $g(x) = 0$:

$-2(x - 2)^2 + 32 = 0$

$-2(x - 2)^2 =$ ___

$(x - 2)^2 =$ ___

$x - 2 = \pm$ ___

$x =$ ___ $\pm$ ___ $=$ ___ or ___

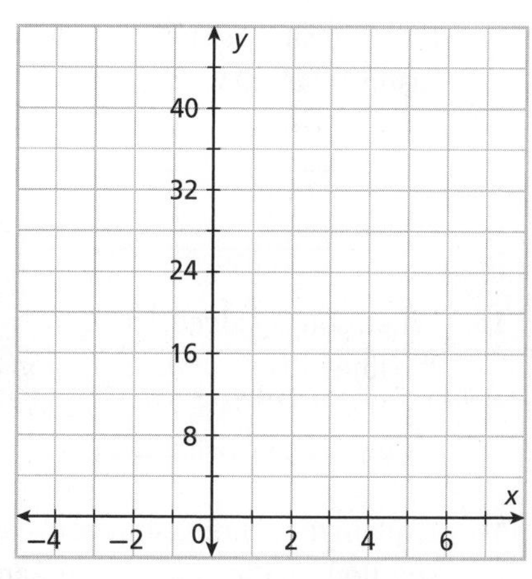

So, the points (___ , 0) and (___ , 0) are on the graph. Use these points and the vertex to draw the graph.

Now graph the linear function. The y-intercept is ____, and the slope is ____.

The line and the parabola intersect at two points. Identify the coordinates of those points.

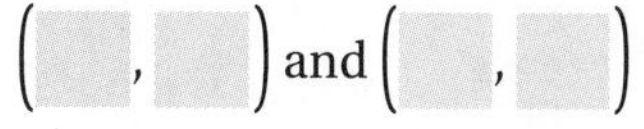

(___ , ___) and (___ , ___)

B Solve the system of equations algebraically.

Write the functions in terms of y.

$$y = -8x + 48$$
$$y = -2(x - 2)^2 + 32$$

Both equations are solved for y, so set the right sides equal to each other and solve for x.

$-8x + 48 = -2(x - 2)^2 + 32$

$-8x + 48 =$ ______ Simplify the right side.

$\underline{8x - 48 = \qquad 8x - 48}$ Add $8x - 48$ to both sides.

$0 =$ ______ Simplify both sides.

$0 = -2(\quad)(\quad)$ Factor the right side.

$x =$ ___ or $x =$ ___ Use the zero-product property to solve for x.

Substitute these values of x into the equation of the line to find the corresponding y-values.

$y = -8(2) + 48 =$ ______

$y = -8(6) + 48 =$ ______

The solutions are (___ , ___) and (___ , ___).

REFLECT

1a. If the linear function was $f(x) = 8x + 48$, how many solutions would there be? Justify your answer.

______

______

1b. When solving algebraically, why do you substitute the x-values into the equation of the line instead of the equation of the parabola?

______

1c. Explain the relationship between the intersection points of the graphs and the solutions of the system of equations.

______

______

1d. Describe how to check that the solutions are correct.

______

______

MCC9–12.A.REI.7

2 EXPLORE Determining the Possible Number of Solutions

In the previous example, the system of equations had two solutions. You can use a graph to understand other possible numbers of solutions of a system of equations involving a linear equation and a quadratic equation.

The graph of the quadratic function $f(x) = -x^2 + 10x - 27$ is shown below.

Graph each linear function below on the same coordinate plane as the parabola.

Line 1: $g(x) = 2x - 11$

Line 2: $h(x) = -2x + 14$

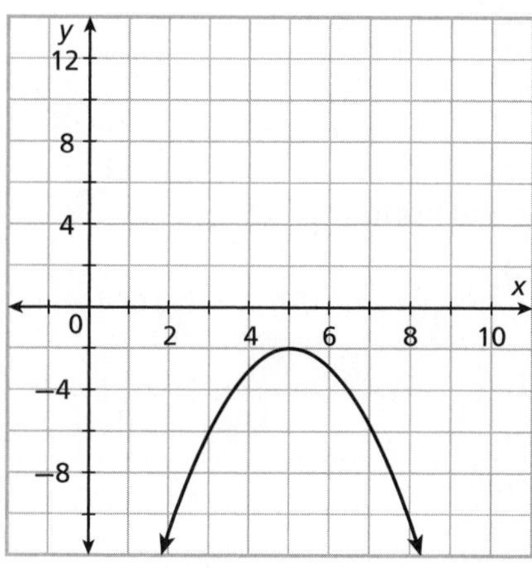

REFLECT

2a. At how many points do the parabola and Line 1 intersect? ________

How many solutions are there for the system consisting of the quadratic function and the first linear function? ________

2b. At how many points do the parabola and Line 2 intersect? ________

How many solutions are there for the system consisting of the quadratic function and the second linear function? ________

2c. A system of equations consisting of one quadratic equation and one linear equation can have ________, ________, or 2 real solutions.

2d. How many solutions does the following system of equations have? Explain your reasoning.

$$f(x) = -x^2 + 10x - 27$$
$$k(x) = -x + 1$$

____

____

2e. How many solutions does the following system of equations have? Explain your reasoning.

$$f(x) = -x^2 + 10x - 27$$
$$p(x) = -2$$

____

____

You can use the Intersect feature on a graphing calculator to solve systems of equations.

MCC9–12.A.REI.7

3 EXAMPLE Solving Systems Using Technology

Use a graphing calculator to solve the system of equations.

$$f(x) = -4.9x^2 + 50x + 25$$
$$g(x) = 30x$$

A Enter the functions as Y_1 and Y_2 on a graphing calculator. Then graph both functions. Sketch the graphs on the coordinate plane at the right.

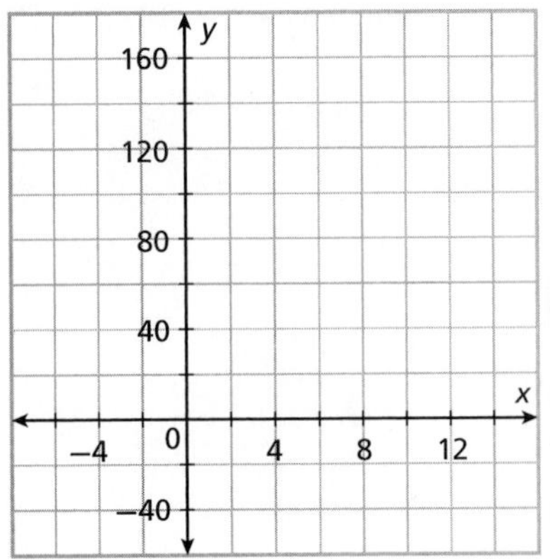

Estimate the solutions of the system from the graph.

____

B Solve the system directly by using the Intersect feature of the graphing calculator.

Press 2nd and CALC, then select Intersect. Press Enter for the first curve and again for the second curve. For Guess?, press the left or right arrows to move the cursor close to one of the intersections, then press Enter again. Repeat, moving the cursor close to the other intersection to find the second solution. Round your solutions to the nearest tenth.

____

REFLECT

3a. Are the solutions you get using the Intersect feature of a graphing calculator always exact? Explain.

____

3b. How can you check the accuracy of your estimated solutions?

____

3c. Use a graphing calculator to solve the system of equations $f(x)$ and $h(x)$ where $h(x) = 30x + 50$. What is the result? Explain.

____

____

PRACTICE

Solve the system of equations algebraically. Round to the nearest tenth, if necessary.

1. $f(x) = x^2 - 2$
$g(x) = -2$

____

2. $y = (x - 3)^2$
$y = x$

____

3. $y = -2x^2 - 4x + 1$
$y = -\frac{1}{2}x + 3$

____

4. $f(x) = x^2$
$g(x) = 1$

____

5. $y = x^2 + 4x - 5$
$y = 3x - 2$

____

6. $f(x) = -16x^2 + 15x + 10$
$g(x) = 14 - x$

____

The graph of a system of equations is shown. State how many solutions the system has. Then estimate the solution(s).

7. ______________________

____

8. 

____

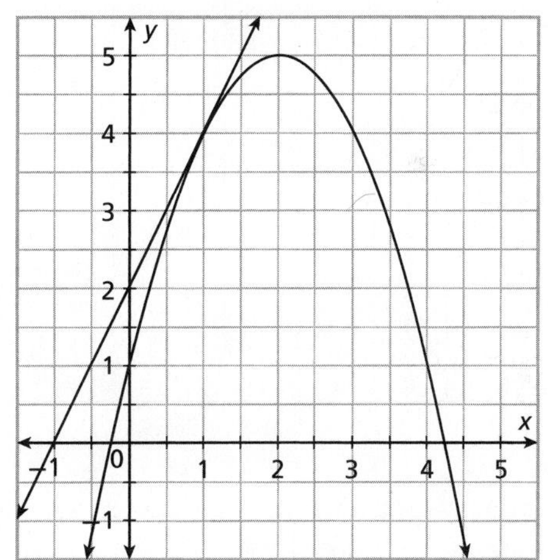

Estimate the solutions to the system of equations graphically. Confirm the solutions by substituting the values into the equations.

9. $f(x) = x^2$

$g(x) = 1$

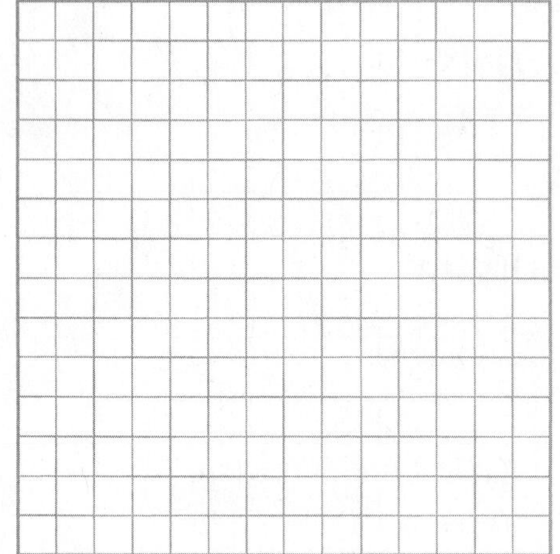

____

10. $y = x^2 - 1$

$y = 0.5x - 3$

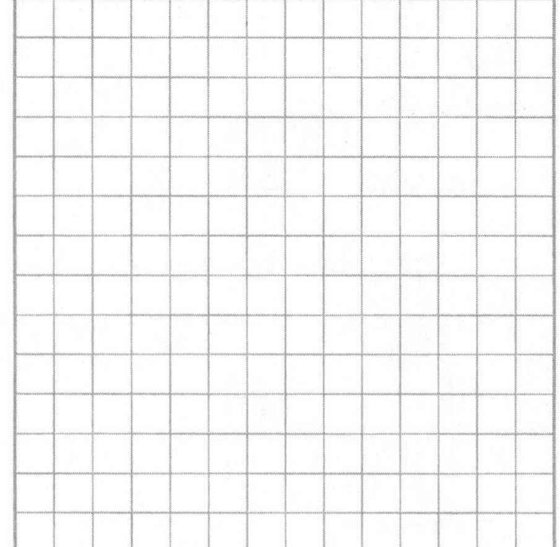

____

11. $f(x) = -16x^2 + 15x + 10$

$g(x) = 14 - x$

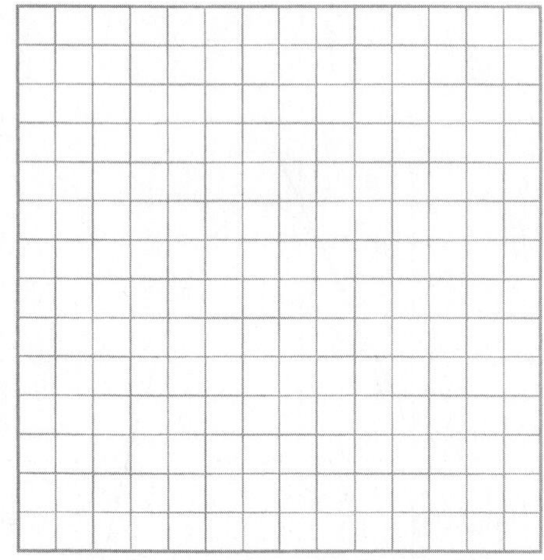

____

12. $f(x) = 3(x - 1)^2 + 4$

$g(x) = -4x + 9$

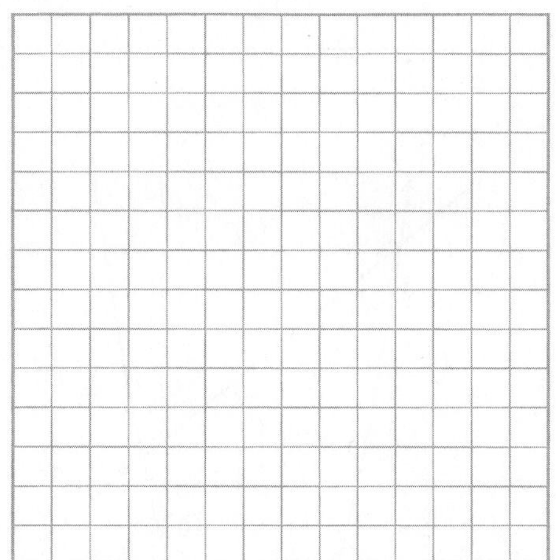

____

Solve the system of equations using the Intersect feature of a graphing calculator. Round your answers to the nearest tenth.

13. $y = -x^2 + 6x + 7$

$y = 2x + 6$

____

14. $f(x) = -x^2 + x - 2$

$g(x) = 2x - 3$

____

Name________________ Class__________ Date__________

Additional Practice

Solve each system by graphing. Check your answers.

1. $\begin{cases} y = x^2 - x - 2 \\ y = -x + 2 \end{cases}$

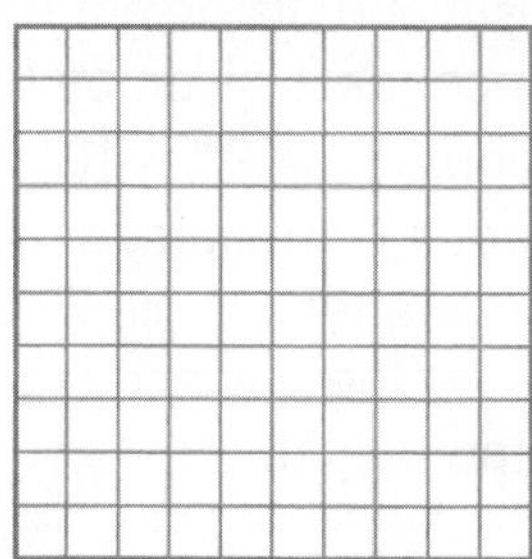

____

2. $\begin{cases} y = x^2 + x - 6 \\ y = -x - 3 \end{cases}$

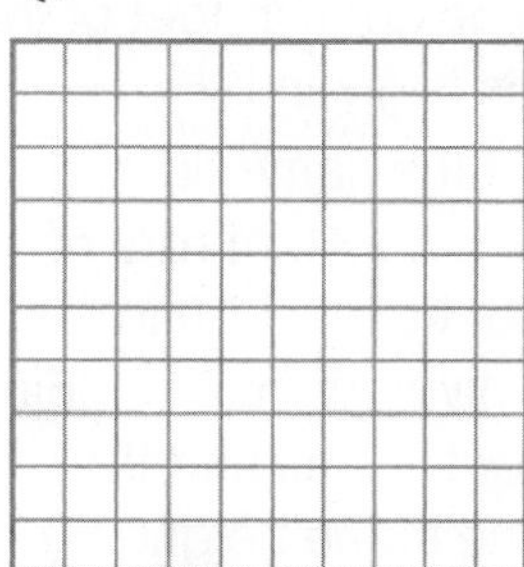

____

Solve each system by substitution. Check your answers.

3. $\begin{cases} y = -2x^2 + x + 4 \\ y = -5x + 8 \end{cases}$

____

4. $\begin{cases} y = -2x^2 - 3x + 2 \\ y = -x + 6 \end{cases}$

____

5. $\begin{cases} y = 3x^2 + 2x - 1 \\ x + y = 5 \end{cases}$

____

6. $\begin{cases} y = x^2 - 16 \\ y = x + 4 \end{cases}$

____

7. $\begin{cases} y = x^2 - 1 \\ x + 2y = 8 \end{cases}$

____

8. $\begin{cases} y = x^2 + 3x + 2 \\ 2x + y = -4 \end{cases}$

____

9. $\begin{cases} y = 2x^2 + 3x - 1 \\ 2x + y = -4 \end{cases}$

____

10. $\begin{cases} y = -x^2 + 2x - 4 \\ 3x + y = -4 \end{cases}$

____

Problem Solving

Write the correct answer.

1. A ball is thrown upward with an initial velocity of 40 feet per second from ground level. The height h in feet of the ball after t seconds is given by $h = -16t^2 + 40t$. At the same time, a balloon is rising at a constant rate of 10 feet per second. Its height h in feet after t seconds is given by $h = 10t$. Find the time it takes for the ball and the balloon to reach the same height.

____

2. A bird starts flying up from the grass in a park and climbs at a steady rate of 0.5 meters per second. Its height h in meters after t seconds is given by $h = 0.5t$. The equation $h = -4.9t^2 + 40t + 3$ models the height h, in meters, of a baseball t seconds after it is hit. Find the time it takes for the ball and the bird to reach the same height.

____

3. A skateboard company's monthly sales income can be modeled by the equation $C(s) = 0.5s^2 + 25s + 500,$ where s represents the number of skateboards sold. The monthly cost of running the business is $C(s) = 25s + 812.5$. How many skateboards must the company sell in a month before the sales income equals or exceeds the cost of running the business?

____

4. The deer population in a park can be modeled by the equation $P(y) = 4y^2 - 10y + 60,$ where y is the number of years after 2010. The deer population in another park can be modeled by $P(y) = 10y + 80$, where y is the number of years after 2010. In which year will the two parks have approximately the same number of deer?

____

Select the best answer.

5. A seagull is flying upwards such that its height h in feet above the sea after t seconds is given by $h = 3t$. At the same time, the height h in feet of a rock falling off a cliff above the sea after t seconds is given by $h = -16t^2 + 50$. Find the approximate time it takes for the rock and the bird to be at the same height.

   A 1.68 seconds C 3.36 seconds

   B 3.13 seconds D 16.67 seconds

6. A juggler at a fun park throws a ball upwards such that the ball's height h in feet above the ground after t seconds is given by $h = -16t^2 + 20t + 5$. At the same time, a scenic elevator begins climbing a tower at a constant rate of 20 feet per second. Its height h in feet after t seconds is given by $h = 20t$. Find the approximate time it takes for the ball and the elevator to reach the same height.

   F 0.56 seconds H 4 seconds

   G 1.12 seconds J 11.18 seconds

Name______________ Class______________ Date______________

UNIT 5

Performance Tasks

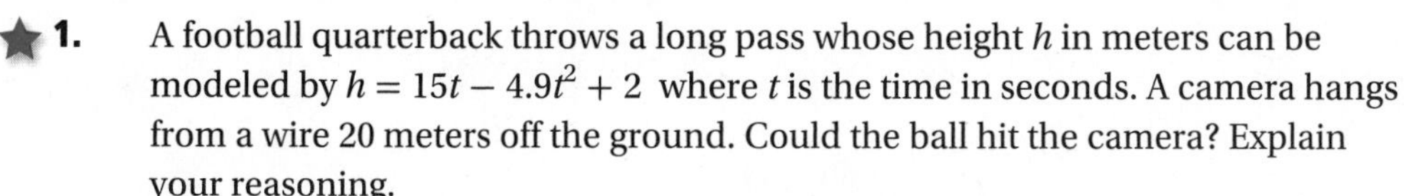

GPS COMMON CORE

MCC9-12.A.SSE.1
MCC9-12.A.SSE.2
MCC9-12.A.SSE.3a
MCC9-12.A.CED.2
MCC9-12.A.REI.4

★ **1.** A football quarterback throws a long pass whose height h in meters can be modeled by $h = 15t - 4.9t^2 + 2$ where t is the time in seconds. A camera hangs from a wire 20 meters off the ground. Could the ball hit the camera? Explain your reasoning.

★ **2.** Baljit builds a square frame that is 1 inch wider than twice the width of a square frame from the store. He writes the area enclosed by his frame with the polynomial $4x^2 + 4x + 1$.

a. Factor the polynomial that Baljit wrote. Explain how the factorization yields an expression for the width of the frame Baljit builds.

b. What is a variable expression for the area enclosed by the frame from the store? Explain how you know.

★★ **3.** Vehicle braking performance data uses 60 mph (or 28 m/s) to 0 mph. However, the published data is often unrealistic for the average driver and road conditions. To calculate how long it takes a vehicle to stop, assuming a constant deceleration, you can use the formula $d = \frac{1}{2}at^2$, where d is the distance traveled while stopping, a is the acceleration (deceleration), and t is the time. For a new hybrid car the published stopping distance is 75 meters and its constant deceleration is 6 m/s^2.

a. Substitute the given values into $d = \frac{1}{2}at^2$ and simplify the equation. Group all the terms on one side of the equation and use factoring to solve.

b. What do the solutions represent? Are all solutions meaningful? Explain.

continued

c. The stopping time provided does not include the driver recognition and reaction time, which can add about 2 seconds to the stopping time. Find the reaction distance by multiplying the speed (before stopping begins) times the reaction time. What is the total distance the vehicle travels, including the reaction distance? Convert this distance to feet using 1 m = 3.3 ft.

★★★ **4.** There are two square workout mats at a gym.

a. Let x represent the length of the larger mat, and let y represent the length of the smaller mat. Write a binomial that represents how much more area the larger mat has than the smaller mat.

b. Factor the binomial for the difference in the mat areas. Interpret what the factors could mean in this context.

c. One mat has 4 times the area of the other mat. Use this to rewrite the binomial from part **a** using only the variable y.

UNIT 5 GPS COMMON CORE PARCC Assessment Readiness

Name ______________________ Class ______________ Date ________

SELECTED RESPONSE

1. The graph of which function is a reflection and vertical stretch of the parent quadratic function?

   A. $f(x) = 3x^2$ **C.** $f(x) = -3x^2$

   B. $f(x) = 0.3x^2$ **D.** $f(x) = -0.3x^2$

2. Which of the following describes the graph of $f(x) = -2x^2$ as a transformation of the graph of the parent quadratic function?

   F. reflection across the x-axis and vertical stretch by a factor of 2

   G. reflection across the y-axis and vertical shrink by a factor of 2

   H. translation 2 units left

   J. translation 2 units down

3. What is the minimum value of $f(x) = 5x^2 + 10x + 10$?

   A. -5 **C.** 1

   B. -1 **D.** 5

4. Jon has rewritten the expression $15x^3 - 10x^2 + 27x - 18$ in order to factor it. Which is a reasonable next step for Jon to perform?

   F. Use the Commutative Property to rewrite the terms in a different order.

   G. Factor 2 from the second and fourth terms.

   H. Group the first two terms and factor out the greatest common factor, $5x^2$.

   J. Factor x from each of the four terms.

5. What is the factored form of $n^2-5n + 6$?

   A. $(n - 6)(n + 1)$

   B. $(n + 6)(n - 1)$

   C. $(n + 2)(n + 3)$

   D. $(n - 2)(n - 3)$

6. What is the factored form of $3c^2 + c - 4$?

   F. $(3c - 2)(c + 2)$

   G. $(3c + 2)(c + 2)$

   H. $(3c + 4)(c - 1)$

   J. $(3c - 1)(c + 4)$

7. Which of the following polynomials have a common binomial factor?

   A. $(x^2 + 4)$ and $(x^2 + 4x + 4)$

   B. $(x^2 + 4)$ and $(x^2 - 4x + 4)$

   C. $(x^2 - 4)$ and $(x^2 + 4x - 4)$

   D. $(x^2 - 4)$ and $(x^2 + 4x + 4)$

8. Which expression is not equivalent to the polynomial $6x^3 + 15x^2 - 9x$?

   F. $3(2x^3 + 5x^2 - 3x)$

   G. $3x(2x^2 + 5x - 3)$

   H. $3x(x + 3)(x - 1)$

   J. $3x(2x - 1)(x + 3)$

CONSTRUCTED RESPONSE

9. Amanda is adding a border to a rectangular quilt with a length of 4 feet and a width of 3 feet. The border has a width of x feet. Write a quadratic function $f(x)$ in standard form for the area of the border in square feet. What is $f(0.5)$ and what does it represent?

10. The function $f(x) = -16x^2 + 40x$ models the height in feet of a football x seconds after it is kicked from the ground.

   a. Graph the function.

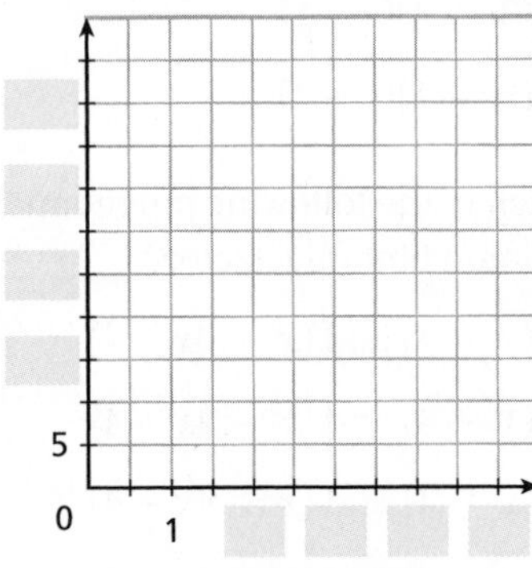

   b. What does the origin of the graph represent?

   c. What is a reasonable domain of the function? Explain.

   d. What is the maximum of the function, and what does it represent in this situation?

11. Complete the diagram and the equation that represent the binomial multiplication shown by the algebra tiles.

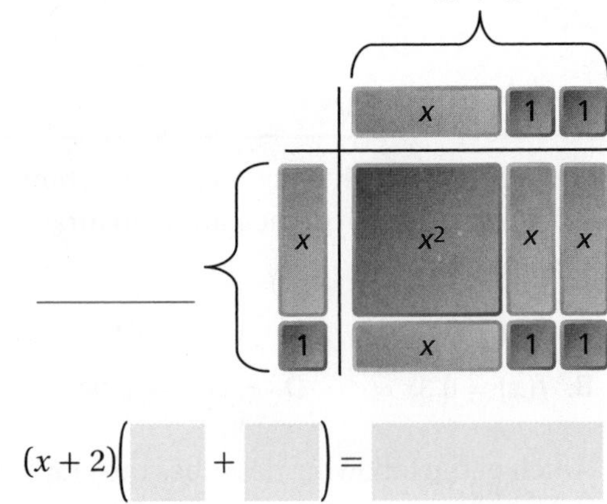

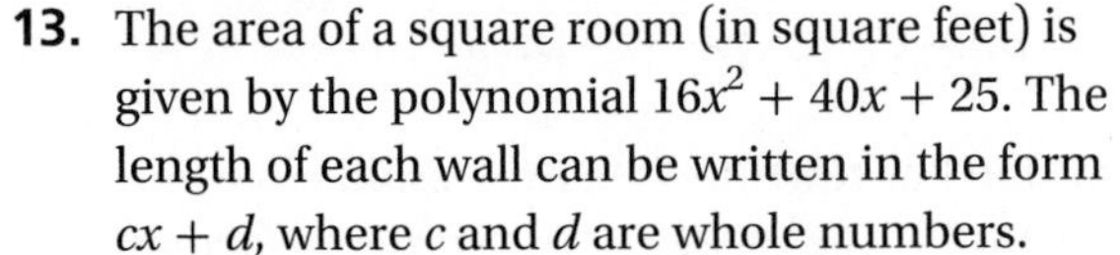

$(x + 2)(\quad + \quad) =$

12. Show how to factor the polynomial $10a^2b - 20ab - 12b + 6ab$ completely.

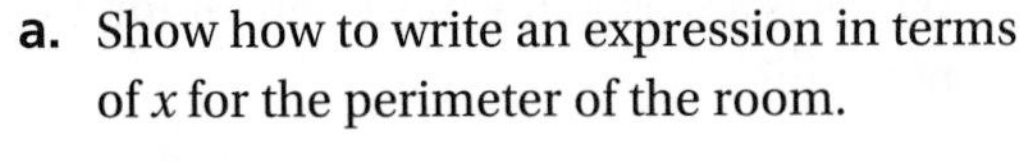

13. The area of a square room (in square feet) is given by the polynomial $16x^2 + 40x + 25$. The length of each wall can be written in the form $cx + d$, where c and d are whole numbers.

   a. Show how to write an expression in terms of x for the perimeter of the room.

   b. Find the perimeter when $x = 2$ feet.

UNIT 6

Modeling Geometry

Unpacking the Standards

Understanding the standards and the vocabulary terms in the standards will help you know exactly what you are expected to learn in this unit.

MCC9-12.G.GPE.1

Derive the equation of a circle of given center and radius using the Pythagorean Theorem; …

Key Vocabulary

circle *(círculo)* The set of points in a plane that are a fixed distance from a given point called the *center of the circle.*

radius of a circle *(radio de un círculo)* A segment whose endpoints are the center of a circle and a point on the circle; the distance from the center of a circle to any point on the circle.

Pythagorean Theorem *(Teorema de Pitágoras)* If a right triangle has legs of lengths a and b and a hypotenuse of length c, then $a^2 + b^2 = c^2$.

What It Means For You

You can use the Pythagorean Theorem to derive the Distance Formula. In turn, you can use the Distance Formula to derive the general form of the equation of a circle.

EXAMPLE

For the circle shown, the distance from the center (h, k) to any point (x, y) on the circle is the radius. The center is at $(-1, 2)$ and the radius is 3. Using the Distance Formula:

$(-1, 2)$, x, y, -4, 0, 2, 4, -2, -4

$$\sqrt{(x-h)^2 + (y-k)^2} = r$$

$$\sqrt{(x-(-1))^2 + (y-2)^2} = 3$$

$$\sqrt{(x+1)^2 + (y-2)^2} = 3$$

Squaring both sides of the equation gives the equation of the circle, $(x + 1)^2 + (y - 2)^2 = 9$.

GPS COMMON CORE

MCC9-12.G.GPE.2

Derive the equation of a parabola given a focus and directrix.

Key Vocabulary

directrix *(directriz)* A fixed line used to define a *parabola*. Every point on the parabola is equidistant from the directrix and a fixed point called the *focus*.

focus of a parabola *(foco de una parábola)* A fixed point F used with a directrix to define a parabola.

parabola *(parábola)* The shape of the graph of a quadratic function. Also, the set of points equidistant from a point F, called the *focus*, and a line d, called the directrix.

What It Means For You

You can use the Distance Formula to derive the general form of the equation of a parabola with focus $F(0, p)$ and directrix $y = p$.

EXAMPLE

A point: the *focus*

A line: the *directrix*

$F(0, p)$, $P(x, y)$, x, y, $y = -p$

The equation of a parabola with focus $F(0, p)$ and directrix $y = -p$ is $y = \frac{1}{4p}(x^2)$. It is sometimes written $x^2 = 4py$.

UNIT 6

MCC9-12.G.GPE.4

Use coordinates to prove simple geometric theorems algebraically.

Key Vocabulary

coordinate *(coordenada)* A number used to identify the location of a point. On a number line, one coordinate is used. On a coordinate plane, two coordinates are used, called the *x*-coordinate and the *y*-coordinate. In space, three coordinates are used, called the *x*-coordinate, the *y*-coordinate, and the *z*-coordinate.

What It Means For You

Positioning geometric diagrams on a coordinate grid makes algebraic tools such as the Midpoint and Distance Formulas available to you to prove geometric relationships.

EXAMPLE

You can use coordinates and the Distance Formula to prove that $\overline{AB}$, which joins the midpoints of $\overline{PR}$ and $\overline{QR}$, is half as long as $\overline{PQ}$.

$$AB = \sqrt{(4-0)^2 + (0-3)^2}$$
$$= \sqrt{16+9}$$
$$= 5$$
$$PQ = \sqrt{(8-0)^2 + (0-6)^2}$$
$$= \sqrt{64+36}$$
$$= 10$$

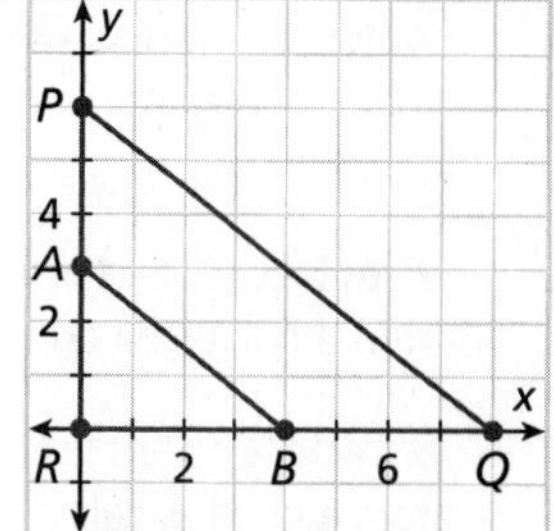

UNIT 6

Key Vocabulary

axis of symmetry *(eje de simetria)* A line that divides a plane figure or a graph into two congruent reflected halves.

circle *(círculo)* The set of points in a plane that are a fixed distance from a given point called the center of the circle.

coordinate *(coordenada)* A number used to identify the location of a point. On a number line, one coordinate is used. On a coordinate plane, two coordinates are used, called the x-coordinate and the y-coordinate. In space, three coordinates are used, called the x-coordinate, the y-coordinate, and the z-coordinate.

directrix *(directriz)* A fixed line used to define a *parabola*. Every point on the parabola is equidistant from the directrix and a fixed point called the *focus*.

parabola *(parábola)* The shape of the graph of a quadratic function. Also, the set of points equidistant from a point F, called the *focus*, and a line d, called the directrix.

radius of a circle *(radio de un círculo)* A segment whose endpoints are the center of a circle and a point on the circle; the distance from the center of a circle to any point on the circle.

vertex of a parabola *(vértice de una parábola)* The highest or lowest point on the parabola.

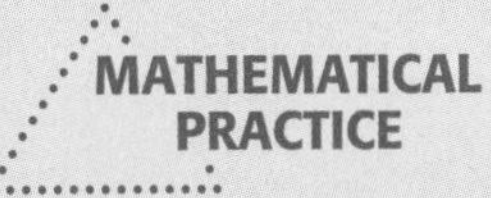

The Common Core Standards for Mathematical Practice describe varieties of expertise that mathematics educators at all levels should seek to develop in their students. Opportunities to develop these practices are integrated throughout this program.

1. **Make sense of problems and persevere in solving them.**
2. **Reason abstractly and quantitatively.**
3. **Construct viable arguments and critique the reasoning of others.**
4. **Model with mathematics.**
5. **Use appropriate tools strategically.**
6. **Attend to precision.**
7. **Look for and make use of structure.**
8. **Look for and express regularity in repeated reasoning**

UNIT 6

Name_______________ Class_______________ Date_______________

17-1

Introduction to Coordinate Proof

Going Deeper

Video Tutor

Essential question: *How do you write a coordinate proof?*

You have already seen a wide range of purely geometric proofs. These proofs used postulates and theorems to build logical arguments. Now you will learn how to write coordinate proofs. These proofs also use logic, but they apply ideas from algebra to help demonstrate geometric relationships.

MCC9–12.G.GPE.4

1 EXAMPLE Proving or Disproving a Statement

Prove or disprove that the triangle with vertices $A(4, 2)$, $B(-1, 4)$, and $C(2, -3)$ is an isosceles triangle.

A Plot the vertices and draw the triangle.

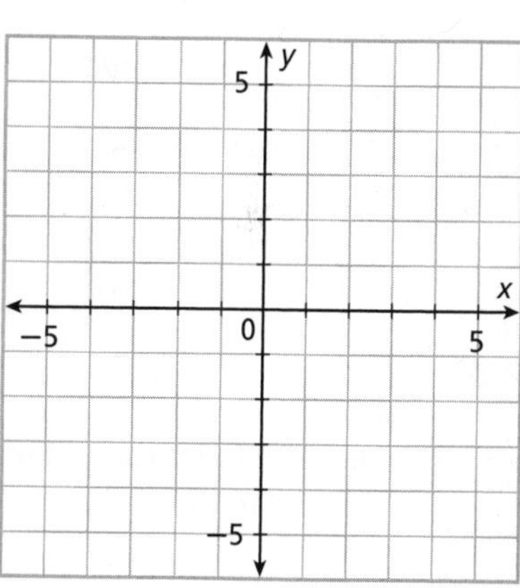

B Use the distance formula to find the length of each side of $\triangle ABC$.

$$AB = \sqrt{(-1-4)^2 + (4-2)^2} = \sqrt{(-5)^2 + 2^2} = \sqrt{29}$$

$BC =$ _______________

$AC =$ _______________

C Draw a conclusion based on your results. State whether or not the triangle is isosceles and why.

____

REFLECT

1a. What other conclusion(s) can you make about the sides or angles of $\triangle ABC$? Explain.

____

____

1b. Suppose you map $\triangle ABC$ to $\triangle A'B'C'$ by the translation $(x, y) \to (x - 3, y - 2)$. Is $\triangle A'B'C'$ an isosceles triangle? Why or why not?

____

____

You can write a coordinate proof to prove general facts about geometric figures. The first step in such a proof is using variables to assign general coordinates to a figure using only what is known about the figure.

MCC9–12.G.GPE.4

2 EXAMPLE Writing a Coordinate Proof

Prove that in a right triangle, the midpoint of the hypotenuse is equidistant from all three vertices.

A Assign coordinates to the figure.

Let the triangle be $\triangle ABC$. Since the triangle is a right triangle, assume $\angle B$ is a right angle. Place $\angle B$ at the origin and place the legs along the positive x- and y-axes.

Since the proof involves a midpoint, use multiples of 2 in assigning coordinates to A and C, as shown.

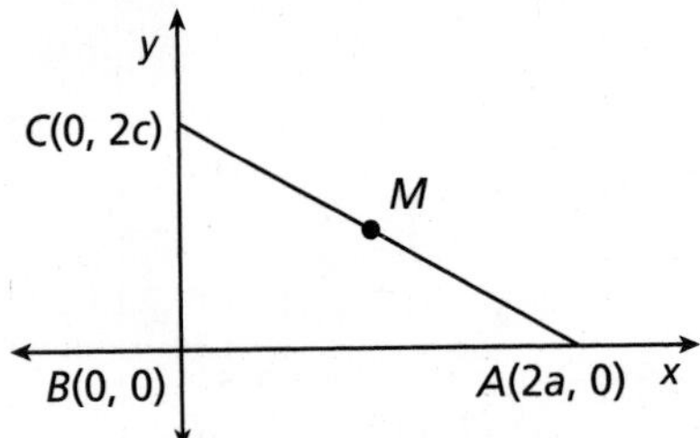

B Let M be the midpoint of the hypotenuse, $\overline{AC}$. Use the midpoint formula to find the coordinates of M.

$$M\left(\frac{\square + \square}{2}, \frac{\square + \square}{2}\right) = M(\square, \square)$$

C Use the distance formula to find MA, MB, and MC.

$$MA = \sqrt{(\square - \square)^2 + (\square - \square)^2} = \sqrt{\square^2 + \square^2}$$

$$MB = \sqrt{(\square - \square)^2 + (\square - \square)^2} = \sqrt{\square^2 + \square^2}$$

$$MB = \sqrt{(\square - \square)^2 + (\square - \square)^2} = \sqrt{\square^2 + \square^2}$$

So, the midpoint of the hypotenuse is equidistant from all three vertices because

____

____

REFLECT

2a. Explain why it is more convenient to assign the coordinates as $A(2a, 0)$ and $C(0, 2c)$ rather than $A(a, 0)$ and $C(0, c)$.

2b. Can you write the proof by assigning the coordinates as $A(2n, 0)$ and $C(0, 2n)$?

PRACTICE

1. Prove or disprove that the triangle with vertices $R(-2, -2)$, $S(1, 4)$, and $T(4, -5)$ is an equilateral triangle.

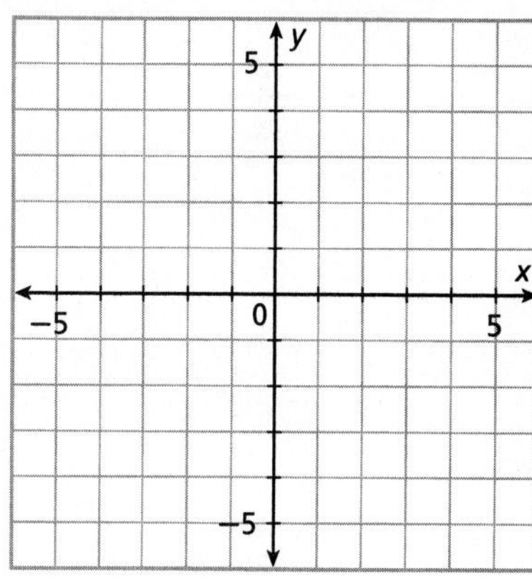

2. Refer to the triangle you drew in Exercise 1 to prove or disprove that the triangle with vertices $R(-2, -2)$, $S(1, 4)$, and $T(4, -5)$ is a right triangle.

3. $\triangle ABC$ has vertices $A(-4, 1)$, $B(-3, 4)$, and $C(-1, 1)$. $\triangle DEF$ has vertices $D(2, -3)$, $E(5, -2)$, and $F(2, 0)$. Prove or disprove that the triangles are congruent.

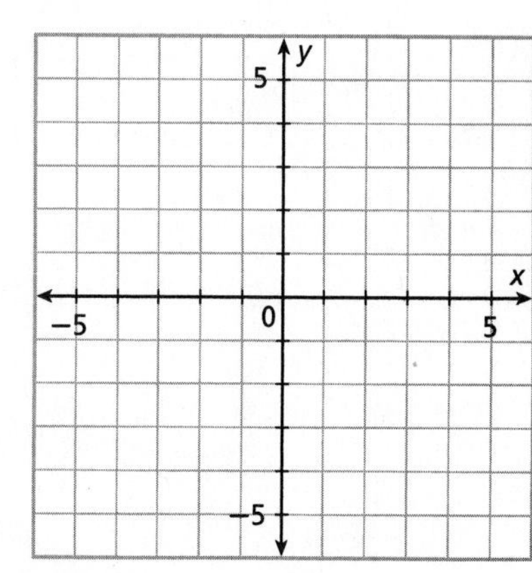

4. Write a coordinate proof to prove that the diagonals of a rectangle are congruent. Use the space at right to show how to assign coordinates. Then write the proof below.

____

____

____

____

5. Error Analysis A student proves that every right triangle is isosceles by assigning coordinates as shown at right and by using the distance formula to show that $PQ = a$ and $RQ = a$. Explain the error in the student's proof.

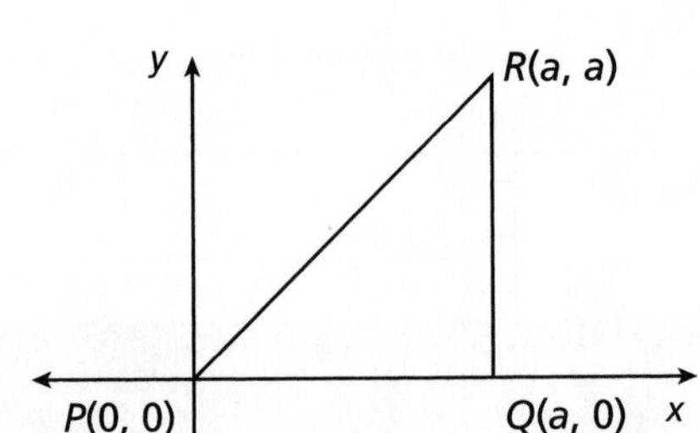

____

____

____

____

Name ______________________ Class ____________ Date ____________

17-1

Additional Practice

Position an isosceles triangle with sides of 8 units, 5 units, and 5 units in the coordinate plane. Label the coordinates of each vertex. (*Hint:* Use the Pythagorean Theorem.)

1. Center the long side on the *x*-axis at the origin.

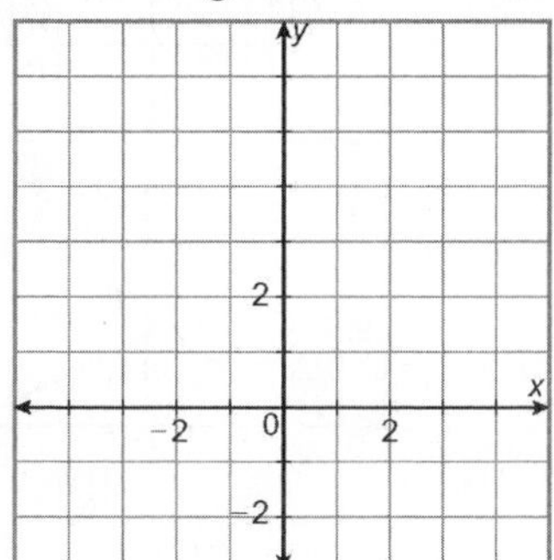

2. Place the long side on the *y*-axis centered at the origin.

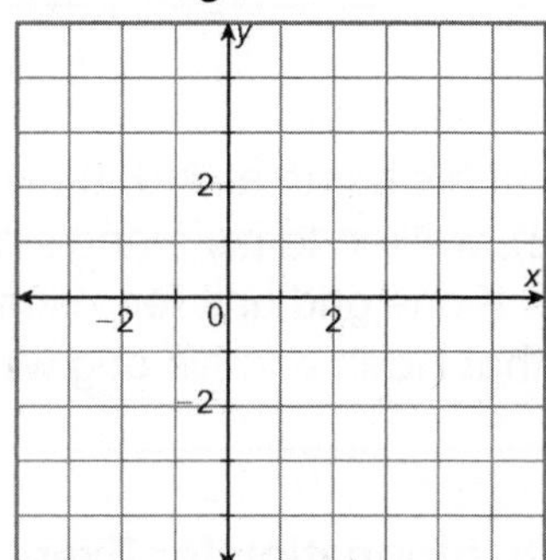

Write a coordinate proof.

3. **Given:** Rectangle *ABCD* has vertices *A*(0, 4), *B*(6, 4), *C*(6, 0), and *D*(0, 0). *E* is the midpoint of $\overline{DC}$. *F* is the midpoint of $\overline{DA}$.

   Prove: The area of rectangle *DEGF* is one-fourth the area of rectangle *ABCD*.

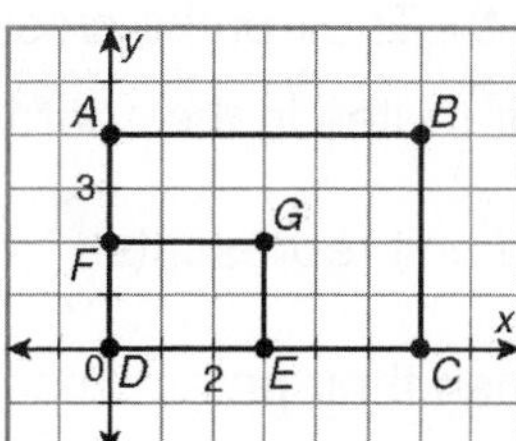

Problem Solving

Round to the nearest tenth for Exercises 1 and 2.

1. A fountain is at the center of a square courtyard. If one grid unit represents one yard, what is the distance from the fountain at (0, 0) to each corner of the courtyard?

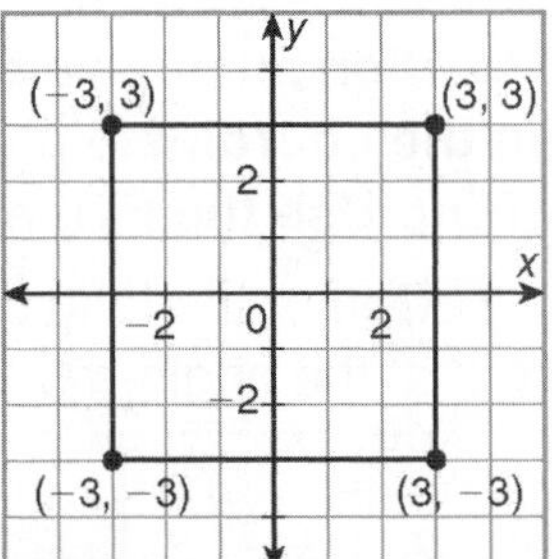

____

2. Noah started at his home at $A(0, 0)$, walked with his dog to the park at $B(4, 2)$, walked to his friend's house at $C(8, 0)$, then walked home. If one grid unit represents 20 meters, what is the distance that Noah and his dog walked?

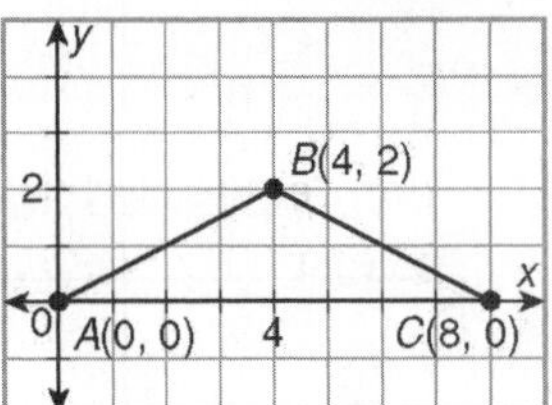

____

Use the following information for Exercises 3 and 4.

Rachel started her cycling trip at $G(0, 7)$. Malik started his trip at $J(0, 0)$. Their paths crossed at $H(4, 2)$.

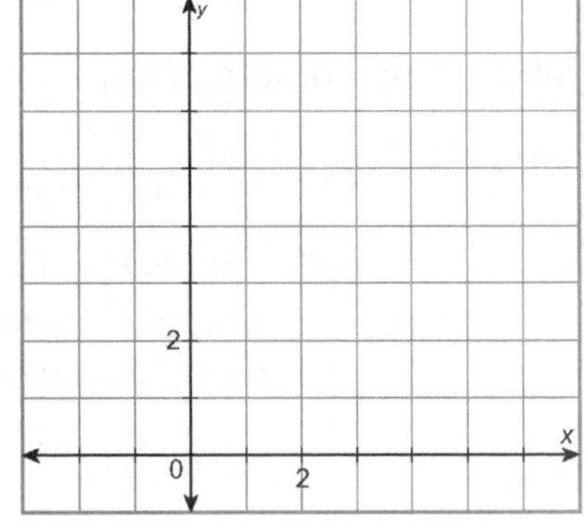

3. Draw their routes in the coordinate plane.

4. If one grid unit represents $\frac{1}{2}$ mile, who had ridden farther when their paths crossed? Explain.

____

____

Choose the best answer.

5. Two airplanes depart from an airport at $A(9, 11)$. The first airplane travels to a location at $N(-250, 80)$, and the second airplane travels to a location at $P(105, -400)$. Each unit represents 1 mile. What is the distance, to the nearest mile, between the two airplanes?

   A 335.3 mi C 490.3 mi

   B 477.9 mi D 597.0 mi

6. A corner garden has vertices at $Q(0, 0)$, $R(0, 2d)$, and $S(2c, 0)$. A brick walkway runs from point Q to the midpoint M of $\overline{RS}$. What is QM?

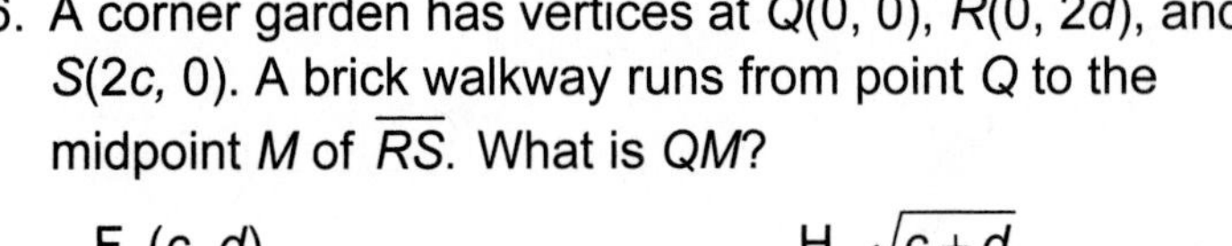

   F (c, d) H $\sqrt{c+d}$

   G $c^2 + d^2$ J $\sqrt{c^2+d^2}$

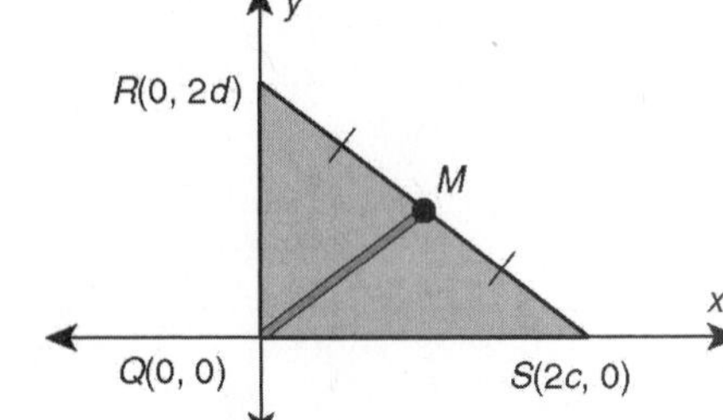

Name ______________________ Class ______________ Date __________

17-2

Circles in the Coordinate Plane

Connection: Completing the Square

Essential question: *How can you write and use equations of circles in the coordinate plane?*

Recall that a circle is the set of all points in a plane that are a fixed distance from a given point. Now you will investigate circles in a coordinate plane.

MCC9–12.G.GPE.1

1 EXPLORE Deriving the Equation of a Circle

Consider the circle in a coordinate plane that has its center at $C(h, k)$ and that has radius r.

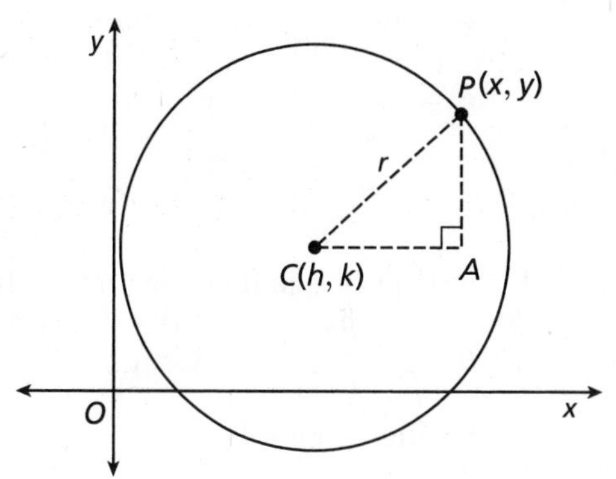

A Let P be any point on the circle and let the coordinates of P be (x, y).

Create a right triangle by drawing a horizontal line through C and a vertical line through P, as shown.

What are the coordinates of point A? ______________

Write expressions for the lengths of the legs of $\triangle CAP$.

$CA =$ ______________; $PA =$ ______________

B Use the Pythagorean Theorem to write a relationship among the side lengths of $\triangle CAP$.

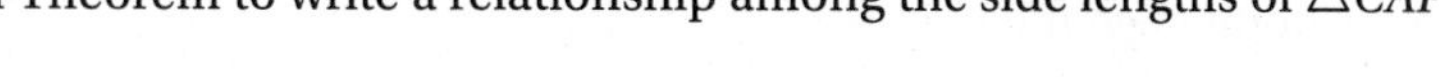

REFLECT

1a. Compare your work with that of other students. Then write the equation of a circle with center (h, k) and radius r.

____

1b. Why do you need absolute values when you write expressions for the lengths of the legs in Step A, but not when you write the relationship among the side lengths in Step B?

____

____

1c. Suppose a circle has its center at the origin. What is the equation of the circle in this case?

____

Equation of a Circle

The equation of a circle with center (h, k) and radius r is $(x - h)^2 + (y - k)^2 = r^2$.

MCC9–12.G.GPE.1

2 EXAMPLE Finding the Center and Radius of a Circle

Find the center and radius of the circle whose equation is $x^2 - 4x + y^2 + 2y = 4$. Then graph the circle.

A Complete the square to write the equation in the form $(x - h)^2 + (y - k)^2 = r^2$.

$x^2 - 4x + \square + y^2 + 2y + \square = 4 + \square$	Set up to complete the square.
$x^2 - 4x + \_\_\_\_ + y^2 + 2y + \_\_\_\_ = 4 + \_\_\_\_\_\_\_\_$	Add $\left(\frac{-4}{2}\right)^2$ and $\left(\frac{2}{2}\right)^2$ to both sides.
$x^2 - 4x + \_\_\_\_ + y^2 + 2y + \_\_\_\_ = 4 + \_\_\_\_$	Simplify.
$(x - \_\_\_\_)^2 + (y + \_\_\_\_)^2 = \_\_\_\_\_\_\_\_$	Factor.

B Identify h, k, and r to determine the center and radius.

$h =$ ______ $k =$ ______ $r =$ ______

So, the center is (______, ______) and the radius is ______.

C Graph the circle.

- Locate the center of the circle.
- Place the point of your compass at the center.
- Open the compass to the radius.
- Use the compass to draw the circle.

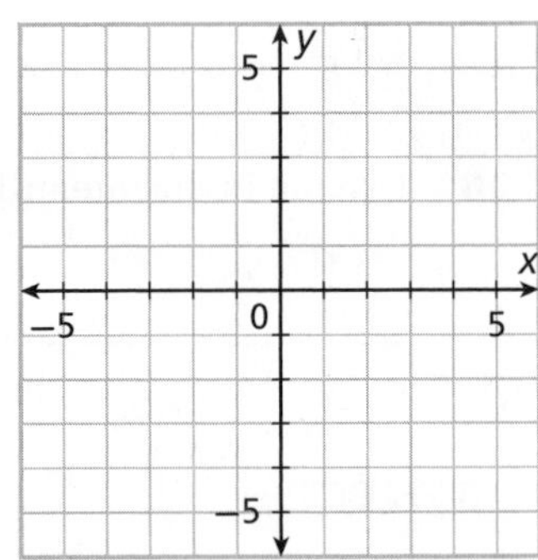

REFLECT

2a. How can you check your graph by testing specific points from the graph in the original equation? Give an example.

____

____

2b. Suppose you translate the circle by the translation $(x, y) \rightarrow (x + 4, y - 1)$. What is the equation of the image of the circle? Explain.

____

____

MCC9–12.G.GPE.4

3 EXAMPLE Writing a Coordinate Proof

Prove or disprove that the point $(1, \sqrt{15})$ lies on the circle that is centered at the origin and contains the point (0, 4).

A Plot a point at the origin and at (0, 4). Use these to help you draw the circle centered at the origin that contains (0, 4).

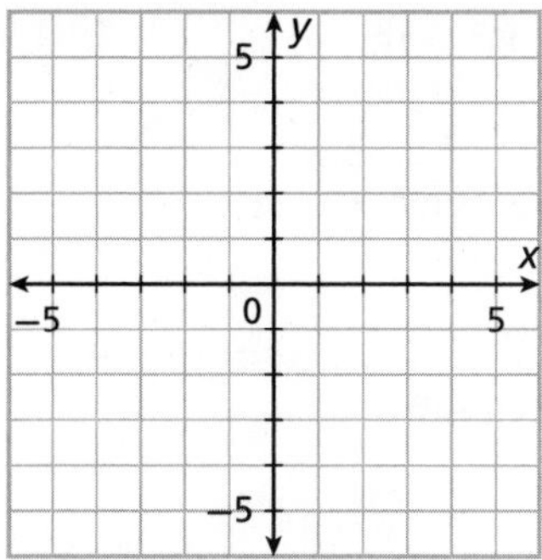

B Determine the radius: $r =$ ____________________

C Use the radius and the coordinates of the center to write the equation of the circle.

____

D Substitute the *x*- and *y*-coordinates of the point $(1, \sqrt{15})$ in the equation of the circle to check whether they satisfy the equation.

$\_\_\_\_\_\_^2 + \_\_\_\_\_\_^2 \stackrel{?}{=} 16$ Substitute.

$\_\_\_\_\_\_ + \_\_\_\_\_\_ = 16$ Simplify.

E So, the point $(1, \sqrt{15})$ lies on the circle because

____

REFLECT

3a. Explain how to determine the radius of the circle.

____

____

3b. Name another point with noninteger coordinates that lies on the circle. Explain.

____

3c. Explain how you can prove that the point $(2, \sqrt{5})$ does *not* lie on the circle.

____

____

Recall that you can solve a system of two equations in two unknowns by graphing both equations and finding the point(s) of intersection of the graphs. You can also solve a system using the algebraic methods of substitution or elimination. In the next Examples, you will see how these techniques may be used with systems that include a quadratic equation.

MCC9–12.A.REI.7

4 EXAMPLE Solving a System by Graphing

Solve the system of equations. $\begin{cases} (x-1)^2 + (y-1)^2 = 16 \\ y = x + 4 \end{cases}$

A The equation $(x-1)^2 + (y-1)^2 = 16$ represents a circle with center ________ and radius ________.

The equation $y = x + 4$ represents a line with slope ________ and y-intercept ________.

B Graph the equations on the coordinate plane below.

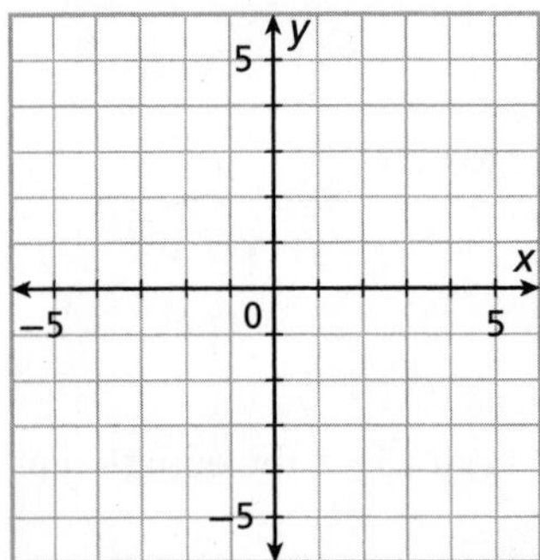

C The solutions of $(x-1)^2 + (y-1)^2 = 16$ are exactly the points on the circle. The solutions of $y = x + 4$ are exactly the points on the line. The solutions of the system are points that lie on both the circle and the line. These are the points of intersection of the circle and the line.

So, the solutions of the system are ________________________.

REFLECT

4a. How can you check your solutions? Check them.

____

____

____

4b. How many solutions are possible when a system of equations involves a circle and a line? Explain.

____

____

MCC9–12.A.REI.7

5 EXAMPLE Solving a System Algebraically

Solve the system of equations. $\begin{cases} x^2 + y^2 = 13 \\ y = -5x \end{cases}$

A Use substitution to write an equation in one variable. The second equation is already solved for y, so substitute this expression for y into the first equation.

$x^2 + y^2 = 13$	Write the first equation.
$x^2 + (\_\_\_\_\_\_)^2 = 13$	Substitute $-5x$ for y in the equation.
$x^2 + \_\_\_\_\_\_ = 13$	Square the expression in parentheses.
$\_\_\_\_\_\_ = 13$	Combine like terms.
$x^2 = \_\_\_\_\_\_$	Use the Division Property of Equality.
$x = \_\_\_\_\_\_$	Take the square root of both sides.
$x = \_\_\_\_\_\_$	Rationalize the denominator.

B Substitute each x-value into one of the original equations to find the corresponding y-values.

Substitute into the simpler equation, $y = -5x$.

When $x =$ ______, $y =$ ______.

When $x =$ ______, $y =$ ______.

So, the solutions of the system are ____________________.

REFLECT

5a. Is it possible to solve this system of equations by graphing? Explain.

____

____

5b. Based on what you know about the graphs of the equations in this system, why does it make sense that there are two solutions?

____

____

MCC9–12.A.REI.7

6 EXAMPLE Solving a System Involving a Parabola

Solve the system of equations. $\begin{cases} y = x^2 - 3 \\ y = 8x - 19 \end{cases}$

A Use substitution to write an equation in one variable. Substitute the expression for y from the second equation into the first equation.

$y = x^2 - 3$	Write the first equation.
________ $= x^2 - 3$	Substitute $8x - 19$ for y in the equation.
$0 =$ ________	Get 0 on one side of the equation.
$0 =$ ________	Combine like terms.
$0 =$ ________	Factor.
$0 =$ ________	Take the square root of both sides.
$x =$ ________	Solve for x.

B Substitute the x-value into one of the original equations to find the corresponding y-value.

Substitute into the equation $y = x^2 - 3$.

When $x =$ ______, $y =$ ______.

So, the solution of the system is ____________.

REFLECT

6a. In Step B, what would happen if you substituted the value of x in the other equation?

____

6b. Verify that the slope of the line that contains $(0, -19)$ and $(4, 13)$ is 8.

____

6c. Since there is only one solution of the system, what does this tell you about the line and the parabola that are represented by the equations?

____

6d. How many solutions are possible when a system of equations involves a parabola and a line? Explain.

____

____

PRACTICE

Write the equation of the circle with the given center and radius.

1. center: (0, 2); radius: 5

____

2. center: (−1, 3); radius 8

____

3. center: (−4, −5); radius: $\sqrt{2}$

____

4. center: (9, 0); radius $\sqrt{3}$

____

Find the center and radius of the circle with the given equation. Then graph the circle.

5. $x^2 - 2x + y^2 = 15$

____

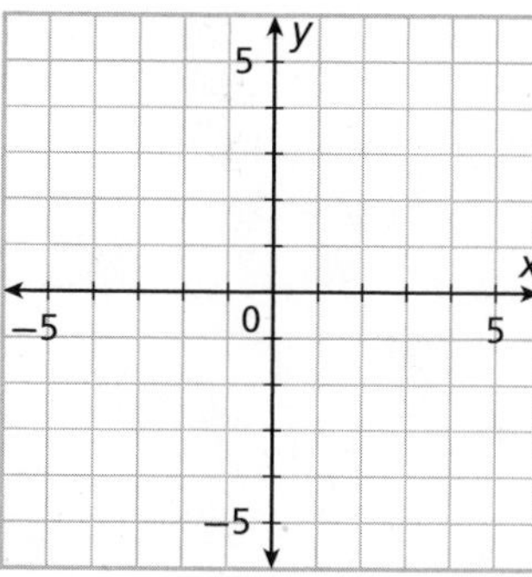

6. 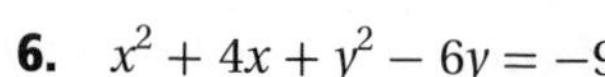 $x^2 + 4x + y^2 - 6y = -9$

____

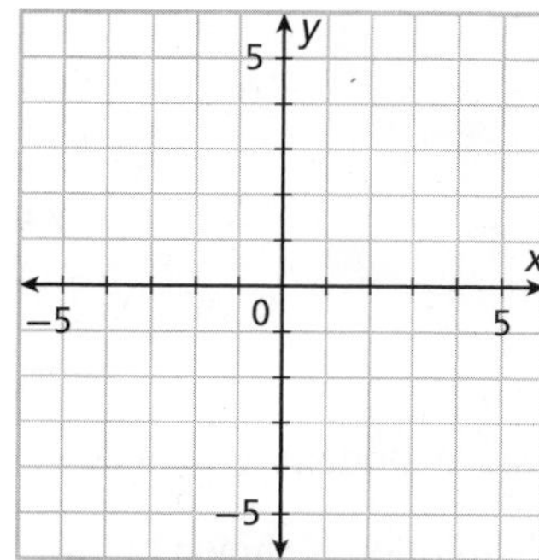

7. Prove or disprove that the point $(1, \sqrt{3})$ lies on the circle that is centered at the origin and contains the point (0, 2).

____

____

____

8. Prove or disprove that the point $(2, \sqrt{3})$ lies on the circle that is centered at the origin and contains the point (−3, 0).

____

____

____

9. Prove or disprove that the circle with equation $x^2 - 4x + y^2 = -3$ intersects the y-axis.

____

____

____

Solve each system of equations by graphing.

10. $\begin{cases} (x-2)^2 + y\text{^}2 = 4 \\ y = -x \end{cases}$

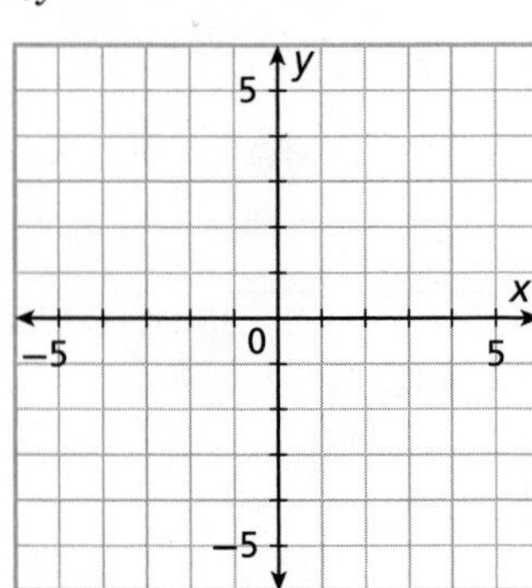

11. $\begin{cases} (x+1)^2 + (y-1)^2 = 9 \\ y = x - 1 \end{cases}$

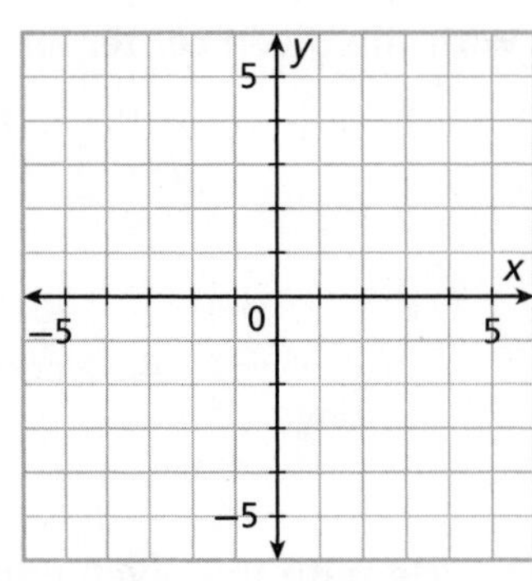

12. $\begin{cases} y = x^2 - 1 \\ y = -x + 1 \end{cases}$

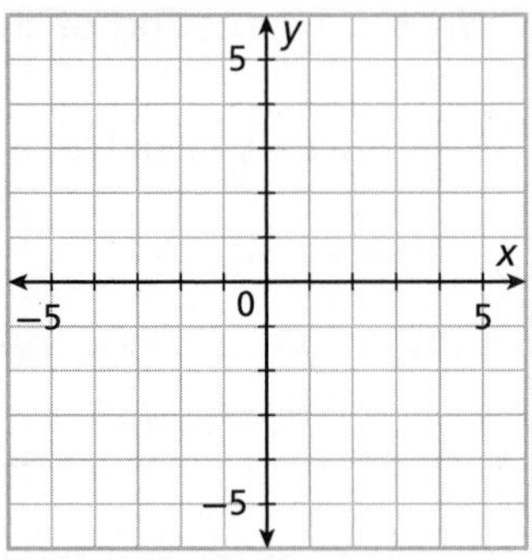

Solve each system of equations algebraically.

13. $\begin{cases} x^2 + y^2 = 10 \\ y = -3x \end{cases}$

14. $\begin{cases} x^2 + y^2 = 25 \\ y = 7x \end{cases}$

15. $\begin{cases} x^2 + y^2 = 13 \\ y = -8x \end{cases}$

16. $\begin{cases} y = x^2 \\ y = -x + 2 \end{cases}$

17. $\begin{cases} y = x^2 + 2 \\ y = 4 \end{cases}$

18. $\begin{cases} y = -x^2 + 2 \\ y = x - 4 \end{cases}$

19. **Error Analysis** A student was asked to solve the system $\begin{cases} x^2 + y^2 = 9 \\ y = x \end{cases}$. The student's solution is shown below. Critique the student's work. If there is an error, give the correct solution.

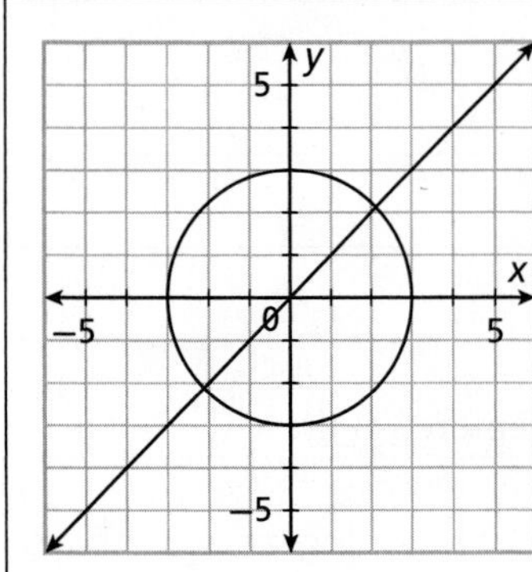

The graph of $x^2 + y^2 = 9$ is a circle centered at the origin with radius 3. The graph of $y = x$ is a straight line through the origin. The graphs intersect at (2, 2) and (−2, −2), so these are the solutions.

Name________________ Class__________ Date__________ **17-2**

Additional Practice

1. Write an equation of a circle with center $B(0, -2)$ that passes through $(-6, 0)$. ________________

Complete the square to rewrite the given equation in the form $(x - h)^2 + (y - k)^2 = r^2$. Identify the center and radius of the circle. Then graph the circle.

2. $x^2 + 2x + y^2 - 6y = -6$

____

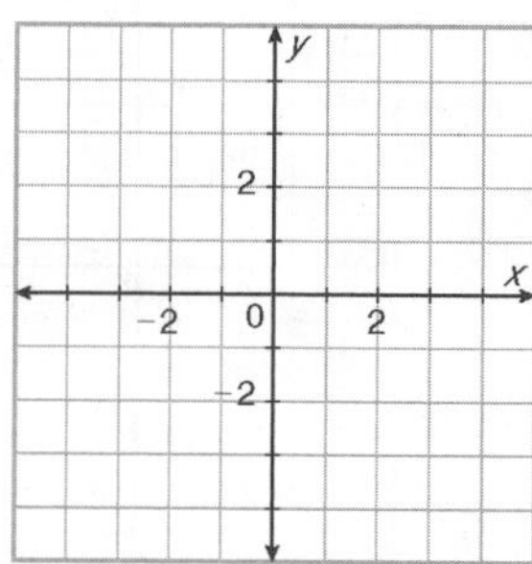

3. $x^2 + 4x + y^2 + 6y = -9$

____

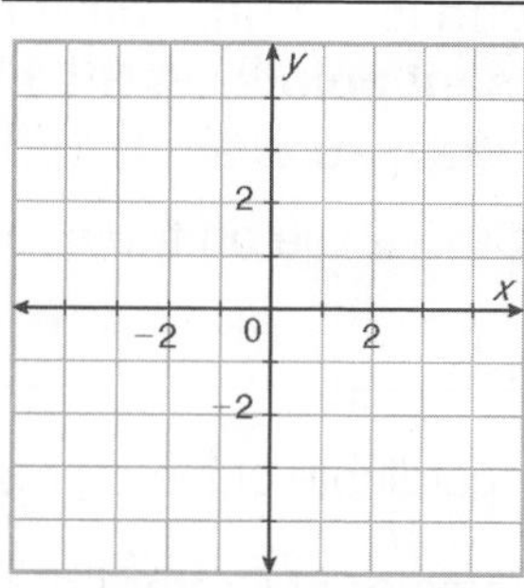

4. $x^2 - 2x + y^2 - 2y = 14$

____

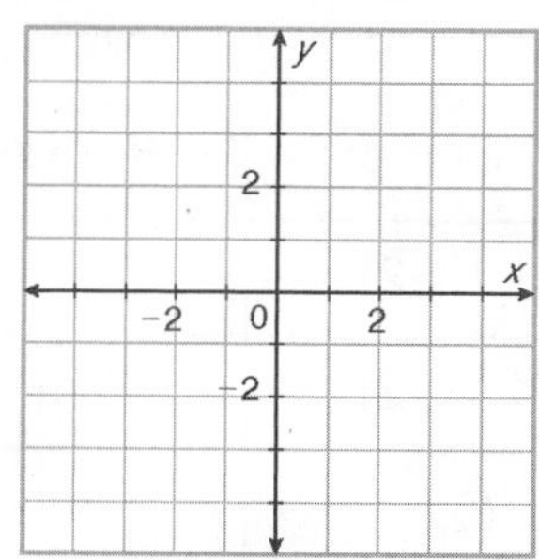

5. $x^2 + y^2 + 6y = -8$

____

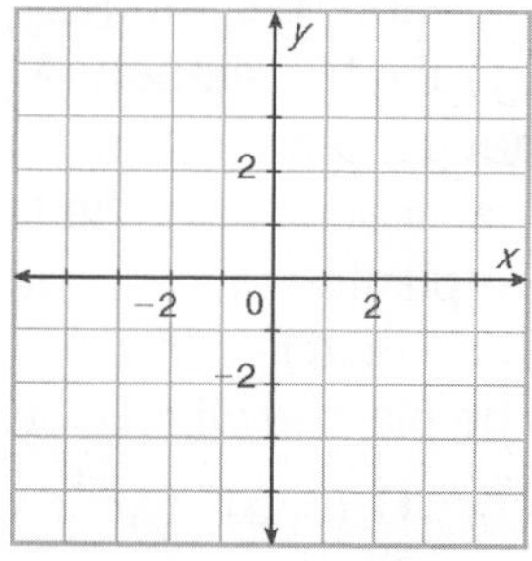

6. Solve the system of equations by graphing.

$$\begin{cases} x^2 + (y - 2)^2 = 9 \\ y = x - 1 \end{cases}$$

____

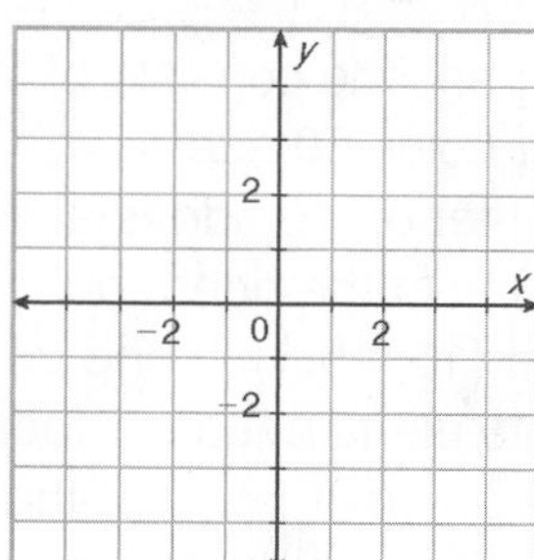

Solve each system of equations algebraically.

7. $\begin{cases} x^2 + y^2 = 25 \\ x - y = 5 \end{cases}$

____

8. $\begin{cases} y = -x^2 \\ y = -x - 2 \end{cases}$

____

9. $\begin{cases} (x - 2)^2 + y^2 = 100 \\ y = -10 \end{cases}$

____

Problem Solving

1. Prove or disprove that the circle that is centered at the origin and contains the point (–4, –3) intersects the line $x = 6$.

____

____

____

Crater Lake in Oregon is roughly circular. Suppose that *A*(–4, 1) and *B*(–2, –3) represent points on the circular shoreline of the lake. The center of the lake is at (1, 1).

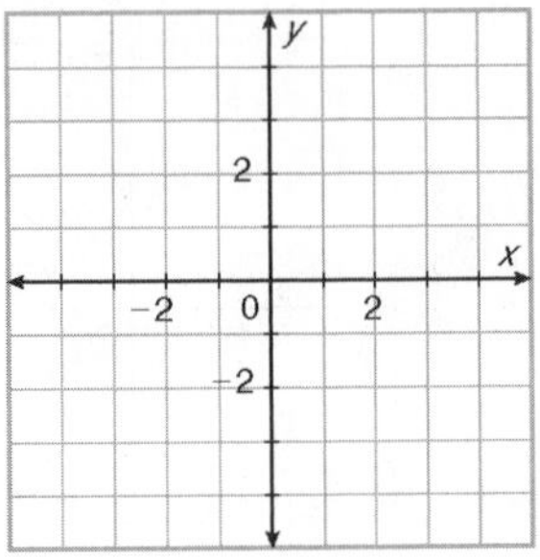

2. Does the point $C(5, -2)$ lie on the shoreline of the lake?

____

3. Each unit of the coordinate plane represents $\frac{3}{5}$ mile. Find the diameter of Crater Lake.

____

Choose the best answer.

4. An English knot garden has hedges planted to form geometric shapes. A blueprint of a knot garden contains three circular hedges as described in the table. Flowers are to be planted in the space that is within all three circles. Which is a point that could be planted with flowers?

   A (7, 1) C (0, 5)
   B (5, 1) D (0, 0)

Circular Hedge	Center	Radius
A	(3, 2)	3 ft
B	(7, 2)	4 ft
C	(5, –1)	3 ft

5. An amusement park ride consists of a circular ring that holds 50 riders. Suppose the center of the ride is at the origin and that one of the riders on the circular ring is at (16, 15.1). If one unit on the coordinate plane equals 1 foot, which is a close approximation of the distance the rider travels during one complete revolution of the circle?

   F 22 ft H 138 ft
   G 44 ft J 1521 ft

6. Which of these circles intersects the circle that has center (0, 6) and radius 1?

   A $(x - 5)^2 + (y + 3)^2 = 4$
   B $(x - 4)^2 + (y - 3)^2 = 9$
   C $(x + 5)^2 + (y + 1)^2 = 16$
   D $(x + 1)^2 + (y - 4)^2 = 4$

7. The center of a circle is (9, 2), and the radius of the circle is 5 units. Which is a point on the circle?

   F (4, 2) H (9, 4)
   G (14, 0) J (9, –5)

Name ______________________ Class ____________ Date ________

17-3

Parabolas

Going Deeper

Essential question: *What are the defining features of a parabola?*

Like the circle, the ellipse, and the hyperbola, the parabola can be defined in terms of distance. A parabola is the set of all points in a plane that are the same distance from a fixed point, called the **focus**, and a fixed line, called the **directrix**. The midpoint of the shortest segment connecting the focus and the directrix is the **vertex** of the parabola. The **axis of symmetry** is a line perpendicular to the directrix and passes through the focus and the vertex.

MCC9–12.G.GPE.2

1 EXPLORE Deriving the Equation of a Parabola

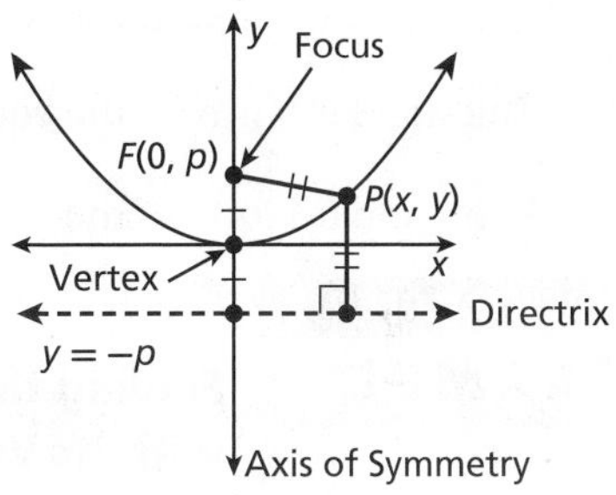

Use distance on the coordinate plane to find the equation of a parabola.

A In the figure, $P(x, y)$ on the parabola is equidistant from the focus $F(0, p)$ and the directrix $y = -p$.
A line perpendicular to the directrix from P intersects the directrix at $D(x, -p)$.

$\sqrt{(x - x_1)^2 + (y - y_1)^2} = \sqrt{(x - x_2)^2 + (y - y_2)^2}$ Distance Formula

$\sqrt{(\quad)^2 + (\quad)^2} = \sqrt{(\quad)^2 + (\quad)^2}$ Substitute (0, p) for (x_1, y_1) and $(x, -p)$ for (x_2, y_2).

$\sqrt{\quad + (\quad)^2} = \sqrt{(\quad)^2}$ Simplify.

$\quad + (\quad)^2 = (\quad)^2$ Square both sides.

$\quad + \quad - \quad + \quad = \quad + \quad + \quad$ Expand the binomials.

$\quad - \quad = \quad$ Subtract y^2 and p^2 from both sides.

$x^2 = \quad$ Add $2yp$ to both sides.

$y = \frac{\quad}{\quad}(x^2)$ Solve for y.

This is the standard form of the equation of a parabola. Sometimes, the equation is given in the form $x^2 =$ __________.

B A parabola has its focus at $F(0, 6)$ and directrix $y = -6$.

The equation of the parabola is $y =$ __________.

C The focus of the parabola $x^2 = 18y$ is __________. The directrix is __________.

REFLECT

1. In the first step of the derivation of the equation of a parabola, the points $(0, p)$ and $(x, -p)$ were substituted for (x_1, y_1) and (x_2, y_2), yielding the equation $\sqrt{(x-0)^2 + (y-p)^2}$ $= \sqrt{(x-x)^2 + (y+p)^2}$. Compare that equation with the equation you would write if the parabola were rotated 90° so that its axis of symmetry were horizontal, as in the figure at the right. How would the remaining equations in the derivation be affected? What would the derivation yield as the standard form of the equation of a parabola with a horizontal axis of symmetry?

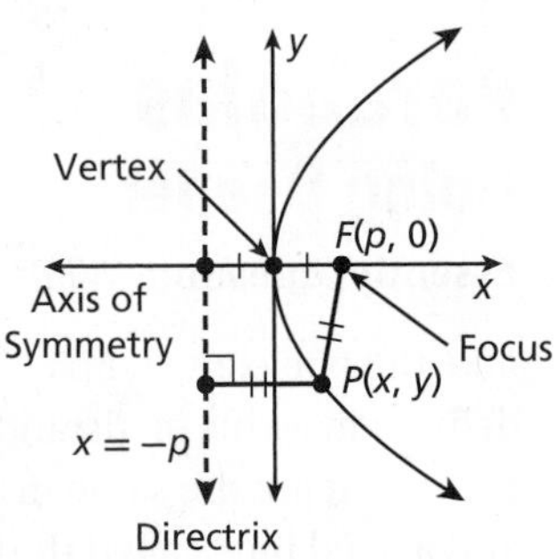

___

___

___

The standard form of the equation of a parabola with a vertical axis is $y = \frac{1}{4p}x^2$.

The standard form of the equation of a parabola with a horizontal axis is $x = \frac{1}{4p}y^2$.

MCC9–12.G.GPE.2

2 EXAMPLE Finding the Equation of a Parabola with its Vertex at the Origin

Write the equation of each parabola in standard form.

A

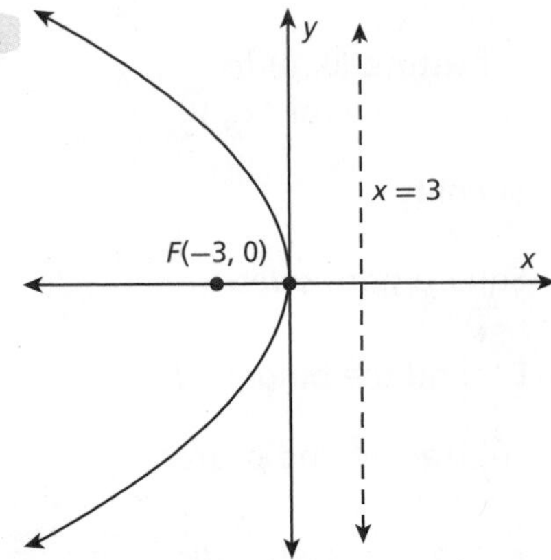

___

B

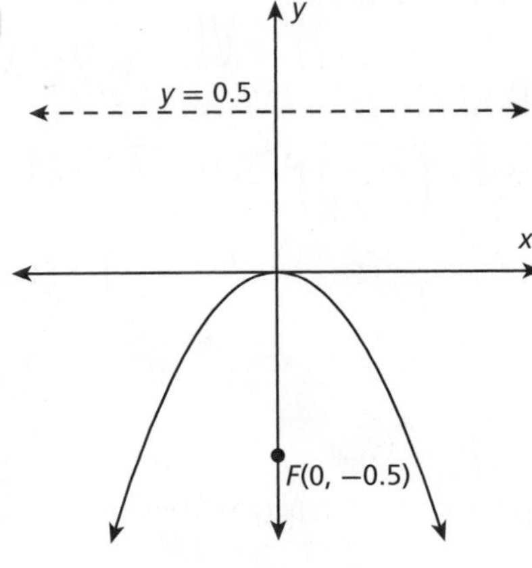

___

REFLECT

2. Describe how the value of p relates to the shape of the parabola.

___

___

___

For the circle, the ellipse, and the hyperbola, translating the center of the conic section from (0, 0) to (h, k) changed x in the standard form of the equation of the figure to $x - h$ and changed y to $y - k$. A similar transformation takes place when the vertex of a parabola is translated from (0, 0) to (h, k).

Direction of Axis of Symmetry	Equation of Axis of Symmetry	Standard Form of the Equation of a Parabola with Vertex at (h, k)
Vertical	$x = h$	$y - k = \frac{1}{4p}(x - h)^2$
Horizontal	$y = k$	$x - h = \frac{1}{4p}(y - k)^2$

MCC9–12.G.GPE.2

3 EXAMPLE Finding the Equation of a Parabola with its Vertex Not at the Origin

Use the focus and directrix to sketch the parabola. Then find the equation of the parabola.

A A parabola has focus (3, 8) and directrix $y = 4$.

The vertex of the parabola is ________. So $h =$ ________ and $k =$ ________.

Use the fact that p equals the distance from the focus to the vertex to find p: $p =$ ________.

Standard form of the equation of the parabola: ________________

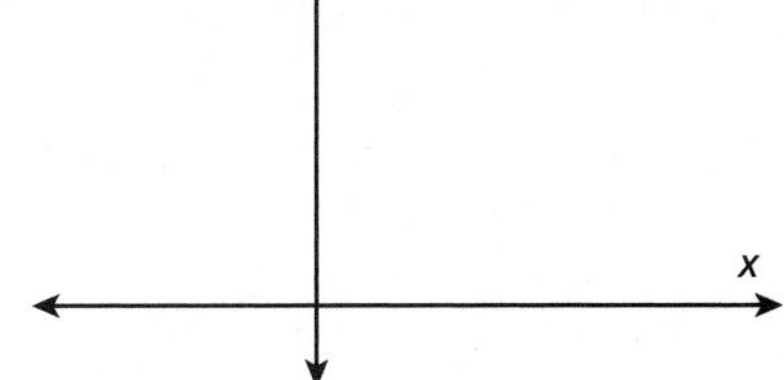

B A parabola has focus (3, −1) and directrix $x = -2$

The vertex of the parabola is ________. So $h =$ ________ and $k =$ ________.

Find p: $p =$ ________.

Standard form of the equation of the parabola: ________________

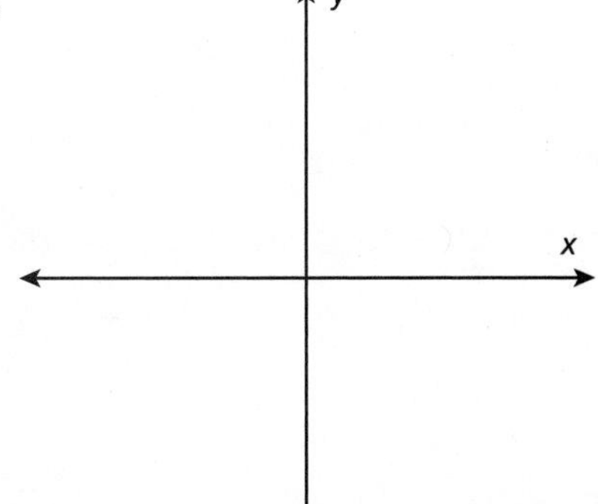

REFLECT

3. During the study of quadratic functions, the standard form of a quadratic function is given as $y = ax^2 + bx + c$. Find values of a, b, and c which show that this equation is equivalent to the standard form given in this lesson $y - k = \frac{1}{4p}(x - h)^2$. Explain how you found the values.

____

____

____

PRACTICE

Write the equation of each parabola in standard form.

	Focus	Directrix	Equation
1.	$F(2, 0)$	$x = -2$	________
2.	$F(0, 8)$	$y = -8$	________
3.	$F(-20, 0)$	$x = 20$	________
4.	$F\left(0, -\frac{1}{12}\right)$	$y = \frac{1}{12}$	________
5.	$F(5, 5)$	$y = -3$	________
6.	$F(3, 0)$	$x = -2$	________
7.	$F(4, -3)$	$y = 6$	________
8.	$F(8, 0)$	$y = 4$	________
9.	$F(10, -3)$	$x = 5$	________
10.	$F(6, 2)$	$x = 4$	________
11.	$F(7, -7)$	$x = -2$	________
12.	$F(-1, 2)$	$y = -1$	________

Name ______________________ Class ______________ Date ______________

17-3

Additional Practice

Use the Distance Formula to find the equation of a parabola with the given focus and directrix.

1. $F(6, 0)$, $x = -3$ ______________________

2. $F(1, 0)$, $x = -4$ ______________________

Write the equation in standard form for each parabola.

3. Vertex (0, 0), directrix $y = -2$ ______________________

4. Vertex (0, 0), focus (9, 0) ______________________

5. Focus (–6, 0), directrix $x = 6$ ______________________

6. Vertex (0, 0), focus (0, –3) ______________________

Find the vertex, value of *p*, axis of symmetry, focus, and directrix of each parabola. Then graph.

7. $x - 1 = -\frac{1}{12}y^2$

____

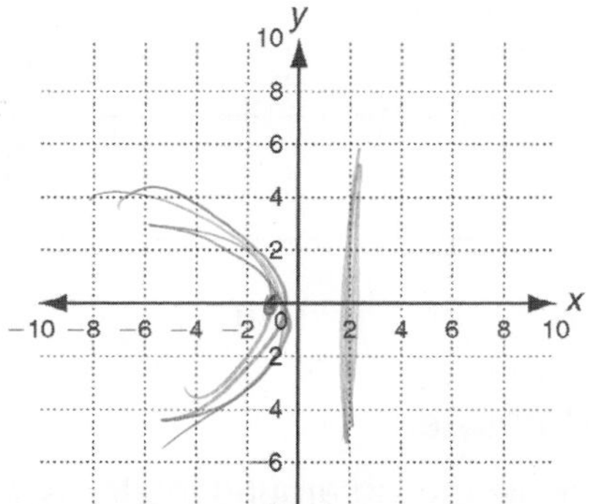

8. $y + 2 = \frac{1}{4}(x - 1)^2$

____

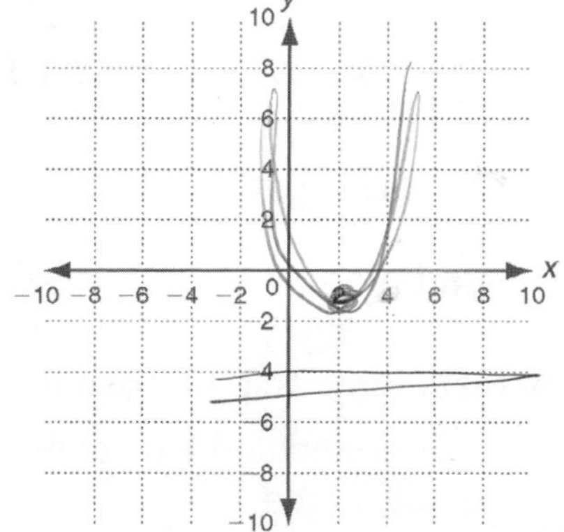

Solve.

9. A spotlight has parabolic cross sections.
   a. Write an equation for a cross section of the spotlight if the bulb is 6 inches from the vertex and the vertex is placed at the origin. ______________________
   b. If the spotlight has a diameter of 36 inches at its opening, find the depth of the spotlight if the bulb is 6 inches from the vertex. ______________________

Problem Solving

At a bungee-jumping contest, Gavin makes a jump that can be modeled by the equation $x^2 - 12x - 12y + 84 = 0$, with dimensions in feet.

1. Gavin wants to know how close he came to the ground during his jump.
    a. Classify the shape of his path. Identify the values for the coefficients of each term, and determine what conic section models his path.

    ____

    b. Write the equation of his path in standard form by completing the square.

    ____

    c. Which point on the path identifies the lowest point that Gavin reached? What are the coordinates of this point? How close to the ground was he?

    ____

2. Nicole makes a similar jump that can be modeled by the equation $x^2 - 4x - 8y + 84 = 0$. She wants to know whether she got closer to the ground than Gavin and by how much.
    a. Write the equation of Nicole's path in standard form.

    ____

    b. How close to the ground did she get? ______________

    c. Did Nicole get closer to the ground than Gavin? ______________

The design for a new auto racetrack can be modeled by the equation $x^2 + 4y^2 - 20x - 32y + 160 = 0$, with dimensions in kilometers. Tracey tests the track. Choose the letter for the best answer.

3. What is the standard form of the equation for the path of the racetrack?

    A $\frac{(x-10)^2}{1^2} + \frac{(y-4)^2}{2^2} = 1$

    B $\frac{(x-10)^2}{2^2} + \frac{(y-4)^2}{1^2} = 1$

    C $\frac{(x-4)^2}{2^2} + \frac{(y-10)^2}{1^2} = 1$

    D $\frac{(x-4)^2}{1^2} + \frac{(y-10)^2}{2^2} = 1$

4. While driving around the track, what is the greatest distance that Tracey will reach from the center of the track?

    F 1 km

    G 2 km

    H 10 km

    J 16 km

Name________________________ Class________________ Date________

UNIT 6

Performance Tasks

GPS COMMON CORE

MCC9-12.G.GPE.1
MCC9-12.G.GPE.2
MCC9-12.G.GPE.4

 **1.** Missy draws a map on the coordinate plane. She plots her house at the origin. She then draws a circle that represents all the places that are exactly 9 miles from the library.

a. The equation $x^2 - 8x + y^2 = 65$ represents the graph of the circle that Missy drew. Complete the square to find the center and radius of the circle.

b. How far does Missy live from the library? Explain.

 **2.** A graphic artist is using a coordinate plane to design a company logo. The logo has an equilateral triangle inscribed in a circle. The circle lies in Quadrant I, is tangent to the x- and y-axes, and has a radius of 10 units. One side of the triangle is parallel to the y-axis, and one vertex is at (20, 10).

a. Write the equation for the circle.

b. What is the length of the sides of the inscribed triangle? Round your answer to the nearest hundredth of a unit and show your work.

c. Use the fact that the base opposite the vertex at (20, 10) is parallel to the y-axis, and your result from part **b** to find the coordinates of the other two vertices. Round the coordinates to the nearest hundredth of a unit and show your work. (*Hint*: The vertices will be the same distance above and below a horizontal line passing through (20, 10)).

3. Chase wants to prove the following: Given a circle with radius r and center (0, 0), if (a, b) is on the circle, then the point $(-a, -b)$ is on the circle.

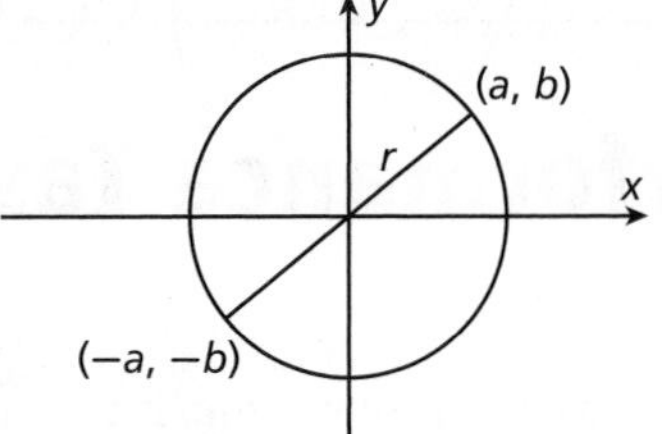

a. Use the figure to write the radius r in terms of a and b. Explain what you did.

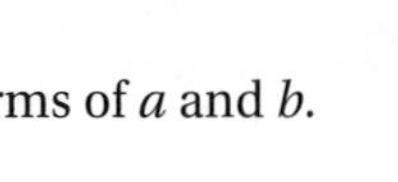

b. Write the equation of the circle using your expression for the radius from part **a**.

c. Use the equation to prove Chase's statement. Justify your answer.

4. In the diagram, $\overline{AC}$ bisects $\overline{BD}$ at K and $\overline{BD}$ bisects $\overline{AC}$ at K.

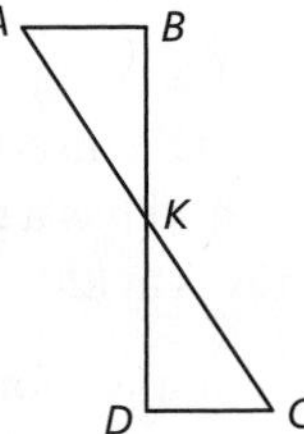

a. What must you know in order to prove that $\overline{AB} \parallel \overline{DC}$?

b. Write a plan to prove the criteria you gave in part **a**.

c. Prove $\overline{AB} \parallel \overline{DC}$.

Name ______________________ Class ______________ Date ________

SELECTED RESPONSE

1. Tyrell's teacher asks him to prove or disprove that the triangle with vertices $A(1, 1)$, $B(2, 5)$, and $C(6, 4)$ is an isosceles triangle. Which of the following should he do?

A. Disprove the statement by using the distance formula to show that $\overline{AB}$, $\overline{BC}$, and $\overline{AC}$ all have different lengths.

B. Prove the statement by using the distance formula to show that $AB = BC$.

C. Prove the statement by using the distance formula to show that $AB = AC$.

D. Prove the statement by using the distance formula to show that $BC = AC$.

2. What is the equation in standard form for the parabola with focus $F(0, -6,)$ and directrix $y = 6$?

F. $y = \frac{1}{24}x^2$

G. $x = \frac{1}{24}y^2$

H. $x = -\frac{1}{24}y^2$

J. $y = -\frac{1}{24}x^2$

3. What is an equation in standard form for the parabola shown?

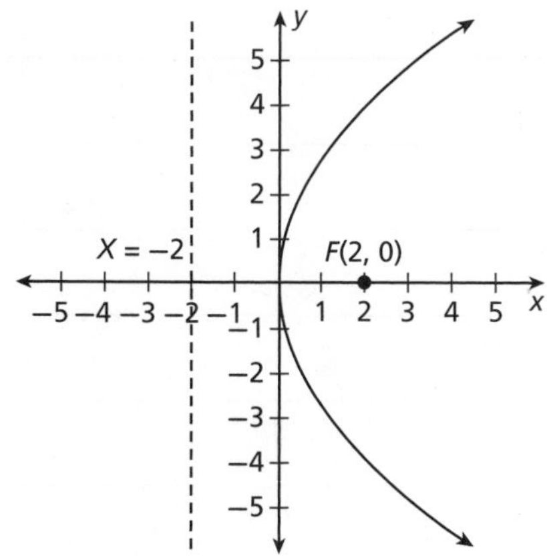

A. $y = -\frac{1}{8}x^2$

B. $y = \frac{1}{8}x^2$

C. $x = \frac{1}{8}y^2$

D. $x = -\frac{1}{8}y^2$

4. Three friends are planning to visit each other. To optimize travel time, they want the meeting place to be equidistant from the three different cities they live in. The cities are located at $A(-16, -1)$, $B(1, 6)$, and $C(1, -18)$. What are the coordinates where the meeting should take place?

F. $(-7.5, 2.5)$

G. $(-7, -9.5)$

H. $(-4.3, -4.3)$

J. $(-4, -6)$

5. Position a right triangle with leg lengths r and $2s + 4$ in the coordinate plane and give the coordinates of each vertex.

A.

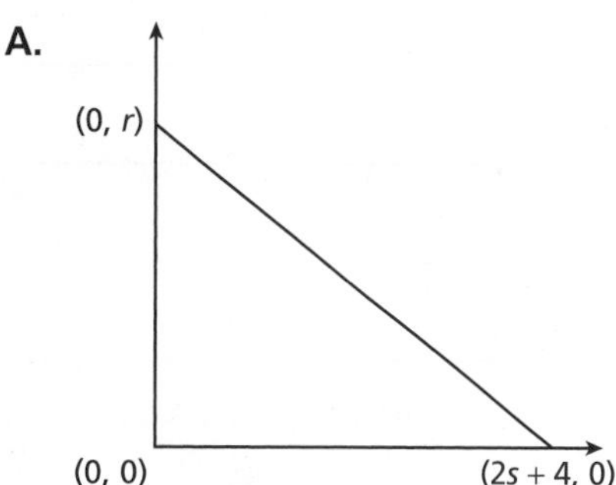

B.

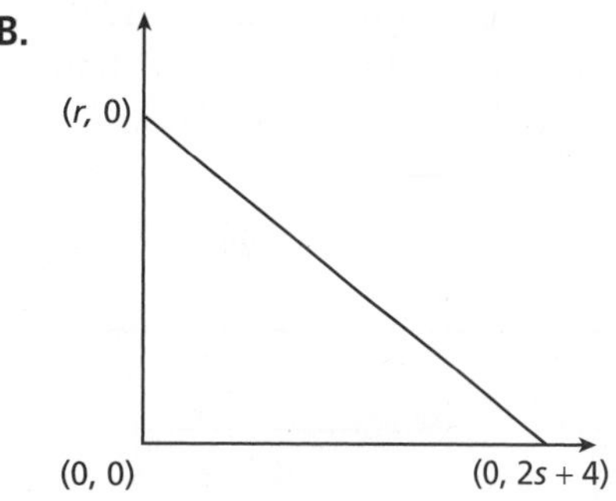

C.

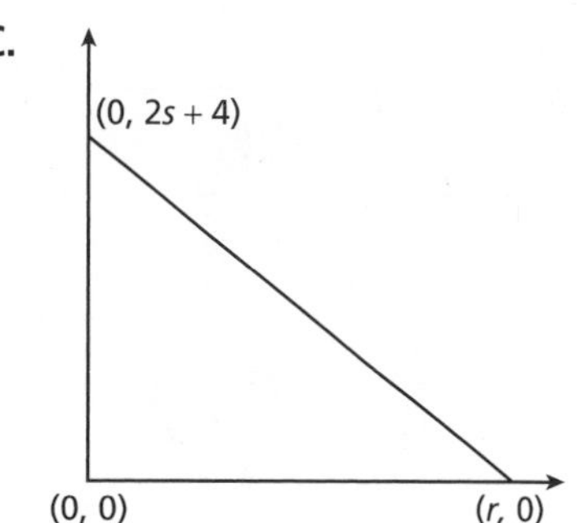

D. Both a. and c.

CONSTRUCTED RESPONSE

6. Prove or disprove that the point $(2, \sqrt{5})$ lies on the circle that is centered at the origin and contains the point $(0, -3)$.

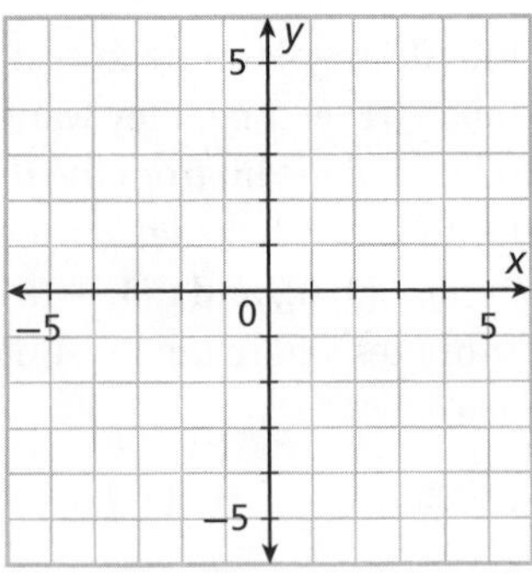

7. What is the equation of the parabola with focus $(4, -1)$ and directrix $x = 1$? Without graphing, tell the direction in which the parabola opens. How do you know?

8. Prove that the angle inscribed in a semicircle below is a right angle.

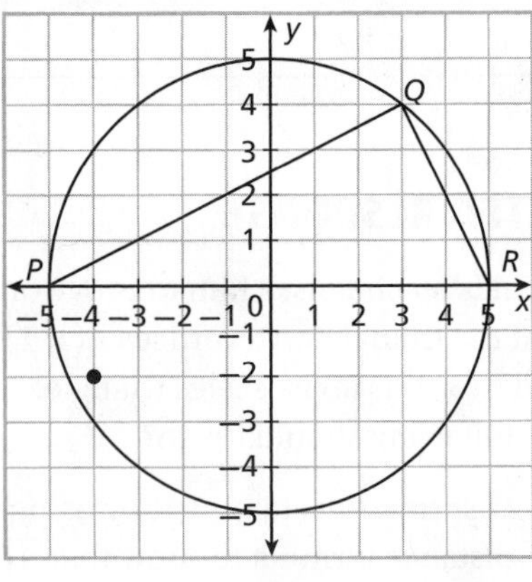

9. Find the point(s) of intersection of the line $x - y = -6$ and the circle $x^2 + y^2 = 18$ by solving the system of equations.

Applications of Probability

Module 18 Probability		
18-1	Geometric Probability	**MCC9-12.S.CP.1**
18-2	Permutations and Combinations	**MCC9-12.S.CP.9(+)**
18-3	Theoretical and Experimental Probability	**MCC9-12.S.CP.1**
Module 19 Conditional Probability		
19-1	Independent and Dependent Events	**MCC9-12.S.CP.2, MCC9-12.S.CP.3, MCC9-12.S.CP.5, MCC9-12.S.CP.6**
19-2	Two-Way Tables	**MCC9-12.S.CP.4**
19-3	Compound Events	**MCC9-12.S.CP.5, MCC9-12.S.CP.7**
	Performance Tasks	
	PARCC Assessment Readiness	

Unpacking the Standards

Understanding the standards and the vocabulary terms in the standards will help you know exactly what you are expected to learn in this unit.

MCC9-12.S.CP.9(+)

Use permutations and combinations to compute probabilities of compound events and solve problems.

Key Vocabulary

permutation *(permutación)*
An arrangement of a group of objects in which order is important. The number of permutations of r objects from a group of n objects is denoted ${}_nP_r$.

combination *(combinación)*
A selection of a group of objects in which order is *not* important. The number of combinations of r objects chosen from a group of n objects is denoted ${}_nC_r$.

probability *(probabilidad)*
A number from 0 to 1 (or 0% to 100%) that is the measure of how likely an event is to occur.

event *(suceso)* An outcome or set of outcomes in a probability experiment.

compound event *(suceso compuesto)* An event made up of two or more simple events.

UNIT 7

What It Means For You

A permutation is an arrangement of objects in which order is important. A combination is an arrangement of objects in which order is not important. Both permutations and combinations can be used to find probabilities.

EXAMPLE **Permutations**

Lindsey will choose two of these pictures to hang next to each other on her bedroom wall.

This is an example of a permutation because the order is important. Hanging the mountain picture to the right of the sunset picture is different from hanging the mountain picture to the left of the sunset picture.

EXAMPLE **Combinations**

You can choose three toppings for your hamburger.

This is an example of a combination because the order is not important. Tomato, onions, and pickles is the same as pickles, tomato, and onions.

MCC9-12.S.CP.1

Describe events as subsets of a sample space (the set of outcomes) using characteristics (or categories) of the outcomes, or as unions, intersections, or complements of other events ("or," "and," "not").

Key Vocabulary

sample space *(espacio muestral)* The set of all possible outcomes of a probability experiment.
outcome *(resultado)* A possible result of a probability experiment.
union *(unión)* The union of two sets is the set of all elements that are in either set, denoted by ∪.
intersection *(intersección de conjuntos)* The intersection of two sets is the set of all elements that are common to both sets, denoted by ∩.
complement of an event *(complemento de un suceso)* All outcomes in the sample space that are not in an event *E*, denoted $\overline{E}$ or E^c.

What It Means For You

To calculate the probability of a particular event, you may need to find the sample space, which is the set of all possible outcomes. You may also need to determine which outcome(s) in the sample space make up the event.

EXAMPLE **Sample Spaces**

1 1	1 2	1 3	1 4	1 5	1 6
2 1	2 2	2 3	2 4	2 5	2 6
3 1	3 2	3 3	3 4	3 5	3 6
4 1	4 2	4 3	4 4	4 5	4 6
5 1	5 2	5 3	5 4	5 5	5 6
6 1	6 2	6 3	6 4	6 5	6 6

The sample space for rolling two standard number cubes is shown. The circled outcomes make up the event "rolling a sum of 10."

GPS COMMON CORE

MCC9-12.S.CP.4

Construct and interpret two-way frequency tables of data when two categories are associated with each object being classified. Use the two-way table as a sample space to decide if events are independent and to approximate conditional probabilities.

Key Vocabulary

frequency table *(tabla de frecuencia)* A table that lists the number of times, or frequency, that each data value occurs.
independent events *(sucesos independientes)* Events for which the occurrence or non-occurrence of one event does not affect the probability of the other event.
conditional probability *(probabilidad condicional)* The probability of event *B*, given that event *A* has already occurred or is certain to occur, denoted $P(B|A)$.

What It Means For You

A two-way table organizes data about two variables. A two-way frequency table can be very helpful when finding probabilities.

EXAMPLE **Finding Conditional Probability**

		Owns a cat: Yes	No	Total
Owns a dog	Yes	0.15	0.24	0.39
	No	0.18	0.43	0.61
	Total	0.33	0.67	1

This two-way frequency table describes data collected by a sociologist who surveyed 100 randomly selected people about their pets. You can use this table to answer the question, "If a person in this survey has a dog, what is the probability that he or she also has a cat?"

UNIT 7

Key Vocabulary

combination *(combinación)* A selection of a group of objects in which order is *not* important. The number of combinations of r objects chosen from a group of n objects is denoted ${}_nC_r$.

complement of an event *(complemento de un suceso)* All outcomes in the sample space that are not in an event E, denoted $\overline{E}$ or E^C.

compound event *(suceso compuesto)* An event made up of two or more simple events.

conditional probability *(probabilidad condicional)* The probability of event B, given that event A has already occurred or is certain to occur, denoted $P(B|A)$.

convenience sample *(muestra de conveniencia)* A sample based on members of the population that are readily available.

dependent events *(sucesos dependientes)* Events for which the occurrence or non-occurrence of one event affects the probability of the other event.

event *(suceso)* An outcome or set of outcomes in a probability experiment.

factorial *(factorial)* If n is a positive integer, then n factorial, written $n!$, is $n \bullet (n-1) \bullet (n-2) \bullet \ldots \bullet 2 \bullet 1$. The factorial of 0 is defined to be 1.

frequency table *(tabla de frecuencia)* A table that lists the number of times, or frequency, that each data value occurs.

independent events *(sucesos independientes)* Events for which the occurrence or non-occurrence of one event does not affect the probability of the other event.

intersection *(intersección de conjuntos)* The intersection of two sets is the set of all elements that are common to both sets, denoted by $\cap$.

mutually exclusive events *(sucesos mutuamente excluyentes)* Two events are mutually exclusive if they cannot both occur in the same trial of an experiment.

outcome *(resultado)* A possible result of a probability experiment.

permutation *(permutación)* An arrangement of a group of objects in which order is important. The number of permutations of r objects from a group of n objects is denoted ${}_nP_r$.

probability *(probabilidad)* A number from 0 to 1 (or 0% to 100%) that is the measure of how likely an event is to occur.

random sample *(muestra aleatoria)* A sample selected from a population so that each member of the population has an equal chance of being selected.

sample space *(espacio muestral)* The set of all possible outcomes of a probability experiment.

union *(unión)* The union of two sets is the set of all elements that are in either set, denoted by $\cup$.

UNIT 7

Name_________________________ Class_______________ Date__________

18-1

Geometric Probability
Connection: Set Theory

Essential question: *How can you use set theory to help you calculate theoretical probabilities?*

Video Tutor

MCC9–12.S.CP.1

1 ENGAGE Introducing the Vocabulary of Sets

You will see that set theory is useful in calculating probabilities. A **set** is a well-defined collection of distinct objects. Each object in a set is called an **element** of the set. A set may be specified by writing its elements in braces. For example, the set S of prime numbers less than 10 may be written as $S = \{2, 3, 5, 7\}$.

The number of elements in a set S may be written as $n(S)$. For the set S of prime numbers less than 10, $n(S) = 4$.

The set with no elements is the **empty set** and is denoted by $\varnothing$ or $\{\ \}$. The set of all elements under consideration is the **universal set** and is denoted by U. The following terms describe how sets are related to each other.

Term	Notation	Venn Diagram
Set A is a **subset** of set B if every element of A is also an element of B.	$A \subset B$	U, B, A
The **intersection** of sets A and B is the set of all elements that are in both A and B.	$A \cap B$	U, A, B
The **union** of sets A and B is the set of all elements that are in A or B.	$A \cup B$	U, A, B
The **complement** of set A is the set of all elements in the universal set U that are not in A.	A^c	U, A

REFLECT

1a. For any set A, what is $A \cap \varnothing$? Explain.

____

____

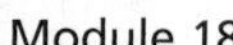

Recall that a *probability experiment* is an activity involving chance. Each repetition of the experiment is a *trial* and each possible result is an *outcome*. The *sample space* of an experiment is the set of all possible outcomes. An *event* is a set of outcomes.

When all outcomes of an experiment are equally likely, the **theoretical probability** that an event A will occur is given by $P(A) = \frac{n(A)}{n(S)}$, where S is the sample space.

MCC9–12.S.CP.1

2 EXAMPLE Calculating Theoretical Probabilities

You roll a number cube. Event *A* is rolling an even number. Event *B* is rolling a prime number. Calculate each of the following probabilities.

A $P(A)$ **B** $P(A \cup B)$ **C** $P(A \cap B)$ **D** $P(A^c)$

A $P(A)$ is the probability of rolling an even number. To calculate $P(A)$, first identify the sample space S.

$S =$ ____________________, so $n(S) =$ __________.

$A =$ ____________________, so $n(A) =$ __________.

So, $P(A) = \frac{n(A)}{n(S)} = \frac{\square}{\square} = \frac{\square}{\square}$.

B $P(A \cup B)$ is the probability of rolling an even number *or* a prime number.

$A \cup B =$ ____________________, so $n(A \cup B) =$ __________.

So, $P(A \cup B) = \frac{n(A \cup B)}{n(S)} = \frac{\square}{\square}$.

C $P(A \cap B)$ is the probability of rolling an even number *and* a prime number.

$A \cap B =$ ____________________, so $n(A \cap B) =$ __________.

So, $P(A \cap B) = \frac{n(A \cap B)}{n(S)} = \frac{\square}{\square}$.

D $P(A^c)$ is the probability of rolling a number that is *not* even.

$A^c =$ ____________________, so $n(A^c) =$ __________.

So, $P(A^c) = \frac{n(A^c)}{n(S)} = \frac{\square}{\square} = \frac{\square}{\square}$.

REFLECT

2a. Explain what $P(S)$ represents and then calculate this probability. Do you think this result is true in general? Explain.

____

____

You may have noticed in the example that $P(A) + P(A^c) = 1$. To see why this is true in general, note that an event and its complement represent all outcomes in the sample space, so $n(A) + n(A^c) = n(S)$.

$$P(A) + P(A^c) = \frac{n(A)}{n(S)} + \frac{n(A^c)}{n(S)}$$ Definition of theoretical probability

$$= \frac{n(A) + n(A^c)}{n(S)}$$ Add.

$$= \frac{n(S)}{n(S)} = 1$$ $n(A) + n(A^c) = n(S)$

You can write this relationship as $P(A) = 1 - P(A^c)$ and use it to help you find probabilities when it is more convenient to calculate the probability of the complement of an event.

Probabilities of an Event and Its Complement

The probability of an event and the probability of its complement have a sum of 1. So, the probability of an event is one minus the probability of its complement. Also, the probability of the complement of an event is one minus the probability of the event.

$$P(A) + P(A^c) = 1$$

$$P(A) = 1 - P(A^c)$$

$$P(A^c) = 1 - P(A)$$

MCC9–12.S.CP.1

3 EXAMPLE Using the Complement of an Event

You roll a blue number cube and white number cube at the same time. What is the probability that you do not roll doubles?

A Let A be the event that you do not roll doubles. Then A^c is the event that you do roll doubles.

Complete the table at right to show all outcomes in the sample space.

Circle the outcomes in A^c (rolling doubles).

White Number Cube

Blue Number Cube	1	2	3	4	5	6
1	1-1	1-2	1-3	1-4	1-5	1-6
2	2-1					
3	3-1					
4	4-1					
5	5-1					
6	6-1					

B Find the probability of rolling doubles.

$$P(A^c) = \frac{n(A^c)}{n(S)} = \frac{\quad}{\quad} = \frac{\quad}{\quad}$$

C Find the probability that you do not roll doubles.

$$P(A) = 1 - P(A^c) = 1 - \frac{\quad}{\quad} = \frac{\quad}{\quad}$$

REFLECT

3a. Describe a different way you could have calculated the probability that you do not roll doubles.

PRACTICE

You have a set of 10 cards numbered 1 to 10. You choose a card at random. Event *A* is choosing a number less than 7. Event *B* is choosing an odd number. Calculate each of the following probabilities.

1. $P(A)$

2. $P(B)$

3. $P(A \cup B)$

4. $P(A \cap B)$

5. $P(A^c)$

6. $P(B^c)$

7. A bag contains 5 red marbles and 10 blue marbles. You choose a marble without looking. Event *A* is choosing a red marble. Event *B* is choosing a blue marble. What is $P(A \cap B)$? Explain.

8. A standard deck of cards has 13 cards (2, 3, 4, 5, 6, 7, 8, 9, 10, jack, queen, king, ace) in each of 4 suits (hearts, clubs, diamonds, spades). You choose a card from a deck at random. What is the probability that you do not choose an ace? Explain.

9. You choose a card from a standard deck of cards at random. What is the probability that you do not choose a club? Explain.

10. **Error Analysis** A bag contains white tiles, black tiles, and gray tiles. $P(W)$, the probability of choosing a tile at random and choosing a white tile, is $\frac{1}{4}$. A student claims that the probability of choosing a black tile, $P(B)$, is $\frac{3}{4}$ since $P(B) = 1 - P(W) = 1 - \frac{1}{4} = \frac{3}{4}$. Do you agree? Explain.

Name__________ Class__________ Date__________ **18-1**

Additional Practice

Set $A = \{2, 4, 6, 8, 10\}$ and Set B is the set of all prime numbers less than 20. List the elements in each of the following sets.

1. B
2. $A \cup B$
3. $A \cap B$

A bag contains 26 tiles, one for each letter of the alphabet. Event A is drawing a tile with a vowel on it. Event B is drawing a tile with the letter A, B, C, D, E, or F on it. Calculate each of the following probabilities.

4. $P(A)$
5. $P(B)$
6. $P(A \cup B)$
7. $P(A \cap B)$
8. $P(A^C)$
9. $P(B^C)$

Find the probability of A^C for each of the following situations.

10. $P(A) = 0.3$
11. $P(A) = \frac{1}{4}$
12. A number cube with sides numbered 1–6 is rolled. A is rolling a 5.
13. A number cube with sides numbered 1–6 is rolled. A is rolling an even number.
14. Give an example of two sets A and B, for which A and $A \cup B$ both contain the exact same elements. Both sets should contain at least two elements, and the sets should not be the same.

Problem Solving

Write the correct answer.

1. The universal set U is the set of all integers from 1 through 20. You select one element of U at random. Event A is choosing 2, 6, or 18. What is $P(A^C)$?

____

2. A bag contains a total of 10 marbles. Four of the marbles are black, and 3 of the marbles are white. If Event A is drawing a black marble and Event B is drawing a white marble, what is $P(A \cup B)$?

____

3. Set $C = \{-2, -1, 0, 1, 2\}$ and Set D is the set of all positive integers. What elements are in the set $C \cap D$?

____

4. You roll two six-sided number cubes at the same time. Event A is rolling a 1 on both cubes. What is $P(A^C)$?

____

Select the best answer.

5. A spinner has four sections of equal size. The sections are painted blue, red, green, and yellow. Event A is spinning a yellow, and Event B is spinning a red. What is $P(A \cup B)$?

A $\frac{1}{4}$

B $\frac{1}{2}$

C $\frac{3}{4}$

D 1

6. What is $P(B^C)$ for the situation described in Exercise 5?

F $\frac{1}{4}$

G $\frac{1}{2}$

H $\frac{3}{4}$

J 1

7. Set $J = \{-\pi, \sqrt{2}, 0, 1\}$ and Set Q is the set of all rational numbers. Which set represents $J \cap Q$?

A $\varnothing$

B $\{0\}$

C $\{0, 1\}$

D Q

8. If you have two sets, A and B, and A and $A \cap B$ have the exact same elements, which statement must be true?

F B is the null set.

G Every element in A is also in B.

H Every element in B is also in A.

J $A \cup B$ is the null set.

Name ____________________ Class ____________ Date ________

18-2

Video Tutor

Permutations and Combinations

Going Deeper

Essential question: *What are permutations and combinations and how can you use them to calculate probabilities?*

A **permutation** is a selection of a group of objects in which order is important. For example, there are 6 permutations of the letters A, B, and C.

ABC	ACB
BAC	BCA
CAB	CBA

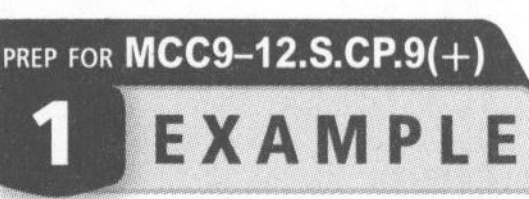

Finding Permutations

The members of a club want to choose a president, a vice-president, and a treasurer. Seven members of the club are eligible to fill these positions. In how many different ways can the positions be filled?

A Consider the number of ways each position can be filled.

There are __________ different ways the position of president can be filled.

Once the president has been chosen, there are __________ different ways the position of vice-president can be filled.

Once the president and vice-president have been chosen, there are __________ different ways the position of treasurer can be filled.

B Multiply to find the total number of different ways the positions can be filled.

President — Vice-President — Treasurer

__________ × __________ × __________ = __________ permutations

So, there are __________ different ways that the positions can be filled.

REFLECT

1a. Suppose the club members also want to choose a secretary from the group of 7 eligible members. In how many different ways can the four positions (president, vice-president, treasurer, secretary) be filled? Explain.

____

1b. Suppose 8 members of the club are eligible to fill the original three positions (president, vice-president, treasurer). In how many different ways can the positions be filled? Explain.

____

The process you used in the example can be generalized to give a formula for permutations. To do so, it is helpful to use factorials. For a positive integer n, n **factorial**, written $n!$, is defined as follows.

$$n! = n \cdot (n-1) \cdot (n-2) \cdot \ldots \cdot 3 \cdot 2 \cdot 1$$

That is, $n!$ is the product of n and all the positive integers less than n. Note that $0!$ is defined to be 1.

In the example, the number of permutations of 7 objects taken 3 at a time is

$$7 \cdot 6 \cdot 5 = \frac{7 \cdot 6 \cdot 5 \cdot \cancel{4} \cdot \cancel{3} \cdot \cancel{2} \cdot \cancel{1}}{\cancel{4} \cdot \cancel{3} \cdot \cancel{2} \cdot \cancel{1}} = \frac{7!}{4!} = \frac{7!}{(7-3)!}.$$

This can be generalized as follows.

Permutations

The number of permutations of n objects taken r at a time is given by

$${}_nP_r = \frac{n!}{(n-r)!}.$$

Recall that the probability of an event is equal to the number of outcomes that result in the event, divided by the number of all possible outcomes.

MCC9–12.S.CP.9(+)

2 EXAMPLE Using Permutations to Calculate a Probability

Every student at your school is assigned a four-digit code, such as 6953, to access the computer system. In each code, no digit is repeated. What is the probability that you are assigned a code with the digits 1, 2, 3, and 4 in any order?

A Let S be the sample space. Find $n(S)$.

The sample space consists of all permutations of 4 digits taken from the 10 digits 0 through 9.

$$n(S) = {}_{10}P_4 = \frac{10!}{(10-4)!} = \frac{10!}{6!} = \frac{10 \cdot 9 \cdot 8 \cdot 7 \cdot \cancel{6} \cdot \cancel{5} \cdot \cancel{4} \cdot \cancel{3} \cdot \cancel{2} \cdot \cancel{1}}{\cancel{6} \cdot \cancel{5} \cdot \cancel{4} \cdot \cancel{3} \cdot \cancel{2} \cdot \cancel{1}} = \underline{\qquad}$$

B Let A be the event that your code has the digits 1, 2, 3, and 4. Find $n(A)$.

The event consists of all permutations of 4 digits chosen from the 4 digits 1 through 4.

$$n(A) = {}_4P_4 = \frac{4!}{(4-4)!} = \frac{4!}{0!} = \frac{\qquad}{\qquad} = \underline{\qquad}$$

C Find $P(A)$.

$$P(A) = \frac{n(A)}{n(S)} = \frac{\qquad}{\qquad} = \underline{\qquad}$$

So, the probability that your code has the digits 1, 2, 3, and 4 is ________.

REFLECT

2a. What is the probability that you are assigned the code 1234? Explain.

____

A **combination** is a grouping of objects in which order does not matter. For example, when you choose 3 letters from the letters A, B, C, and D, there are 4 different combinations.

ABC **ABD** **ACD** **BCD**

PREP FOR MCC9–12.S.CP.9(+)

3 EXAMPLE Finding Combinations

A restaurant offers 8 side dishes. When you order an entree, you can choose 3 of the side dishes. In how many ways can you choose 3 side dishes?

Side Dishes	
Beets	Rice
Potatoes	Broccoli
Carrots	Cole slaw
Salad	Apple sauce

A First find the number of ways to choose 3 sides dishes when order does matter. This is the number of permutations of 8 objects taken 3 at a time.

$${}_8P_3 = \frac{8!}{(8-3)!} = \frac{8!}{5!} = \frac{}{} = \underline{}$$

B In this problem, order does not matter, since choosing beets, carrots, and rice is the same as choosing rice, beets, and carrots.

Divide the result from Step A by ${}_3P_3$, which is the number of ways the 3 side dishes can be ordered.

$${}_3P_3 = \frac{}{} = \frac{}{} = \underline{}$$

So, the number of ways you can choose 3 side dishes is $\frac{}{} = \underline{}$.

REFLECT

3a. Suppose the restaurant offers a special on Mondays that allows you to choose 4 side dishes. In how many ways can you choose the side dishes?

____

3b. In general, are there more ways or fewer ways to select objects when order does not matter? Why?

____

____

The process you used in the example can be generalized to give a formula for combinations. In order to find ${}_8C_3$, the number of combinations of 8 objects taken 3 at a time, you first found the number of permutations of 8 objects taken 3 at a time, then you divided by 3! That is,

$${}_8C_3 = \frac{8!}{(8-3)!} \div 3! \text{ or } \frac{8!}{3!(8-3)!}.$$

This can be generalized as follows.

Combinations

The number of combinations of n objects taken r at a time is given by

$${}_nC_r = \frac{n!}{r!(n-r)!}.$$

MCC9–12.S.CP.9(+)

4 EXAMPLE Using Combinations to Calculate a Probability

There are 5 boys and 6 girls in a school play. The director randomly chooses 3 of the students to meet with a costume designer. What is the probability that the director chooses all boys?

A Let S be the sample space. Find $n(S)$.

The sample space consists of all combinations of 3 students taken from the group of 11 students.

$$n(S) = {}_{11}C_3 = \frac{11!}{3!(11-3)!} = \frac{11!}{3! \cdot 8!} = \frac{11 \cdot 10 \cdot 9 \cdot \cancel{8} \cdot \cancel{7} \cdot \cancel{6} \cdot \cancel{5} \cdot \cancel{4} \cdot \cancel{3} \cdot \cancel{2} \cdot \cancel{1}}{3 \cdot 2 \cdot 1 \cdot \cancel{8} \cdot \cancel{7} \cdot \cancel{6} \cdot \cancel{5} \cdot \cancel{4} \cdot \cancel{3} \cdot \cancel{2} \cdot \cancel{1}} = \underline{\qquad\qquad}$$

B Let A be the event that the director chooses all boys. Find $n(A)$.

Suppose the 11 students are B_1, B_2, B_3, B_4, B_5, G_1, G_2, G_3, G_4, G_5, G_6, where the Bs represent boys and the Gs represent girls.

The combinations in event A are combinations like $B_2B_4B_5$ and $B_1B_3B_4$. That is, event A consists of all combinations of 3 boys taken from the set of 5 boys.

So, $n(A) = {}_5C_3 = \frac{\qquad}{\qquad} = \frac{\qquad}{\qquad} = \frac{\qquad}{\qquad} = \underline{\qquad\qquad}$.

C Find $P(A)$.

$$P(A) = \frac{n(A)}{n(S)} = \frac{\qquad}{\qquad} = \underline{\qquad\qquad}$$

So, the probability that the director chooses all boys is ________.

REFLECT

4a. Is the director more likely to choose all boys or all girls? Why?

PRACTICE

1. An MP3 player has a playlist with 12 songs. You select the shuffle option for the playlist. In how many different orders can the songs be played?

2. There are 10 runners in a race. Medals are awarded for 1st, 2nd, and 3rd place. In how many different ways can the medals be awarded?

3. There are 9 players on a baseball team. In how many different ways can the coach choose players for first base, second base, third base, and shortstop?

4. You have 15 photographs of your school. In how many different ways can you arrange 6 of them in a line for the cover of the school yearbook?

5. A bag contains 9 tiles, each with a different number from 1 to 9. You choose a tile, put it aside, choose a second tile, put it aside, and then choose a third tile. What is the probability that you choose tiles with the numbers 1, 2, and 3 in that order?

6. There are 11 students on a committee. To decide which 3 of these students will attend a conference, 3 names are chosen at random by pulling names one at a time from a hat. What is the probability that Sarah, Jamal, and Mai are chosen in any order?

7. **Error Analysis** A student solved the problem at right. The student's work is shown. Did the student make an error? If so, explain the error and provide the correct answer.

A bag contains 6 tiles with the letters A, B, C, D, E, and F. You choose 4 tiles one at a time without looking and line up the tiles as you choose them. What is the probability that your tiles spell BEAD?

Let S be the sample space and let A be the event that the tiles spell BEAD.

$$n(S) = {}_6P_4 = \frac{6!}{(6-4)!} = \frac{6!}{2!} = 360$$

$$n(A) = {}_4P_4 = \frac{4!}{(4-4)!} = \frac{4!}{0!} = 4! = 24$$

So, $P(A) = \frac{n(A)}{n(S)} = \frac{24}{360} = \frac{1}{15}$.

8. A cat has a litter of 6 kittens. You plan to adopt 2 of the kittens. In how many ways can you choose 2 of the kittens from the litter?

9. An amusement park has 11 roller coasters. In how many ways can you choose 4 of the roller coasters to ride during your visit to the park?

10. A school has 5 Spanish teachers and 4 French teachers. The school's principal randomly chooses 2 of the teachers to attend a conference. What is the probability that the principal chooses 2 Spanish teachers?

11. There are 6 fiction books and 8 nonfiction books on a reading list. Your teacher randomly assigns you 4 books to read over the summer. What is the probability that you are assigned all nonfiction books?

12. A bag contains 26 tiles, each with a different letter of the alphabet written on it. You choose 3 tiles from the bag without looking. What is the probability that you choose the tiles containing the letters A, B, and C?

13. You are randomly assigned a password consisting of 6 different characters chosen from the digits 0 to 9 and the letters A to Z. As a percent, what is the probability that you are assigned a password consisting of only letters?

14. Calculate ${}_{10}C_6$ and ${}_{10}C_4$.

a. What do you notice about these values? Explain why this makes sense.

b. Use your observations to help you state a generalization about combinations.

15. Use the formula for combinations to make a generalization about ${}_nC_n$. Explain why this makes sense.

Name______________________ Class______________ Date______________ **18-2**

Additional Practice

Use the Fundamental Counting Principle.

1. The soccer team is silk-screening T-shirts. They have 4 different colors of T-shirts and 2 different colors of ink. How many different T-shirts can be made using one ink color on a T-shirt? ________________

2. A travel agent is offering a vacation package. Participants choose the type of tour, a meal plan, and a hotel class from the table below.

Tour	Meal	Hotel
Walking	Restaurant	4-Star
Boat	Picnic	3-Star
Bicycle		2-Star
		1-Star

How many different vacation packages are offered? ________________

Evaluate.

3. $\dfrac{3!6!}{3!}$

4. $\dfrac{10!}{7!}$

5. $\dfrac{9!-6!}{(9-6)!}$

________________ ________________ ________________

Solve.

6. In how many ways can the debate team choose a president and a secretary if there are 10 people on the team? ________________

7. A teacher is passing out first-, second-, and third-place prizes for the best student actor in a production of *Hamlet*. If there are 14 students in the class, in how many different ways can the awards be presented? ________________

Evaluate.

8. ${}_5P_4$

9. ${}_3C_2$

10. ${}_8P_3$

________________ ________________ ________________

Solve.

11. Mrs. Marshall has 11 boys and 14 girls in her kindergarten class this year.
    a. In how many ways can she select 2 girls to pass out a snack? ________________
    b. In how many ways can she select 5 boys to pass out new books? ________________
    c. In how many ways can she select 3 students to carry papers to the office? ________________

Problem Solving

Rosalie is looking at locks. The label *combination lock* confuses her. She wonders about the number of possible permutations or combinations a lock can have.

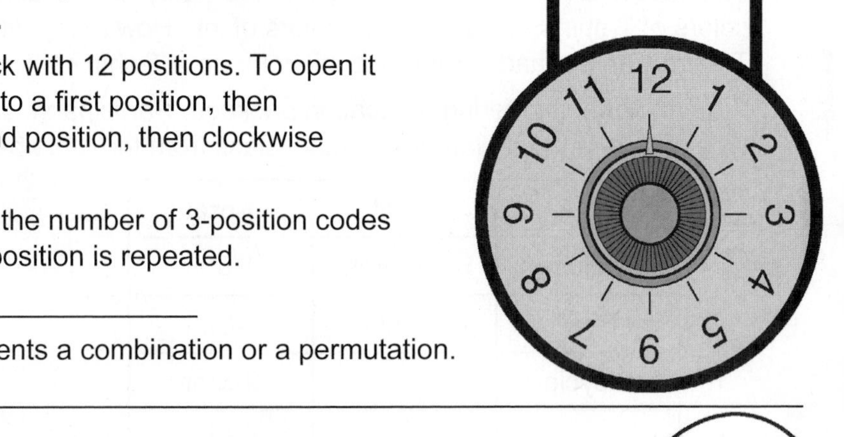

1. She looks at one circular lock with 12 positions. To open it she turns the dial clockwise to a first position, then counterclockwise to a second position, then clockwise to a third position
   a. Write an expression for the number of 3-position codes that are possible, if no position is repeated.

   ____

   b. Explain how this represents a combination or a permutation.

   ____

2. Rosalie looks at cable locks. Each position can be set from 0 to 9. How many different codes are possible for each lock if no digits are repeated in each code?
   a. a 3-digit cable lock

   ____

   b. a 4-digit cable lock

   ____

   c. a 6-digit cable lock

   ____

3. Rosalie needs 2 cable locks, but there are 13 types of locks to choose from.

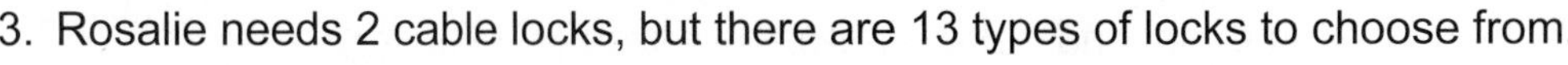

   a. In how many ways can she choose 2 different locks? ______________
   b. Explain how this represents a permutation or a combination.

   ____

4. Explain why you think Rosalie might be confused by the label *combination lock.*

Rosalie wants to lock her bicycle near the library. There are 7 slots still open in the bike rack. Choose the letter for the best answer.

5. Rosalie arrives at the same time as 2 other cyclists. In how many ways can they arrange their bikes in the open slots?

   A 7   C 210

   B 35   D 343

6. Suppose Rosalie arrived just ahead of the 2 other cyclists and selected a slot. In how many ways can the others arrange their bikes in the open slots?

   F 2   H 24

   G 15   J 30

Name________________________ Class________________ Date__________

18-3

Theoretical and Experimental Probability

Connection: Sampling

Essential question: *How can you use probabilites to help you make fair decisions?*

PREP FOR MCC9–12.S.MD.6(+)

1 ENGAGE Introducing a Decision-Making Problem

A small town has 25 residents. The state has given the town money that must be used for something that benefits the community. The town's mayor has decided that the money will be used to build a teen center or a senior center.

In order to make a decision about the type of community center to build, the mayor plans to survey a subset of town residents. There are two survey methods: a random sample and a convenience sample. The convenience sample will be conducted by surveying town residents at a local movie theater.

In the table below, each resident of the town is identified by a number from 1 to 25. The table shows each resident's preference: T for the teen center, S for the senior center. The table also gives the probability that each resident is at the movie theater when the convenience-sample survey is conducted.

1 S 0.2	**2** S 0.3	**3** T 0.8	**4** S 0.1	**5** T 0.8
6 T 0.7	**7** S 0.2	**8** T 0.8	**9** S 0.1	**10** S 0.3
11 S 0.1	**12** T 0.7	**13** S 0.2	**14** S 0.2	**15** S 0.4
16 T 0.6	**17** S 0.7	**18** S 0.1	**19** S 0.1	**20** T 0.6
21 S 0.3	**22** S 0.2	**23** S 0.3	**24** S 0.1	**25** T 0.9

REFLECT

1a. Based on the data in the table, what percent of all residents favor the teen center? the senior center?

____

1b. If it were possible for the mayor to survey every resident, what decision do you think the mayor would make? Why?

____

Using a Random Sample

Suppose the mayor of the town is not able to survey every resident, so the mayor decides to survey a random sample of 10 residents.

A You can use your calculator to simulate the process of choosing and surveying a random sample of residents.

- Go to the MATH menu.
- Use the right arrow key to access the PRB menu.
- Use the down arrow key to select **5:randInt(** .
- Use "randInt(1,25)" as shown at the right.
- Each time you press Enter, the calculator will return a random integer from 1 to 25.

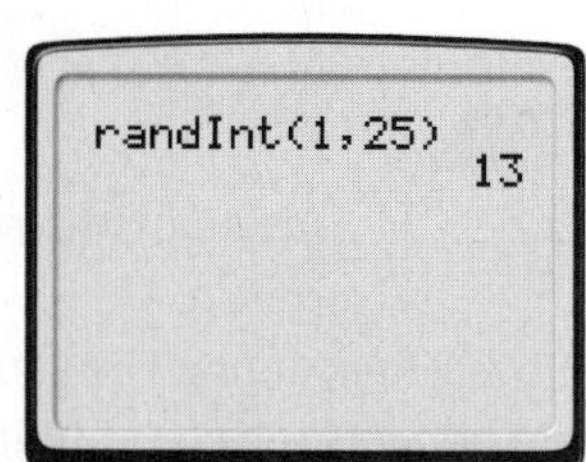

Generate 10 random integers in this way. For each integer, note the corresponding preference (T or S) of that resident of the town. (If a number is selected more than once, ignore the duplicates and choose a new number. This ensures that no resident is surveyed more than once.) Record your results in the table.

Resident Number										
Preference (T or S)										

B Based on the random sample, what percent of residents favor the teen center? the senior center?

____

REFLECT

2a. What is the probability that any resident is chosen to be part of the random sample? Explain.

____

____

2b. What decision do you think the mayor would make based on the random sample? Why?

____

2c. Compare your results with those of other students. In general, how well do the results of the random sample predict the preferences of the town as a whole?

____

MCC9–12.S.MD.6(+)

3 EXPLORE Using a Convenience Sample

The mayor of the town decides to use a convenience sample by surveying the first 10 residents of the town to leave a local movie theater.

A You can use slips of paper to simulate the process of choosing and surveying this convenience sample.

- For each resident, prepare 1 to 10 small slips of paper with the resident's number on them. The number of slips of paper is determined by the probability that the resident is at the movie theater when the survey is conducted. For example, Resident 1 has a 0.2 probability of being at the theater, so prepare 2 slips of paper with the number 1; Resident 2 has a 0.3 probability of being at the theater, so prepare 3 slips of paper with the number 2; and so on.

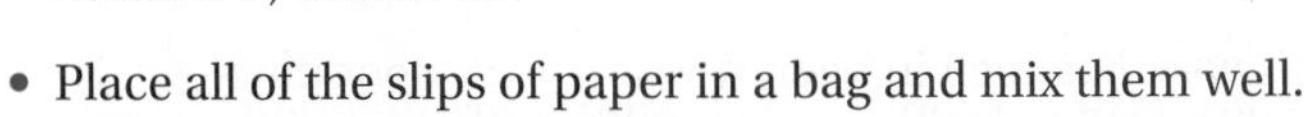

- Place all of the slips of paper in a bag and mix them well.
- Choose slips of paper one at a time without looking.

Choose 10 residents in this way. For each resident, note the corresponding preference (T or S) using the table on the first page of the lesson. (If a resident is selected more than once, ignore the duplicates and choose a new number from the bag. This ensures that no resident is surveyed more than once.) Record your results in the table.

Resident Number										
Preference (T or S)										

B Based on the convenience sample, what percent of residents favor the teen center? the senior center?

____

REFLECT

3a. Why do some residents of the town have more slips of paper representing them than other residents? How does this connect to the way the convenience sample is conducted?

____

____

____

____

3b. What decision do you think the mayor would make based on the convenience sample? Why?

____

3c. Compare your results with those of other students. In general, how well do the results of the convenience sample predict the preferences of the town as a whole?

____

____

3d. Which sampling method is more likely to lead to fair decision-making? Explain.

____

____

3e. What factors might explain why the results of the convenience sample are different from the results of the random sample?

____

____

____

3f. When you conduct the random-sample simulation is it possible that you might choose 10 residents who all favor the senior center? Is this result possible when you conduct the convenience-sample simulation? In which simulation do you think this result is more likely?

____

____

____

3g. What are some limitations or drawbacks of the simulations?

____

____

____

3h. In a town of 25 residents, it is likely that the mayor could actually survey all the residents, instead of using a random sample or convenience sample. What are some reasons that sampling might be used in situations involving populations that are much larger than 25?

____

____

____

Name________________________ Class______________ Date______________

Additional Practice

The table represents a class of 30 students. Each student was asked if he or she would prefer having a written report (R) or an oral presentation (O) for the final. Use the table for Exercises 1–4.

1 R	2 R	3 O	4 R	5 O
6 R	7 R	8 R	9 O	10 R
11 O	12 O	13 R	14 R	15 R
16 R	17 O	18 R	19 R	20 R
21 R	22 R	23 O	24 R	25 R
26 O	27 R	28 O	29 R	30 R

1. Use a calculator or slips of paper to choose 10 random numbers from 1 to 30. Circle the 10 numbers you generate.
2. What is the probability of any given student being chosen for your sample?

____

3. According to your sample, what percent of the class would prefer to have a written report as the final?

____

4. What percent of the class would prefer to have a written report if you take into account *all* of the students? How does this compare to what you found in your sample?

____

____

5. Another teacher wants to survey his classes with the same question. He has three classes of 90 students each. Explain a way he could collect responses from a random sample of 10% of his students. The sample should have equal representation for each of the three classes.

____

____

Problem Solving

The council of a city of 200,000 people is deciding on one of two improvement projects. The two proposed projects are (1) creating bike lanes in the downtown area and (2) repairing a road that passes through the suburbs. An employee of the city takes a survey of 50 people near his house in the suburbs. Of those surveyed, 45 people said they would prefer the road repair. Use this information for Exercises 1–4.

1. According to the survey, what percent of the city residents prefer the road repair project?

____

2. The city employee calculates that every city resident had a $\frac{50}{200,000} = \frac{1}{4,000}$ probability of being chosen for his survey. Do you agree? Explain why or why not.

____

____

3. Is the sample a random sample or a convenience sample? Explain your reasoning.

____

____

4. Do you think it's likely that the sample represents the population as a whole? Explain why or why not.

____

____

____

Select the best answer.

5. A survey asks a question of 30 people out of a total of 3,000 visiting a mall in one day. If the sample is random, what is the probability of any given person being surveyed?

   A 1% C 10%

   B 3% D 30%

6. A survey finds that 65% of town residents support leash laws. If that number was found by taking a sample of 40 residents, how many people in the sample support leash laws?

   F 12 H 40

   G 26 J 6

Name _______________ Class _______________ Date _______________

19-1

Independent and Dependent Events

Going Deeper

Video Tutor

Essential question: *How do you find the probability of independent and dependent events?*

Two events are **independent events** if the occurrence of one event does not affect the occurrence of the other event. For example, rolling a 1 on a number cube and choosing an ace at random from a deck of cards are independent events.

If two events A and B are independent events, then the fact that event B has occurred does not affect the probability of event A. In other words, for independent events A and B, $P(A) = P(A \mid B)$. You can use this as a criterion to determine whether two events are independent.

MCC9–12.S.CP.4

1 EXAMPLE Determining If Events are Independent

An airport employee collects data on 180 random flights that arrive at the airport. The data is shown in the two-way table. Is a late arrival independent of the flight being an international flight? Why or why not?

	Late Arrival	On Time	TOTAL
Domestic Flight	12	108	120
International Flight	6	54	60
TOTAL	18	162	180

A Let event A be the event that a flight arrives late. Let event B be the event that a flight is an international flight.

To find $P(A)$, first note that there is a total of ________ flights.

Of these flights, there is a total of ________ late flights.

So, $P(A) = \frac{\square}{\square} =$ ________.

To find $P(A \mid B)$, first note that there is a total of ________ international flights.

Of these flights, there is a total of ________ late flights.

So, $P(A \mid B) = \frac{\square}{\square} =$ ________.

B Compare $P(A)$ and $P(A \mid B)$.

So, a late arrival is independent of the flight being an international flight because

____

____

REFLECT

1a. In the example, you compared $P(A)$ and $P(A \mid B)$. Suppose you compare $P(B)$ and $P(B \mid A)$. What do you find? What does this tell you?

____

You can use a tree diagram to help you understand the formula for the probability of independent events. For example, consider tossing a coin two times. The outcome of one toss does not affect the outcome of the other toss, so the events are independent.

The tree diagram shows that the probability of the coin landing heads up on both tosses is $\frac{1}{4}$ because this is 1 of 4 equally-likely outcomes at the end of Toss 2. This probability is simply the product of the probabilities of the coin landing heads up on each individual toss: $\frac{1}{2} \cdot \frac{1}{2} = \frac{1}{4}$.

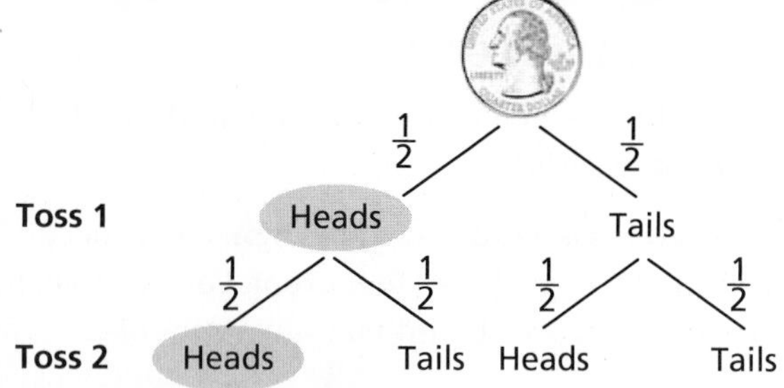

Probability of Independent Events

A and *B* are independent events if and only if $P(A \text{ and } B) = P(A) \cdot P(B)$.

MCC9–12.S.CP.3

2 EXAMPLE Using the Formula

You spin the spinner at right two times. What is the probability that you spin an even number on the first spin followed by an odd number on the second spin?

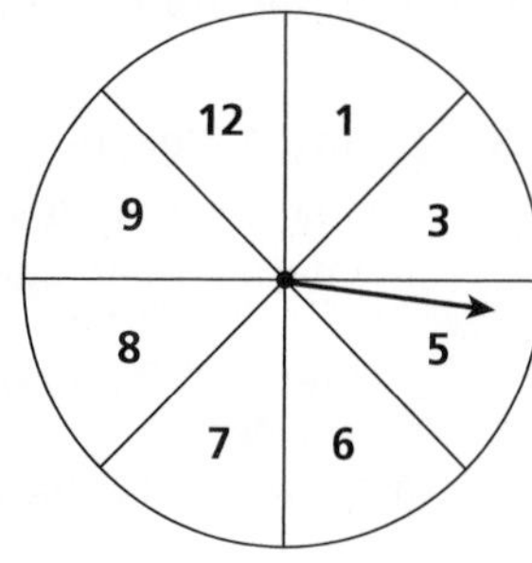

A Let event *A* be the event that you spin an even number on the first spin. Let event *B* be the event that you spin an odd number on the second spin.

$P(A) = \frac{}{}$ $P(B) = \frac{}{}$

B The outcome of the first spin does not affect the outcome of the second spin, so the events are independent events.

$P(A \text{ and } B) = P(A) \cdot P(B)$ Use the formula for independent events.

$= (\_\_\_\_\_\_) \cdot (\_\_\_\_\_\_)$ Substitute.

$= \_\_\_\_\_\_\_\_$ Simplify.

So, the probability that you spin an even number on the first spin followed by an odd number on the second spin is ________.

REFLECT

2a. What is the probability that you spin an odd number on the first spin followed by an even number on the second spin? What do you notice?

The formula for the probability of independent events gives you another way to determine whether two events are independent. That is, two events A and B are independent events if $P(A \text{ and } B) = P(A) \cdot P(B)$.

MCC9–12.S.CP.2

3 EXAMPLE Showing that Events are Independent

The two-way table shows the data from the first example. Show that a flight arriving on time and a flight being a domestic flight are independent events.

	Late Arrival	On Time	TOTAL
Domestic Flight	12	108	120
International Flight	6	54	60
TOTAL	18	162	180

A Let event A be the event that a flight arrives on time. Let event B be the event that a flight is a domestic flight.

To find $P(A)$, $P(B)$, and $P(A \text{ and } B)$ note that there is a total of ________ flights.

There is a total of ________ on-time flights.

So, $P(A) = \frac{\square}{\square} = \frac{\square}{\square}$.

There is a total of ________ domestic flights.

So, $P(B) = \frac{\square}{\square} = \frac{\square}{\square}$.

There is a total of ________ on-time domestic flights.

So, $P(A \text{ and } B) = \frac{\square}{\square} = \frac{\square}{\square}$.

B Compare $P(A \text{ and } B)$ and $P(A) \cdot P(B)$.

$P(A) \cdot P(B) = (\_\_\_\_) \cdot (\_\_\_\_) = \_\_\_\_$

So, the events are independent events because

____

REFLECT

3a. Describe a different way you can show that a flight arriving on time and a flight being a domestic flight are independent events.

____

____

PREP FOR MCC9–12.S.CP.8(+)

4 ENGAGE Introducing Dependent Events

Two events are **dependent events** if the occurrence of one event affects the occurrence of the other event.

Suppose you have a bag containing 2 blue marbles and 2 black marbles. You choose a marble without looking, put it aside, and then choose a second marble. Consider the following events.

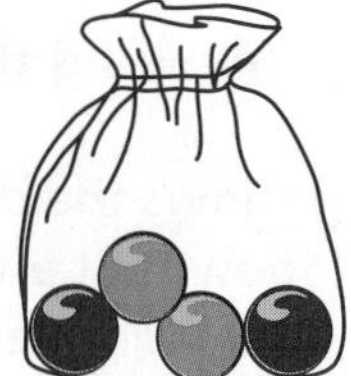

Event A: The first marble you choose is blue.

Event B: The second marble you choose is black.

Events A and B are dependent events, because the marble you choose for your first pick changes the sample space for your second pick. That is, the occurrence of event A affects the probability of event B.

Recall that you developed the following formula for conditional probability.

$$P(B \mid A) = \frac{P(A \text{ and } B)}{P(A)}$$

Multiplying both sides by $P(A)$ results in $P(A) \cdot P(B \mid A) = P(A \text{ and } B)$. This is known as the Multiplication Rule.

Multiplication Rule

$P(A \text{ and } B) = P(A) \cdot P(B \mid A)$, where $P(B \mid A)$ is the conditional probability of event B, given that event A has occurred.

You can use the Multiplication Rule to find the probability of dependent or independent events. Note that when A and B are independent events, $P(B \mid A) = P(B)$ and the rule may be rewritten as $P(A \text{ and } B) = P(A) \cdot P(B)$, which is the rule for independent events.

REFLECT

4a. How can you write the Multiplication Rule in a different way by starting with the formula for the conditional probability $P(A \mid B)$ and multiplying both sides of that equation by $P(B)$?

____

____

MCC9–12.S.CP.8(+)

5 EXAMPLE Finding the Probability of Dependent Events

There are 5 tiles with the letters A, B, C, D, and E in a bag. You choose a tile without looking, put it aside, and then choose another tile. Find the probability that you choose a consonant followed by a vowel.

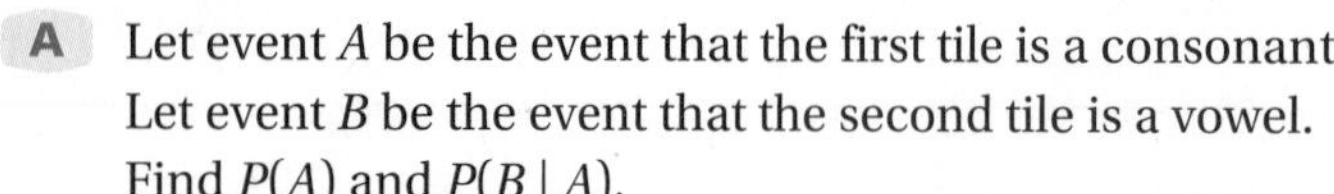

A Let event A be the event that the first tile is a consonant.
Let event B be the event that the second tile is a vowel.
Find $P(A)$ and $P(B \mid A)$.

$P(A) = \frac{\square}{\square}$ Of the 5 tiles, 3 are consonants.

$P(B \mid A) = \frac{\quad}{\quad} = \frac{\quad}{\quad}$ Of the 4 remaining tiles, 2 are vowels.

B Use the Multiplication Rule.

$P(A \text{ and } B) = P(A) \cdot P(B \mid A)$ Use the Multiplication Rule.

$= (\_\_\_\_) \cdot (\_\_\_\_)$ Substitute.

$= \_\_\_\_\_\_$ Multiply.

So, the probability that you choose a consonant followed by a vowel is ________.

REFLECT

5a. Complete the tree diagram below. Then explain how you can use it to check your answer.

1st tile A B C

2nd tile B C D E A C D E

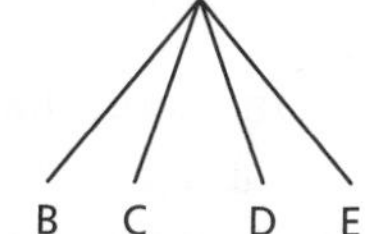

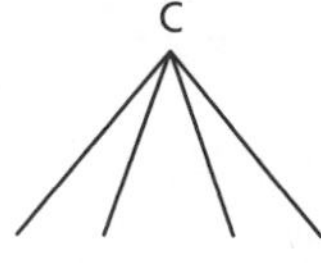

____

____

____

5b. What does your answer tell you about the likelihood of choosing a consonant followed by a vowel?

____

PRACTICE

1. A farmer wants to know if an insecticide is effective in preventing small insects called aphids from living on tomato plants. The farmer checks 80 plants. The data is shown in the two-way table. Is having aphids independent of being sprayed with the insecticide? Why or why not?

	Has Aphids	No Aphids	TOTAL
Was sprayed with insecticide	12	40	52
Was not sprayed with insecticide	14	14	28
TOTAL	26	54	80

____

____

2. A student wants to know if right-handed people are more or less likely to play a musical instrument than left-handed people. The student collects data from 250 people, as shown in the two-way table. Show that being right handed and playing a musical instrument are independent events.

	Right Handed	Left Handed	TOTAL
Plays a musical instrument	44	6	50
Does not play a musical instrument	176	24	200
TOTAL	220	30	250

3. A basket contains 6 bottles of apple juice and 8 bottles of grape juice. You choose a bottle without looking, put it aside, and then choose another bottle. What is the probability that you choose a bottle of apple juice followed by a bottle of grape juice?

4. You have a set of ten cards that are numbered 1 through 10. You shuffle the cards and choose a card at random. You put the card aside and choose another card. What is the probability that you choose an even number followed by an odd number?

5. There are 12 boys and 14 girls in Ms. Garcia's class. She chooses a student at random to solve a geometry problem at the board. Then she chooses another student at random to check the first student's work. Is she more likely to choose a boy followed by a girl, a girl followed by a boy, or are these both equally likely? Explain.

6. A bag contains 4 blue marbles and 4 red marbles. You choose a marble without looking, put it aside, and then choose another marble. Is there a greater than or less than 50% chance that you choose two marbles with different colors? Explain.

Name ______________________ Class ______________ Date ____________

Additional Practice

Find each probability.

1. A bag contains 5 red, 3 green, 4 blue, and 8 yellow marbles. Find the probability of randomly selecting a green marble, and then a yellow marble if the first marble is replaced. ____________
2. A sock drawer contains 5 rolled-up pairs of each color of socks, white, green, and blue. What is the probability of randomly selecting a pair of blue socks, replacing it, and then randomly selecting a pair of white socks? ____________

Two 1–6 number cubes are rolled—one is black and one is white.

3. The sum of the rolls is greater than or equal to 6 and the black cube shows a 3.
   a. Explain why the events are dependent.
   ____
   b. Find the probability. ____________
4. The white cube shows an even number, and the sum is 8.
   a. Explain why the events are dependent.
   ____
   b. Find the probability. ____________

The table below shows numbers of registered voters by age in the United States in 2004 based on the census. Find each probability in decimal form.

Age	Registered Voters (in thousands)	Not Registered to Vote (in thousands)
18–24	14,334	13,474
25–44	49,371	32,763
45–64	51,659	19,355
65 and over	26,706	8,033

5. A randomly selected person is registered to vote, given that the person is between the ages of 18 and 24. ____________
6. A randomly selected person is between the ages of 45 and 64 and is not registered to vote. ____________
7. A randomly selected person is registered to vote and is at least 65 years old. ____________

A bag contains 12 blue cubes, 12 red cubes, and 20 green cubes. Determine whether the events are independent or dependent, and find each probability.

8. A green cube and then a blue cube are chosen at random with replacement. ____________
9. Two blue cubes are chosen at random without replacement. ____________

Problem Solving

The table shows student participation in different sports at a high school. Suppose a student is selected at random.

Sports Participation by Grade					
	Track	**Volleyball**	**Basketball**	**Tennis**	**No Sport**
Grade 9	12	18	15	9	66
Grade 10	6	20	12	2	95
Grade 11	15	11	8	5	61
Grade 12	7	6	10	12	50

1. What is the probability that a student is in grade 10 and runs track?
   a. Find the probability that a student is in grade 10, $P(10)$. ________________
   b. Find the probability that a student runs track, given that the student is in grade 10, $P(Tr \mid 10)$, ________________
   c. Find P (10 and Tr) $= P(10) \cdot P(Tr \mid 10)$. ________________
2. What is the probability that a student is in grade 12 and runs track or plays tennis?
   a. Find the probability that a student is in grade 12, $P(12)$. ________________
   b. Find the probability that a student runs track or plays tennis, given that the student is in grade 12, $P(Tr$ or $Te \mid 12)$. ________________
   c. Find P(12 or (Tr or Te)). ________________
3. During a fire drill, the students are waiting in the parking lot. What is the probability that one student is in grade 12 and runs track or plays tennis, and the student standing next to her is in grade 10 and runs track?
   a. Find the probability for the first student. ________________
   b. Find the probability for the second student. ________________
   c. Find the probability for the event occurring. ________________
   d. Are these events independent or dependent? Explain.

____

Samantha is 1 of 17 students in a class of 85 who have decided to pursue a business degree. Each week, a student in the class is randomly selected to tutor younger students. Choose the letter for the best answer.

4. What is the probability of drawing a business student one week, replacing the name, and drawing the same name the next week?

   A 3.4   C 0.04

   B 0.2   D 0.002

5. What is the probability of drawing Samantha's name one week, not replacing her name, and drawing the name of another business student the next week?

   F $\frac{1}{85} \cdot \frac{16}{84}$ H $\frac{17}{85} \cdot \frac{16}{84}$

   G $\frac{1}{85} \cdot \frac{17}{84}$ J $\frac{17}{85} \cdot \frac{17}{84}$

Name________________ Class__________ Date________

19-2

Two-Way Tables

Going Deeper

Essential question: *How do you calculate a conditional probability?*

Video Tutor

The probability that event B occurs given that event A has already occurred is called the **conditional probability** of B given A and is written $P(B \mid A)$.

MCC9–12.S.CP.6

1 EXAMPLE Finding Conditional Probabilities

One hundred people who frequently get migraine headaches were chosen to participate in a study of a new anti-headache medicine. Some of the particpants were given the medicine; others were not. After one week, the participants were asked if they got a headache during the week. The two-way table summarizes the results.

	Took Medicine	No Medicine	TOTAL
Headache	12	15	27
No Headache	48	25	73
TOTAL	60	40	100

A **To the nearest percent, what is the probability that a participant who took the medicine did not get a headache?**

Let event A be the event that a participant took the medicine. Let event B be the event that a participant did not get a headache.

To find the probability that a participant who took the medicine did not get a headache, you must find $P(B \mid A)$. You are only concerned with participants who took the medicine, so look at the data in the "Took Medicine" column.

There were ________ participants who took the medicine.

Of these participants, ________ participants did not get a headache.

So, $P(B \mid A) = \frac{\square}{\square} =$ ________.

B **To the nearest percent, what is the probability that a participant who did not get a headache took the medicine?**

To find the probability that a participant who did not get a headache took the medicine, you must find $P(A \mid B)$. You are only concerned with participants who did not get a headache, so look at the data in the "No headache" row.

There were ________ participants who did not get a headache.

Of these participants, ________ participants took the medicine.

So, $P(A \mid B) = \frac{\square}{\square} \approx$ ________.

REFLECT

1a. In general, do you think $P(B \mid A) = P(A \mid B)$? Why or why not?

1b. How can you use set notation to represent the event that a participant took the medicine and did not get a headache? Is the probability that a participant took the medicine and did not get a headache equal to either of the conditional probabilities you calculated in the example?

MCC9–12.S.CP.3

2 EXPLORE Developing a Formula for Conditional Probability

You can generalize your work from the previous example to develop a formula for finding conditional probabilities.

A Recall how you calculated $P(B \mid A)$, the probability that a participant who took the medicine did not get a headache.

You found that $P(B \mid A) = \frac{48}{60}$.

Use the table shown here to help you write this quotient in terms of events A and B.

		Event A		
		Took Medicine	No Medicine	TOTAL
	Headache	12	15	27
Event B	No Headache	48 = $n(A \cap B)$	25	73 = $n(B)$
	TOTAL	60 = $n(A)$	40	100

$P(B \mid A) = \frac{\square}{\square}$

B Now divide the numerator and denominator of the quotient by $n(S)$, the number of outcomes in the sample space. This converts the counts to probabilities.

$P(B \mid A) = \frac{\square / n(S)}{\square / n(S)} = \frac{\square}{\square}$

REFLECT

2a. Write a formula for $P(A \mid B)$ in terms of $n(A \cap B)$ and $n(B)$.

2b. Write a formula for $P(A \mid B)$ in terms of $P(A \cap B)$ and $P(B)$.

You may have discovered the following formula for conditional probability.

Conditional Probability

The conditional probability of B given A (the probability that event B occurs given that event A occurs) is given by the following formula:

$$P(B \mid A) = \frac{P(A \cap B)}{P(A)}$$

MCC9–12.S.CP.3

3 EXAMPLE Using the Conditional Probability Formula

In a standard deck of playing cards, find the probability that a red card is a queen.

A Let event Q be the event that a card is a queen. Let event R be the event that a card is red. You are asked to find $P(Q \mid R)$. First find $P(R \cap Q)$ and $P(R)$.

$R \cap Q$ represents cards that are both red and a queen; that is, red queens.

There are __________ red queens in the deck of 52 cards, so $P(R \cap Q) =$ __________.

There are __________ red cards in the deck, so $P(R) =$ __________.

B Use the formula for conditional probability.

$P(Q \mid R) = \frac{P(Q \cap R)}{P(R)} = \frac{\square}{\square}$ Substitute probabilities from above.

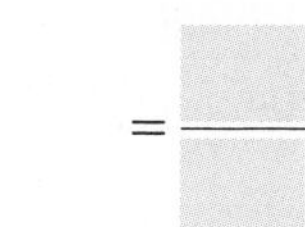

$= \frac{\square}{\square}$ Multiply numerator and denominator by 52.

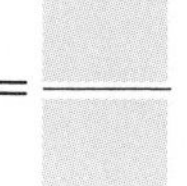

$= \frac{\square}{\square}$ Simplify.

So, the probability that a red card is a queen is __________.

REFLECT

3a. How can you interpret the probability you calculated above?

____

____

3b. Is the probability that a red card is a queen equal to the probability that a queen is red? Explain.

____

PRACTICE

1. In order to study the connection between the amount of sleep a student gets and his or her school performance, data was collected about 120 students. The two-way table shows the number of students who passed and failed an exam and the number of students who got more or less than 6 hours of sleep the night before.

	Passed Exam	Failed Exam	TOTAL
Less than 6 hours of sleep	12	10	22
More than 6 hours of sleep	90	8	98
TOTAL	102	18	120

   a. To the nearest percent, what is the probability that a student who failed the exam got less than 6 hours of sleep? ________

   b. To the nearest percent, what is the probability that a student who got less than 6 hours of sleep failed the exam? ________

   c. To the nearest percent, what is the probability that a student got less than 6 hours of sleep and failed the exam? ________

2. A botanist studied the effect of a new fertilizer by choosing 100 orchids and giving 70% of these plants the fertilizer. Of the plants that got the fertilizer, 40% produced flowers within a month. Of the plants that did not get the fertilizer, 10% produced flowers within a month. Find each probability to the nearest percent. (*Hint:* Construct a two-way table.)

   a. Find the probability that a plant that produced flowers got the fertilizer. ________

   b. Find the probability that a plant that got the fertilizer produced flowers. ________

3. At a school fair, a box contains 24 yellow balls and 76 red balls. One-fourth of the balls of each color are labeled "Win a prize." Find each probability as a percent.

   a. Find the probability that a ball labeled "Win a prize" is yellow. ________

   b. Find the probability that a ball labeled "Win a prize" is red. ________

   c. Find the probability that a ball is labeled "Win a prize" and is red. ________

   d. Find the probability that a yellow ball is labeled "Win a prize." ________

In Exercises 4–9, consider a standard deck of playing cards and the following events: *A*: the card is an ace; *B*: the card is black; *C*: the card is a club. Find each probability as a fraction.

4. $P(A \mid B)$ ________

5. $P(B \mid A)$ ________

6. $P(A \mid C)$ ________

7. $P(C \mid A)$ ________

8. $P(B \mid C)$ ________

9. $P(C \mid B)$ ________

Name________________________ Class______________ Date______________ **19-2**

Additional Practice

1. The table shows the results of a customer satisfaction survey of 100 randomly selected shoppers at the mall who were asked if they would shop at an earlier time if the mall opened earlier. Complete the table below and use it to answer parts **a** and **b**.

	Ages 10–20	Ages 21–45	Ages 46–65	Ages Over 65
Yes	13	2	8	24
No	25	10	15	3

	Ages 10–20	Ages 21–45	Ages 46–65	Ages Over 65	Total
Yes					
No					
Total					

a. To the nearest whole percent, what is the probability that a shopper who is in the age range 21 to 45 said that he or she would shop earlier?

____

b. To the nearest whole percent, what is the probability that a shopper who would shop earlier is in the age range 65 and older?

____

2. Jerrod collected data on 100 randomly selected students, and summarized the results in a table.

		Owns an MP3 player	
		Yes	**No**
Owns a Smart phone	**Yes**	28	12
	No	34	26

a. If you are given that a student owns an MP3 player, what is the probability that the student also owns a smart phone? Round your answer to the nearest hundredth.

____

b. If you are given that a student owns a smart phone, what is the probability that the student also owns an MP3 player? Round your answer to the nearest hundredth.

____

Problem Solving

1. The table shows the number of students who would drive to school if the school provided parking spaces. Complete the table below and use it to answer parts **a** and **b**.

	Lowerclassmates	Upperclassmates
Always	32	122
Sometimes	58	44
Never	24	120

a. To the nearest whole percent, what is the probability that a student who said "always" is an upperclassmate?

____

b. To the nearest whole percent, what is the probability that a lowerclassmate said "always" or "sometimes"?

____

2. Gerry collected data and did a table of marginal relative frequencies on the number of students who participate in chorus and the number who participate in band.

		Chorus	
		Yes	**No**
Band	**Yes**	38	29
	No	9	24

a. If you are given that a student is in chorus, what is the probability that the student also is in band? Round your answer to the nearest hundredth.

____

b. If you are given that a student is not in band, what is the probability that the student is in chorus? Round your answer to the nearest hundredth.

____

Use the table in Exercise 2 to answer Exercises 3 and 4. Select the best answer.

3. What is the probability if a student is not in chorus, then that student is in band?

A 0.29 B 0.38
C 0.43 D 0.55

4. What is the probability that if a student is not in band then the student is not in chorus?

F 0.09 G 0.33
H 0.44 J 0.73

Name________________________ Class______________ Date__________

19-3

Compound Events

Going Deeper

Video Tutor

Essential question: *How do you find the probability of mutually exclusive events and overlapping events?*

Two events are **mutually exclusive events** if the events cannot both occur in the same trial of an experiment. For example, when you toss a coin, the coin landing heads up and the coin landing tails up are mutually exclusive events.

PREP FOR MCC9–12.S.CP.7

1 EXAMPLE Finding the Probability of Mutually Exclusive Events

A dodecahedral number cube has 12 sides numbered 1 through 12. What is the probability that you roll the cube and the result is an even number or a 7?

A Let event A be the event that you roll an even number. Let event B be the event that you roll a 7. Let S be the sample space.

Complete the Venn diagram by writing all outcomes in the sample space in the appropriate region.

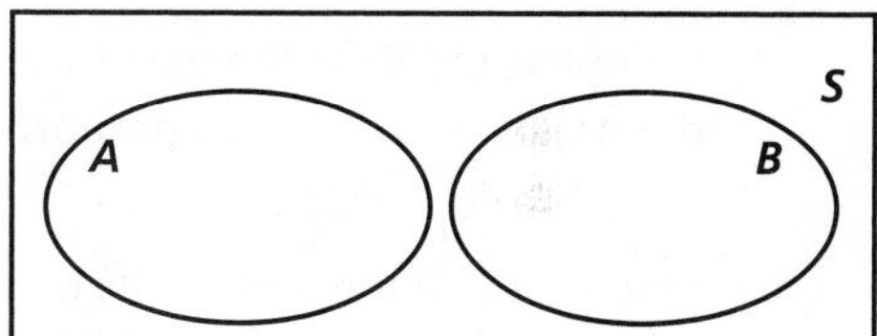

B You must find the probability of A or B.

$n(S) =$ ________

$n(A \text{ or } B) = n(A) + n(B)$ — A and B are mutually exclusive events.

$=$ ________ $+$ ________ — Use the Venn diagram to find $n(A)$ and $n(B)$.

$=$ ________ — Add.

So, $P(A \text{ or } B) = \frac{n(A \text{ or } B)}{n(S)} = \frac{}{}$.

REFLECT

1a. Does the probability you calculated seem reasonable? Why?

____

____

1b. Is it always true that $n(A \text{ or } B) = n(A) + n(B)$? Explain.

____

1c. How is $P(A \text{ or } B)$ related to $P(A)$ and $P(B)$? Do you think this is always true?

____

____

The process you used in the example can be generalized to give a formula for the probability of mutually exclusive events.

Mutually Exclusive Events

If A and B are mutually exclusive events, then $P(A \text{ or } B) = P(A) + P(B)$.

Two events are **overlapping events** (or *inclusive events*) if they have one or more outcomes in common.

PREP FOR MCC9–12.S.CP.7

2 EXAMPLE Finding the Probability of Overlapping Events

What is the probability that you roll a dodecahedral number cube and the result is an even number or a number greater than 7?

A Let event A be the event that you roll an even number. Let event B be the event that you roll a number greater than 7. Let S be the sample space.

Complete the Venn diagram by writing all outcomes in the sample space in the appropriate region.

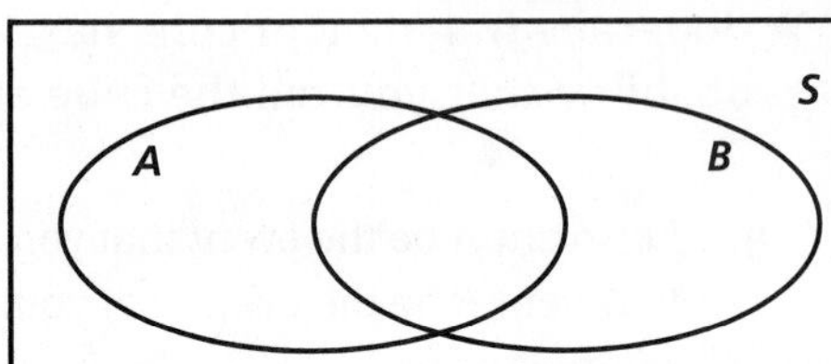

B You must find the probability of A or B.

$n(S) =$ ________

$n(A \text{ or } B) = n(A) + n(B) - n(A \text{ and } B)$ — A and B are overlapping events.

$=$ ________ $+$ ________ $-$ ________ — Use the Venn diagram.

$=$ ________ — Simplify.

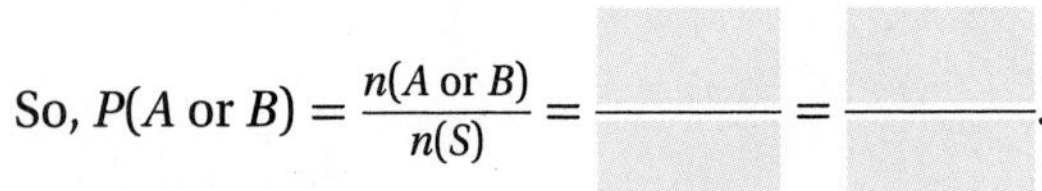
So, $P(A \text{ or } B) = \frac{n(A \text{ or } B)}{n(S)} = \frac{\square}{\square} = \frac{\square}{\square}$.

REFLECT

2a. Why is $n(A \text{ or } B)$ equal to $n(A) + n(B) - n(A \text{ and } B)$?

____

____

____

____

2b. Is $P(A \text{ or } B)$ equal to $P(A) + P(B)$ in this case? Explain.

____

In the previous example you saw that for overlapping events A and B, $n(A \cup B) = n(A) + n(B) - n(A \cap B)$. You can convert these counts to probabilities by dividing each term by $n(S)$ as shown below.

S
A
$A \cap B$
B

$$\frac{n(A \cup B)}{n(S)} = \frac{n(A)}{n(S)} + \frac{n(B)}{n(S)} - \frac{n(A \cap B)}{n(S)}$$

Rewriting each term as a probability results in the following rule.

Addition Rule

$P(A \text{ or } B) = P(A) + P(B) - P(A \text{ and } B)$

Notice that when A and B are mutually exclusive events, $P(A \text{ and } B) = 0$, and the rule becomes the simpler rule for mutually exclusive events on the previous page.

MCC9–12.S.CP.7

3 EXAMPLE Using the Addition Rule

You shuffle a standard deck of playing cards and choose a card at random. What is the probability that you choose a king or a heart?

A Let event A be the event that you choose a king. Let event B be the event that you choose a heart. Let S be the sample space.

There are 52 cards in the deck, so $n(S) =$ ________.

There are 4 kings in the deck, so $n(A) =$ ________ and $P(A) =$ ________.

There are 13 hearts in the deck, so $n(B) =$ ________ and $P(B) =$ ________.

There is one king of hearts in the deck, so $P(A \text{ and } B) =$ ________.

B Use the Addition Rule.

$P(A \text{ or } B) = P(A) + P(B) - P(A \text{ and } B)$

= ________ + ________ − ________ Substitute.

= ________ or ________ Simplify.

So, the probability of choosing a king or a heart is ________.

REFLECT

3a. What does the answer tell you about the likelihood of choosing a king or a heart from the deck?

____

____

PRACTICE

1. A bag contains 3 blue marbles, 5 red marbles, and 4 green marbles. You choose a marble without looking. What is the probability that you choose a red marble or a green marble?

____

2. An icosahedral number cube has 20 sides numbered 1 through 20. What is the probability that you roll the cube and the result is a number that is less than 4 or greater than 11?

____

3. A bag contains 26 tiles, each with a different letter of the alphabet written on it. You choose a tile without looking. What is the probability that you choose a vowel or a letter in the word GEOMETRY?

____

4. You roll two number cubes at the same time. Each cube has sides numbered 1 through 6. What is the probability that the sum of the numbers rolled is even or greater than 9?

____

5. You shuffle a standard deck of playing cards and choose a card at random. What is the probability that you choose a face card (jack, queen, or king) or a club?

____

6. You have a set of 25 cards numbered 1 through 25. You shuffle the cards and choose a card at random. What is the probability that you choose a multiple of 3 or a multiple of 4?

____

7. The two-way table provides data on the students at a high school. You randomly choose a student at the school. Find each probability.

	Freshman	Sophomore	Junior	Senior	TOTAL
Boy	98	104	100	94	396
Girl	102	106	96	108	412
TOTAL	200	210	196	202	808

a. The student is a senior. _______

b. The student is a girl. _______

c. The student is a senior and a girl. _______

d. The student is a senior or a girl. _______

8. A survey of the 1108 employees at a software company finds that 621 employees take a bus to work and 445 employees take a train to work. Some employees take both a bus and a train, and 312 employees take only a train. To the nearest percent, what is the probability that a randomly-chosen employee takes a bus or a train to work? (*Hint:* Make a Venn diagram.)

____

9. Suppose A and B are complementary events. Explain how you can rewrite the Addition Rule in a simpler form for this case.

____

Additional Practice

A can of vegetables with no label has a $\frac{1}{8}$ chance of being green beans and a $\frac{1}{5}$ chance of being corn.

1. Explain why the events "green beans" or "corn" are mutually exclusive.

____

2. What is the probability that an unlabeled can of vegetables is either green beans or corn? ____________

Ben rolls a 1–6 number cube. Find each probability.

3. Ben rolls a 3 or a 4. ____________
4. Ben rolls a number greater than 2 or an even number. ____________
5. Ben rolls a prime number or an odd number. ____________

Of the 400 doctors who attended a conference, 240 practiced family medicine and 130 were from countries outside the United States. One-third of the family medicine practitioners were not from the United States.

6. What is the probability that a doctor practices family medicine or is from the United States? ____________
7. What is the probability that a doctor practices family medicine or is not from the United States? ____________
8. What is the probability that a doctor does not practice family medicine or is from the United States? ____________

Use the data to fill in the Venn diagram. Then solve.

9. Of the 220 people who came into the Italian deli on Friday, 104 bought pizza and 82 used a credit card. Half of the people who bought pizza used a credit card. What is the probability that a customer bought pizza or used a credit card?

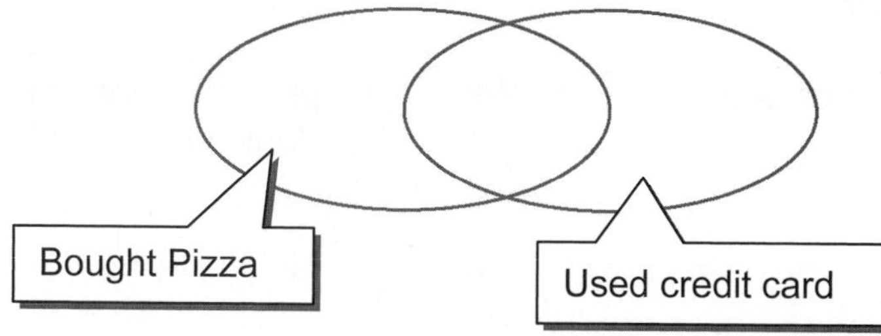

____

Solve.

10. There are 6 people in a gardening club. Each gardener orders seeds from a list of 11 different types of seeds available. What is the probability that 2 gardeners will order the same type of seeds? ____________

Problem Solving

Of 100 students surveyed, 44 are male and 54 are in favor of a change to a 9-period, 4-day school week. Of those in favor, 20 are female. One student is picked at random from those surveyed.

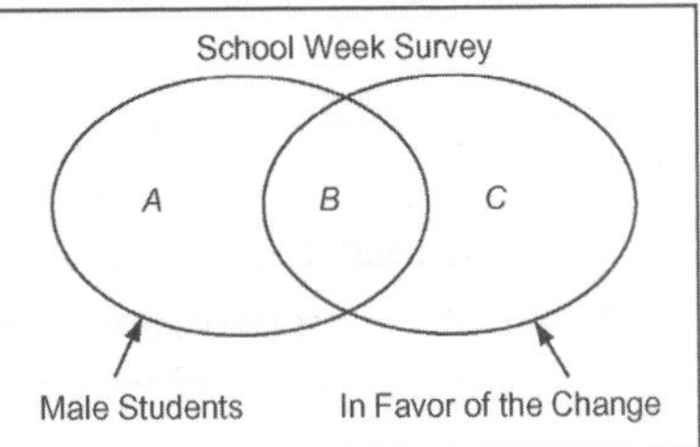

1. What is the probability that the student is male or favors the change? Use the Venn diagram.
   a. What is represented by the total of $A + B$?

   ____

   b. What is represented by the total of $B + C$?

   ____

   c. How many of those in favor of the change are male? ______________
   d. Find the values for A, B, and C and label the diagram.
   e. Write and evaluate an expression for the probability that the student is male or favors the change. ______________
2. What is the probability that the student is female or opposes the change?
   a. How many students are female? ______________
   b. How many students oppose the change? ______________
   c. If you draw a Venn diagram to show females and those opposed to the change, what is the meaning and value of the overlapping area?

   ____

   d. Write and evaluate an expression for the probability that the student is female or opposes the change. ______________
3. Of the students surveyed, 27 plan to start their own businesses. Of those, 18 are in favor of the change to the school week. Write and evaluate an expression for the probability that a student selected at random plans to start his or her own business or favors the change.

   ____

Sean asks each student to cast a vote for the type of class he or she would prefer. Of the students, 55% voted for online classes, 30% voted for projects, and 15% voted for following the textbook. Choose the letter for the best answer.

4. Which description best describes Sean's experiment?

   A Simple events

   B Compound events

   C Mutually exclusive events

   D Inclusive events

5. What is the probability that a randomly selected student voted for online classes or projects?

   F $\frac{33}{200}$ H $\frac{1}{4}$

   G $\frac{7}{10}$ J $\frac{17}{20}$

Name ____________ Class ____________ Date ________

Performance Tasks

GPS COMMON CORE
MCC9-12.S.CP.1
MCC9-12.S.CP.2
MCC9-12.S.CP.3
MCC9-12.S.CP.5
MCC9-12.S.CP.6
MCC9-12.S.CP.7
MCC9-12.S.CP.9(+)

★ **1.** Sam is playing a board game. He rolls a number cube to see how many spaces he can move. To win, he must land on the WIN! square. If he passes it, he must move back to the beginning of the board.

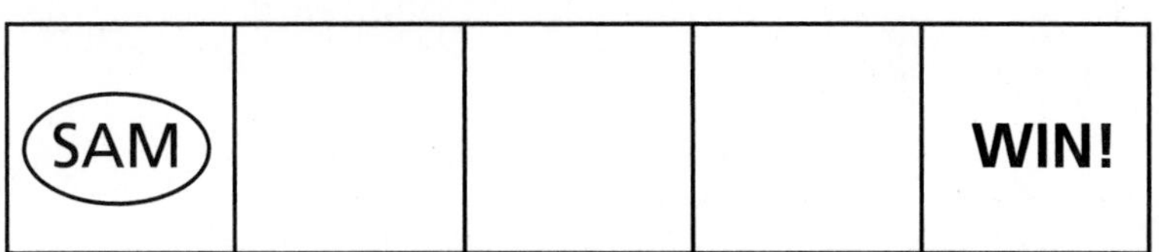

What is the probability that Sam wins on this roll? Is this event the complement of the event "Sam moves back to beginning"? Explain.

★ **2.** Kiki surveyed a random sample of 30 registered voters in a neighborhood and asked if they had voted in the last election. Twelve voters answered yes. The neighborhood has 525 registered voters. Based on this data, what is the probability that a person in the neighborhood voted in the last election given that he or she is a registered voter?

★★ **3.** The Teacup serves 20 different teas. Of the 20 teas, 14 of them contain caffeine, and 12 of them are organic. Alice selects a tea at random. Her friend Mel then randomly selects a different tea than Alice.

continued

a. Let A be the event that Alice selects a tea with caffeine, and B be the event that Mel selects a tea with caffeine. Are the events independent? Explain.

b. Two of the teas are neither caffeinated nor organic. Draw a Venn diagram to show how many of each type of tea there are.

c. A tea is selected at random. Determine P(tea is organic | tea is caffeinated).

★★★ 4. Shannon is designing a target of 3 concentric circles. From inside to outside, the colors are yellow, blue, and white. She wants the probabilities of randomly hitting yellow to be 15%, of randomly hitting blue to be 35%, and of randomly hitting white to be 50%. The radius of the entire target will be 9 inches.

a. Find the radius of each concentric circle to the nearest tenth of an inch. Show your work.

b. How wide will the blue and white circular bands be? Round to the nearest tenth of an inch.

Name ______________________ Class ______________ Date ________

SELECTED RESPONSE

1. You spin a spinner with 10 equal sections that are numbered 1 through 10. Event A is rolling an odd number. Event B is rolling a number greater than 5. What is $P(A \cap B)$?

   A. $\frac{1}{8}$ C. $\frac{1}{2}$

   B. $\frac{1}{5}$ D. $\frac{4}{5}$

2. There are 9 players on a basketball team. For a team photo, 4 of the players are seated on a row of chairs and 5 players stand behind them. In how many different ways can 4 players be arranged on the row of chairs?

   F. 24 H. 180

   G. 126 J. 3024

3. There are 5 peaches and 4 nectarines in a bowl. You randomly choose 2 pieces of fruit to pack in your lunch. What is the probability that you choose 2 peaches?

   A. $\frac{5}{36}$ C. $\frac{2}{5}$

   B. $\frac{5}{18}$ D. $\frac{5}{9}$

4. You shuffle the cards shown below and choose one at random. What is the probability that you choose a gray card or an even number?

1	2	4	5	7	9
10	11	13	16	18	19

   F. $\frac{1}{10}$ H. $\frac{5}{6}$

   G. $\frac{35}{144}$ J. 1

The two-way table provides data about 240 randomly chosen people who visit a movie theater. Use the table for Items 5 and 6.

	Discount Admission	Regular Admission	TOTAL
Purchases a snack	24	72	96
Purchases no snack	36	108	144
TOTAL	60	180	240

5. Consider the following events.

   Event A: Pays for a regular admission.
   Event B: Purchases a snack.

   Which is the best description of the two events?

   A. complementary events

   B. dependent events

   C. independent events

   D. mutually exclusive events

6. What is the probability that a visitor to the movie theater purchases a snack given that the visitor pays for a discount admission?

   F. 0.1 H. 0.4

   G. 0.25 J. 0.75

7. A bag contains 8 yellow marbles and 4 blue marbles. You choose a marble, put it aside, and then choose another marble. What is the probability that you choose two yellow marbles?

   A. $\frac{7}{18}$ C. $\frac{4}{9}$

   B. $\frac{14}{33}$ D. $\frac{2}{3}$

8. Events A and B are independent events. Which of the following must be true?

F. $P(A \text{ and } B) = P(A) \cdot P(B)$

G. $P(A \text{ and } B) = P(A) + P(B)$

H. $P(A) = P(B)$

J. $P(B|A) = P(A|B)$

9. Which expression can you use to calculate the conditional probability of event A given that event B has occurred?

A. $P(A) + P(B) - P(A \text{ and } B)$

B. $P(B) \cdot P(A|B)$

C. $\frac{P(A \text{ and } B)}{P(B)}$

D. $\frac{P(A)}{P(B)}$

CONSTRUCTED RESPONSE

10. It is known that 1% of all mice in a laboratory have a genetic mutation. A test for the mutation correctly identifies mice that have the mutation 98% of the time. The test correctly identifies mice that do not have the mutation 96% of the time. A lab assistant tests a mouse and finds that the mouse tests positive for the mutation. The lab assistant decides that the mouse must have the mutation. Is this a good decision? Explain.

11. Two students, Naomi and Kayla, play a game using the rules shown below. The winner of the game gets a box of 80 fruit chews.

Game Rules

- One student repeatedly tosses a coin.
- When the coin lands heads up, Naomi gets a point.
- When the coin lands tails up, Kayla gets a point.
- The first student to reach 8 points wins the game and gets the fruit chews.

The game gets interrupted when Naomi has 7 points and Kayla has 5 points. How should the 80 fruit chews be divided between the students given that the game was interrupted at this moment? Explain why your answer provides a fair way to divide the fruit chews.